Eugenie Grandet and Nanon

A scene from Balzac's novel

John Ridd arrested by Colonel Kirke's men

A scene from " Lorna Doone "

A Cheat's Guide
to the
CLASSICS

ACKNOWLEDGMENTS

The editor wishes to acknowledge his grateful thanks to the following for permission to make digests of the copyright works mentioned:—

To Macmillan & Co., Limited, and the executors of Thomas Hardy for *Tess of the D'Urbervilles*.

To George Allen & Unwin, Limited, for the translation by Eden and Cedar Paul of Marx's *Capital*.

First printed in Great Britain by The Whitefriars Press Ltd., London and Tonbridge.

This edition published in 2003 by Bounty Books, a division of Octopus Publishing Group Ltd, 2-4 Heron Quays, London E14 4JP

Reprinted 2005, 2006

ISBN 0 7537 0814 0
ISBN 13 9 780753 708149

Printed and bound in Great Britain by Mackays of Chatham plc, Chatham, Kent

CONTENTS

LIST OF ILLUSTRATIONS

PRIDE AND PREJUDICE

By JANE AUSTEN

*" Pride and Prejudice " is perhaps the best-loved work of
Jane Austen's (1775–1817) small but popular output.
It contains her greatest satiric characters, Mr. Collins and
Lady Catherine, and is easily the most readable by anyone
making their first excursion into early nineteenth-century
English literature.*

"My dear Mr. Bennet," said his lady to him one day,
"have you heard that Netherfield Park is let at
last?"

Mr. Bennet replied that he had not.

Mrs. Bennet, overwhelmed with delight at the good fortune
that had befallen the neighbourhood, furnished him with a
long account of the new master of Netherfield Park. He was
a young man—by name Mr. Bingley—unmarried, of good
fortune—four or five thousand a year, it was believed. He had
lately come from the north of England, but it was hoped that
he meant to settle in Hertfordshire.

Mrs. Bennet was a foolish woman of little intelligence,
uncertain temper and no self-control. After three-and-
twenty years of marriage, she had no understanding of her
husband. He, whose fancy as a young man had been caught
by a pretty face, had lived to be disappointed of her wit and
understanding, to become indifferent, and to withdraw himself
as much as he could from the cares and responsibilities of his
family. Yet even he, as the father of five unmarried daughters,
could not be blind to the advantage of making the acquaintance
of his new neighbour. Accordingly he called upon Mr.
Bingley.

Within a few days Mr. Bingley returned the call. He had
hoped to meet the young ladies of the establishment, the two
eldest of whom, Jane and Elizabeth, were famous local
beauties. He was disappointed, seeing only the father. The
young ladies, however, fared better. They glimpsed Mr.
Bingley from the upstairs room where they sat, and the result
of their observations was that they could add to the information
about him that he wore a blue coat and rode a fine black horse.

Not all the questions Mrs. Bennet or her daughters could ask could draw from Mr. Bennet a satisfactory description of Mr. Bingley. They were obliged to rely on the intelligence of Lady Lucas, their near neighbour, whose eldest daughter, Charlotte, was the close friend of Lizzie and Jane. Mr. Bingley, they learned, was quite young, and quite wonderfully handsome. To crown all, he had expressed his intention of being present, with a large party, at the next assembly. Nothing could be more delightful. To be fond of dancing was a certain step toward falling in love. Very lively hopes were entertained of capturing Mr. Bingley's heart.

On the night of the assembly, all eyes turned to witness the arrival of Mr. Bingley's party. It resolved itself into five: Mr. Bingley's two sisters, one who was married to a Mr. Hurst being accompanied by her husband; Mr. Bingley himself, and his particular friend Mr. Darcy. Mr. Bingley was good-looking and gentleman-like; his sisters were fine women, with an air of decided fashion. His brother-in-law, Mr. Hurst, merely looked the gentleman; but his friend Mr. Darcy soon drew the attention of the room by his fine, tall person, handsome features, noble mien; and by the report, which was in general circulation within five minutes after his entrance, of his having ten thousand a year.

Elizabeth Bennet suffered a particular slight at his hands, for when Bingley came up to him as he stood near her, and begged him to join in the dancing, he replied, looking at Jane:

"You are dancing with the only handsome girl in the room."

"Oh! She is the most beautiful creature I ever beheld! But there is one of her sisters sitting down just behind you, who is very pretty, and I dare say, very agreeable. Do let me ask my partner to introduce you."

"Which do you mean?" and turning round he looked for a moment at Elizabeth, till, catching her eye, he withdrew his own and coldly said: "She is tolerable, but not handsome enough to tempt me; and I am in no humour at present to give consequence to young ladies who are slighted by other men."

Relations between the young ladies of Longbourn and those of Netherfield were soon established firmly. Miss Bingley and her sister voted the mother intolerable, and the younger sisters not worth speaking to, but for the two eldest Miss

Bennets they expressed warm friendship. Elizabeth felt in their friendship a degree of superciliousness which she could not but suspect and resent, but the gentle Jane extended to the sisters of Mr. Bingley a happy, trusting affection. Elizabeth, seeing her beloved sister blossoming into radiant, though quiet happiness as the bond between her and Mr. Bingley strengthened, had not the heart to warn her to be on her guard.

Occupied in observing Mr. Bingley's attentions to her sister, Elizabeth was far from suspecting that she was herself becoming an object of some interest in the eyes of Mr. Darcy. He began to wish to know her better, and to observe her closely when they met. Of this she was perfectly unaware—to her he was only the man who made himself agreeable nowhere, and who had not thought her handsome enough to dance with.

Mr. Darcy was soon to have an opportunity of making himself better acquainted with Elizabeth. Jane had been invited to dine at Netherfield, and had been unlucky enough to catch a severe chill which necessitated her staying there overnight. Elizabeth, more anxious than her mother, insisted on walking over to see her sister. She found Jane so unwell that she was thankful to accept Miss Bingley's suggestion that she should stay with her.

Miss Bingley and her sister noted with concern, not only their brother's increasing partiality for Jane, but Mr. Darcy's admiration for Elizabeth. Elizabeth, indeed, felt ill at ease in the house. She knew that they would not approve of a match between Mr. Bingley and Jane; she knew, too, that Miss Bingley hoped to become the wife of Darcy, and mistress of his vast estates at Pemberley in Derbyshire, but so great was her prejudice against him that she could only feel that he deserved such a fate. She, no less than her hostess, was glad when the improvement in Jane's health was such that they could return to Longbourn.

Mr. Bennet's estate and fortune were entailed, and as he himself had no son, and his wife's fortune was small, his daughters looked to fare very ill in the event of their father dying. No patient explanations, no reasonable arguments could persuade Mrs. Bennet that the entail was anything but a piece of deliberate cruelty on the part of someone—and that Mr. Bennet could order it otherwise if he chose. A few days after their return, Mr. Bennet received a letter from his cousin and heir, Mr. Collins.

Hunsford, nr. Westerham, Kent.
15th October.

DEAR SIR,

The disagreement subsisting between yourself and my late honoured father, always gave me much uneasiness, and since I have had the misfortune to lose him, I have frequently wished to heal the breach; but for some time I was kept back by my own doubts, fearing least it might seem disrespectful to his memory for me to be on good terms with any one, with whom it had always pleased him to be at variance. My mind, however, is now made up on the subject, for having received ordination at Easter, I have been so fortunate as to be distinguished by the patronage of the Right Honourable Lady Catherine de Bourgh, widow of Sir Lewis de Bourgh, whose bounty and beneficence has preferred me to the valuable rectory of this parish, where it shall be my earnest endeavour to demean myself with grateful respect towards her Ladyship, and be ever ready to perform those rites and ceremonies which are instituted by the Church of England. As a clergyman, moreover, I feel it my duty to promote and establish the blessings of peace in all families within the reach of my influence; and on these grounds I flatter myself that my present overtures of good-will are highly commendable, and that the circumstances of my being next in the entail of Longbourn estate, will be kindly overlooked on your side, and not lead you to reject the olive branch. I cannot be otherwise than concerned at being the means of injuring your amiable daughters, and beg leave to apologise for it, as well as to assure you of my readiness to make amends—but of this hereafter. If you should have no objection to receive me into your house, I propose myself the satisfaction of waiting on you and your family, Monday, November 18th, by four o'clock, and shall probably trespass on your hospitality till the Saturday se'night following, which I can do without any inconvenience, as Lady Catherine is far from objecting to my occasional absence on a Sunday providing that some other clergyman is engaged to do the duty of the day. I remain, dear sir, with respectful compliments to your lady and daughters, your well-wisher and friend,

WILLIAM COLLINS.

Mr. Collins presented himself punctual to the hour, and was cordially received. He was a tall, heavy-looking young man of five-and-twenty who talked incessantly of his own good fortune in acquiring the living at Hunsford, and of the virtues of his patroness, Lady Catherine de Bourgh. He had come to Longbourn with the intention of marrying one of the daughters if their good looks and amiable characters were all that was reported. When he saw Jane's lovely face, he found no cause to alter his mind, but on a delicate hint from Mrs. Bennet that the eldest Miss Bennet's affections were engaged, to change from Jane to Elizabeth was soon done—done as Mrs. Bennet stirred the fire.

A mile from the village of Longbourn, where the Bennets resided, was Meryton, a convenient distance for the young ladies, who were usually tempted thither three or four times a week, to visit their Aunt Phillips, a sister of their mother, and no less foolish.

The two youngest of the family, Catherine and Lydia, were particularly frequent in their visits to their aunt. Their minds were more vacant than their elder sisters', and the gossip of Meryton was their chief amusement. At present, indeed, they were well supplied with news and happiness by the recent arrival of a militia regiment, which was to be quartered in the district for the winter and whose headquarters was Meryton itself.

On the morning after Mr. Collins' arrival, the young ladies, with the exception of Mary, set off to walk to Meryton escorted by their cousin. Lydia wished to find out if a certain Lieutenant Denny had returned yet, and great was her joy in espying him almost directly they reached the town. On observing them, Mr. Denny came up, and begged to introduce his friend, a Mr. Wickham, who had returned with him to take a commission in the regiment. The whole party were still standing and talking very amiably when Mr. Bingley and Mr. Darcy were observed riding down the street. They came up to salute the ladies. Mr. Bingley was remarking that they had been about to call at Longbourn and Mr. Darcy was corroborating it with a bow when he was suddenly arrested by the sight of the stranger. Elizabeth happened to observe both their countenances, and was astonished at the effect of the meeting. One turned red, and the other white. After a moment, Mr. Wickham touched his hat—a salutation which Mr. Darcy just deigned to return. What could be the meaning of it?—It was impossible to imagine; it was impossible not to long to know.

Elizabeth's curiosity was satisfied not long afterwards, for at a party given by her aunt Phillips, Wickham sitting by her opened the subject by asking hesitantly how long Darcy had been in the neighbourhood. He then went on to tell Elizabeth that he himself had known Darcy from his infancy. His father had been steward of the Pemberley estates, and he himself was the godson of Darcy's father.

"—— and I can never be in company with this Mr. Darcy without being grieved to the soul by a thousand tender recollections. His behaviour to myself has been scandalous, but I verily believe I could forgive him anything and everything rather than his disappointing the hopes and disgracing the memory of his father.")

Later in the evening, Wickham heard Collins mention Lady Catherine de Bourgh, and enquired of Elizabeth his relationships with her. Elizabeth explained her cousin's position.

" You know," said Wickham, " that Lady Catherine and Lady Anne Darcy were sisters; consequently she is aunt to the present Mr. Darcy. Her daughter, Miss de Bourgh, will have a very large fortune, and it is believed that she and her cousin will unite the two estates."

Elizabeth smiled, thinking of the vain hopes of Miss Bingley.

After this occasion, Elizabeth was forced to admit to herself that the handsome Mr. Wickham occupied a great deal of her thoughts. His wrongs at the hands of Mr. Darcy made her yield more readily to this partiality, and when Mr. Bingley gave the long-promised ball at Netherfield, she anticipated with much pleasure the thought of meeting him again.

She was bitterly disappointed, for Wickham did not make his appearance at all. And in everything else, the evening accorded with her mood. She was continually teased by the heavy courtesies of her cousin, Mr. Collins; she was forced to dance with Mr. Darcy; she could learn nothing new of Mr. Wickham, and to her it appeared that had her family made an agreement to expose themselves as much as they could during the evening, it would have been impossible for them to play their parts with more spirit or finer success. Her mother's loud rejoicings at Jane's success with Mr. Bingley, the unrestrained behaviour of Lydia and Catherine, and the determined efforts of Mary to usurp the place of honour at the piano all filled her with shame. That Bingley's two sisters and Mr. Darcy should have such an opportunity of ridiculing her relations was bad enough, and she could not determine whether the silent contempt of the gentleman, or the insolent smile of the ladies was more intolerable. Only when she saw Jane's happiness was she consoled for her sufferings during that wretched evening.

The next day opened a new scene at Longbourn. Mr.

Collins made his declaration in form. Elizabeth was forced to listen to a long and weary dissertation on his reasons for marrying, his reasons for selecting her, and the inestimable blessings of their future life under the patronage of Lady Catherine de Bourgh. In vain did Elizabeth, torn between annoyance and humour, attempt to end the interview. He would not believe her when she declined the honour.

" I know it to be the established custom of your sex to reject a man on the first application, and perhaps you have even now said as much to encourage my suit as would be consistent with the true delicacy of the female character."

" Really, Mr. Collins," cried Elizabeth with some warmth, " you puzzle me exceedingly. If what I have hitherto said can appear to you in the form of encouragement, I know not how to express my refusal in such a way as may convince you of its being true." And despite his attempts to detain her with awkward gallantry, Elizabeth withdrew.

Mrs. Bennet knew Elizabeth's character better than Mr. Collins. When she heard of her refusal she was in no doubt that Elizabeth was determined in what she said. Her own ill temper when she saw one of her dearest plans coming to naught knew no bounds. She hurried immediately to her husband, and poured out the tale to him. He listened to her patiently, then summoned Elizabeth to the library.

" Come here, child," cried her father as she appeared. " I have sent for you on an affair of importance. I understand that Mr. Collins had made you an offer of marriage. Is it true? " Elizabeth replied that it was. " Very well—and this offer of marriage you have refused? "

" I have, sir."

" Very well. We now come to the point. Your mother insists upon your accepting it. Is not it so, Mrs. Bennet? "

" Yes, or I will never see her again."

" An unhappy alternative is before you, Elizabeth. From this day you must be a stranger to one of your parents. Your mother will never see you again if you do *not* marry Mr. Collins, and I will never see you again if you *do*! "

*   *   *   *   *

Elizabeth's attention was distracted from Mr. Collins, however, both by the return of Mr. Wickham, who told her that he had felt it better to avoid Mr. Darcy's company, and that therefore he had not attended the Netherfield ball, and more by the affairs of Jane. For Jane received a letter from

Miss Bingley bidding her an affectionate farewell, and stating plainly that Mr. Bingley had not the intention of returning to Netherfield that winter.   There was one passage in the letter which gave Jane particular hurt:—

> " Mr. Darcy is impatient to see his sister, and to confess the truth, *we* are scarcely less eager to meet her again.   I really do not think Georgiana Darcy has her equal for beauty, elegance and accomplishments; and the affection she inspires in Louisa and myself is heightened into something still more interesting from the hope we dare to entertain of her being hereafter our sister."

Elizabeth tried to console Jane by saying that it was merely an attempt of Miss Bingley to part her brother and Jane, and at last had the happiness of seeing her sister hope again.

Mr. Collins, it has been stated, came to Hertfordshire with the intention of finding a wife.   He did not mean to be crossed in his purpose.   After his rebuff by Elizabeth, he found consolation at the hands of Charlotte Lucas.   Charlotte meant to marry him.   He was neither sensible nor agreeable; his society was irksome, and his attachment to her must be imaginary.   But still, he would be her husband—it was an excellent match, and Charlotte was twenty-seven.   She might do a lot worse.   He proposed, and was accepted with alacrity.

The news was received in the Bennet household with varying emotions.   Elizabeth and Jane were frankly shocked, then grieved that their friend should have shown so little sensibility as to marry such a man.   Mr. Bennet was amused, Mrs. Bennet hysterically outraged.   When Mr. Collins at length took his departure, she could barely be civil.

The Monday after he had gone, Mrs. Bennet had the pleasure of receiving her brother and his wife, who came as usual to spend Christmas at Longbourn.   Mr. Gardiner was a sensible, gentleman-like man, greatly superior to his sisters, as well by nature as education.   The Netherfield ladies would have had difficulty in believing that a man who lived by trade could have been so well bred and agreeable.   Mrs. Gardiner was an amiable, intelligent, elegant woman, and a great favourite with all her Longbourn nieces.   Between the two eldest, and herself especially, there subsisted a very particular regard.

From Mrs. Bennet, Mrs. Gardiner heard many grievances and complaints: how two of her girls were on the point of being married, and how nothing came of it all.   From

Elizabeth and Jane she heard the other side of the story. At Elizabeth's plight she could laugh, but the patient, gentle unhappiness of Jane was a different matter. To Elizabeth she suggested that they should take Jane back to town with them, where a change of scene and relief from her mother's constant bewailings might ease her. Elizabeth was exceedingly pleased with this proposal and felt persuaded of her sister's acquiescence.

During their stay at Longbourn, the Gardiners saw much of the officers stationed at Meryton, who did, indeed, constitute most of the society of the district. At most gatherings Mr. Wickham was present, and Mrs. Gardiner, rendered suspicious by Elizabeth's warm commendation of him, narrowly observed them both. Their preference for each other was enough to make her uneasy, and she felt it her duty to warn her niece of the imprudence of encouraging such an attachment. For both Mr. Wickham and herself were without any sort of fortune.

Elizabeth was too sensible to resent her aunt's gentle interference, or not to realize she spoke truly, and she promised to consider carefully her feelings towards Mr. Wickham.

Scarcely had the Gardiners returned to town taking Jane with them, than Mr. Collins returned for his wedding. Charlotte left for her new life at Hunsford with no admission of her doubts of being very happy other than an earnest plea to Elizabeth to pay her a visit as soon as she could.

In those early weeks of the new year, nothing so occupied her mind as the unhappiness of her sister. Jane wrote that Miss Bingley had called at last, but that her coldness left her in no doubt as to the altered state of her affections. Of Mr. Bingley there had been no sign.

March took Elizabeth to Hunsford in the company of Sir William and Maria Lucas. She had at first contemplated the visit with some misgivings, but now was all eagerness. For one thing, she would see her sister as they passed through London; for another, Mr. Wickham's attentions were now engrossed by another—a Miss King who had lately inherited ten thousand pounds. Elizabeth admitted that her vanity rather than her heart was touched, but she was none the less glad to be gone.

Their arrival at Hunsford was greeted by Charlotte with delight, and by Mr. Collins with a profusion of tedious courtesies and the promise of a sight of Lady Catherine de

Bourgh the following Sunday. The honour of their presentation to Mr. Collins' patroness came sooner than that, for Lady Catherine having heard of the visitors' arrival, and being consumed by an overwhelming curiosity and a passion for interfering in other people's affairs, invited them to dine the next day.

Elizabeth found her to be very much the type of woman she had expected, haughty, overbearing and stupid. Her daughter Ann was a sickly, peevish girl, who had inherited too many of her mother's less pleasant characteristics, but had not her commanding personality.

They had been at Hunsford a little over a week, and Sir William, having satisfied himself that Charlotte was happily settled, had returned into Hertfordshire, when Mr. Collins came in one morning with the intelligence that Mr. Darcy and a cousin, a Colonel Fitzwilliam, had arrived on a visit to their aunt. Mr. Collins hastened to Rosings the next morning. To the great amazement of both Charlotte and Elizabeth he returned accompanied by the gentlemen. Mr. Darcy enquired civilly after the family at Longbourn. Elizabeth answered him in the usual way, adding: " My eldest sister has been in Town these three months. Have you never happened to see her there? " His slight look of confusion, as he told her he had not had the pleasure, informed Elizabeth that he had some consciousness of what had passed between the Bingleys and Jane. Not long afterwards, she had her suspicions confirmed, for Colonel Fitzwilliam told her how Mr. Darcy had saved a young friend of his from an imprudent match, and that he believed the friend to be Mr. Bingley. Though she had always believed Darcy to have had a share in Jane's unhappiness, this sudden revelation threw her into such a violent state of emotion that she hardly knew how to bear herself.

She was sitting by herself the next morning, reading over Jane's unhappy letters, when Mr. Darcy was announced. Anger kept her silent except to answer his greetings with cold civility. Mr. Darcy was agitated; he paced the room, then suddenly came towards her and burst out:

" In vain have I struggled. It will not do. My feelings will not be repressed. You must allow me to tell you how ardently I admire and love you! "

Elizabeth's astonishment was beyond expression. She could not have prevented his continuing. There were feelings besides those of the heart to be detailed, and he was not more

eloquent on the subject of tenderness than of pride. He spoke
of the inferiority of her family and of her connections, and
when at last he ceased the colour rose in Elizabeth's cheeks.
"—— if I could feel gratitude, I would now thank you,"
she said, "but I cannot—I have never desired your good
opinion, and you have certainly bestowed it most unwillingly!" She was sorry to have caused him pain, but
"—— had not my own feelings decided against you, had they
been indifferent, or had they even been favourable, do you
think that any consideration would tempt me to accept the
man who has been the means of ruining, perhaps for ever,
the happiness of a most beloved sister?" Then with steadily
growing anger, she went on to accuse him of terrible injustice
to Wickham. Darcy heard her to the end, then with a few
cold words of regret for his presumption he left her.

The next morning he delivered himself to her a letter which
he begged she would read. She found it contained no renewal
of his proposal, but an answer to the charges she had brought
against him. He admitted that he had used his influence
with Bingley to separate him from Jane. He said he felt the
match to be an imprudent one from his friend's point of view,
but he believed—and he assured Elizabeth of his utter sincerity
on this point—that when Bingley left Hertfordshire, Jane's
attachment for him was not strong. On this point he admitted now he might have been mistaken, and he deeply
regretted the sorrow he had caused.

Then he went on to deal with Elizabeth's second charge—
his treatment of Wickham. On this point he wrote at greater
length. He admitted his father's partiality for Wickham—his
godson—and also that in his will he had recommended to his
son that he should be given a living in his gift. But, Darcy
went on, even before the death of his father, Wickham had
become a profligate, dissolute young man. His vices he was
careful to conceal from his patron, but could not conceal from
the son. When the elder Darcy died, Wickham wrote saying
that he did not wish to go into orders, but desired to study
law, and needed monetary help. He accepted from Darcy
the sum of three thousand pounds and in return relinquished
all claim on the living. In little more than a year he had
squandered all the money, and wrote again saying he had
decided after all to take orders, and was ready to step into the
living. Not unnaturally, Darcy refused his claim. But that
was not the end of his villainy. He went down to Ramsgate,

where Darcy's sister, then just out of school, was staying with her chaperone. He so duped the child—an heiress in her own right—with his easy charm, that she consented to elope with him. Mercifully Darcy found out just in time to save his sister.

It can be imagined with what mixed feelings Elizabeth read this letter. She still felt that Darcy had interfered unwarrantably in her sister's affairs, but admitted the sincerity of his actions. In the affair of Wickham she knew herself to have been wholly wrong, and burned with shame when she realized how she had been misled.

That day Darcy and Fitzwilliam left. Elizabeth was thankful that she too was to return home. She yearned to be able to unburden herself to Jane.

Elizabeth and Maria Lucas broke their journey in London, and when they set out again for Hertfordshire, Jane was with them. Elizabeth was pleased to see an improvement in her sister's health, but could see that try as she would to conquer her unhappiness, Jane was still in very low spirits. She confided Darcy's proposal, and his account of Wickham. On her own affairs she felt it kinder to keep silence. Jane was deeply shocked, but as Wickham was removing from the neighbourhood they felt it better to keep their own counsel.

Then Lydia was transported with delight by an invitation from Mrs. Forster, Colonel Forster's lady, to accompany her to Brighton, whence the militia had moved to summer quarters. In vain Elizabeth pleaded with her father not to let Lydia go. Her father could not face the storm that his refusal would bring on his head, so to Brighton Lydia went, and after Catherine had got over her disappointment at not being asked as well, the house settled down to peace once more.

In July Elizabeth was to tour in Northern England with the Gardiners. She had been looking forward to this holiday, and it was with great pleasure that she left Longbourn again in the company of her aunt and uncle. She did not know whether she was glad or sorry when her aunt expressed her desire to visit Pemberley, which she had known well as a child.

Elizabeth was reassured by the housekeeper that the family was still away, so that she was able to enjoy wandering over the fine old house, and admiring the beauties of the park.

They were walking across the lawn towards the gates, and had turned to take a last look at the house, when the owner of it himself suddenly appeared. Both he and Elizabeth were startled, but Darcy recovered himself first, and coming up to her greeted her, asked after her family and begged to be introduced to her friends.

In the days that followed Elizabeth was astonished at the change in the master of Pemberley. His manner was quiet and subdued, he made every effort to please Elizabeth, and her aunt and uncle. She met his sister Georgiana, who obviously also desired to be pleasing. This much-talked-of heiress Elizabeth found not to be proud at all, as Wickham had reputed her to be, but only painfully shy. Bingley and his sister were staying at Pemberley, and Bingley's manner led Elizabeth to believe that Longbourn would soon have the pleasure of a visit from him.

But just when it seemed that all misunderstandings were at an end, Elizabeth received a letter from Jane, begging her to return home, where they were in great distress. Lydia had eloped with Wickham, and no trace could be found of the fleeing couple, but it was feared that they had not married.

Elizabeth had just read this dreadful news when Darcy was announced, and she could not hide from him her agitation and distress. He heard her news with grave concern, and having done what he could for her, left her.

Within an hour of the receipt of the letter Elizabeth, her uncle and aunt were on their way home. The journey to Longbourn was terrible to Elizabeth. Again and again she blamed herself for not having spoken openly of what she knew of Wickham. Then her thoughts wandered to Mr. Darcy. She would never see him again, she thought. This last shame had lost him to her for ever. Now that it was too late, she knew she did indeed love him.

At last Longbourn was reached. Elizabeth found a sorry state of affairs. Her mother, in constant hysterics, kept to her room. Jane was worn out, her father had gone to London to try to trace the fugitives. Then Mr. Gardiner followed immediately, and the women settled down to wait for news with what patience they could muster.

Weary days passed. Mr. Bennet returned home, leaving the search to his more capable brother-in-law; then at last Mr. Gardiner wrote. He had found them, they were unmarried, but if Mr. Bennet would agree to a very moderate settlement, they could be married immediately. The stricken household could lift its head again.

It had been Mr. Bennet's fixed intention to refuse to see his daughter again; but calmer counsels prevailed. Wickham was to go north very shortly to join a regiment there. Mr. Bennet reluctantly gave permission for the newly-married pair to come to Longbourn to make their farewells.

In describing her marriage to Elizabeth, Lydia mentioned that Mr. Darcy had been present at the ceremony. Elizabeth's curiosity could not be subdued. She wrote to her aunt Gardiner begging for an explanation. She received, in due course, an answer which gave her a sense of mingled joy and astonishment. For it had been Mr. Darcy who had traced the fugitives, Darcy who had persuaded Wickham to marry Lydia by settling his debts, buying him a new commission and setting him up again. Elizabeth dared not acknowledge even to herself, what she knew in her heart to be true—he had done this for her.

The Wickhams left, regretted by no one except Mrs. Bennet, and her lamentations speedily turned to rejoicings, for Mr. Bingley arrived again at Netherfield.

He called, accompanied by Mr. Darcy. It was very plain that only a few days would pass before Mr. Bingley declared himself to Jane, but Elizabeth was puzzled by Mr. Darcy's behaviour. He was grave and silent, and watched her always, but he said very little.

" Why, if he came only to be silent, grave and indifferent," said she, " did he come at all? "

At one point *she* at least could not remain silent. A few days after Jane had become engaged to Mr. Bingley. Elizabeth found herself walking alone with Darcy, and while her courage was high she told him she must thank him for what he had done for Lydia.

"—— I thought only of you," he replied. Elizabeth could find nothing to say, and he went on: " You are too generous to trifle with me. If your feelings are still what they were last April, tell me so at once. My affections and wishes are unchanged, but one word from you will silence me on this subject for ever."

Elizabeth forced herself to speak, and to tell him how great was the change in her feelings towards him, and how happy she was in his present assurances. They walked on, scarcely knowing where they went, so much was there to be felt and thought and said.

Elizabeth suffered the last retribution of her oft violently expressed prejudice against Darcy when her family was in-

formed of her engagement. They could not believe her
serious at first. But when at last she persuaded them of her
great happiness, they rejoiced with her. Her mother received
the news in her own fashion.

"Good gracious! Lord bless me! only think! dear me!
Mr. Darcy! Who would have thought it! Oh, my sweetest
Lizzie! how rich and how great you'll be!—— Dear, dear
Lizzie! A house in Town! Three daughters married! Ten
thousand a year! Oh, Lord! What will become of me? I
shall go distracted."

Mr. Bennet's reaction was equally characteristic.

"I admire all my three sons-in-law highly," said he.
"Wickham, perhaps, is my favourite: but I think I shall like
your husband quite as well as Jane's."

There is little more to tell. Elizabeth took up her new life
at Pemberley, happy in the love of her husband and her dearly
loved new sister, Georgiana. Jane and her husband bought an
estate near to them, and sold Netherfield, which was a little
too near Mrs. Bennet for comfort. To them came often, as a
welcome visitor, Mr. Bennet, and Catherine, who in the society
of her elder sister's friends became much improved.

With the Gardiners they were always on the most intimate
terms. Darcy, as well as Elizabeth, really loved them, and
they were both sensible of the warmest gratitude towards the
persons who, by bringing her into Derbyshire, had been the
means of uniting them.

EUGÉNIE GRANDET

By HONORÉ DE BALZAC

" Eugénie Grandet " (published 1833), *a novel from Balzac's " Scenes of Provincial Life ", is one of his greatest works.   The story is slight, but the careful building up of the characters, of the miser Grandet and his household, must be read* in extenso *for the student to gain a full idea of the exquisite observation and discrimination that have gone to their creation.*

THE stranger who climbs the dark and narrow street that winds through Saumur might almost believe the old market-town had been evacuated by its inhabitants at some time during the Middle Ages, if now and then a pale, cold face did not appear above a window-sill at the sound of an unaccustomed step on the echoing cobbles.   There is no sign of life about the shops, which are not easy to distinguish from the houses, for they have no front windows and no show-cases, but only a wooden door, the top half of which is bolted back, while the lower forms a kind of gate that jangles a bell when you push it open.   You enter—and find yourself in a dim cavern amid a few tubs of codfish or bales of sail-cloth or iron hoops, according to the nature of the business. A young girl with red arms and white kerchief lays aside her knitting and calls her father, who serves you without betraying the least sign of emotion, whether you spend two sous or twenty thousand francs.   He seems to possess nothing but some old planks or two or three bundles of laths, but his timber-yard on the river supplies all the coopers in Anjou; he knows to a stave how many casks he can sell if the vine harvest is good; a sunbeam can enrich him, a shower ruin him; in a single morning the price of a puncheon can fall from eleven francs to six.

At the top of the street, shadowed by the ancient ramparts of the town, stands the house of Monsieur Grandet.   He cultivated a hundred acres of vineyard, and possessed in addition thirteen farms and a hundred and twenty-seven acres of meadow.   But only two people could hazard a guess as to the amount of his invested capital—Monsieur Cruchot the notary,

who had charge of the vine-dresser's loans throughout the
province, and Monsieur Des Grassins, the wealthiest banker
in Saumur, in whose profits Monsieur Grandet shared at his
discretion and convenience.

"He must be worth at least six million francs," people
were saying of Père Grandet in 1819, when this story opens.
Though seventy-six years old, he looked no more than fifty.
He was sturdy and thickset in every inch of his five feet,
with broad shoulders, a straight back, and hands like legs of
mutton. His face was sunburnt and wrinkled, and his eyes
had in them the calm and eerie light which legend attributes
to the basilisk. The end of his nose was adorned with a
blue-veined wen. If this dilated ever so slightly, it was
regarded in Saumur as ominous as a sign of bad weather.

He had dressed for more than thirty years in exactly the
same manner—Quaker hat, black cravat, full-skirted brown
coat over a velvet waistcoat with yellow and violet stripes,
short breeches of coarse brown cloth with silver buckles,
milled cotton stockings, and stout black shoes.

In the course of years, his growing fortune began to cast
an aura of gold over everything he did or said. His speech,
his clothes, his gestures, the movements of his eyes, acquired
the force of law in the province. "It'll be a hard winter,"
some one would say. "Père Grandet has put on his fur
gloves." Or "Père Grandet is getting in lots of staves, there'll
be plenty of wine this year."

Monsieur Grandet never bought any food for his household, which consisted of his wife, his only daughter, Eugénie,
and the servant, Nanon. His tenants brought him every week
a stock of flour, poultry, eggs, butter and vegetables by way
of rent. His only known expenses were for bread for the
Communion, his wife's and daughter's dresses and their chairs
at the church, light, Nanon's wages and the cost of re-tinning
her saucepans, taxes, repairs and outlays on farming operations.

The whole town envied Monsieur and Madame Grandet
their servant. She had been an inmate of the Grandet mansion for thirty-five years. She was twenty-two years old when
she came to Saumur in a vain search for work. Grandet
ran his eye over the girl as she was turned away from one
door after another. The trade of master-cooper gave him an
unerring eye for physical strength; he saw how much toil
might be extracted from a woman built on the model of a
Hercules, planted on her feet like a sixty-year oak on its roots,

strong-hipped, square-backed, and with the hands of a carrier. Neither the pocks and warts that embellished her martial face, nor her brick-red skin, nor her sinewy arms, nor her rags, dismayed the cooper, who was still at an age when the heart is easily moved. He clothed, shod, and fed the poor girl, gave her wages and employed her. Nanon wept for joy, and henceforth obeyed him like a dog.

Now and then an impulse of pity would seize Grandet as he reflected that Nanon had never known any of the joys of normal womanhood. He would look at her and mutter "Poor Nanon!" This exclamation was always followed by an indescribable glance of devotion from the old servant. Grandet, noting with approval that nothing was ever wasted in her neat, cold kitchen, became quite fond of her, and allowed her many a small treat. "Go and eat your fill, Nanon," he often said to her in seasons when the fruit trees in his orchard were so laden with plums and nectarines that he was obliged to feed them to the pigs.

*　　*　　*　　*　　*

"Well, as it's Eugénie's birthday, I think we'll have a fire," said Grandet one evening in the middle of November, 1819, as he sat with his wife and daughter in the *salle* of their home.

Grandet's present to Eugénie on her birthday was always a curious gold piece of some kind or other—an old foreign coin worth far more than its face value. He also gave her one or more such coins every New Year's Day and on certain saints' days. He loved to tease her about this little hoard, and on each New Year's Day he asked to see it.

Grandet had invited Cruchot his notary, Des Grassins his banker, with their wives to call round after dinner for a game of loto in celebration of Eugénie's birthday. Des Grassins was the wealthiest banker in Saumur. Scarcely had Nanon lighted the fire, when there was a knock at the door, and a few moments later the guests entered the *salle*.

They took up their positions in two groups on either side of the great table. No stranger to the province would ever have guessed from their smiles and pleasant nods that enmity had arisen between these two families as remorseless as that which formerly existed between the Medicis and the Pazzis.

The secret combat between the Cruchots and the Des Grassins for the hand of Eugénie Grandet, the wealthiest heiress in Saumur, was the talk of the entire town. Would she marry Monsieur Cruchot's nephew, the brilliant young lawyer who had just been appointed president of the court of first instance at Saumur, or Monsieur Adolphe Des Grassins, whose parents were not only rich, but of noble birth as well? None could say with certainty, least of all perhaps Eugénie herself, who appeared quite unaware of the intrigues that went on around her.

The Cruchot faction consisted of the Abbé Cruchot, a plump little man with shrewd and restless eyes, his brother Monsieur Cruchot the notary, a tall and dignified figure who rarely spoke if he could avoid doing so, and the lanky, conceited, red-haired young President Cruchot, who now advanced and offered Eugénie a huge bouquet of flowers that were rare at Saumur.

" Permit me, mademoiselle, to wish you many happy years and a continuance of the health you enjoy," he said in a falsetto voice, then, taking Eugénie by the elbows, he kissed her on both sides of the neck so awkwardly that she blushed with humiliation.

It was now the turn of young Adolphe Des Grassins. He was a tall, fair-haired stripling, pale and slender, and still rather bashful, though he had spent ten thousand francs over his allowance as a student in Paris on learning to be a man of the world. He walked up to Eugénie, kissed her on both cheeks, and offered her a workbox with " E. G." engraved on the crest. Eugénie opened it, and the sight of the silver-gilt utensils made her tremble with joy. She glanced interrogatively at her father, and Grandet uttered a " Take it, my child! " in an accent that would have done credit to a great actor.

Madame Des Grassins looked round triumphantly at the Cruchots. She was one of those buxom and attractive women, with faces white and pink as a doll's, who, thanks to the monastic régime and virtuous habits of the provinces, maintain their youth to the age of forty. She dressed very well and set the fashion in Saumur. Her husband, a former quartermaster of the Imperial Guard, retained the free-and-easy manner of a military man in spite of his dignity as a banker and his regard for his host.

By half-past eight, the game of loto was in full swing. Madame Grandet had just won a pool of sixteen sous—the biggest ever played for in that room—and Nanon did not try to conceal her delight. She never could look at her mistress without a twinge of pity. Madame Grandet was a thin, dried-up woman, yellow as a quince, and awkward and slow of movement. She had large bones, a large nose, a large forehead, large eyes, and she reminded one of a stringy fruit without either savour or juice. But everyone admired and respected her. She was an angel of piety, kindliness and resignation.

She had brought Grandet as her marriage portion the sum of three hundred thousand francs. Occasionally he would give her six francs for pin money. But whenever he ran short of small change, he never hesitated to say to her, as if they had this fund in common, " Can you let me have a few sous, *maman*? "

Suddenly there was such a thunderous knocking at the door that the women jumped from their seats in alarm. Nanon hastened to the door, followed by Grandet. A moment afterwards, a fashionably-dressed young man entered the *salle*, accompanied by a porter struggling with two enormous trunks and a number of carpet-bags.

The young man gave a letter to Grandet, raised a small monocle to his eye, and drawled affectedly, " I presume I have the honour of addressing my uncle. I am the son of your brother Guillaume of Paris."

A peacock in a farmyard would have appeared less out of place than this exquisite young fop among the astounded circle of his beholders.

Eugénie gazed at him with breathless awe. She had never even imagined a man could be so attractive in person and costume. The perfume that exhaled from his glossy curls made her senses swim with delight. She was enchanted by the smallness and whiteness of his hands, the freshness of his complexion, the delicacy of his features. She would have given anything in the world just to touch the satiny kid of his dainty gloves.

Adolphe Des Grassins and President Cruchot, suddenly conscious of their worn and rumpled cravats, snuff-stained shirts, shiny coats, and creased pantaloons, exchanged glances of dismay. Could it be possible that young Charles Grandet had come from Paris in order to ask for the hand of Eugénie in marriage? They had often been told by their elders that Guillaume Grandet had far loftier views of his son's future. One of the richest wholesale dealers in wines in Paris, mayor of an arrondissement, colonel in the National Guard, judge of the tribunal of commerce, it was said that he disowned the

Grandets of Saumur, and intended to form an alliance with some ducal family by the favour of Napoleon.

"Let us call off the game and keep our sous," said Madame Des Grassins. The players each took two sous from an old chipped bowl which held the pool, and rose from the table.

Grandet looked up from his letter. "Have you finished?" he said.

"Yes, yes," replied Madame Des Grassins. There was a flush in her plump white cheeks. She glanced at Charles Grandet, lolling indolently on his chair by the fireside. The young dandy smiled at her. Her eyes, full of the reserve and caution habitual to middle-aged women in the provinces, suddenly glowed with a prurience that reminded Charles of the nights he had spent recently in the arms of his lovely Annette, before her suspicious husband took her with him on a tour of Scotland.

Monsieur Des Grassins glanced at his wife, then said to Grandet, "We don't want to intrude. You may wish to talk with your nephew, so we will bid you good-night."

The guests took their leave. Grandet read the letter for the third time.

My Brother,

When you have this letter in your hands, I shall have ceased to live, for I have determined not to face the disgrace of bankruptcy. The failures of my broker and of Roguin, my notary, have swept away my last resources and left me nothing. Poor Charles, whom I idolize, knows nothing of this. Oh my unhappy son, my son! Grandet, dying, I entrust Charles to you. I view my pistols without sorrow, knowing that you will be another father to him. Brother, Charles is an upright, brave young man. Lend him enough money to go to the Indies, where he can work to regain the fortune of which I have deprived him.

Adieu, brother. May all God's blessings rest upon you in the fulfilment of the trust I confide to you, and which you will accept, I doubt not. There will be one voice then that will pray unceasingly for you in the world to which we must all go some day and where I already am.

GUILLAUME GRANDET.

Grandet folded up the letter, put it in his pocket, and glanced with an almost timid air at his nephew. "Well, Charles, if you're ready," he said, "I'll show you to your room. It won't be a fine gentleman's apartment, faith! but you will excuse a poor vine-dresser who hasn't a sou. Taxes swallow up everything."

As Charles glanced at the yellow, grimy walls of the staircase, and felt the worm-eaten rail tremble under his hand, his heart sank, and he said to himself, " What the devil did father send me here for? "

*　　*　　*　　*　　*

There is a delicious hour in the life of every young girl when the golden beams of the sun reawaken in her the thrill she felt as a child on seeing them for the first time, when every flower reveals its thoughts to her, and when her heart beats with a vague, sweet torment that will allow her no rest. Such a season of rapture began for Eugénie as she sat at the window of her bedroom and looked into the garden on the morning after her cousin's arrival.

" I am not pretty enough; he'll never take any notice of me," she thought despondently, as she gazed into the mirror, and her fine grey eyes filled with tears. Her beauty was in truth of the kind that enchants the artist rather than a lover— somewhat too regular and cold in its lines. Her features, the contours of her round face, suggested noble devotion rather than passion; her mouth, though red as a cherry, was marked with countless little lines that were instinct with the kindness and sympathy of a maturer age than twenty-three; her neck was divinely graceful; only her swelling corsage would have made the pulses of a gay young Parisian beat more quickly.

Eugénie sat by the window until she heard Nanon astir in the kitchen. Then she ran downstairs and cried to the old servant:

" Let's make a cake for him, Nanon."

Nanon gaped at her in astonishment. " Who'll give me wood for the oven, and flour and butter? " she asked. " Must I steal from Monsieur Grandet to feast your cousin? See, there's your father now, coming in from the orchard; you'd better ask him yourself." But at the sight of her father, Eugénie had already turned and fled in alarm into the garden.

Père Grandet walked into the kitchen, took a key from his pocket, and unlocked the door of the pantry.

" Is there any bread left from yesterday? " he said to Nanon.

" Not a crumb, monsieur."

Grandet took a coarse round loaf from the pantry and was about to cut it, when Nanon said, " There are five of us to-day, monsieur."

" True," replied Grandet, " but this loaf weighs six pounds and there'll be plenty left over. Besides, you'll see that this fine young gentleman from Paris won't deign to eat bread."

" Give me some flour and butter, and I'll make a cake."

" Do you think just because the fellow's my nephew I'm going to let him eat us out of house and home? "

" No, monsieur, I thought it would be a treat for all of us. But you've only put out six lumps of sugar for the coffee. I must have eight."

" Look here, Nanon, I don't know what nonsense has got into your head. If I've any more of it, you'll pack your things and go. Six lumps are all we need."

" But what will your nephew sugar his coffee with? "

" With two lumps; I'll go without."

" I'd rather buy you two lumps out of my own pocket," said Nanon boldly.

" Silence! " roared Grandet. He glanced at his watch, took his hat, and set off along the banks of the Loire to see if his workmen were making progress in clearing his fields of poplars.

An hour later, young Charles Grandet was sitting down to the noon breakfast that Eugénie had prepared for him. This meal was always a simple one in the household, and consisted merely of a little bread and butter and a glass of wine or cup of coffee. But Eugénie had sent Nanon out to the shops and had made, in the old servant's words, " a real spread " for her cousin—two boiled eggs, plates of fruit, a bottle of white wine, a bowl of coffee, preserve, and a saucer heaped high with lumps of sugar.

Charles, humming gaily to himself as he sampled the eggs, appeared quite unconscious of this honour, but the women kept glancing round furtively at the door, dreading every minute that Grandet would return before Charles had finished.

" 'Pon honour, my dear cousin," he murmured, " if you were in a box at the Opera, I promise that you would cause much sinning in the way of envy among the men and jealousy among the women."

Eugénie did not understand the compliment, but it made her heart throb wildly with delight. Before she could reply, there was a rap at the door that made all three women jump to their feet. Eugénie removed the saucer of sugar, Nanon hurried into the kitchen with the egg-plate, and Madame Grandet quivered like a startled deer.

"What in heaven's name is the matter with you all?" cried Charles.

Monsieur Grandet entered the *salle*, darted a piercing glance at the table, then at Charles. "Ah, so you've been feasting our young gentleman, eh?" he muttered. "When the cat's away, the mice run round the larder."

The three women held their breath as he came nearer the table and saw the lumps of sugar Eugénie had left on the cloth. Grandet turned and glared at his wife, who had closed her eyes and gone deathly pale.

He leaned over and whispered into her ear, "Where—did—you—get—that—sugar?"

"Nanon went to Fessard's for it."

At this moment of crisis, Charles tasted his coffee and, finding it not sweet enough, looked round for the saucer of sugar.

"What do you want, nephew?" asked Grandet.

"The sugar."

"Put in some milk," rejoined the master of the house hoarsely; "your coffee's a bit too strong, that's all."

Eugénie put the saucer of sugar back on the table in front of Charles, and looked her father squarely in the eyes. No heroine who ever risked death for her lover was braver than Eugénie Grandet at that moment.

The old vine-dresser strangled a noise in his throat. "When you have finished, nephew," he grunted, "we will take a turn in the garden together. I have things to tell you that are not . . . *sugared* !"

"What do you mean, uncle?" exclaimed Charles. "Since my poor mother's death"—his voice softened—"no misfortune could affect me."

"Come," said Grandet. The colour ebbed from Charles's face as he rose to his feet and followed his uncle into the garden. As he did so, Madame Grandet whispered to Eugénie the fatal news of the letter which her husband had read to her late the previous night.

"Courage, cousin!" shouted Eugénie, her face white.

The girl's tone froze Charles's blood. Grandet strolled up and down the gravel paths in silence for a few minutes before he broke the news of his brother's death.

Charles, who was only twenty-one years old, and had not yet learnt to control his emotions, burst into tears.

" That too is nothing, my poor nephew," added Grandet
in a kindlier tone; " that is nothing, you will get over your
grief, but——"

" Never! never! O my father, my dear father!"

" He has ruined you . . . you are penniless," said Grandet,
his voice breaking with pity.

" What do I care for that? I want my father! Father!"
screamed Charles again and again until the high walls around
the garden echoed and re-echoed with his cries. Suddenly he
turned away from his uncle, rushed blindly into the house, up
the staircase and into his room, where he flung himself on his
bed and sobbed as if his heart would break.

Grandet returned to the *salle*.

" I hope you do not intend to continue your extravagance,
Madame Grandet," he said. " I do not give you my money
to stuff that young fellow with sugar."

" Mother had nothing to do with it," said Eugénie. " I
was the one who——"

" Is it because you are of age," interrupted Grandet sternly,
" that you dare to disobey me? "

" But, father, your own brother's son ought not to go
without——"

" Ta, ta, ta, ta!" said the cooper in four different keys.
" My nephew here, my brother's son there. Charles is nothing
to us; he hasn't a sou to his name; his father has failed; and
when this young beau has wept his fill he'll have to take himself
off. I'm not going to let my house be turned upside down
on his account."

" What does failing mean, father?" asked Eugénie.

" To fail," Grandet replied solemnly, " is to commit
the most dishonourable of all acts that a man can
imagine."

" But daddy, couldn't you have helped uncle Guillaume *not*
to fail? "

" He did not consult me. Besides, he owed . . . millions of
francs."

" Millions of francs!" cried Eugénie, aghast. " *Mon Dieu,
mon Dieu!* Why, no one could have helped him. There can't
be anyone in all France with as much money as that!"

Père Grandet rubbed his chin, and the wen on his nose
seemed to expand a little.

" Whatever will become of poor cousin Charles?" asked
Eugénie.

"He's going to the Indies, where he will try to make his fortune as his father wished."

"But has he any money to get there?"

"I will pay for his journey as far as—yes—as far as Nantes." Eugénie flung her arms around her father's neck.

"Oh, father, how good you are!"

At that moment a hollow groan from the attic made Eugénie and her mother start with terror.

"Nanon, go and see if he's killing himself," said Grandet. His wife and daughter turned pale at these words. "Enough of this nonsense," he snapped. "I am going out for a chat with the Dutch wine merchants—they're leaving to-day."

The vine-dresser did not return until late in the evening. He entered the *salle* in high good-humour. Having taken off his gloves, he rubbed his hands together hard enough to bring the skin off, had it not been tanned like Russian leather. He strode to and fro ecstatically. At last his secret escaped him.

"Wife," he said, "I have outwitted the lot of them. Our wine is sold! The owners of all the other vineyards are holding on to their crops; I didn't say a word to prevent them. Besides, we'd all agreed not to sell. Our Dutchman was in despair. I got him up to two hundred francs the cask and sold him a thousand, ready cash, *gold*! Here are six francs for you. In three months the price of wine will drop like a stone."

"A thousand casks, daddy?" said Eugénie.

"Yes, *fifille*," said the vine-dresser, using a term of endearment that always meant he was delighted with her.

"That makes two hundred thousand francs," she said.

"Yes, Mademoiselle Grandet," he jested.

"Then, daddy, you could lend Charles enough to start a little business in the Indies."

Veins of purple stood out on the old cooper's neck. "Damnation!" he exploded. "Ever since that young popinjay set foot inside my home, everything has been turned topsy-turvy. You give yourself fine airs and graces. You buy sweetmeats. You set out wedding banquets. Well, I've had all I can stand of it, d'ye hear? Any more of this foolishness, young lady, and I'll pack you straight off to a convent. Now get to bed at once—both of you," he added, with a furious look at his wife.

That night, Eugénie thought she heard the moan of a dying man. Perhaps Charles had killed himself. . . . She sprang out of bed, wrapped herself in a *pelisse*, and opened the door a little. A light streamed through the aperture and she saw

before her on the landing her father and Nanon yoked together
by a staff that rested on their shoulders, and from which
swung at the end of a thick rope a heavy, ironbound cask.
A single candle placed between two uprights of the banisters
illumined the eerie scene.

Grandet had overheard the gossip of a travelling carpenter
to a farmer on the riverside that evening, who said that arma-
ments had begun on such a huge scale that gold had doubled
in value. Speculators were already at Angers trying to buy
what gold they could. By taking to Angers overnight all the
gold in his office, including the two hundred thousand louis the
Dutchman had just paid him, Grandet reckoned he could
clear a profit in Treasury bills of more than a million francs—
provided Des Grassins and the other Saumur bankers did not
get wind of his venture and forestall him.

Eugénie's eye met her father's, and she saw in it a look,
vague and unmeaning, but which none the less made her feel
as if hell itself were opening suddenly before her. With a gasp
of terror, she closed the door. She stood trembling in the
darkness while her father and Nanon slowly and clumsily
descended the stairs. She heard the neighing of horses, the
shout of a driver, and the sound of carriage wheels driving
away. At last all was quiet again. Gently, Eugénie opened
the door and tiptoed upstairs to her cousin's attic.

Charles was asleep in an old easy-chair, with his head
hanging over the arm, and one hand, from which a pen had
dropped, almost touching the floor. She lifted his head
and laid it against the back of the chair, and he submitted like
a child who even in his sleep knows his mother and is not
disturbed by her caresses. Then she leaned towards him
timidly and kissed his hair. Charles did not stir. Her glance
fell upon an open letter lying on the table. Quivering with
passion and curiosity, she picked it up. It began with the
words " My dear Annette ".

My DEAR ANNETTE,

Nothing could ever have parted us if a disaster which
shatters all my hopes had not overwhelmed me. My father has
committed suicide to escape bankruptcy, and his fortune and
mine have entirely disappeared. Dear Anna, even if you should
give up all your pleasures and your luxuries, your toilet and your
box at the Opera we could not retrench enough to meet my debts
in Paris. Nor could I accept so great a sacrifice. And so we
part to-day, for ever.

" Blessed Virgin, he renounces her!" thought Eugénie, her heart bounding for joy. She read on—

I had thought of trying my luck in the Indies or America, but I haven't even the hundred francs I need for my passage, no, not even one franc, for that matter. I want above all to restore my father's honour and my own by settling some day the immense debts he has left behind him. Then perhaps I could think of marriage—and I must confess that I have found here at Saumur, in my uncle's house, a cousin whose manners, face, mind and heart would please you, and who, moreover, seems to possess——

" He must have been very tired to have stopped writing," thought Eugénie. " Poor Charles! I did well to read his letter. I have plenty of money; I can help him."

She stole back to her room, lighted a candle, and opened the locked drawer of an old oaken chest. From this she took a large red velvet purse with tassels of gold thread. With a thrill of keen pleasure, which somehow reminded her of her father, she poured out its contents—rare coins, glistening like suns—*portugaises*, *genovines*, Spanish gold quadruples of Philip V, given her by her maternal grandmother, a hundred Dutch ducats coined in 1756, etc., etc., all worth much more than their face value. Finest of all were a number of rupees with the sign of the Balance or the Virgin, valued at fifty francs apiece by connoisseurs. Altogether, the hoard was worth nearly six thousand francs.

She scooped the coins back into the purse and went upstairs again. Just as she appeared in the doorway of the attic, Charles awoke and stared at his cousin in amazement. Eugénie entered the room, poured out the coins on the table and said in a trembling voice, " Here are my savings, Charles. Take them and go seek your fortune in the Indies." He did not answer. She fell on her knees, and took his hand in her own. " You will, won't you? " she said, weeping for joy. " This gold will bring you luck; some day you can repay me; we're partners if you like."

His eyes filled with tears. " You are an angel, Eugénie," he said hoarsely. Then, rising to his feet, he took from one of his trunks a square casket richly chased with gold.

" This dressing-case was a present from my mother," he said. He opened it, and displayed to his wondering cousin the exquisite workmanship of the gold inlay, and the finely-chased articles of toilet. " But that is nothing," he added. He pressed a spring and revealed a secret compartment, which

" Life is sweet, brother, who would wish to die? "

A scene from " Lavengro "

The lunatic sprang and grappled his throat vigorously

A scene from " Jane Eyre "

held two portraits, masterpieces by Madame de Mirbel, each
in a frame of pearls.

"My father and mother," he said. "Eugénie, I will
accept your gift—as a loan—if you will keep this treasure safe
for me. If I should die and lose your little fortune, this gold
will more than make it up to you. As for the portraits, there
is no one but you to whom I would entrust them, and, should
I not return, they are yours, too."

He took her hand and kissed it. "Angel of purity," he said,
" between us money will never be of any importance. Let the
world go hang, that's how we feel towards each other, eh ? "

The young couple spent most of the next day walking in the
garden. Charles said little to her, but his fond glances showed
from time to time that he was beginning to return her affection.
In this quiet sanctuary he was realizing for the first time in his
life that love could be tranquil; hitherto his dear Annette
had showed him only its storms and tempests.

That evening, Charles announced to the family that he
wanted to leave for Nantes as soon as possible. Grandet
immediately displayed great interest in aiding the young
man's departure with the utmost dispatch and economy.

On the last morning, as Charles and Eugénie were seated
pensively on the bench in the garden, he said to her, " I know
that we feel deeply for each other . . . but I cannot think of
returning for several years. Perhaps an opportunity for you
to make a wealthy marriage will present itself——"

" Do you love me? " she said, abruptly.

" More than my life," he replied with intense earnestness.

" Then I will wait." He moved nearer to kiss her.

" My father is at the window," she said, and ran into the
house.

He ran after her and caught her in the darkest part of the
corridor. He put his arm around her waist and drew her to
him. She raised her face and gave him the sweetest, purest
and frankest of all kisses.

" Dear Eugénie," said Charles, " a cousin is even better
than a brother, for he can marry you."

" Amen ! " cried Nanon, flinging open the door of her
kitchen, and laughing with joy as the lovers fled in dismay into
the *salle*.

*   *   *   *   *

Two months had elapsed since the day Charles left for the
Indies.

On the morning of January 1, 1820, Nanon entered Madame Grandet's bedroom crying, "What in the world's the matter with Monsieur Grandet? 'Happy New Year, you great ninny,' he says to me; 'run along and make a fire in my wife's room; it's freezing cold!' But you could have knocked me down with a feather when he reached out his hand and gave me a crown of six francs! He's a good man, madame, a fine man indeed. The older some men grow, the harder they get, but he's turning as sweet as your currant wine."

A few moments later, the old vine-dresser himself entered the room. "Happy New Year," he said jovially, and he bent forward and kissed his wife on the forehead.

"You're in high spirits this morning, monsieur," said the poor woman in a solemn tone.

"Always merry and bright, that's me. We're going to have a slap-up feed this morning, old girl. Des Grassins has sent along a *pâte-de-foie gras* with truffles!"

Grandet owed his cheerfulness to the sudden rise of the Funds from eighty-nine to ninety-two after he had invested in this stock all the Treasury notes he had got for his gold at Angers. He calculated that by reinvesting the interest, he would clear at least six million francs in the next five years.

After Nanon had cleared away the breakfast things, Grandet turned to his daughter and said, "Now for your little treasure. Little? Faith, no. Five thousand nine hundred and fifty-nine francs, and the forty you get this morning'll make it six thousand, less one. Well, I'll tell you what I'm going to do, *fifille*, I'm going to give you this franc to make up the round sum. So run along, sweetheart, and don't keep your father waiting."

Eugénie did not move.

"Listen, Eugénie. I'm asking you for your gold. You wouldn't refuse your poor old daddy, would you?" he wheedled. "I haven't any more gold left myself. I had a few old coins, but I let them all go. There isn't a grain of gold in the house, apart from yours. I'll give you six thousand francs for your gold, and you can put them into the Government Funds, so that you'll get nearly two hundred francs interest every six months. You ought to kiss me for telling you the secret of how money grows and multiplies like men and women," he added, with a horrible expression on his face. "So go and fetch me your treasure at once, my pet."

The two women sat as if petrified. But suddenly Eugénie

remembered Charles. "For him," she thought, "for him I would suffer a thousand deaths." And she glanced at her mother, to whom she had confided her secret, with eyes gleaming with resolution. Then she turned and faced her father.

"I no longer have my gold," she said.

Grandet reared like a horse that hears a cannon explode within ten feet of him.

"You are joking, Eugénie."

"No."

"By my father's pruning-knife!"

When the cooper swore like that, the rafters trembled.

"Mother of God!" cried Nanon, "see how pale madame has gone."

"Grandet, your anger will kill me," murmured the poor woman.

Eugénie sank on her knees beside her. "Father," she said, "mother is very ill—look!"

Grandet was terrified at the grey pallor of his wife's face, so yellow a moment before.

"Nanon, come and help me to bed," said the mother feebly. "I am dying." The old servant and Eugénie carried the swooning woman upstairs to her room.

When Eugénie came downstairs again, her father said to her fiercely, "Where is your treasure?"

Eugénie did not answer.

"You little b——, where is it? You're murdering me in cold blood. Did you lend it to Charles? But no, that's impossible, no daughter of mine could have been such a fool as to let that beggar in kid boots get his paws on it. At least you didn't part with it for nothing? Damnation, she won't budge, she won't move an eyelash, she's more of a Grandet than I am. Go to your room. You will stay there until I allow you to leave it. Nanon will bring you bread and water!"

In the months that followed, the old cooper visited his wife in her bedroom several times each day, but he never spoke to his daughter, never uttered her name or made the slightest allusion to her. Madame Grandet did not leave her room, and from day to day her condition grew worse. When visitors called to see her, she said nothing about Grandet's ill-treatment of Eugénie, for she was hoping to effect a reconciliation of father and daughter without an open scandal. But one

evening towards the close of spring, she was so overwhelmed
with grief that she betrayed to Monsieur Cruchot the true cause
of her suffering.

"Rest assured, madame," said the notary. "I will put an
end to this nonsense to-morrow."

Early the next morning, he found the old vine-dresser in the
garden. Grandet was in the habit now of standing behind the
walnut tree each morning at this hour, so that, unobserved,
he could watch his daughter brushing her luxuriant chestnut
tresses at the window of her room.

"Look here, Grandet," began the notary without more ado,
"everyone in Saumur is saying that you're killing your wife
by your cruelty to Eugénie."

The old cooper glared at him with blood-flecked eyes.
"What business is it of theirs," he said, thickly, "or of yours,
either, for that matter?"

"Do you realize what your position would be if your wife
died? Eugénie is her mother's heir. You and your wife hold
all your property in common. Your daughter would have the
right to demand half of everything you've got. The cost of
drawing up the inventory and partition alone would at at least
four hundred thousand francs."

These words were like a thunderbolt to Grandet.

"What must I do?" he gasped.

"Eugénie might be persuaded to abandon her claim. But
if you want to obtain a concession like that, you'll have to make
your peace with her, of course."

When the notary had gone, Grandet went into the house and
crept stealthily upstairs to his wife's room. Eugénie had just
brought the dressing-case to her mother's bedside, and the
two women were gazing with delight at the portrait of Charles's
beautiful mother.

Like a tiger Grandet pounced upon the dressing-case.

"Father!" cried Eugénie in such a piercing tone that Nanon
hurried upstairs in terror. Grandet inserted his knife under one
of the little gold plates and levered it up a little.

Eugénie seized a long steel paper-knife that was lying beside
a book on the table.

"Father," she said in a low tense voice, "if you do not stop
this instant, I will plunge this into my heart!"

Madame Grandet fainted.

"She is dying!" screamed Nanon.

Grandet threw the dressing-case on the bed. "Here,

daughter, let's not quarrel over a box.   Nanon, fetch a doctor—
Monsieur Bergerin's the nearest.   Come, come, mother," he
said, kissing his wife's hand, " it's nothing, we've made it up,
haven't we, *fifille*?   No more dry bread; you shall eat whatever
you want.   Ah, she opens her eyes.   Look, mother, I am kissing
Eugénie, look *mémère*, *timère*.   She loves her cousin, she shall
marry him, she shall keep her little box.   But you must live a
long time, dear wife."

He went into his office, and returned with a handful of louis,
which he scattered over the bed. "Here, Eugénie, here, wife, these
are for you," he said, fingering the coins incessantly.   Madame
Grandet and her daughter gazed at each other in amazement.

" Take them, father, we need nothing but your affection."

" Oh well, just as you say," said Grandet, pocketing the coins
swiftly.   " Let's all go down to the *salle* and play loto for—for
two sous a hundred.   Cheer up!   We're going to have a
wonderful time! "

In spite of Grandet's longing for his wife's restoration to
health, his immediate compliance with all her wishes, the
medical skill of Monsieur Bergerin, and Eugénie's loving care,
the good woman rapidly drew near her end.

On the day after her mother's death, Eugénie was summoned
by her father into the *salle*, where she found Monsieur Cruchot
awaiting her.

After some preamble the notary said: " You must sign this
document, whereby you renounce your claim to your mother's
property, and allow your father the usufruct, of which he
guarantees you the reversion——"

" I don't understand in the least what you're saying,"
Eugénie interrupted.   " Give me the paper and show me where
I am to sign."

*   *   *   *   *

Five years passed without any event of importance in the
monotonous life of Eugénie and her father.   She had never
once heard from Charles.   Mademoiselle Grandet's profound
sadness was no secret in Saumur, but no one besides Grandet or
Nanon ever learnt its cause.

Towards the end of 1827, Grandet, who had reached the age
of eighty-two, was stricken by a paralysis so grave that Monsieur
Bergerin told Eugénie that he had only a few more weeks to live.
Eugénie nursed her father with devoted care.   A woman in
love knows no purpose in life but love—and Charles was not
there.

The days of the death-agony arrived. The cooper insisted upon sitting in a chair outside his office, so that he could watch the door leading into it from his bedroom. He pulled off all the clothes that were put upon him, saying to Nanon, " Put these away, so that they won't be stolen." Often he called out to Eugénie. " I'm shivering with cold. Spread some money out." His daughter would strew louis over the table, and Grandet would smile weakly like a child. " I feel warm again now," he would say.

When the curé of the parish came to administer the sacrament, Grandet's eyes, dulled and filmed for some hours, brightened at the sight of the Cross and the silver candlesticks. The priest put the gilt crucifix to his lips to kiss. The vinedresser made a ghastly clutch at it, and this final effort cost him his life.

" Take good care of everything," he gasped painfully to Eugénie, struggling with the rattle in his throat. " You'll have to settle accounts with me . . . over there! "

The total amount of the property left to Eugénie was estimated at nearly nineteen millions.

*　　*　　*　　*　　*

While the poor young heiress wept out her heart in the cold dark *salle*, Charles was on his way home from the Indies. Fortune had smiled upon him. He had devoted himself so ardently to business that he had had little time to think of Eugénie, and after a few orgies with Nautch girls and mulattresses, the image of that pure young face no longer troubled his conscience.

As the handsome brig *Marie-Caroline* neared Bordeaux, he reflected with some complacency that he would now be able to assume the station in life that befitted a gentleman. For he possessed nineteen hundred thousand francs in three kegs of gold dust, upon which he expected to make seven or eight per cent. on having it coined in Paris.

On board the brig that took him home was a distinguished gentleman of the King's bedchamber, the Marquis D'Aubrion. The Marquise D'Aubrion was very proud of her husband's title, though he himself frequently complained that his fortune was now so reduced by his wife's extravagance that he found it impossible to maintain any longer the dignity of his rank. An even greater tribulation was the future of his only daughter, whose charms were not of the kind that recommended themselves without the aid of a substantial *dot*. Mademoiselle D'Aubrion was long and lanky, with a sneering mouth, over which hung a long nose, yellow in its normal state, but bright red after meals.

Charles had become very intimate with the Marquise D'Aubrion during the homeward voyage, and she in turn had spared no effort to capture so wealthy a son-in-law. They travelled to Paris together, and Charles was installed as a guest in the D'Aubrion mansion, which was fine and imposing, and riddled with mortgages.

Des Grassins was in Paris at the time, and, hearing of Charles's arrival, he thought he would try to do him a service.

He called a meeting of Guillaume Grandet's creditors. They had refrained hitherto from declaring Charles's father a bankrupt, because they had hoped that Père Grandet of Saumur might settle their claims. The old vine-dresser, who, to his credit, had some concern for his dead brother's honour, had authorized Des Grassins to fob off the creditors from time to time with promises of a settlement. They now informed Des Grassins that they were willing to accept twelve hundred thousand francs in full payment of all claims.

On hearing this, Des Grassins immediately sought an interview with Charles.

*   *   *   *   *

A fortnight later, Eugénie was seated on the little wooden bench in the garden, when Nanon brought her a letter.

Eugénie broke the seal with a trembling hand. " My Dear Cousin——"

" I am no longer Eugénie," she thought, and her heart went numb with anguish.

" You——"

" He used to call me *thou*! " Tears filled her eyes. At last she began to read the letter :—

My Dear Cousin,

You will be glad to hear that I succeeded in my task. You brought me good luck; I have returned very rich. I was sorry to hear of the deaths of your parents, and hope that by now you are consoled. Nothing resists the effects of time, as I know from experience. Yes, my dear cousin, for me the period of illusions is past. I went away a child, I returned a man. You are free of my claims upon you, dear cousin, though I myself shall never forget the little wooden bench——

Eugénie sprang to her feet as quickly as if she had been sitting on red-hot embers——

——the little wooden bench where we swore to love each other forever. Alas, love plays little part in a marriage *à la mode*. My fortune makes it possible for me to ally myself with the D'Aubrion family, and thus obtain for myself a title, the post of honorary gentleman-in-waiting to His Majesty, and a most brilliant social position. I will confess to you, my dear cousin, that I have not the slightest affection for Mademoiselle D'Aubrion. But one must sacrifice oneself for one's children. Had fate ordained that I should renounce my social ambitions, how glad I should have been to share for the rest of my days your pure and simple happiness.

Your devoted cousin,
CHARLES.

P.S. I enclose herewith a draft on the bank of Des Grassins to your order for eight thousand francs, payable in gold, being principal and interest for the sum you were kind enough to lend me. You may send my dressing-case by diligence to the Hotel D'Aubrion, Rue Hillerin-Bertin, Paris.

" By diligence! " said Eugenie. " And I would have given my life for it." She walked slowly into the house. Nanon had just admitted Madame Des Grassins, who approached her with another letter.

" My husband would be very grateful for your advice, Mademoiselle Grandet. If you would be good enough to read what he has written to me——"

Eugénie took the letter and stared at it dully for some moments before she could take in the sense of the opening lines.

MY DEAR WIFE,

Charles Grandet has returned from the Indies; he has been in Paris for a month. He is trying to marry into the D'Aubrion family; the whole town is talking of nothing else. But the match is far from certain; the Marquis D'Aubrion will never give his daughter to a bankrupt's son. I had to dance attendance twice before I could obtain an audience with this young coxcomb, and when I told him about the clever manoeuvres I had used to keep the creditors quiet all this time, he had the face to reply to me that *his father's affairs were no concern of his !*

The creditors want twelve hundred thousand francs, and if they don't get this sum in the next few days, they are going to have his father declared a bankrupt. Now, although the would-be

Comte D'Aubrion may have little care for his honour, mine is of the utmost importance to me. I went into this affair on the word of that old crocodile Grandet, and I made definite promises, which Charles is now able, but unwilling, to fulfil. Therefore, I propose to explain my position to the creditors. Nevertheless, I have too much respect for Mademoiselle Eugénie, whom in happier times I had hoped to call my daughter-in-law, to take any step which may not meet with her approval, and so I should be glad if you would discuss the matter with her and——

Eugénie read no more. "Thank you," she said, coolly returning the letter to Madame Des Grassins. "*We will see about that.*"

During the past few months, President Cruchot had renewed his courtship of the heiress. Immediately Madame Des Grassins had taken her leave, Eugénie sent for him.

"Monsieur le Président," said Eugénie in an unsteady voice, when they were alone in the *salle*, "I know what it is you like in me. Swear that you will leave me free throughout my life, that you will never use any of the rights that marriage would give you over me, and my hand is yours. I do not wish to deceive you, monsieur. Friendship is the only sentiment I can offer my husband; I do not propose either to insult him or to ignore the laws of my heart. But you can possess my hand and my fortune only at the price of a great service."

"I am ready to do anything in the world for you," said the president fervently.

"Here are fifteen hundred thousand francs, Monsieur le Président," she went on, giving him a bill drawn upon the Bank of France. "Start for Paris, not to-morrow, not to-night, but this moment. Call together my uncle's creditors, and pay them principal and interest at five per cent. on all his debts. See that a general receipt is given, attested by a notary in proper form. When you have the receipt, monsieur, you will take it to my cousin Grandet, and hand it to him with this document and this letter. On your return I will keep my word. Entrusting myself to your promise, I will face the perils of life under the shelter of your name. We have known each other so long, we are almost relations; you would not want to make me unhappy."

The president fell at the wealthy heiress's feet, his heart beating fast with rapture.

"I will be your slave!" he said.

The president travelled post and reached Paris the following

evening. He met Charles returning to his apartment after a crushing interview with the old marquis; he had told Charles that he would not allow him to marry his daughter until every franc of Guillaume Grandet's debts had been paid.

The president gave Charles the letter from Eugénie.

MY COUSIN,

President Cruchot has undertaken to hand you a receipt for all the sums owed by my uncle, and also a document in which I acknowledge having received the necessary funds from you. I have heard some talk of bankruptcy! It occurred to me that a bankrupt's son might not be able to marry Mademoiselle D'Aubrion. To make you happiness complete, I can do no more than offer you your father's honour.

EUGÉNIE.

" Now we can both announce our marriages," said the president with a smile, as he handed the rest of the papers to Charles.

" Ah! so you are to marry Eugénie," said Charles. " Good, I am glad to hear it, she's a fine girl. By the way," he added, as a ray of light flashed through his mind, " she must be rich? "

" Four day ago," rejoined the president lightly, " she had nearly nineteen millions. But now it's only about seventeen millions."

Charles's jaw dropped and he gazed stupidly at the president.

" Seventeen mil——" he groaned.

" Seventeen millions, yes, monsieur," said the president, taking his hat and walking towards the door. " Mademoiselle Grandet and I will have about seven hundred and fifty thousand francs a year. Adieu, *cousin*! "

" That Saumur cockatoo was laughing at me," thought Charles savagely. " I'd like to run six inches of cold steel into his belly." He hurried to the door. The president had vanished.

* * * * * ,

President Cruchot kept strictly to his word after his marriage to Eugénie. He showed an infinite concern to fulfil her slightest wish. He was scrupulous to the point of ridicule in his observance of her desire for solitude.

His forbearance towards Eugénie aroused the pity of all the married women in Saumur. " The president is the most chivalrous man in France," they would say. " Why does she refuse to give him an heir? Do you know, I think there's something cold and horrible about her."

Eugénie herself began to feel sorry for the president, though for a different reason. Her long habit of meditation had endowed her with an exquisitely keen insight into everything that happened within her little sphere. She knew that the president was even more loth than herself that she should have a child. She knew that the deepest yearning in his heart was that she should die and leave him in sole command of their immense fortune.

The president himself had drawn up the marriage contract. It stated that the parties thereto should give to each other " in case they should have no children, all and singular their property, real and personal, without exception or reservation, in fee simple, dispensing with the formality of an inventory, etc., etc." Never in all his career as a lawyer had he exercised greater skill and care than in setting down its clauses. When he had finished this difficult task, he rubbed his hands together gleefully. " Not a loophole anywhere! " he said to himself.

God, who sees everything, found a loophole. Six months after his marriage, the president died of cancer.

* * * * *

Madame Eugénie Cruchot is a widow at thirty-three, with an income of nearly eight hundred thousand francs a year, still beautiful, but with the beauty of a woman approaching forty. Despite her great wealth, she lives as poor Eugénie Grandet lived, lights a fire in her room only on the days when her father would have permitted a fire, and dresses as her mother dressed. The mansion at Saumur, a cold, sunless house, is the image of her life. She hoards her income, but pious and charitable foundations, hospitals for the old and infirm, Christian schools for children, public libraries richly endowed, and restored churches bear witness each year against any charge of avarice. Everywhere in Saumur Madame Eugénie inspires a feeling of reverence.

Loneliness of heart such as few have known is the fate ordained for her for the rest of her days. " You are the only one who loves me now," she often says to Nanon.

Lately, the family of the Marquis de Froidfond has begun to seek Eugénie's favour, just as the Cruchots and Des Grassins did in earlier years. The marquis owns a large and derelict estate adjoining her property. It is whispered that he has already won Nanon to his interest. Nothing could be further from the truth. Nanon is too simple ever to understand the corruption of society.

LORNA DOONE

By R. D. BLACKMORE

" Lorna Doone ", by Richard Doddridge Blackmore (1825–1900), is the author's only novel which has survived the passing of time. It was published in 1869 and still brings its annual trail of pilgrims to Exmoor and the " Lorna Doone " country.

WHEN, at the age of twelve years, John Ridd was taken from school and rode from Tiverton to Exmoor beside a grimly silent farm-hand, the boy knew tragedy was in the air. For one thing, John Fry was never silent by habit. For another, when summoned from school, it was always his father who came for him.

All through that horrible ride, the boy speculated on what might have happened. And, when Plover's Barrows farm was reached at last, the worst of his fears were realized. His mother and two sisters were weeping from heartbreak. The terror of the Doones had struck at the peaceful farm. Cruelly murdered because he had resisted robbery, John Ridd, the father, lay dead, and Plover's Barrows had a new master only twelve years old.

The hand of the Doones had lain heavy on Exmoor for years. Driven from Scotland by litigation and foolish crime, Sir Ensor Doone had determined to live honestly no more. Settling in a dark valley of the western hills that was defended by natural gates of rock and slope, he had founded the murderous colony over which he ruled. And, since that day, no man might feel safe in his bed.

The King's writ ran slowly or ran not at all in the lonely moor country. Roads did not exist. There was not a wheel on Exmoor. And the troopers of the King had no love for riding in soaking mists and falling in quagmires. Exmoor could go hang. On that the Doones battened. But, from the day his father was brought home dead, John Ridd practised in the use of the long gun and shattered the barn door with vast pellets of lead cut from the church guttering.

So he grew up, landlord of a five-hundred-acre farm that had been with a Ridd since the days of Alfred. All the time he

perfected his aim with the long gun, not because he had a mad
lust for revenge, but because, if the chance came his way, he
would take it, and, meanwhile, his womenfolk must have
protection.

Then came a day which began a new life for John Ridd.
Two years after his father's death, his mother seemed to be
ailing, and he thought of catching her some loaches, the dainty
little fish of turbulent moor rivers.   It was St. Valentine's Day
and very cold.

But loaches were lacking in the Lynn River.   John Ridd,
led on by resolve not to go home without fish, turned into the
dark Bagworthy water that crashed through trees and down a
vast slide of rock from the lip of the Doone stronghold.

Lured on and on, but spearing fish at last, he essayed the
last great torrent, was knocked and thrown by the icy water
until, half-drowned, he staggered on to soft grass and fainted.

When he recovered, a little girl of some eight years was
bathing his forehead and imploring him to get better.   After
their shyness melted:

"I never saw any one like you before," said John.   "My
name is John Ridd.   What is your name?"

"Lorna Doone," she answered, in a low voice, as if afraid.

But John Ridd saw the gold that even the dread name could
not dull.

"Don't cry," he said, "whatever you do.   I am sure you
have never done any harm.   I will give you all my fish, Lorna,
and catch some more for mother."

So, though they little knew it, John Ridd and Lorna Doone
plighted their troth.

Next moment, Lorna saved John's life, for rascally Doones
came running and calling for their "Queen".   She showed
him a hidden cave and, when they had gone, John Ridd went
fearfully back through the icy stream that now was blackened
by night and very terrible.

Then farm life undisturbed by any outward thing.   The
sheep-shearing came, and the hay season next, and then the
harvest of small corn, and the digging of the root called
"batata" (a new but good thing in our neighbourhood, which
our folk have turned into "taties"), and then the sweating of
the apples, and the turning of the cider-press, and the stacking
of the fire-wood, and netting of the woodcocks, and the
springles to be minded, in the garden, and by the hedgerows.
In November, Tom Faggus came into John's life.   Mister

Faggus was a highwayman, a cousin to John, and a man well loved in many places.

He hung about Plover's Barrows, made eyes at John's sister, Annie, and displayed the jumping and galloping powers of his beautiful strawberry roan, Winnie. John's mother was afraid, for, though she liked Tom Faggus, he was a wild man and no safe husband for a Ridd.

That Christmas, old Reuben Huckaback, uncle to Mrs. Ridd, rode from Dulverton to spend the season at his niece's farm. And, for the second time, the hand of the Doones descended on the family. The old man was robbed on the wild moors and sent on, tied backwards on his horse. It was a sorry day for the murdering rascals when they did that act. Reuben Huckaback was no moor-farmer, used to the Doones and over-busy to worry too much at them.

He dragged John to the Lord of the Manor at Ley to testify to murder and robbery and ask for warrants. But he had no comfort from them. Then he made John take him to a high point which gave a view of Glen Doone. And, after gazing long into the robber stronghold, he returned to Dulverton. His last word was to bid John be ready at call for a long journey.

On St. Valentine's Day, seven years since he had first climbed in through the Doone Gate, John Ridd went there again to see if Lorna still had her bower by the stream. He found her and, though they talked only for a minute, knew that the love of his life was found in her. For now she was grown almost to young womanhood, but gravity was in her eyes. She was watched, and men of the Doones were taking a newer, more unpleasant interest in her.

When they parted, John promised not to put her in peril by going again to the Doone Gate. But he made her swear to signal to him if in danger by putting a dark mantle over a great white stone that gleamed in the face of the cliff.

A slow, lovely Spring went by and Lorna gave no sign of danger. Then, one day, came a stranger to Plover's Barrows, a rider in the King's service with a summons for John Ridd. Old Reuben Huckaback's influence in London had begun to bear fruit. John never did himself better service when he took the weary traveller in and, before asking even his business, fed him and gave him strong waters. Thereby he made a mighty friend and a friend for life. Jeremy Stickles was apparitor to the King's Bench and, more weighty still, the agent of Judge Jeffreys, then a rising power in the land. John was called to

London to give evidence on certain matters imperilling the peace of the realm in the West.

Jeffreys was a thick-set, burly, and bulky man, with a blotchy, broad face, and great square jaws and fierce eyes full of blazes. But he knew, at that time, an honest man when he saw one.

The Doones were not his worry. He scoffed at them and said the trained bands could smoke out the nest. He had other things on his mind. There was talk of unrest in Devon and Somerset and Dorset. The Duke of Monmouth was like to set himself up as Pretender. What did John Ridd know of all this?

The farmer of Exmoor knew nothing of it, though his straight answers pleased Jeffreys and earned the great man's favourable regard. He said outright that he had had it in mind to make John his secret agent in the West, but now he saw he was too honest and open to play such a part. Another would be sent. John parted with Jeremy Stickles and posted home alone. He found the danger signal on the white stone and climbed to the gateway to find out its cause.

Lorna was there, with new fear in her eyes. She knew now that Carver Doone, giant leader of the robber band, wanted her for himself, while a younger man, Charleworth Doone, had aims at her as well. In the first panic of the knowledge, she had signalled during the weary weeks that John was away in London. But now she thought that Carver would not touch her yet. Now, too, she returned John's love and the world seemed green and fair but for the shadow of the Doones. But still she bade John keep away unless she signalled.

Strange things were happening on the moor. Weird sounds frightened people. Old Reuben Huckaback came more often to Plover's Barrows and made mysterious journeys into lonely places. As he was terrified of the Doones, it roused more curiosity than usual. Apart from all that, farm life went on and John saw Lorna at rare intervals. Harvest came and went. Tom Faggus gave up highway robbery and courted Annie. Then Jeremy Stickles came again and the air of peace vanished. As the agent of the law talked of sedition and quested for details like a hound, John grew restive.

Because of it, he dared to penetrate the Doone stronghold to its very heart, worried into fearing for Lorna's safety. Luck held with him, and a whispered talk through her window arranged a new signal that could be worked if Lorna could no longer go to the Doone Gate. Her little Cornish maid could climb like a cat. Over the crest was a high tree with seven rooks' nests in it. The maid would take one away if Lorna was in danger and two if Carver Doone carried her off.

Easier in mind, John fell back to work on the farm, though interruptions grew more frequent. Some time afterwards, he saw three men creeping through the brushwood with long guns and a deal of whispered talk. He heard enough to know that they meant to ambush and kill Jeremy Stickles, not liking his inquiring ways whether he was concerned with actions of the Doones or not. A mad run by tracks he knew well allowed John to save Jeremy's life and double a firm friendship.

As winter frost set in, Sir Ensor Doone died, and his death gave great fear to John, for he knew the old man was the last obstacle between Lorna and the desires of Carver Doone. So, as a frost greater than any in living memory gripped the moor, John watched the rooks' nests and prayed for his love.

Winter strove against him, gave him work that took every waking minute. The sheep were buried deep in snow and had to be rescued, vast piles of wood had to be cut to feed the farm fires and keep out the cold. John fashioned snowshoes from a picture in an old book and made himself master of them. It was in the nick of time. On a bitter evening, one rooks' nest vanished, and John took to the snow the same night and struggled upward to the Doone valley, heart heavy with foreboding.

He risked his life to reach the house again and found Lorna starving. Every valley was snowbound. No man could move any distance. So the Doones had no food for the first time in their black lives.

Staying only to give what bread he had, John went back to the farm to prepare. He had decided to take Lorna from the clutches of the Doones, no matter what the consequences. It was only just in time.

When he crept again into Glen Doone, the door of the house was open and Lorna in the grasp of Charleworth Doone, who hoped to steal a march on Carver. A second man was struggling with the maid.

John Ridd seized upon them in the glory of his great strength and they went to grave injury through the window. Their weak cries were smothered by deep snow as John took Lorna and the maid over the snowbound moor to where he had left a sledge. And then it was only a matter of time before Plover's Barrows was reached, warmth and cordials had revived the fugitives and John's mother had been faced with her son's intended wife. She crept into motherly affection as easily as she had invaded John's great heart.

" And so she went to mother's heart, by the very nearest road, even as she had come to mine; I mean the road of pity, smoothed by grace, and youth, and gentleness."

Lorna had nothing of property save her clothes and a necklace of brilliants, a childhood plaything. Nobody thought twice of that till Tom Faggus, whose judgment of valuables was infallible, pronounced it of great worth and gave John another worry. For, if Carver Doone did not pursue Lorna for herself, he might well come after the necklace.

His fears were real. A few days afterwards, while Lorna was gathering flowers by the river, Carver Doone appeared among the trees on the opposite bank. With refined cruelty, he fired a bullet between her feet and said :

" I have spared you this time only because it suits my plans; and I never yield to temper. But unless you come back to-morrow, pure, and with all you took away, and teach me to destroy that fool, who has destroyed himself for you, your death is here, your death is here, where it has long been waiting."

Meanwhile, Jeremy Stickles had decided to storm the Doone fortress, for, even though the robbers might have no immediate connection with any rebellion conjectured in the West, many mutterings would be stopped by it and people would have a salutary lesson in the fate of evil-doers.

While he waited for troops to come from Exeter, the Doones attacked the farm. They came in a small band, at dead of night, but the look-outs John had posted for some time past, saw them in the moonlight. And, as they came to the yard, intent on firing the ricks as a start, they were hotly greeted. Two dead Doones and two flung into prison was the price they paid. John knocked Carver into a muckheap when he might have killed him. But he knew his leniency was wasted by the malevolent gleam in Carver's eye.

When that attempt on the farm failed, the Doones tried another way. He whom they called the Counsellor, a very old man, but the craftiest rogue of all, came in peace to talk to Lorna Doone. He was admitted and treated with courtesy, but, when he went, Lorna's necklace went with him. The old man played on the superstitions of Annie Ridd and got her to fetch it from its hiding-place to show her a witch's way of charming cream from milk.

In the middle of the preparations for the attack, Jeremy Stickles discovered great things. He stumbled on a story of a child who had been kidnapped by the Doones years before, and there was little doubt the child was Lorna. For the last act of the mother had been to put a diamond necklace over the child's head. So said an old Italian nurse, found living in a Devonshire tavern. The name and estates of the baby were being argued in Chancery.

Jeremy was dispirited about the attack. In their wisdom, the authorities refused leave to move troops from the coast, and he had to be content with a body of Somerset militia in yellow coats and a band from Devon in red. Half-trained and without officers, each side hated the other like poison. Jeremy had all the ingredients of civil war with him as he led a hundred and twenty men into the hills, pulling three culverins, to the positions he had chosen.

So it proved. The swift thrust of Jeremy and John failed because no backing came at all. The Devon men, who were to attack from the opposite side to the yellow coats, dropped the first charge from their culverin right among the Somerset ranks. In an instant a reply came, and the Doones were forgotten in a red-hot country feud.

John Ridd fought his way out of a grim struggle, with Jeremy badly wounded, to find the attack a complete failure and the Doones triumphant.

Jeremy mended slowly. Long before he was about again, the Italian nurse had been brought to Plover's Barrows, and Lorna still remembered her. It was known then that Lorna was no child of the moor bandits, but daughter to the late Earl of Dugal. Almost at the same time came messengers from Chancery bidding Lorna to London to claim her estate and enter into guardianship. And, in due time, she went.

John was left to work his farm and hate the Doones and wonder if he had lost Lorna. Tom Faggus received a pardon from the King, married Annie and settled down. And old Reuben Huckaback, hoping to make John marry his niece, showed the secret which made him go so much into the moor. It was a mine in which he extracted gold with the aid of a Cornish metal expert. The engine that crushed the ore was responsible for the strange noises that sometimes throbbed in the air above the lonely waste.

As it became known that Charles II was sick unto death, Jeremy Stickles was ordered south to watch the coast. London feared that, with the accession of a Catholic king, Monmouth's long-talked-of rebellion might break at last.

It was not only London that feared. Wives and daughter of honest farming people were afraid for their husbands and fathers. Simple craftsmen and yeomen were caught up by the cry and lost their heads. The handsome Duke had a way with him, but not a winning way.

John Ridd would have none of it. He was a deal too level in the head. But he feared for his friends as the others did. And, when Charles had breathed his last, he saw how real that fear was. Proclamations appeared from nowhere. Arms of ancient make were culled from hiding-places almost forgotten. But John, when he was handed a Monmouth proclamation in Brendon town, thrust it into the blacksmith's fire, and blew the bellows thrice at it. It had been well for many a man had he done the same.

He returned home with a heavy heart to find his sister Annie, a baby at her breast, weeping to break her heart. She had come flying from South Molton to implore John's help. For Tom Faggus had gone with the rebel army.

John swore he could not go after Tom Faggus while the farm was all open to an attack by the Doones. Without a thought, Annie went bravely to Glen Doone and, on her knees before the Counsellor, prayed for an armistice while John Ridd was away. She succeeded. With a lighter heart, but scarcely trusting any promise given by a Doone, John saddled up and rode away to bring Tom Faggus back to his young wife.

That was a nightmare ride. John found no direct trail. He need must follow scraps of information that led him from Bath to Frome, from Wells to Wincanton and on through Glastonbury, Shepton and Somerton to Bridgwater.

From there, he heard the crash of muskets in the night and rode out to Zoyland, following the sound, in time to see the ghastly slaughter at Sedgmoor.

"Would that I had never been there! Often in the lonely hours, even now it haunts me: would, far more, that the piteous thing had never been done in England! Flying men, flung back from dreams of victory and honour, only glad to have the luck of life and limbs to fly with, mud-bedraggled, foul with slime, reeking both with sweat and blood, which they could not stop to wipe, cursing, with their pumped-out lungs, every stick that hindered them, or gory puddle that slipped the step, scarcely able to leap over the corses that had dragged to die. And to see how the corses lay; some, as fair in death as in sleep; with the smile of placid valour, and of noble manhood, hovering yet on the silent lips. These had bloodless hands put upwards, white as wax, and firm as death, clasped (as on a monument) in prayer for dear ones left behind, or in high thanksgiving. And of these men there was nothing in their broad, blue eyes to fear. But others were of different sort; simple fellows unused to pain, accustomed to the billhook, perhaps, or rasp of the knuckles in a quickset hedge, or making some to-do, at breakfast, over a thumb cut in sharpening a scythe, and expecting their wives to make more to-do. Yet here lay these poor chaps, dead, after a deal of pain."

Amid that pitiful shambles stood Tom Faggus's strawberry roan. She whinnied to John and led him through the grim field just as, in the distance, the King's Guards charged and smashed the remnants of Monmouth's deserted army into a bloody heap.

In a low, black shed, Tom Faggus lay wounded. Tightly bandaged, revived by brandy and able to sit well on his beloved mare, John sent him from the battlefield and lay down to rest, secure in his own clear conscience. He woke to find himself surrounded by the terrible troopers of Colonel Kirke that men afterwards called " lambs " in sarcasm. And, when the cold-hearted commander himself came on the scene, a rope and a tree held John's life by a thread.

In that fateful moment, Jeremy Stickles appeared and whispered words into the ear of Colonel Kirke. The name of " Jeffreys " was the only word John caught but it worked as magic. Kirke dropped his prisoner with a snarl and John rode off with Jeremy.

There was no rest for John even then. Jeremy knew the sort of justice that was being dealt out in the West, knew that John had no chance at all if caught again. His only hope was to sue for trial or pardon in London, where honest law still existed.

So to Churchill, the great man who afterwards became Marlborough, and now in command in Somerset. Jeremy Stickles had some influence with him and soon had leave to take his man to London.

There, while waiting for the law's slow wheels to turn and

show his name, John heard much of Lorna and glimpsed her once at a great function. She was ward to the Earl of Brandir, her dead mother's uncle, and a toast at Court.

Lorna felt John's eyes on her in all that crowd and he went humbly to the Earl's house, only to find that his love was unchanged, still the unspoilt girl he had known on Exmoor. Because of that visit, and others that followed, John did great service to Lorna's guardian.

He saw two men lurking in a thicket near the house one night and followed them about. When, as he had thought, they entered the house at dark, he followed again and caught them as they threatened the Earl of Brandir with pistols and strove to take his great chest of money. In the fierce fight that came after, one was shot, but two John bound and gave to justice. Once more, his lucky star was with him. The men were no ordinary thieves but political desperados long wanted by the law, friends of Titus Oates and Carstairs, men the King himself feared.

When the story got round, James sent for the Earl of Brandir and then for John. He asked what he could give John to show his gratitude and favour, and John said, as for a joke:

" My mother always used to think that having been schooled at Tiverton, with thirty marks a year to pay, I was worthy of a coat of arms."

And James took him up on the words, bade him kneel and clapped a sword to his back, saying: " Arise, Sir John Ridd ! "

" This astonished and amazed me to such extent of loss of mind that when I got up I looked about. And I said to the King, without forms of speech:

" ' Sir, I am very much obliged. But what be I to do with it ? ' "

But John had his coat of arms and he had greater equality with Lorna's rank. He had also the sense to use his new-found favour and secure pardon for anything he had been charged with after Sedgmoor. He rode home, leaving Lorna still in London, to find that, though the Doones had kept their word not to molest Plover's Barrows, they were ranging the country worse than ever. Before the winter was out, they went far beyond their usual limits and roused the whole moor country to white anger, a thing that had never happened before. It was their end.

Led by Carver, a band of them descended on a small farm while the man was away, stole his food and goods, killed his

child and took the wife to outrage and captivity. All honest
people came to John Ridd and swore he must lead an expedition again. But John's honesty refused to let him go without
first warning the Doones, because they had at least kept their
word about Plover's Barrows.

So he went up to Glen Doone under a white flag, but with
a Bible over his heart and another on his spine in case of
treachery. Carver sneered at the request for the return of the
farmer's wife and hidden men fired on John as he turned away.
Luckily he had seen their gun-muzzles in the cave and dodged
in time. Before they could reload, he was away down the glen.

The attack was to be at dawn and some guile was to be used.
Old Reuben Huckaback's gold expert, who had a score
against the Doones like most others, agreed to lure some of the
robbers to the mine by pretending treachery to his employer
and a willingness to hand over a pile of gold. He was given
a store of liquor to entertain the guests and would pour water
on the primings of their guns while they caroused.

Yeomen were to go and finish the drunkards at the mine
while the rest fell on Glen Doone in two bodies, one in a noisy
feint, the other in the real assault.

It fell out just as it was designed. When full daylight came,
no Doone was left alive save Carver, who was not there, and
the Counsellor, who was spared because of his age.

Now came Lorna to the West Country, tired of peacocking at
Court and longing only for marriage with her John. Because
of the favour he once had given John Ridd, aided by a sum of
money from Lorna's estate, Jeffreys gave Chancery permission for the wedding. And, on Whit-Tuesday, a beautiful
day, the two went to the altar.

Then, as the parson's words ended and Lorna turned to her
love, eyes brimming with emotion, a shot rang out and bright
red blood leaped out on Lorna's snowy dress. John laid her
quietly in his mother's arms and, taking no weapon, mounted
his horse and went madly, but coldly, after Carver.

Nothing could stop him. A bullet struck him as the chase
narrowed, but he scarcely noticed it. Then, as Carver turned
to charge down on him, John felled his horse with an oak branch
wrenched off with herculean strength as he rode. The two
men were together in fight at last, and the death-grip came soon
in that lonely hollow of the moor.

" I heard my rib go; I grasped his arm, and tore the muscle
out of it (as the string comes out of an orange); then I took him

by the throat, which is not allowed in wrestling; but he had
snatched at mine; and now was no time of dalliance. In vain
he tugged, and strained, flung himself on me, with gnashing
jaws. Beneath the iron of my strength—for God that day was
with me—I had him helpless in two minutes, and his blazing
eyes lolled out."

Even then John offered Carver his life if he swore to repent and
go away. But it was too late. Even if he had yielded in his
ravening frenzy, for his beard was frothy as a mad dog's jowl;
even if he would have owned that, for the first time in his life,
he had found his master; it was all too late.

The black bog had him by the feet; the sucking of the
ground drew on him, like the thirsty lips of death.

John leaped back with difficulty and "scarcely could I
turn away, while, joint by joint, he sank from sight."

And then, going slowly home, as he thought, to his dear, dead
one, John Ridd found her faintly living, saved by good nursing
from a doctor who would have killed her by further bleeding.

As John recovered from the bullet wound and the terrible
squeeze of Carver's arms, Lorna recovered, too. Until, one
day, they were together in strength and beauty, and there was
no shadow at all over Plover's Barrows or the great thrust of
the sunlit hills above.

LAVENGRO

By GEORGE BORROW

" Lavengro " (published 1851) though complete in itself, is really the first half of a work of which the second half is " The Romany Rye ". This explains why the book ends so abruptly. Petulengro is the name given by Borrow to Ambrose Smith, a real gipsy from Norfolk, who was his contemporary. George Borrow (1803–1881) is famous for his assistance with the compilation of the " Newgate Calendar " and his amazing gift for languages. All his novels have a strong autobiographical basis.

I WAS not the only child of my parents; I had a brother some three years older than myself, with such dauntless spirit and beauty that, even in infancy, people would follow his nurse to gaze on his lovely face. For myself I was ever a lover of nooks and brooding. I remember always a peculiar heaviness, a strange sensation almost amounting to horror, which overwhelmed me sometimes and for which I could never find cause. When strangers addressed me I not infrequently turned my head from them; if they persisted in their attentions I burst into tears—singularities of behaviour which by no means tended to dispose people in my favour. One day—they told me about it long after—a travelling Jew knocked at the door whereat I sat in the sunshine, drawing strange lines in the dust. The maid told him I was her mistress's younger son, tapping her brow as if to show I was weak *there*.

The Jew leaned forward to stare at the lines I had traced. Of a sudden he started back, growing as white as a sheet. Taking off his hat, he made curious gestures at me, cringing, chattering, showing his teeth, before he departed, muttering something about " holy letters ".

We once lived within the canvas walls of a camp at Pett in Sussex, and there it chanced that my brother and I played one evening alone in a sandy lane when a glorious object glided into my view, moving across like a line of gold light. Uttering a cry of pleasure, I sprang forward and seized it. Despite its sunlike appearance, its contact was numbing and

56

cold. The thing was a viper, as my brother's shrieks quickly informed me, but it made not the slightest struggle to escape from my infant grasp. When I dropped the captive at length, as our mother came running towards me, it hissed furiously at my brother and quickly made its escape, yet of my interference it had taken no notice at all. Thus I learned for the first time of the inherent power which some individuals, myself included, possess in the taming of brutes and of reptiles.

At this time my father's regiment was stationed at Norman Cross, serving as guard to French prisoners from the war then being waged against Napoleon. I met an old man there, a catcher of serpents, who made it his business to prepare from the vipers he caught an ointment good against the rheumatism. He gave me a snake from which he had taken the fangs, which I carried often in my shirt. One day as I rambled down a green, little-used lane I came on two carts and a tent, a caldron beside it, by which sat a man and a woman. They were rough and wild-looking. When they saw me they rushed to attack me, shouting words which, young as I was, I remarked to be very different from any I ever had heard.

"So I have caught you at last," said the man. "I'll drown you now in the toad-pond over the hedge!"

"Drown me, will you?" said I, not running away. "I should like to see you! What's all this about?"

"I'll strangle thee," said the beldame, dashing at me. "Come spying on us . . ."

But at this moment up poked the head of my viper, menacing them with its eyes.

"I say, wifekin," the man said in faltering tones, "did you ever see the like of this here?"

The woman stared, with an expression part terror, part curiosity on her loathly face. She and the man fell to muttering together in their strange tongue. When they addressed me again their whole manner had altered. In place of reviling me, she called me her "tiny tawny", her "gorgeous angel", bidding me eat of a sweetmeat and bide with them in their tent. Instead of a spy, they now took me for some sort of goblin, who would bring them good luck if they kept me. I ate of the candied fruit that they offered, and very soon told them the truth; yet they seemed not a wit less surprised at my power with the viper, and still begged that I should stay with them. This I could not do, though much tempted; but before I left them I met their son Jasper, whose father bade him shake my hand, for we were to be brothers.

"What, a sap-engro!" whined Jasper, using their curious jargon. But he took my hand and declared we should meet again.

Years passed, taking me to schools in the north and in Scotland, wherever my father's duties called him to go. In Edinburgh Castle his regiment was stationed at last, and there at Edinburgh I went to High School. The Scots are pugnacious people. My schoolfellows fought for any reason at all, very often for none. With other callants among them I climbed the sheer rocky heights and fought with the best. In the autumn of 1815 my father was ordered to Ireland, and thither we went in the troopship. His regiment was stationed close by the mountains of Tipperary. My brother, an ensign now, had his own small troop, garrisoned in a tiny blockhouse far out on a moor, where I visited him. But my chief adventure was one with a cob, an Irish cob, on which I took my first ride.

"He'll soon teach you to ride," the groom told me. "He's the best riding-master in Ireland; and the best friend I had till I struck him, which he's never forgot or forgiven."

The cob was led forth; what a tremendous creature! He was barely fifteen hands, but he had the girth of a metropolitan dray-horse; his head was small in comparison with his immense neck, which curved down nobly to his wide back; his chest was broad and fine, and his shoulders models of symmetry and strength; he stood well and powerfully upon his legs, which were somewhat short.

"I'm half afraid," said I; "I had rather you would ride him. And where's the saddle?"

"If you are ever to be a frank rider, you must begin without a saddle. Now, before you mount, make his acquaintance—see there, how he kisses you and licks your face, and see how he lifts his foot; that's to shake hands. Now you are on his back at last—hold the bridle gently, gently."

In less than two hours I had made the circuit of the Devil's Mountain, and was returning along the road, bathed with perspiration, but screaming with delight; the cob laughing in his equine way, scattering foam and pebbles to the left and right. Oh, that ride! that first ride! People may talk of first love—it is a very agreeable event, I dare say—but give me the flush and triumph and glorious sweat of a first ride, like mine on the mighty cob! My whole frame was shaken, it is true; and during one long week I could hardly move foot or hand; but what of that? By that one trial I had become free, as I may say, of the whole equine species.

But Ireland and the cob were left behind. We returned to a fine old city in Eastern England. There, with the aid of a tessara-glot grammar (a strange old book which pretended to be an easy guide to the acquirement of French, Italian, Low Dutch and English) and a certain banished Norman priest, I began—or rather proceeded with, for I had already learned some Latin, Greek and Irish—that philological knowledge which was to be one of my chief attainments. French and Italian I learned, the last with great facility, and a knowledge of Spanish as well. In my leisure I fowled and I fished. One day I went to a neighbouring horse-fair. I was watching some wild-looking folk engaged in trick-riding when I felt someone's eyes staring at me.

"Lor! the sap-engro!" a voice cried, and Jasper, the Rommany boy, now grown to a man, greeted me as his brother and led me away to his camp. His friend Tawno Chikno welcomed me there, with other ones of their Rommany tribe. Jasper told me his father and mother were exiled now, that he was king of the Rommanys, and that his whole name was Jasper Petulengro, "which means the horse-shoe master, as sap-engro means the snake-fellow".

"And you are what is called a Gypsy King?"

"Ay, ay; a Rommany Kral."

"Are there other kings?"

"Those who call themselves so; but the true Pharaoh is Petulengro."

"Pharaoh lived in Egypt."

"So did we once, brother."

"And you are not English?"

"We are not gorgios."

"And you have a language of your own?"

"Avali."

"This is wonderful."

"'Tis called Rommany."

"Would you teach it me?"

"None sooner."

"Not while I am here," screamed Jasper Petulengro's mother-in-law, fixing two eyes upon me which shone like burning coals. "A pretty manoeuvre, truly; and what would be the end of it? I goes to the farming ker to tell a fortune and earn a few sixpences for the chabes. I sees a jolly pig in the yard, and I says to my sister, speaking Rommany, ' Do so and so,' which the farming man hearing, asks what we are talking about. ' Nothing at all, master,' says I; ' something about the weather '; when who starts up from behind a pale, where he has been listening, but this ugly gorgio, crying out, ' They are after poisoning your pigs, neighbour ! ' An ill day to the Romans when he masters Rommany; and when I says that, I pens a true dukkerim."

" What do you call God, Jasper? "

" You had better be jawing," said the woman, raising her voice to a terrible scream; " you had better be moving off, my gorgio; hang you for a keen one, sitting there by the fire, and stealing my language before my face. Do you know whom you have to deal with? Do you know that I am dangerous? My name is Herne, and I comes of the hairy ones ! "

And a hairy one she looked ! No she-bear from Lapland ever looked more fierce and hairy than did that woman.

" I call God Duvel, brother."

" It sounds very like Devil. Would it not be a rum thing if divine and devilish were originally one and the same word? "

" It would, brother, it would——"

From that time I had frequent interviews with Jasper, soon finding that I had become acquainted with a most singular people, whose habits and pursuits awakened within me the highest interest. Where did this speech come from, and who were they who spoke it? " Whoever we be, brother," Jasper told me, " we are an old people, and not what folks in general imagine, broken gorgios; and if we are not Egyptians, we are at any rate Rommany Chals ! "

My rapid progress in their language astonished while it delighted him.

" We'll no longer call you Sap-engro, brother," said he; " but rather Lav-engro which in the language of the gorgios meaneth Word Master."

But by now I had reached sixteen, and my father decided to put me to some profession. He himself would gladly have seen me enter the Church, yet feared I should steer an erratic course if sent to a university, and, having excellent common sense, did not press me to adopt a career requiring qualities of mind he saw I did not possess. In the end they put me to law, and for many long months I worked eight hours a day, happy enough in the womb of a lofty deal desk, whereat, though remaining a novice in law, I somehow made myself perfect master of the Welsh tongue!

Yet sometimes I gravely wondered wherefore I was born, or of what profit life was. I told Jasper Petulengro my doubts as we sat on the heath watching the downgoing sun.

"What is your opinion of death, Mr. Petulengro?" I asked.

"My opinion of death, brother, is this. When a man dies, he is cast into the earth, and his wife and child sorrow over him. If he has neither wife nor child, then his father and mother, I suppose; and if he is quite alone in the world, why, then, he is cast into the earth, and there is an end of the matter."

"And do you think that is the end of man?"

"There's an end of him, brother, more's the pity."

"Why do you say so?"

"Life is sweet, brother. There's night and day, sun, moon and stars, all sweet things, brother; there's likewise a wind on the heath. Life is very sweet, brother; who would wish to die?"

"I would wish to die——"

"You talk like a gorgio—which is the same as talking like a fool. Were you a Rommany Chal you would talk wiser. Wish to die, indeed!—a Rommany Chal would wish to live for ever!"

"In sickness, Jasper?"

"There's the sun and the stars, brother."

"In blindness, Jasper?"

"There's the wind on the heath, brother; if I could only feel that, I would gladly live for ever. Dosta, we'll now go to the tents and put on the gloves; and I'll try to make you feel what a sweet thing it is to be alive, brother!"

My father declined and died despite all our care, when I was eighteen years old. My brother, who had forsaken the army to become an artist, returned to our home to stand by his parent's death-bed. Then I quitted the lawyer's office and, with a small sum of money and certain writings, set out on the coach for London, leaving the desolate home and my brother to comfort my mother. In dingy lodgings I took my abode, determined to live by my pen.

The publisher to whom I carried a letter of introduction was a tall, stout man, about sixty, with a sinister, somewhat bilious expression. He welcomed me, but refused to have anything to do with my translations from the Danish ballads or the Welsh of AB GWILYM which I had brought him. This

caused me grave disappointment, but he gave me some consolation by telling me that he intended to start a new magazine,
the *Oxford Review*, for which I should write contributions
confined to belles-lettres and philology. He suggested that I
might also try my hand at some popular, evangelical tales on
the style of the " Dairyman's Daughter ", which I promised
him I would consider. Finally, however, it was decided that,
beside other contributions, I should make my main work a
compilation of Newgate lives and trials; six volumes, each
holding not less than one thousand pages, for which, when
completed, he said he would pay fifty pounds. I was to bear
any cost incurred in procuring books, papers and manuscripts.
In addition, the publisher said I should have the very great
privilege of translating his own book of philosophy into the
German tongue.

I compiled the Chronciles of Newgate; I reviewed books
for the *Review*; and I occasionally tried my best to translate
into German portions of the publisher's philosophy. Of these
three occupations I found the " Newgate Lives and Trials "
most to my taste, full of wild and racy adventures—and in
what racy, genuine language they were told. I often sighed
that it was not my fortune to render these lives into German,
rather than the publisher's philosophy, which I found dull and
difficult enough; for it is one thing to translate from a foreign
into one's own tongue, but quite another to change good
English (which my publisher's philosophy was not, being inter-
larded with much unintelligible Greek and Latin) into abstruse
German. Also the publisher interfered with my work, often
changing his mind as to how the " Lives and Trials " were to
be presented, so that at the last, after many weary months'
labour, I was not altogether either surprised or distressed to
find him stamping with fury upon certain fragments of paper.

" Sir," said he, " you know nothing of German; I have
shown your translation to several Germans; it is utterly
unintelligible to them."

" Did they see the Philosophy? " I replied.

" They did, sir, but they did not profess to understand
English."

" No more do I," I replied, " if that Philosophy be English."

The publisher was furious, but I said no more. The compilation completed, I was paid in the usual manner and
forthwith left him.

And now what was I to do? Turn porter? I had little

enough money left and nothing to do. An Armenian acquaintance offered me work as his clerk. At first I refused, but
when, necessity urging, I decided to take his suggestion, I
found he had just taken mine and left to wage war on the
Persians who troubled his country. Another, more intimate
friend, a dashing young Irishman, offered to lend me one
hundred pounds for me to disport down at Brighton with his
belle amie's sister; but this I renounced out of hand, not considering his plan as one likely to lead either to profit or rest.

On my way home I found myself in a street of which I had
some recollection, and stopped before the window of a shop
in which various publications were exposed; that of the
bookseller to whom I had last applied in the hope of selling
my ballads. A paper was affixed to the glass with wafers, with
something written upon it. In a fair round hand was in-
scribed—" A Novel or Tale is much wanted."

That night over bread and water, along in my lonely apartment, I considered what I should do. Had I the imagination
requisite to write a tale or a novel? Filled with desperation
and doubts, at last I started to write. The story I chose was
the " Life and Adventures of Joseph Sell ", a subject straight
from my mind. That night my pen moved sluggishly; yet
rest seemed to bring inspiration. In four days, working early
and late, with nothing but bread and water to urge me along,
I completed my story. On the fifth day I took it round to
the bookseller, who, after a little bargaining, paid me twenty
pounds for my work. I left the Big City and started to walk
to the south-west.

A coach carried me as far as ——, where I shouldered my
bundle and stick and walked down a road in the dark. It
was late in the night, or towards dawn, I scarcely knew which;
but I came at length to some mighty pillars of stone, which
I knew were no less than Stonehenge. There I cast myself
down on the ground to rest, but rose with the day and, after
some talk with a shepherd, went on my way, travelling many
long miles afoot and meeting with more than one strange
character upon my way or in taverns. At length I came to a
cottage with a notice outside it, " Good Beer ". I entered
and sat in its kitchen and called for a great jug of ale. Four
other persons sat there, a tinker, his wife and their children,
who all looked so draggled and miserable that I offered
them a drink from the three pints I bought for five pennies.
I told them that I was a blacksmith.

Tinker. Well, I shouldn't have thought you had been a blacksmith by your hands. Where did you serve first?

Myself. In Ireland. What's the matter with you; what are you all crying about?

Tinker. I can't bear to think of it. The life of Eden it is, the tinker's life; and now I'm to give it all up. How hard to be frightened to death, to be driven off the roads!

Myself. Who has driven you off the roads?

Tinker. Who! the Flaming Tinman; the biggest rogue in England, and the cruellest, or he wouldn't have served me as he has done. For six or seven years we were the happiest people breathing, up and down on our beat, pitching our tent by the hedges, when along comes this Black Jack, this flaming tinman, driven as they say out of Yorkshire. Now, no beat will support two tinkers, though mine was a good one. Presently he finds me out and offers to fight me for it, knocks me down, threatens to cut my throat, and goes his way. Well, I was woundily frightened, and for several months I contrived to keep out of his company. But yesterday after dinner I sat down to mend three kettles when up comes this king of the tinkers, with Grey Moll, his wife, at his side, springs from his cart and comes at me, knocking me here and there, like an elephant fighting a fly. My wife tries to help, but Grey Moll sets upon her and was like to kill the poor soul. I can't bear that so I shouts out, "Hold!" promising and swearing to leave the road and my beat to them.

Myself. I'm half inclined to buy your cart and pony, and your beat too.

And, to be short, despite the poor tinker's warnings that my head would soon be knocked off by the Flaming Tinman, I paid him five pounds and ten shillings, took over his horse, cart and gear, and set off away on my own.

Down green lanes I made my way, through thickets of sweet briar and hazel, till I came to a great ash tree, under which I camped; and here I spent two or three days, trying my hand at my new trade of mending kettles. One morning a visitor came to see me, a girl of about thirteen with a little dog. She was of the Rommany people, as I knew by the song which she sang. She begged me to give her a kekaubi or kettle, but when she learned that I spoke Rommany too, she stared at me with a curious expression of fear, intermingled with hate.

On her second visit she brought me two cakes, baked for

me, she said, by her grandbebee in return for the kettle. I
had no sooner eaten one than I felt ghastly ill. I lay in my
tent, groaning, vomiting, writhing, unable to get to my feet,
when the girl appeared with her grandbebee, who was no
less a person than my old acquaintance, Mrs. Herne of the
Hairy Ones.

"Ha, ha! bebee, here he lies, poisoned like a hog," exulted
the girl, and she sang the gypsy poison song:

> "The Rommany chi
> And the Rommany chal,
> Shal jaw tasaulor
> To drab the bawlor,
> And dook the gry
> Of the farming rye."

"Do you hear that, sir?" said Mrs. Herne; "you were
always fond of what was Roman. Shall I tell your fortune,
sir; your dukkerin? God bless you, pretty gentleman; much
trouble will you have to suffer, and much water to cross; but
never mind, pretty gentleman, you shall be fortunate at the
end, and those who hate shall take off their hats to you."

"Hey, bebee!" cried the girl; "what is this? what do
you mean? You have blessed the gorgio!"

"Blessed him! no, sure: what did I say? Oh, I remember, I'm mad: well, I can't help it, I said what the dukkerin
dook told me; woe's me, he'll get up yet."

She and her granddaughter did their best to prevent such
a recovery, striking at my unguarded head with staves, and
even setting the juggal or dog at my face, while I lay there
helpless. But, fortunately for me, they were interrupted by
the arrival of some good people, some itinerant Welsh preachers,
who antidoted the poison with oil and cared for me, taking
me with them as far as the borders of Wales, until I got
well.

Jasper Petulengro met with me soon after I left them,
and, hearing me say that I wished above all for solitude,
showed me a hidden dingle where I might find calm and peace.
I settled there, happy enough, but had not been there many
days before my quiet was disturbed. I heard a boisterous
shout, voices and cartwheels moving, as into my dingle came
three carts and horses, with three strange figures in charge.
One was a tall, strapping girl, one a raddled, coarse-looking
woman, but the third was a man whom, by the poor tinker's

description, I knew must surely be the redoubtable Flaming Tinman himself. He did not waste many words. Though I said, with truth, I was feeble still from my illness, and had no wish or spirit to fight, he came flying at me with fury. He was about six feet high, and sported an immense pair of whiskers, but with here and there a grey hair, for his age could not be much under fifty. On his black head was a kind of red nightcap, round his bull neck a Barcelona handkerchief.

To a flush hit in the mouth he paid as little attention as a wild bull would have done; in a moment his arms were around me, and in another, he had hurled me down, planted his knee on my breast, and seized my throat with two huge, horny hands. I gave myself up for dead, but the tall girl caught hold of the handkerchief round his neck and wrenched him from off me.

"Do you call that fair play?" said she, as he sprang up and aimed a blow at her. "I'll be the boy's second, and Moll can pick you up when he happens to knock you down."

The battle during the next ten minutes raged with considerable fury, but it so happened that during this time I was never able to knock the Flaming Tinman down, but on the contrary received six knock-down blows myself.

"Why don't you use Long Melford?" asked the girl Belle, as I sat on her knee, spitting out blood. "It's no use flipping at him with your left hand."

"I don't know what you mean by Long Melford," said I.

"Why, this long right of yours," said Belle, feeling my right arm—"if you do, I shouldn't wonder if you yet stand a chance."

I rose from my second's knee as well as my weakness would let me. On he came, striking left and right, though his eyes were considerably swelled, and his nether lip cut in two. At last he aimed a blow, which, had it taken effect, would doubtless have ended the battle, but owing to his slipping, the fist only grazed my left shoulder, and came with terrific force against a tree. Before the tinman could recover himself, I collected all my strength, and struck him beneath the ear, a right-handed blow, and then fell to the ground exhausted.

"Hurrah for Long Melford!" I heard Belle exclaim: "there is nothing like Long Melford for shortness all the world over."

It was some time before we revived him. Then he and the ugly woman got ready to go.

" It was all due to you, you limmer," she told the tall girl;
" had you not interfered, the old man would soon have settled
the boy."

" I'm for fair play and Long Melford," said the other;
" no foul work for me. Now let us all shake hands, let
bygones be bygones, and camp here with the young man."

But they paid no attention to her, but left her with me
down there in the dingle, flogging their horses and cursing.

" They were bad people," she said, looking after them, tears
in her eyes, " and I did not like them, but they were my only
acquaintance in the wide world."

I learned that her name was Isopel Berners, that she was
the daughter of a small milliner and a sea-officer, who was
killed on the very day before he was about to return to marry
her mother. She had been born in the workhouse and brought
up there, her mother having soon died, till at fourteen she
was put to work on a farm. The farmer's wife treated her
badly, so Isopel knocked her down, and did the same to her
next employer, another farmer, who sought to seduce her.
Then she took up with the travelling life, with a woman who
sold silks and linen. When she died Isopel inherited her
stock-in-trade and her cart; since when she had gone up and
down the country, and for the last few months had kept with
Grey Moll and the Flaming Tinman, finding even their company better than none.

So there we lived in the dingle in our separate tents, Isopel
Berners and I. Few visitors we had, though there was one,
a black Jesuit priest, who came often to talk and drink of the
Hollands gin which I gave him. One night a terrible storm
broke upon us, and while it was raging a coach floundered
close to our dingle and we gave the postilion shelter. When
we had warmed him with fire and with liquor he sat in our
tent and conversed, and the manner of his conversation was
this—

" I'll be bound," said he, " you two come from Gretna
Green; young man has run from his college, and the young
gentlewoman from boarding-school. I should like nothing
better than to have the driving of you when you go home to
your governors. There will be a grand meeting between the
two families, who, after a few reproaches, will give you their
blessing. They won't give you much for the first year, five
hundred at the most, to show they are not altogether satisfied
with you; but the second, if you don't get a cool thousand,

may I catch cold, especially should young madam here present a son and heir for the old people to fondle."

"Really," said I, "you are getting on swimmingly."

"And what do you say to all this?" I demanded of Belle; but before she could answer, the postilion finished his speech.

"Wait a moment," he said, "I have yet one more word to say. When you are surrounded by comforts, keeping your nice little barouche and pair, your coachman and livery, and visited by all the carriage-people in the neighbourhood, I shouldn't wonder if now and then you look back with longing and regret to the days when you lived in the damp, dripping dingle, had no better equipage than a pony or donkey-cart, and saw no better company than a tramper or Gypsy, except once, when a poor postilion was glad to seat himself at your charcoal fire. Now, young gentleman, I will take a spell on your blanket—young lady, good-night."

JANE EYRE

By CHARLOTTE BRONTË

Charlotte (1816–1855), the eldest of the three Brontë sisters, produced only three novels, of which "Jane Eyre", the first (published 1847), is her most popular work. Here is a book whose characterization is so detailed, whose passion so burning that any digest can give only a faint echo of the force and tumult of the original.

My childhood at Gateshead Hall was worse than miserable: it was pitiless. My aunt, Mrs. Reed, was a woman strict and efficient in the management of her estate. She had promised her husband on his deathbed to look after me, his dead brother's child, as she would her own child. She resented her promise and never let me forget my obligations to her as an orphan. Her spoilt children, the headstrong Eliza, the insolent, pretty Georgiana, and the vicious, bullying John, conforming to their mother's wishes, were content to exclude me from the privileges intended for happy children. I was regarded as a pariah, made a perpetual scapegoat and butt for spite. When I was ten years old, locked up in a gloomy room alone, as a punishment for some " misdeed ", my little mind collapsed under the strain, and I suffered some kind of fit.

Three months later, during which time I had been confined to the nursery, I was called into the awful region of the breakfast-room, and there, as a little girl whom it was necessary to cure of deceit and keep humble, introduced by Mrs. Reed to a stony stranger, a Mr. Brocklehurst.

" Humility is a Christian grace," said Mr. Brocklehurst, " and one peculiarly appropriate to the pupils of Lowood school, where the fare is plain, the attire simple and the girls are taught virtues equally unsophisticated."

Mrs. Reed wholeheartedly approved of a frugal discipline for me, and at once decided that I should be placed as a pupil in that nursery of chosen plants, Lowood Institute, a charity school for orphans. The interview closed and Mrs. Reed and I were left alone. I felt I could submit no longer to cant and unfairness. Speak I must: my soul cried out for retaliation.

" I am not deceitful! " I cried.　Shaking from head to foot
with excitement and experiencing a strange, exulting sense of
liberation, I continued: " I am *glad* you are no relation of
mine.　It is *you* who are deceitful! "

Mrs. Reed looked frightened.

" Deceit is *not* my fault! " I cried fiercely.

" Now, Jane, return to the nursery and lie down, there's a
dear."

" I am not your dear:　I cannot lie down:　I hate to live
here:　send me to school soon."

" I will indeed," murmured Mrs. Reed, and left me in the
room victor of the hardest fight I had fought.

At Lowood Institute, together with the rest of the eighty
pupils, I endured an insufficiency of human comforts pro-
portionate to a surfeit of spiritual rigour.　For the bad food,
the inadequate clothes, and the intense cold in winter, I found
compensation in the companionship and moral instruction of
my friend, Helen Burns.　But under-nourishment and an
unhealthy locality beckoned Death to Lowood.　Typhus
decimated the ranks of the children, and beloved, long-suffering
Helen, stricken by consumption, was also carried to the last
haven.　Eight years I remained within the grim walls of the
Institute, the last two in the capacity of teacher.　But the
resignation and marriage of the superintendent, the kind
Miss Temple, abstracted for me everything memorable from
the place, and, eager for liberty, I advertised for a governess's
post.

In September, when I arrived at Thornfield Hall, situated
in the environs of Millcote, my reception was warm and homely,
not at all what I expected as due to a governess.　The housekeeper, Mrs. Fairfax, a neat, quiet, elderly lady, explained my
duties to me.　I was to give tuition to Miss Adele Varens, the
eight-year-old ward of the absentee owner, Mr. Rochester, to
whom Mrs. Fairfax was distantly related.

Everything about Thornfield was stately:　the long gallery,
the large hall, the imposing dining-room, the great oak clock.
A gentleman's manor house of three storeys, its battlements
were set picturesquely over a meadow peopled with mighty
old thorn trees against the background of an ancient rookery.
I felt it rather a misfortune that I, with my pale, irregular
features and over-thin figure, was not more in accord with
my surroundings, though my Quaker style of dress was not
without dignity or merit.

" Is Mr. Rochester a fastidious sort of man? " I asked Mrs.
Fairfax as she showed me over the house.

" Not particularly so; but his tastes are gentlemanly. All
the land in the neighbourhood has been owned by the Rochesters
for generations."

" But is he liked for himself? "

" *I* like him, and he is judged a liberal landlord by his
tenants: though he is very rarely at home for more than a
fortnight at a time."

" But what is his character? "

" Unimpeachable, I suppose. Rather peculiar: he has
travelled a great deal. Sometimes he is a little disconcerting.
You cannot always be sure whether he is in jest or in
earnest."

The third storey of Thornfield Hall, to which all the antique
furniture had been relegated, possessed the strangest atmosphere
—like a shrine of memory, the haunt of a ghost. Even as I
passed through the corridor, I heard a weird, mirthless laugh
echoing in the air. To my startled query Mrs. Fairfax replied:
" One of the servants very likely: Grace Poole, I expect."
And to dispel my perturbation Grace Poole appeared in the
door: no one more solid than this square-made woman could
be imagined.

One afternoon in the following January I went walking in a
lane noted for its wild summer roses and autumn blackberries.
Though ice was on the road I was warm in my mantle and
muff, and sat down on a stile, delighting in the hushed life of
the evening. The clatter of a horse's hooves broke the stillness.
A large dog came bounding ahead of a tall steed and rider, who
passed by me. Suddenly with a sliding and what sounded like
curses man and horse were down, having slipped on the ice.
I went to the help of the traveller.

" Can I do anything? " I asked.

" You must just stand on one side," he answered as he rose
" I have no bones broken—only a sprain."

In the lingering twilight I could trace his stern features and
heavy brow. Of middle height, broad-shouldered, deep-
chested, he seemed past youth; perhaps he might be thirty-
five.

" I cannot think of leaving you, sir, till I see you fit to mount
your horse for home."

" I should think you ought to be home yourself. Where do
you come from? "

"From just below."

"Do you mean from that house with the battlements?"
He pointed to Thornfield Hall.

"Yes, sir."

"Whose house is it?"

"Mr. Rochester's."

"You are not a servant at the Hall, of course. You are——"
He seemed puzzled.

"I am the governess."

"Ah, the governess! Deuce take me, if I had not forgotten!
Excuse me," he continued, "necessity compels me to make
use of you." He laid his heavy hand on my shoulder, and with
my support limped to his horse and mounted. With a touch of
the spur, the horse, the dog and rider vanished into the darkness.

The act pleased me, as it lifted me out of the passivity of my
existence. When I reached Thornfield I found the same dog
seated by the fire, and learnt from Mrs. Fairfax that the master,
Mr. Rochester, had returned.

The next evening I was introduced to him. Grim of mien,
more characterful than handsome, he catechized me in his
commanding manner about my life at Lowood, and after
complimenting me on some sketches I had done, he abruptly
dismissed Adele, Mrs. Fairfax and myself out of the room.
On other evenings Mr. Rochester, in his blunt somewhat
arrogant fashion, was pleased to converse with me about his
own past life. I was as direct with him as was proper to my
position. To his sudden query whether I considered him
handsome, I replied: "No, sir." Further, I suggested that
perhaps he was no philanthropist. For, indeed, his abrupt
style of intercourse showed few signs of benevolence.

"I have a conscience," he asserted. "I once had a kind
of rude tenderness of heart. But Fortune has kneaded me with
her knuckles, and now I flatter myself I am tough as an India-
rubber ball; pervious, though, through a chink or two still.
Does that leave hope for me?"

Adele's dancing appearance in a satin dress elicited the
comment from him: "I have been green, and my departed
Spring has left that floweret on my hands. I keep it and rear
it to expiate my numerous sins." I thought he had had de-
cidedly too much wine.

During the next weeks his manner towards me became more
uniform. His fits of chilly hauteur were less frequent. When
he met me unexpectedly the encounter seemed welcome to

him. The evening conferences with which he honoured me seemed to be as much for his benefit as mine. The tribute to my discretion was very acceptable to me. He seemed more a relation than a master. I grew to like him, but none the less did not dismiss his faults of imperious severity and scowling moodiness. I was dozing and musing thus after lying down one night in bed, when I was chilled with fear at hearing what seemed the groping of fingers on the panelling of my door. I had scarcely relapsed into slumber, when a freezing demoniac laugh sounded outside my chamber. I heard steps retreating to the third storey staircase. " Was that Grace Poole? Is she possessed with the Devil? " I asked myself. I opened my door to go to Mrs. Fairfax. Outside the air was dim with blue smoke rushing in clouds from Mr. Rochester's room. In an instant I was inside. Flames licked the curtains round the bed in which Mr. Rochester lay stupefied by the smoke. I deluged the burning hangings with water from the basin and ewer, and succeeded in extinguishing the fire. The liberal splashing roused Mr. Rochester at last, and he fulminated strangely at finding himself drenched.

" Have you plotted to drown me, Jane Eyre, you witch? " he demanded.

I informed him of the circumstances. He ordered me to remain where I was while he investigated. After a short while he returned pale and gloomy.

" It is just as I thought," said he. " Grace Poole. She laughs in that way. She is an eccentric person." He requested me to keep the incident to myself. As I was about to go, he took my hands in his and thanked me for saving his life. " People talk of natural sympathies," he concluded in a speech oddly hesitant for him, " there are grains of truth in the wildest fable. My cherished preserver, goodnight! " Strange energy was in his voice; strange fire in his eye.

Mr. Rochester, nevertheless, took no steps to give Mrs. Poole into custody, nor even dismiss the dangerous miscreant. The day after the incident the master went away, and nothing was heard of him for a fortnight; during which time my imagination strayed so far from the fold of common-sense that a plain rebuke had to be administered to it. I pronounced judgment that a greater fool than Jane Eyre never existed nor surfeited herself on sweet lies. To think of herself a favourite of Mr. Rochester!

The master sent notice that he would return with a number

of guests. The whole establishment of Thornfield was refurbished: such polishing, scrubbing, dusting, scouring, of pots and pans, carpets and mirrors, bedrooms and hearths as I never beheld. The gorgeous company of haughty ladies arrived, among them Miss Blanche Ingram, who, Mrs. Fairfax told me, was the object of Mr. Rochester's interest. If Mr. Rochester had a taste for the majestic, she was the very type of majesty. Her undoubted beauty carried with it an equally unmistakable pride. She was sufficiently condescending to take notice of me and remark in my hearing that she had nothing but contempt for governesses. I waited after dinner while Mr. Rochester finished a song in his fine bass voice to an accompaniment played by Miss Blanche, and then slipped away. But while tying up my sandal outside in the hall, Mr. Rochester came upon me. He looked at me for a minute.

"You look depressed," he said. "Tell me what about." He noticed I was near tears. "If I were not in mortal dread of some prating servant passing, I would know what this means. Good night, my . . ." he bit his lip and abruptly left me.

The days passed for the guests at Thornfield Hall in a merry round of entertainment, songs and charades, all of which seemed designed to throw Mr. Rochester and Miss Ingram more closely together. The day when Mr. Rochester was called away on business was marked by the arrival of two visitors. The first was a tall stranger from Jamaica, a Mr. Mason, who claimed acquaintance with Mr. Rochester and desired permission to wait till his return. The second was a fortune-teller from a gypsy encampment, who insisted on telling the fortunes of all the ladies present, including myself. She told Miss Ingram something which mightily displeased her, and to me she put strange questions and told things she must have learnt from sources other than my palm. But the *dénouement* took me by surprise. The gypsy was my master in masquerade. He begged my forgiveness for his trick, but I withheld it till I had thought things over. Then I remembered the stranger. Mr. Rochester was severely shaken by the name—Mason.

"My little friend," said he, "I wish I were in a quiet island with only you; and trouble, and danger, and hideous recollections removed from me."

But later he was cheerful enough showing the new visitor to a guest-chamber.

That night was moon-lit and crystal clear when I awoke. Its solemn midnight silence was rent by a shrill savage sound.

Good God! What a cry! My pulse stopped beating. The sound came from overhead, from the third storey. It was accompanied by the noise of a struggle. A muffled voice cried for help. Shaking with terror, I dressed hurriedly and ran out into the passage. Mr. Rochester was there, calming the whole household. A servant had had a nightmare, he explained. But to me he came later and bade me get up and follow him. He led me to Grace Poole's room, where on the bed the stranger, Mason, was lying white as ashes, the linen round one arm soaked in blood. Mr. Rochester bade me fetch salts and a sponge, and stay with the victim while he went for a surgeon. The surgeon noted wounds made not by a knife but by teeth. By dawn the wounded man was dressed and, under Mr. Rochester's direction, circumspectly removed from the house in a coach. The sun was rising when Mr. Rochester called " Jane " and took me into the orchard down a walk edged with stocks and sweet-williams. He gathered a rose and offered it to me. We spoke about Grace Poole and Mr. Mason, from whom, he said, he was in no fear of danger, but who might through carelessness deprive him of happiness for ever.

A dream of an infant had troubled me on the night of the cry, and it recurred the night before Mrs. Reed's coachman came to visit me. He told me that his mistress was likely to die of a stroke at hearing of the suicide of her profligate son John. She had been murmuring my name and asking for me. Mr. Rochester gave me permission to visit her, but our parting seemed a little too cool for his liking.

I returned to that hostile roof at Gateshead with a surer trust in myself and in my powers, forgiving past wrongs and purified of resentment. But Mrs. Reed could not so easily eradicate her natural antipathy to me. She confessed she had done me two vengeful wrongs: in not bringing me up as her child according to her vow; and in keeping a note to herself that she had received three years previously from my uncle in Madeira, who wanted to adopt his niece. She relieved her conscience by this confession, but carried her hatred of me to the grave.

I overstayed my week's leave of absence at Gateshead by three weeks. It was a fair and soft summer's evening when I walked through the fields of Millcote that were being raked by the haymakers. The sky, with its cloud-strata high and thin, promised well for the future. When I saw Mr. Rochester sitting on the stone steps of the Hall reading, it was only with difficulty I regained the mastery over myself.

" Truant, truant ! " he cried. " Absent from me a whole month, and forgetting me quite, I'll be sworn."

Maintaining his bantering attitude, he took me to see the new coach he had bought for his wife-to-be.

But in the fortnight that followed I was surprised there were no continual visits to Ingram Park, which was only twenty miles off. Resolutely as I tried to set my face against the future and its warning of separation and grief, at the times when I was called into Mr. Rochester's presence—and they were more frequent than ever before—my spirits were dejected. Yet never had he been kinder to me, and never, alas! had I loved him so well.

The summer shone splendidly over England. On midsummer's eve I wandered into the garden. With the scents of jasmine, southernwood and rose mingled the aroma of Mr. Rochester's cigar. Mr. Rochester was examining a great moth that had attached itself to a plant at his foot. I tried to avoid him, but he called quietly: " Jane, come and look at this fellow." As always at a crisis, I was tongue-tied, and obeyed.

" Jane," he said after a while, " you must have become attached to Thornfield."

" Indeed I have, sir,"

" You would be sorry to depart ? "

" Yes."

" Pity ! " he said, and sighed.

" Must I leave ? " I asked.

" I am sorry, Jane, but I believe you must."

" Then you *are* going to be married, sir ? "

" Precisely ! And remember, when Rumour first intimated that I was to enter into the holy estate of matrimony with Miss Ingram, it was you yourself who suggested that you and Adele should forthwith trot. I have already found you a position as governess to the five daughters of Mrs. O'Gall of Bitternutte Lodge in Ireland."

" It is a long way off, sir."

" From what, Jane ? "

" From England, and from Thornfield, and . . ."

" Well ? "

" From you, sir."

The tears flowed from my eyes involuntarily, but I avoided sobbing. We came to the giant chestnut-tree in the orchard.

" Come, let us sit here in peace to-night and talk over the voyage."

But my heart was too full to risk answering his questions. The nightingale was singing in the wood. My whole body quivered with acute distress. But at last I gained control of myself, and spoke of my grief at leaving the place where I had experienced expansion in communion with so vigorous and original a mind; but that it must be so, if necessity—in the form of his bride—commanded it.

" My bride! I have no bride! "

" But you will have."

" Yes, I will!—I will! " He set his teeth. " But you must, you can, stay. I swear it."

" Ah! I tell you I must go! " I retorted, roused to something like passion. " Do you think I can stay to become nothing to you? Do you think I am an automaton? Do you think that because I am poor and plain, I have no soul, no feelings? If God had gifted me with wealth and beauty, I would have made it as hard for you to have left me. It is my spirit that speaks to you now, as though equal at God's foot with yours."

" As we are! " repeated Mr. Rochester, and he took me in his arms, held me to his breast and pressed his lips to mine: " so, Jane! "

" Yet not so," I rejoined, " for you are as good as a married man."

" Jane, be still; don't struggle so. I summon you as my wife: it is you only I intend to marry."

I was incredulous till he proved his intentions by his earnestness. And sitting by him, his cheek laid on mine, the paradise of union taking the place of a nightmare of parting, I could not see the fierce quality of his exultation. Happiness entirely took hold of me. " It will atone," he murmured. " Have I not found her friendless, comfortless? It will expiate at God's tribunal. For man's opinion—I defy it." As he was speaking, a livid spark of lightning was followed by the rushing rain of a storm. Back in the hall, he kissed me goodnight. Next morning little Adele ran to tell me that the great chestnut-tree at the bottom of the orchard had been struck by lightning.

Two nights before my marriage, my sleep was disturbed by dreams. Again the foreboding dream of a child took hold of me. And in my second dream I saw Thornfield Hall empty as a broken shell, a ruin haunted by owls and bats. I woke to find someone in my room holding a candle and surveying my wedding dress and veil. It was not the maid, nor Mrs. Fairfax, nor even Grace Poole, but a large woman with thick, dark hair, dressed in white. I saw her savage face reflected in the mirror, ghastly, red and rolling of eye, swollen and purplish in feature. The creature put my veil on its gaunt head, then, removing it, tore it furiously in pieces and stamped on it. When the horror turned and stooped over me in bed, I lost consciousness. I related the whole story to Mr. Rochester. " Thank God! " he said, " only the veil was harmed. It must have been Grace Poole." He promised to tell me, after we had been married a year and a day, why he kept such a woman in the house.

No bridegroom ever looked so grimly resolute, I am sure, nor was ever so impatient of delay, as Mr. Rochester on his wedding day. The ceremony was to take place in the church just beyond the gates of Thornfield, and none was to be present but Mr. Rochester and I, Mr. Wood, the clergyman, and his clerk. The service had proceeded to the point where the clergyman was saying: " If either of you know any impediment why ye may not lawfully be joined together in matrimony," when one of two strangers who had entered the church stepped forward, and in a distinct voice alleged that an insuperable impediment to the marriage existed.

When pressed to explain, he continued steadily: " Mr. Rochester has a wife now living."

Mr. Rochester's face was colourless rock, his eye spark and flint: with a strong grip he rivetted me to his side.

" Gentlemen," said Mr. Rochester, reckless in discovery, " my plan is broken up. Wood, close your book and take off your surplice. There will be no wedding to-day. What this lawyer and his client say is true. Wood, I daresay you have heard gossip about the mysterious lunatic kept under lock and key at the Hall. She is my wife, whom I married fifteen years ago—Bertha Mason by name, sister of this other personage here, who was severely attacked by her three months ago. Bertha Mason is mad; and she came of a mad family. I invite you all up to the house to visit Mrs. Poole's patient, *my wife*! "

There, in Grace Poole's room, the creature who had trampled on my veil prowled as savage and as vicious as a wild beast. At Mr. Rochester's entrance, she sprang at him, grappled his throat viciously and bared her teeth at his flesh. Mr. Rochester mastered her and bound her with rope to a chair. He turned to the spectators and said desolately: " That is my wife."

In the ebb of the afternoon I sat wrestling with the coils of my predicament. My mind told me : " Leave Thornfield at once," but my heart fought against so cruel a decision. Mr. Rochester came to me with such remorse in his eye, and with a story offering so many justifications for his conduct, that I willingly forgave him all. He exerted all his strength and determination to break down that barrier in my character and conscience which made me reject, though after the most agonising ordeal, his so persuasive claim on my fidelity and love. But my intolerable duty beckoned clearly in the one word—" Depart ! "

Next morning I escaped from the house before the servants stirred. My last shilling I gave to a coachman to convey me far from the scene of my agony. For days I wandered on the moors where I was set down, hunger reducing me to beggary, fatigue and desolation to a total prostration of hope. At last Providence directed me across the marshes to a house where I was granted refuge.

I emerged from a period of fever to find my saviours, the Misses Diana and Mary Rivers and Mr. St. John Rivers, kindly, generous and sensitive to my desire to be uncommunicative about my recent tribulation. I told them my name was Jane Elliot. The more I knew of the handsome, vigorous Diana and of the docile, intelligent Mary, whom I taught to draw and paint, the more I liked them. But their brother, Mr. St. John, of the Athenian features and hard, eager expression, was less open to intimacy than his two sisters. Yet as minister he secured for me the humble post of schoolmistress to the cottagers' children in his parish at £30 a year.

I had the opportunity of watching St. John's resolute and icy Christianity shaken, but not broken, by the dazzling assault of beautiful Rosamund Oliver, the daughter of a wealthy proprietor. Yet St. John began to evince a curious interest in me and my family connections. Having by chance come across the vital link in a chain of evidence, he one day announced to me that it was I who was the missing heiress of a fortune of £20,000 left by his uncle, and which he and his sisters had expected to inherit.

As the time approached for St. John to take up his missionary work in the East, his interest in me developed with a cold, controlling persistence. He asked me to marry him. " God intended you for a missionary's wife," he asserted. " Jane, you are diligent, constant, docile ; very gentle and very heroic. Your assistance to me will be invaluable." His persuasion contracted round me like an iron shroud. " I will accompany you as your cousin," I agreed, " but not as your wife." But he would not consent to any other basis of co-operation than his own. The night before he left home, with a gentleness well-nigh irresistible, he once more urged me to accompany him. More excited by his renewed offer than I ever had been, I entreated of Heaven: " Show me, show me the path!" My heart beat fast. Suddenly it stood still. I heard a voice somewhere cry:

" Jane! Jane! Jane!"

" O God! What is it?" I gasped.

I might have said " Where is it?" for it did not seem in the room; nor in the house, nor in the garden. And it was the voice of a human being: a known, loved, well-remembered voice—that of Edward Fairfax Rochester; and it spoke eerily, urgently, in pain and woe.

" I am coming!" I cried. " Wait for me! Oh! I will come!" I rushed to the door: the passage was dark. I ran to the garden: it was void.

I left at dawn and travelled by coach to Thornfield, feeling like a messenger-pigeon flying home. With what feelings I welcomed the trees I knew, the woods, the lanes, the clustered rookery! I came to a sudden stop in front of the great mansion. Like a lover thinking to come upon his love sleeping sweetly and finding her stone dead, I looked at that stately house: I saw a blackened ruin, hollowed out by conflagration. Horrified, I returned to the inn and asked questions of the host.

" Is Mr. Rochester living at Thornfield Hall now?"

" No, ma'am: oh, no! No one is living there. The hall was burnt down last autumn just about harvest time. A terrible spectacle. I witnessed it myself."

" Was it known how the fire originated?"

" They guessed, ma'am. There was a—a—lunatic kept in the house. She was kept in very close confinement, ma'am. And she had a woman to take care of her, by the name of Mrs. Poole—an able woman in her line, but she was addicted to gin and took a drop over-much occasionally. When Mrs. Poole was fast asleep after the gin, the mad lady would take the keys out of her pocket and roam the house. On this night she set fire to the room next to her own, and to the former governess's chamber."

" Was Mr. Rochester at home when the fire broke out?"

" Yes, indeed he was. He got the servants out of their

beds and went back to fetch his mad wife. But she climbed to the battlements. We saw Mr. Rochester approach her, and then, ma'am, she yelled and gave a spring, and the next minute she lay smashed on the pavement."

" Did any one else lose their life? "

" No—perhaps it would have been better if there had."

" What do you mean? "

" Poor Mr. Edward! " he ejaculated.

" You said he was alive? " I exclaimed.

" He is stone blind," he said at last. " He was crushed in the ruins as they collapsed. One eye was knocked out by a falling beam, and one hand had to be amputated. The other eye became inflamed, and he lost the sight of that also. Now is he helpless indeed."

" Where is he? Where does he live? "

" At Ferndean, a manor house about thirty miles off: quite a desolate spot."

I arrived at Ferndean, a house buried deep in a wood, just ere dark. The house and its unkempt estate looked lifeless. But suddenly the front door opened and a figure came into the twilight, a man stretching forth his hand to feel whether it rained. I recognized him—my master, Edward Rochester—his countenance changed, marked with the brooding of despair. I saw him grope his way back into the house. I followed him, and, with the housekeeper's permission, carried a tray of glasses and water into the parlour to him.

" Will you have a little water, sir? " I asked.

" Who is it? Who speaks? "

He groped forward: I took his outstretched hand.

" Her very fingers! " he cried.

" And this her voice," I added.

" Jane Eyre!—Jane Eyre! " was all he said.

" My dear master," I said, " I am come back to you."

" My crippled strength, my seared vision," he murmured regretfully. " I am no better than the old lightning-struck chestnut tree at Thornfield."

But, Reader, I married him, and Mr. Rochester partially regained the sight of one eye two years after our marriage.

WUTHERING HEIGHTS

By EMILY BRONTË

Though her single novel excels any of her sisters' books in raging splendour and sombre passion, Emily, the second of the Brontë sisters, is ultimately renowned as a poet. Perhaps it is the same poetic genius that produced such fine lyrics as " Remembrance " and " Last Lines " that shines at times through her prose with such an unearthly gleam.

IN the year 1801 Mr. Lockwood, the new tenant of Thrushcross Grange, called on his landlord, Mr. Heathcliff, at the isolated farm, high up on the Yorkshire moors, known as Wuthering Heights. He found a queer household. Mr. Heathcliff, tall, black-browed, of gypsy-like aspect, and of rude and forbidding manners, evidently resented the call, and took no pains to conceal it. Within the house Mr. Lockwood found an aged and disagreeable servant called Joseph, who grumbled audibly at his intrusion and constantly cursed the other members of the household as heathens and idlers. The housekeeper, Zillah, seemed normal enough, and was the only person to come to his assistance when he was set upon by dogs. There was also a handsome but surly and boorish youth, coarse in language and manners, who did the farm work, yet was evidently not a servant.

In the parlour was an exquisitely beautiful young woman, very fair, dressed in black; a girl to all appearances, but addressed as Mrs. Heathcliff. After making two unfortunate blunders, Mr. Lockwood discovered that she was the widow of Mr. Heathcliff's son. Mr. Heathcliff behaved roughly, even violently, towards her, and she treated everybody with contempt and silence.

A heavy snowstorm obliged Mr. Lockwood to stay the night, though he was offered no hospitality. Zillah, the housekeeper, secretly showed him to a room. In it was a queer old bed in an oak chest which enclosed the window embrasure. On the window-sill Mr. Lockwood saw the names Catherine Earnshaw, Catherine Linton, Catherine Heathcliff, scratched over and over again on the paint. He turned over an old

Bible with the name Catherine Earnshaw in it, and idly read a few scraps of a child's diary written on the fly-leaves.

He fell asleep and had a terrible dream. He dreamed that he was in the same chest bed by the window, with the storm swirling outside. A branch of a fir tree was tapping against the window-pane, and in his dream he rose, determined to silence it. But the casement would not open, so he broke the glass and stretched out an arm to seize the branch; but instead, his fingers closed on a little, ice-cold hand. He tried to draw back, but the hand clung to his and a voice sobbed: " Let me in; I'm Catherine Linton." Obscurely he saw a child's face peering through the glass. In terror he rubbed the creature's wrist on the broken pane until the blood flowed. Still it clung to him, and Mr. Lockwood screamed.

The scream was real, and brought Mr. Heathcliff to the door. He showed the greatest surprise and anger at finding Mr. Lockwood in the room, but when he heard of the dream he became extremely agitated and rushed to the window calling in a grief-stricken voice: " Cathy, come in, come in."

Mr. Lockwood returned to Thrushcross Grange with a severe chill, and while he was confined to his bed his house-keeper, Nelly Dean, told him the story of the inhabitants of Wuthering Heights.

The farm belonged to a very old family, the Earnshaws, and Nelly Dean's mother had been nurse to Hindley Earnshaw, and she herself was brought up with the family. There was a younger Earnshaw child, Catherine. One day old Mr. Earn-shaw brought home a black-haired, black-eyed, dirty little waif that he had picked up in the streets of Liverpool. They called him Heathcliff, and he was brought up with the other children. Old Mr. Earnshaw took a great fancy to him, but Hindley, the son, detested and maltreated him. Catherine and Heathcliff, however, became fast friends, although they often quarrelled, both having violent tempers. The two were mainly looked after by Joseph, the canting old servant, and Nelly.

Old Mr. Earnshaw died, and Hindley became head of the house. He took advantage of his position to vent his hatred of Heathcliff to the full. He dismissed his tutor, degraded him to the position of a servant, and bullied him in all possible ways. Heathcliff grew up with two consuming passions, love for Catherine and hatred for Hindley.

Hindley married and had a son. His wife died of consumption, and Hindley, crazed with grief, took to drink. Meanwhile Catherine had grown into a beautiful girl, wild and wayward and passionate. She was devoted to Heathcliff. In time a neighbour, Edgar Linton of Thrushcross Grange, fell in love with her and asked her to marry him. Very uncertainly she accepted. Edgar Linton was entirely her opposite, very fair in appearance (the Earnshaws were all dark), gentle and scholarly.

When Heathcliff heard of the engagement he suddenly disappeared. Catherine spent a whole night looking and waiting for him in the rain, and then fell terribly ill of a fever. After this illness her constitution was permanently weakened, so that the violence of her passions was a constant source of danger to her health.

Three years later, Catherine married Edgar Linton, and went to live at the Grange. Nelly Dean, who until then had been nurse to Hindley's little son Hareton, went with her. Nothing more had been heard of Heathcliff. Contrary to Nelly's expectations, the first six months of the marriage passed in peaceful happiness. Catherine seemed to have grown gentler. But it was the lull before the storm.

Suddenly Heathcliff reappeared. He called to see Catherine, a full-grown, handsome man with a gentlemanly bearing and amply supplied with money. No one ever knew where he had been during the intervening years, nor how he had transformed himself from a rustic savage into a man of education and substance. There was still something wild and savage, however, about his handsome gypsy face.

Catherine was madly delighted to see him, while Edgar was sad and angry, for Heathcliff treated him with open contempt. Heathcliff called frequently, and Isabella, Edgar's eighteen-year-old sister, fell in love with him. Catherine, amused, told Heathcliff, but, genuinely concerned for the girl, gave her a true description of Heathcliff's real character, violent, cruel and ruthless, bent on one object in life: the destruction of his enemies. Catherine loved him, not because she did not see him in his true colours, but because he was part of herself. Isabella, however, did not believe her, and continued to cherish her passion.

Meanwhile Heathcliff had ensconced himself once more at Wuthering Heights. Hindley had two passions, drink and gambling, and Heathcliff indulged him liberally in both. Hindley was easy game, and Heathcliff had soon ruined him.

Hindley mortgaged all the Earnshaw property to him to pay his gambling debts.

Next to the Earnshaws, Heathcliff hated the Lintons, who had stolen Catherine from him. The news of Isabella's infatuation showed him the way to revenge himself on Edgar. He began to pay surreptitious court to Isabella. He was caught one day by Nelly, who told Catherine. The result was a terrible scene between Catherine, Heathcliff, and Edgar. Catherine at first defended the Lintons, but when Edgar threatened Heathcliff, she turned in defence of the man she really loved. Blows were struck, Heathcliff left the house and was bid never return, and Catherine gave way to a sort of wild emotional fit. She locked herself in her room, refused food for three days, and then fell dangerously ill of a brain fever.

The same night that she fell ill, Isabella eloped with Heathcliff. To mark this first successful stage of his revenge on the Lintons, Heathcliff hanged Isabella's little dog at the park gates. Nothing was heard of the fugitives for six weeks, and then Nelly received a letter from Isabella written from Wuthering Heights. She had already, she said, been long cured of her love for Heathcliff. From the first he had treated her with the greatest brutality, making no pretence at concealing his hatred for her. She was now a prisoner at Wuthering Heights with no companions but the half-crazy, drink-sodden Hindley, who was constantly threatening to murder Heathcliff, the servant Joseph, and the child Hareton, who, under Heathcliff's influence, had degenerated into a wild little animal.

Catherine recovered at length, but her reason was impaired. Nelly meanwhile found out that during the whole of Catherine's illness Heathcliff had been lurking in the garden at night. He forced her to arrange for him to see Catherine, and one evening, while Edgar and the servants were at church, Heathcliff came into the forbidden house and spoke to Catherine. Overcome by emotion, Heathcliff took the poor, wasted invalid in his arms, and thus they were found by Edgar on his return. But Catherine was in a dead faint. That night she gave birth to a seven months' child and died.

The baby was a girl, and christened Catherine. In default of a male heir to Edgar, on his death all the Linton property would pass to Isabella and her children. Thus it would inevitably fall into the hands of Heathcliff, who already held the Earnshaw property. Grimly Heathcliff watched his schemes maturing. Catherine's death cut him off from the one creature he loved. He was crazed with grief. The whole night long he spent by her grave. His terrible sorrow made him the more brutal to Isabella. At last she managed to escape and fled over the moors one night to the Grange. Not daring to spend more than an hour at home, she merely changed her drenched clothes and continued her flight. Eventually she settled in the south, and some months afterwards a son was born to her. Heathcliff did not molest her again.

Meanwhile, Hindley, his health broken by drink and despair, died still a young man. Heathcliff now came into full possession of Wuthering Heights, and the little Hareton was completely in his power. He planned to degrade him as Hindley had degraded *him*. He refused to have him taught even his letters, and instead encouraged him in every sort of bad behaviour. Yet Hareton, though he grew up ignorant and unmannerly, had a native intelligence and a good heart that nothing could corrupt.

The little Cathy grew up into an exquisite girl, very fair and quite unlike her mother except for her dark eyes. In time Isabella died, and Edgar brought her son Linton, a sickly, fretful invalid of sixteen, back to the Grange. Scarcely had he arrived than Heathcliff sent for him to Wuthering Heights. Fearing the worst from Heathcliff's cruelty, Nelly Dean took him to his father. Heathcliff, however, although manifesting his dislike for his son in brutal terms, nevertheless had him treated with every care, thus marking the difference between *his* son and Hareton.

Cathy had taken a great fancy to her cousin during the one evening Linton had spent at the Grange. She was very upset when she found that he had been spirited away to Wuthering Heights and that she was not to be allowed to visit him. Cathy inherited the rebellious will of her mother. On her sixteenth birthday, a beautiful sunny day in March, she tempted Nelly out for a walk on the moor, and, on the pretext of looking for grouse nests, deliberately wandered right on to Wuthering Heights land.

Here they met Heathcliff and his son out walking. Heathcliff, whom Cathy had never seen, made himself tolerably agreeable, and invited them into the house. Nelly did her best to prevent Cathy from acceding to the proposal, but she was overborne by Heathcliff and Cathy herself, who was delighted to see Linton and who had no inkling of her uncle's malevolence.

Nelly, who was now the only person in the world for whom Heathcliff felt some regard, told him outright that he was behaving very wrongly in encouraging Cathy, and that she was convinced that he was doing it from no good motive. Heathcliff replied openly that he intended Linton to marry Cathy. To which Nelly returned that Cathy should never approach his house again.

Linton did not make himself very agreeable to his cousin. He was peevish and apathetic. Hareton was in the house, and Cathy discovered, much to her disgust, that this loutish, unlettered boor was also her cousin. When she asked him about the inscription: " Hareton Earnshaw 1500 " over the door, he replied that it was some damnable writing, he could not read it. Heathcliff, following out his dark designs, took care to bait Hareton on his manners, in order to render him effectively tongue-tied and unattractive. To Nelly he confided his fiendish pleasure in the success of his degradation of Hareton, how he had turned this intelligent, sensitive nature into a coarse, boorish yokel. " And the best of it is, that Hareton is damnably fond of me. You'll confess I've out-matched Hindley there." Yet he admitted that he could have had a real regard for Hareton, whereas he utterly despised his own son.

Linton, finding Cathy much kinder and more indulgent than his own family, begged her to come again, and in this he was seconded by his father. Back at the Grange, however, Cathy was forbidden by Edgar to hold further communication with Wuthering Heights. In order to convince her of the villainy of Heathcliff's character, in which she was not at first disposed to believe, Edgar told Cathy something of the history of Heathcliff's conduct towards Isabella and the manner in which Wuthering Heights had become his property. Cathy was deeply shocked at this new view of human nature, but nevertheless nothing could damp her solicitude for Linton.

Many weeks later Nelly discovered an illicit correspondence between the two cousins. They were regular love-letters, of a childish, romantic kind. Cathy's were simple and spontaneous, but Linton's, to Nelly's eye, bore signs of strict surveillance by Heathcliff, who had obviously prevented him from giving way to his natural complaining fretfulness, and had composed his letters for him, inspiring them with a fictitious ardour and manliness.

Summer passed, autumn came on. Edgar's health was

visibly declining, and with it Cathy's spirits. One October afternoon she and Nelly took a walk in the Grange park. They arrived at the wall surrounding the park, and Cathy, anxious to pick some berries, climbed on to the top. Her hat fell into the road, so she scrambled down to fetch it. But once on the other side she found she could not climb back. There was a door in the wall, but it was locked. Just at this moment Heathcliff came by on his horse.

While Nelly on the park side vainly tried to force the lock of the gate, at the same time abjuring Cathy not to listen to Heathcliff, the latter was pouring a fearful tale of Linton's state of health into the ears of the frightened girl. He said that Linton was seriously ill through fretting after Cathy, and that if she did not relent and come to see him, he might die through her fault. From the other side of the door, Nelly shouted that it was all a lie, but Heathcliff replied that he would be away from home all the week, and that Nelly could go and see for herself.

" I swear that Linton is dying," he said, " and that grief and disappointment are hastening his death." At that point the lock at last gave way, Nelly pulled the girl in, and Heathcliff rode away.

The next day Cathy insisted on going to see her cousin. It was very wet and cold, and they found Linton alone in the parlour fretfully scolding Joseph for not bringing more coals. Joseph himself was calmly smoking by the kitchen fire and deliberately ignoring his young master. Cathy began to pet and nurse Linton, but a chance remark about their respective parents led to a violent quarrel. It was cut short by a horrible paroxysm of coughing in Linton, followed by a fit of moaning which he obviously prolonged in order to punish Cathy. Cathy, however, did not see through his tricks, and was deeply concerned. She promised she would come and see him again the next day.

When they got home, however, Nelly went to bed with a chill, and remained laid up for three weeks. Cathy divided her day between the two sick-beds of her father and her nurse. But when Nelly got up again, she discovered that Cathy had been riding over to see Linton every evening. Cathy told her that there had been several scenes at Wuthering Heights, once when Hareton, who hated Linton, had pushed him out of the room, and Linton had had a sort of fit. Cathy now had no illusions about Linton's temper, but she felt that nevertheless he really loved her and that he could not help himself, and above all that he needed her.

Nelly immediately told Edgar of the visits, and he once more forbade Cathy to go to Wuthering Heights, but at the same time he wrote to Linton inviting him to come to the Grange whenever he pleased. Since Linton was obviously very ill, and a most unattractive son-in-law, Heathcliff had no intention of allowing Edgar to see him. He therefore made him write to Edgar explaining that Heathcliff would not permit him to visit the Grange, but saying that he was heartbroken at being cut off from Cathy, and begging to be allowed to meet her out riding under the chaperonage of Mr. Linton himself. (Heathcliff knew well that Edgar was too ill to go out.)

Spring came on. Both Edgar and Linton were fast declining. Heathcliff was afraid that his son would die before Edgar, in which case he would not inherit Edgar's property. He determined to hurry on the marriage. Edgar himself, knowing nothing of Linton's real condition, began to consider the marriage favourably. At last he consented to Cathy and Linton meeting for a ride on the moors.

The meeting-place was fixed near the Grange grounds, but when Cathy and Nelly arrived, a herd-boy gave them a message that Linton was waiting at a spot much nearer Wuthering Heights. They found him looking very sick and downcast and frightened. He extracted a promise from Cathy that if she met Heathcliff on her way back she would tell him that Linton had been gay and cheerful, which he certainly had *not* been, and also she was to tell her own father that Linton's health was much improved. They arranged to meet again the following week.

It was a beautiful, hot August afternoon. Cathy and Nelly found Linton on the moor at the same spot as before. He seemed iller than ever, and abjectly terrified of something. He behaved so strangely that Cathy threatened to go home. Whereupon Linton threw himself at her feet, implored her to stay, saying he would be killed if she went away. He said there was a secret, but he dared not tell her, he dreaded his father so. Soon Heathcliff himself appeared and asked them to walk into the farmhouse. Cathy agreed, despite Nelly's disapproval. Linton could scarcely walk, and Cathy had to help him in. Once inside, Heathcliff locked the door.

He said they should stay to tea, adding to Nelly, indicating the two cousins: " Had I been born where laws are less strict and tastes less dainty, I should treat myself to a slow vivisection of those two as an evening's amusement."

Cathy, her eyes flashing, stepped up to Heathcliff and demanded the key. She tried to wrench it from his hand. He seized her and gave her a shower of terrific slaps on the head. Then he made tea and went out to loose their horses. Linton, who, having played his prescribed part in luring Cathy to the house, was now no longer in mortal terror of his father, told them that Heathcliff planned to keep them prisoners overnight and to marry Cathy and himself in the morning. When Heathcliff returned, Cathy begged him to release her, promising to marry Linton if only she might go back to her father that night. Heathcliff replied that nothing could please him better than to give pain to Edgar.

The housekeeper was away, and Nelly and Cathy were locked into her room for the night. At seven the next morning Heathcliff came for Cathy; Nelly was kept a prisoner for four days longer, seeing no one but Hareton, who brought her food. When she was released she found that Cathy was married to Linton and kept a prisoner in his room. Nelly went back to the Grange to comfort the dying Edgar. Cathy eventually perusaded Linton to let her out, and ran alone through the night to her father. She arrived just in time, and Edgar died believing her to be happily married.

Thrushcross Grange and Cathy were now in Heathcliff's hands. He fetched his young daughter-in-law back to Wuthering Heights, but obliged Nelly to stay at the Grange as housekeeper. Linton did not long outlast his father-in-law, for Heathcliff now would have no doctor nor attendance for him. After his death Cathy fell ill from the strain of nursing him alone. When she came downstairs again, she was changed from a gay, warm-hearted young girl to a cold, bitter woman, with nothing but unconcealed hatred for every member of Wuthering Heights.

This was the household which Mr. Lockwood had encountered. He took a sudden aversion to Thrushcross Grange, and, having recovered from his chill, returned immediately to London. The following summer he was travelling in the neighbourhood again and decided to call on Mr. Heathcliff to arrange the details of the termination of his tenancy of the Grange. On his arrival at Wuthering Heights, however, he found that all had changed. No dogs flew at him, the gate was unbarred, flowers grew in the garden and Cathy and Hareton were seated with their heads together over a book. Nelly

Dean was installed as housekeeper. On his inquiring for Heathcliff, she told him the rest of the story.

She had been summoned to Wuthering Heights only a fortnight after Mr. Lockwood had left the Grange. Heathcliff began to act more strangely than ever. He became more and more solitary and could scarcely bear to speak to any mortal. One evening he confided in Nelly.

Ever since Catherine's death, he said, he had been trying to reach her spirit. She was always almost within reach, and always she eluded him. She had tormented him during life, and she tormented him still. This straining of all his mental powers to find Catherine had been his real preoccupation all these years. While Edgar's grave was being dug beside Catherine's, Heathcliff had gone to the churchyard at night and had unscrewed her coffin and looked once more on her face.

After this he grew daily more withdrawn. Meanwhile Hareton and Cathy drew together. Cathy, sorry that she had teased him so shamefully, offered to teach him to read. Hareton was sulky at first, but his admiration for Cathy soon overcame him, and it was not long before the cousins were thoroughly in love with each other. Heathcliff saw, but seemed too wrapped up in something else to care.

One April day he came into the house with a wild, abstracted look of joy on his dark face. He was pale and trembling and had a strange fixed smile. All that day he did not eat. The next day was the same.

The third day he retired into the child Catherine's room with the oak chest bed, and was heard all day muttering and groaning to himself. That night was windy and wet. In the morning when Nelly went in she found the casement open and Heathcliff lying on his back with his eyes wide open, drenched with rain. He was dead.

Cathy and Hareton were now to be married and live at the Grange, and Nelly was to go with them. This was the end of Nelly's story. She added that there were tales in the village that Heathcliff and Catherine were seen wandering about the moors at night. Mr. Lockwood took his leave, and on his way back, looked at the three graves of Catherine, Edgar and Heathcliff. He watched the moths fluttering among the heath and harebells, listened to the soft wind breathing through the grass, and wondered how any one could ever imagine unquiet slumbers for the sleepers in that quiet earth.

DON QUIXOTE

By MIGUEL DE CERVANTES SAAVEDRA

This remarkable work, first published in 1605, began as a burlesque of the then fashionable romances of chivalry. Soon, however, the characters grew into a life outside their creator's original intentions and became the world-famous persons as we know them to-day. " Don Quixote " has many times been translated into English, but the finest is that of Motteux (1712), from whose version this digest is taken.

A T a certain village in La Mancha which I shall not name, there lived not long ago one of those old-fashioned gentlemen who are never without a lance upon a rack, an old target, a lean horse, and a greyhound. His diet consisted more of beef than mutton; and with minced meat on most nights, lentils on Fridays, griefs and groans on Saturdays, and a pigeon extraordinary on Sundays, he consumed three-quarters of his revenue: the rest was laid out in a plush coat, velvet breeches, with slippers of the same, for holidays; and a suit of the very best homespun cloth, which he bestowed on himself for working days. His whole family was a housekeeper something turned of forty, a niece not twenty, and a man that served him in the house and in the field, and could saddle a horse, and handle a pruning-hook. The master himself was nigh fifty years of age, of a hale and strong complexion, lean-bodied, and thin-faced, an early riser and a lover of hunting. Some say his surname was Quixada, or Quesada (for authors differ in this particular): however, we may reasonably conjecture he was called Quixana (*i.e.* lanthorn-jaws), though this concerns us but little, provided we keep strictly to the truth in every point of this history.

You must know, then, that when our gentleman had nothing to do (which was almost all the year round), he passed his time in reading books of knight-errantry; which he did with that application and delight, that at last he in a manner wholly left off his country sports, and even the care of his estate; nay, he grew so strangely besotted with those amusements, that he sold many acres of arable land to purchase books of that kind; by which means he collected as many of them as were to be had.

He would often dispute with the curate of the parish, a man of learning, and with Master Nicholas, barber of the same town, who was the better knight, Palmerin of England, or Amadis of Gaul?

In fine, he gave himself up so wholly to the reading of romances, that a-nights he would pore on until it was day, and a-days he would read on until it was night; and thus, by sleeping little and reading much, the moisture of his brain was exhausted to that degree, that at last he lost the use of his reason. A world of disorderly notions, picked out of his books, crowded into his imagination; and now his head was full of nothing but enchantments, quarrels, battles, challenges, wounds, complaints, amours, torments, and abundance of stuff and impossibilities.

Having thus lost his understanding, he unluckily stumbled upon the oddest fancy that ever entered into a madman's brain; for now he thought it convenient and necessary, as well for the increase of his own honour as the service of the public, to turn knight-errant, and roam through the whole world, armed *cap-à-pie* and mounted on his steed, in quest of adventures; that thus imitating those knights-errant of whom he had read, redressing all manner of grievances, and exposing himself to danger on all occasions, at last, after a happy conclusion of his enterprises, he might purchase everlasting honour and renown.

The first thing he did was to scour a suit of armour that had belonged to his great-grandfather, and had lain time out of mind carelessly rusting in a corner. Next, he went to view his horse, whose bones stuck out like the corners of a Spanish Real. He was four days considering what name to give him. After many names which he devised, rejected, changed, liked, disliked, and pitched upon again, he concluded to call him Rozinante.

When he had thus given his horse a name so much to his satisfaction, he thought of choosing one for himself; and having seriously pondered on the matter eight whole days more, at last he determined to call himself Don Quixote.

And now, he perceived he wanted nothing but a lady, on whom he might bestow the empire of his heart. Near the place where he lived dwelt a good, comely country lass, for whom he had formerly had a sort of an inclination, though it is believed she never heard of it, nor regarded it in the least. Her name was Aldonza Lorenzo, and at last he resolved to call her Dulcinea, with the addition of del Toboso, from the place where she was born.

These preparations being made, he found his designs ripe for action, and thought it now a crime to deny himself any longer to the injured world, that wanted such a deliverer. So one morning, before day, without acquainting anyone with his design, he armed himself *cap-à-pie*, grasped his lance, mounted Rozinante, and at the private door of his back-yard sallied out.

He travelled almost all that day without meeting any adventure; which put him in a kind of despair, for he desired nothing more than to encounter immediately some person on whom he might try the vigour of his arm. At last, towards evening, he espied an inn. And, as whatever our knight-errant saw, thought, or imagined, was all of the romantic cast, he no sooner saw the inn, but he fancied it to be a castle.

It happened at the very moment that a swineherd winded his horn; and Don Quixote presently imagined this was the wished-for signal, which some dwarf gave to notify his approach; therefore, with the greatest joy in the world, he rode up to the inn. When the landlord observed such a strange disguise of human shape he could hardly forbear laughing. " Sir Knight," said he, " if your worship be disposed to alight, you will fail of nothing here but a bed; as for all other accommodations, you may be supplied to your mind."

Don Quixote, observing the humility of the governor of the castle (for such the innkeeper seemed to him), " Señor Castellano," said he, " the least thing in the world suffices me; for arms are the only things I value, and combat is my bed of repose."

As soon as he had done supper, he called his host, and shut him and himself up in the stable, and falling at his feet, " I will never rise from this place," cried he, " most valorous knight, till you have graciously vouchsafed to grant me a boon which will redound to your honour and the good of mankind." The innkeeper, at a loss, endeavoured to make him rise, but all in vain till he had promised to grant him what he asked.

" I expected no less from your great magnificence, noble sir," replied Don Quixote, " and therefore I make bold to tell you, that the boon which I beg, and you generously condescend to grant me, is, that to-morrow you will be pleased to bestow the honour of knighthood upon me. This night I will watch

my armour in the chapel of your castle and then in the morning
you shall gratify me."

When he heard him talk after this manner, the innkeeper was
fully convinced of the disorder in his guest's understanding;
and, to make sport that night, resolved to humour him in his
desires. He told him that his castle at present had no chapel, it
being pulled down in order to be new built, but he knew his
arms might lawfully be watched in the courtyard of the castle;
and in the morning (God willing) all the necessary ceremonies
should be performed, so that he might assure himself he should
be dubbed a knight. And so they disposed everything in order
to his watching his arms in a great yard that adjoined the inn.
To which purpose, the knight, having got them all together,
laid them in a cistern close by a well in that yard; then, bracing
his target and grasping his lance, just as it grew dark, he began
to walk about by the horse-trough with a graceful deportment.
In the meantime, the innkeeper and all such as were in the house
went out to observe him at a distance; where they saw him
sometimes walk about with a great deal of gravity, and sometimes lean on his lance, with his eyes all the while fixed upon
his arms.

While he was thus employed, a carrier who lodged in the
inn came out to water his mules, which he could not do without
removing the arms out of the trough. With that, Don Quixote,
who saw him make towards him, cried out to him aloud, "O
thou, whosoever thou art, rash knight, that prepares to lay thy
hands on the arms of the most valorous knight-errant that ever
wore a sword, take heed; do not audaciously attempt to profane
them with a touch, lest instant death be the too sure reward of
thy temerity."

But the carrier never regarded these dreadful threats; and,
laying hold on the armour by the straps, without any more
ado threw it a good way from him. Don Quixote no sooner
saw this than, lifting up his eyes to heaven, and addressing his
thoughts, as it seemed, to his lady Dulcinea, "Assist me, lady,"
cried he, "in the first opportunity that offers itself to your faithful slave!" Repeating suchlike ejaculations, he lifted up his
lance with both his hands and gave the carrier such a terrible
knock on his inconsiderate pate with his lance, that he laid
him at his feet in a woeful condition. This done, Don Quixote
took up his armour, laid it again on the horse-trough, and then
walked on, backwards and forwards, with as great unconcern
as he did at first.

The innkeeper, who began somewhat to disrelish these mad tricks of his guest, resolved to dispatch him forthwith, and bestow on him that unlucky knighthood, to prevent further mischief: so, coming to him, he excused himself for the insolence of that base scoundrel. He said that the knight had already fulfilled the obligation of watching his arms, and, having fetched the book in which he used to set down the carrier's accounts for straw and barley, he ordered Don Quixote to kneel; then, reading in his manual, as if he had been repeating some pious oration, in the midst of his devotion he lifted up his hand, and gave him a good blow on the neck, and then a gentle slap on the back with the flat of his sword.

These extraordinary ceremonies being thus hurried over in a kind of post-haste, Don Quixote could not rest till he had taken the field in quest of adventures.

He had not gone above two miles, but he discovered a company of people riding towards him, who proved to be merchants of Toledo. The knight no sooner perceived them, but he imagined this to be some new adventure, and so, with a dreadful grace and assurance, fixing himself in his stirrups, couching his lance, and covering his breast with his target, he posted himself in the middle of the road. "Hold," cried he; "let all mankind stand, nor hope to pass on farther, unless all mankind acknowledge and confess, that there is not in the universe a more beautiful damsel than the Empress of La Mancha, the peerless Dulcinea del Toboso."

Conjecturing the poor gentleman had lost his senses, one of the company, who loved raillery, undertook to talk to him. "Señor cavalier," cried he, "we do not know this worthy lady you talk of; so be pleased to let us see her before we own the truth which you would extort from us."

"Had I once showed you that beauty," replied Don Quixote, "what wonder would it be to acknowledge so notorious a truth? The importance of the thing lies in obliging you to believe it, confess it, confirm it, swear it, and maintain it, without seeing her."

"Sir knight," replied the merchant, "I beseech your worship will vouchsafe to let us see some portraiture of that lady, and I verily believe that though her picture should represent her to be blind of one eye, and distilling vermilion and brimstone at the other, yet, to oblige you, we should be ready to say in her favour whatever your worship desires."

"Distil, ye infamous scoundrels!" replied Don Quixote.

Heathcliffe attacks Cathy

A scene from " Wuthering Heights "

The sail hurled away both knight and horse along with it

A scene from " Don Quixote "

" Distil, say you? Know that nothing distils from her but amber and civet. You shall all severely pay for your horrid blasphemy."

Saying this, with his lance couched, he ran so furiously at the merchant who had provoked him that, had not good fortune so ordered it that Rozinante should stumble and fall in the midst of his career, the audacious trifler had paid dear for his raillery.

One of the grooms, coming up to Don Quixote as he lay wallowing, snatched his lance, and, having broke it to pieces, he so belaboured the knight's sides with one of them that, in spite of his arms, he thrashed him like a wheat-sheaf.

At last the mule-driver was tired, and the merchants pursued their journey.

At length, kind fortune so ordered it that a ploughman happened to pass by, as he came from the mill with a sack of wheat. The good man took off the battered adventurer's armour as well as he could and endeavoured to set him upon his legs; at last, with a great deal of trouble, he heaved him upon his own ass, and with a bundle of the poor knight's arms tied to the back of Rozinante, he led them all towards the village.

The curate and the barber, together with Don Quixote's niece and housekeeper, whom they happened at the time to be visiting, all ran out of doors, and the one finding it to be her uncle, and the other to be her master, and the rest their friend, they all ran to embrace him; to whom Don Quixote, " Forbear," said he, " for I am sorely hurt, by reason that my horse failed me; carry me to bed, and if it be possible, let the enchantress Urganda be sent for to cure my wounds."

Full fifteen days did our knight remain quietly at home, without betraying the least sign of his desire to renew his rambling; during which time there passed a great deal of pleasant discourse between him and his two friends; while he maintained there was nothing the world stood so much in need of as knights-errant; wherefore he was resolved to revive the order.

In the meantime Don Quixote earnestly solicited one of his neighbours, a country labourer, and a good honest fellow, if we may call a poor man honest, for he was poor indeed, poor in purse and poor in brains; and, in short, the knight talked so long to him, plied him with so many arguments, and made him so many fair promises, that at last the poor silly clown consented to go along with him, and become his squire. Among other inducements to entice him to do it willingly, Don Quixote forgot not to tell him that it was likely such an adventure would present itself as might secure him the conquest of some island, and then the squire might promise himself to be made governor of the place. Allured with these large promises, Sancho Pança (for that was the name of the fellow) forsook his wife and children to be his neighbour's squire.

They stole out of the village one night, not so much as suspected by anybody.

As they jogged on, " I beseech your worship, Sir Knight-errant," quoth Sancho to his master, " be sure you do not forget what you promised me about the island; for, I dare say, I shall make shift to govern it, let it be never so big."

" You must know, friend Sancho," replied Don Quixote, " that it has been the constant practice of knights-errant in former ages to make their squires governors of the islands or kingdoms which they conquered. Now, I am not only resolved to keep that laudable custom, but even to improve it. Now, if thou and I do live, it may happen that I may conquer some kingdom, having many other kingdoms annexed to its imperial crown; then would I presently crown thee king of one of them."

" Why, should this come to pass," quoth Sancho Pança, " and I be made a king by some such miracle as your worship says, then happy-be-lucky, my Mary Gutierrez would be at least a queen, and my children infantas and princes."

" Who doubts of that? " cried Don Quixote.

" I doubt it," replied Sancho; " for I cannot help believing, that though it should rain kingdoms down upon the face of the earth, not one of them would fit well upon Mary Gutierrez's head; for I must needs tell you, she is not worth two brass jacks to be made a queen of: no, Countess would be better for her, if it please you."

As they were thus discoursing, they discovered some thirty or forty windmills; and, as soon as the knight had spied them, " Fortune," cried he, " directs our affairs better than we ourselves could have wished: look yonder, friend Sancho; there are at least thirty outrageous giants, whom I intend to encounter; and, having deprived them of life, we will begin to enrich ourselves with their spoils: for they are lawful prize; and the extirpation of that cursed brood will be an acceptable service to heaven."

" What giants? " quoth Sancho Pança. " Those thou seest yonder," answered Don Quixote, " with their long-extended arms; some of that detested race have arms of so immense a size, that sometimes they reach two leagues in length."

"Pray look better, sir," quoth Sancho Pança; "those things yonder are no giants, but windmills, and the arms you fancy are their sails, which, being whirled about by the wind, make the mill go."

"It is a sign," cried Don Quixote, "thou are but little acquainted with adventures. I tell thee, they are giants; and, therefore, if thou art afraid, go aside and say thy prayers, for I am resolved to engage in a dreadful, unequal combat against them all." This said, he clapped spurs to his horse Rozinante, without giving ear to his squire Sancho, who bawled to him they were windmills, not giants. But he was so full possessed with a strong conceit to the contrary, that he did not so much as hear his squire's outcry, nor was he sensible of what they were, although he was already very near them.

"Stand, coward," cried he as loud as he could, "stand your ground, ignoble creatures, and fly not basely from a single knight, who dares encounter you all."

At the same time, the wind rising, the mill-sails began to move, which, when Don Quixote spied, "Base miscreants," cried he, "though you move more arms than the giant Briareus, you shall pay for your arrogance."

He most devoutly recommended himself to his lady Dulcinea, imploring her assistance in this perilous adventure; and so, covering himself with his shield, and couching his lance, he rushed with Rozinante's utmost speed upon the first windmill he could come at, and, running his lance into the sail, the wind whirled about him with such swiftness, that the rapidity of the motion presently broke the lance into shivers, and hurled away both knight and horse along with it, till down he fell, rolling a good way off in a field.

Sancho Pança ran as fast as his ass could drive to help his master, whom he found lying, and not able to stir, such a blow he and Rozinante had received. "Mercy on me!" cried Sancho, "did I not give your worship fair warning? Did not I tell you they were windmills, and that nobody could think otherwise, unless he had also windmills in his head?"

"Peace, friend Sancho," replied Don Quixote: "there is nothing so subject to the inconstancy of fortune as war. I am verily persuaded the cursed necromancer Freston has transformed these giants into windmills to deprive me of the honour of the victory; such is his inveterate malice against me; but, in the end, all his pernicious wiles and stratagems shall prove ineffectual against the prevailing edge of my sword."

"Amen, say I," replied Sancho; and so, heaving him up again upon his legs, once more the knight mounted poor Rozinante, that was half shoulder-slipped with his fall.

They rode on for some time in silence, when Don Quixote, perceiving a thick cloud of dust arise right before them in the road, "The day is come," said he, turning to his squire, "the day is come, Sancho, that shall usher in the happiness which fortune has reserved for me; this day shall the strength of my arm be signalized by such exploits as shall be transmitted even to the latest posterity. Seest thou that cloud of dust, Sancho? It is raised by a prodigious army marching this way, and composed of an infinite number of nations."

"Why then, at this rate," quoth Sancho, "there should be two armies; for yonder is as great a dust on the other side."

With that, Don Quixote looked, and was transported with joy at the sight, firmly believing that two vast armies were ready to engage each other in that plain. For his imagination was so crowded with those battles, enchantments, surprising adventures, amorous thoughts, and other whimsies which he had read of in romances, that his strong fancy changed everything he saw into what he desired to see; and thus he could not conceive that the dust was only raised by two large flocks of sheep that were going the same road from different parts, and could not be discerned till they were very near. He was so positive they were two armies that Sancho firmly believed him at last.

"Well, sir," quoth the squire; "what are we to do, I beseech you?"

"What shall we do," replied Don Quixote, "but assist the weaker and the injured side? For know, Sancho, that the army that now moves towards us is commanded by the great Alifanfaron, emperor of the vast island of Taprobana; the other that advances behind us is his enemy, the king of Garamantians, Pentapolin with the naked arm; so called because he always enters into battle with his right arm bare."

"Why," cried Sancho, "you had as good tell me it snows; the devil of any knight, giant, or man can I see; who knows but all this may be witchcraft and spirits?"

"How," replied Don Quixote; "dost thou not hear their horses neigh, their trumpets sound, and their drums beat?"

"Not I," quoth Sancho; "I prick up my ears like a sow in

the beans, and yet I can hear nothing but the bleating of sheep. Oh, that I was ever born to see this day!"

But Don Quixote, still riding on, deaf and lost to good advice, outroared his expostulating squire. "Courage, brave knights," cried he; "march up, fall on all of you who fight under the standard of the valiant Pentapolin!" And so saying, he charged the squadron of sheep with that gallantry and resolution, that he pierced, broke, and put it to flight in an instant, charging through and through, not without a great slaughter of his mortal enemies, whom he laid at his feet, biting the ground and wallowing in their blood.

The shepherds, seeing their sheep go to rack, called out to him; till, finding fair means ineffectual, they unloosed their slings, and began to ply him with stones as big as their fists. While the stones flew about his ears, one unluckily fell upon his small ribs, and had like to have buried two of the shortest deep in his body. The knight thought himself slain, or at least desperately wounded, and calling to mind an earthen jar of precious balsam he carried, he clapped it to his mouth: but, before he had swallowed a sufficient dose, souse comes another of those bitter almonds, that spoiled his draught, and hit him so pat upon the jug, hand, and teeth, that it broke the first, maimed the second, and struck out three or four of the last. These two blows were so violent, that the boisterous knight, falling from his horse, lay upon the ground as quiet as the slain; so that the shepherds, fearing he was killed, got the flock together with all speed, and carrying away their dead, which were no less than seven sheep, they made what haste they could out of harm's way.

When the shepherds were safely gone, up runs Sancho. "Ah, master," quoth he. "This comes of not taking my counsel. Did I not tell you it was a flock of sheep, and no army? May I never stir if ever I set eyes on a more dismal figure in my born days; and I cannot tell what should be the cause of it, unless your being tired after this fray, or the want of your worship's teeth, but I think you should rather be called the Knight of the Ill-favoured Countenance."

"All the knights of yore," cried Don Quixote, "assumed some appellation; for one was called the Knight of the Burning Sword, another of the Unicorn, a third of the Phoenix; by which by-names and distinctions they were known all over the globe. Therefore, doubtless, that learned sage, my historian, has inspired thee with the thought of giving me

that additional appellation of the Knight of the Ill-favoured
Countenance."

After they had rested awhile and Don Quixote had rinsed his
bloody jaws in a brook, they mounted again and, turning to
the right hand, struck into a highway, where they had not
gone far before they discovered a horseman, who wore upon his
head something that glittered like gold. The knight had no
sooner spied him, but turning to his squire. " Sancho," cried
he, " in all probability yonder comes the man who wears on his
head Mambrino's helmet."

" I do not know," says Sancho, " but I am sure, were I
suffered to speak my mind, mayhap I would give you such main
reasons that yourself should see you are wide of the matter."

" How can I be mistaken, thou eternal misbeliever? " cried
Don Quixote. " Dost thou not see that knight that comes
riding up directly towards us upon a dapple grey steed, with a
helmet of gold on his head? "

" I see what I see," replied Sancho, " and the devil of anything I can spy but a fellow upon such another grey ass as mine
is, with something that glistens on top of his head."

Now, the truth of the story was this : There were in that part
of the country two villages, one of which was so little that it had
not so much as a shop in it, nor any barber; so that the barber
of the greater village served also the smaller. And thus a
person happening to have occasion to be let blood, and another
to be shaved, the barber was going thither with his brass basin,
which he had clapped upon his head to keep his hat from being
spoiled by the rain.

When Don Quixote saw the imaginary knight draw near, he
fixed his lance, or javelin, to his thigh, and without staying to
hold a parley, flew at his adversary as fiercely as Rozinante
would gallop, crying out in the midst of his career, " Caitiff!
wretch! defend thyself, or immediately surrender that which is
so justly my due! "

The barber, who as he peaceably went along saw that terrible
apparition come thundering upon him at unawares, had no
other way to avoid being run through with his lance but to
throw himself off from his ass to the ground; and then, as
hastily getting up, he took to his heels, leaving his ass and his
basin behind him.

Don Quixote ordered Sancho to take up the helmet.

" On my word," quoth Sancho, " it is a special basin, and
as well worth a piece of eight as a thief is worth a halter."

With that he gave it to his master, who presently clapped it on his head, turning it every way to find out the beaver or vizor; and at last, seeing it had none. " Doubtless," said he, " the Pagan for whom this famous helmet was first made had a head of prodigious size; but the worst is that there is at least one half of it wanting."

Sancho could not forbear smiling to hear his master call the barber's basin a helmet.

Proceeding on their quest of adventures, Don Quixote and his simple squire met a noble duke and his duchess who were hawking in a forest glade. When they discovered who the strange figure was who approached them with such grave courtesy, the duke and duchess remembered to have heard tales of the rare exploits of the errant knight and his squire. They therefore invited Don Quixote to sojourn with them in their castle, intending to have much rare sport with the knight's strange fantasies and the simplicity of his squire.

Don Quixote having solemnly accepted the invitation, and the company having returned to the castle, the duke and his duchess lost no time in starting the frolic.

After dinner in the castle gardens there entered suddenly a herald of prodigious size, with a white beard stretching to his waist. He asked audience for his mistress, the Disconsolate Matron, Trifaldi. When this was granted, twelve elderly waiting-women entered the garden, all clad in mourning habits, over which they had veils of white calico. After them came the Countess Trifaldi, handed by her squire Trifaldin.

Then, in a voice rather hoarse and rough than clear and delicate, " Most invincible knight," said she, addressing Don Quixote, " I prostrate myself at these feet, the foundations and pillars of chivalry errant, the supporters of my drooping spirits, whose indefatigable steps alone can hasten my relief."

The Disconsolate Matron then proceeded to tell her story. She had come far over the seas from Candaya, where she had once been duenna to the queen dowager's daughter, Antono-masia. Unfortunately, she had been the occasion of the queen's death, from mere anger and shame when it was brought to light that her daughter had secretly married an upstart courtier, introduced into her chamber by the Countess Trifaldi herself. At news of the queen's death, her brother, a most prodigious fiend and enchanter, the notorious Malambruno, had changed the young husband and wife into a hideous crocodile and a brazen she-monkey of unknown metal. By the same malign influence the duenna and all her maids-in-waiting had felt the pores of their faces to open, and all about them perceived an itching pain, like the pricking of pins and needles. Clapping their hands to their faces, they had found them all rough with bristly beards.

"Thus," ended the countess, after she and her attendants had thrown back their veils and exposed the most horrible thick beards, "hath that murthering and bloody-minded Malambruno served us, and planted these rough and horrid bristles on our faces, otherwise most delicately smooth."

The duke and duchess marvelled at the unnatural sight, and then the Disconsolate Lady continued: "You must know then, sir, from this place to the kingdom of Candaya, by computation, we reckon is about five thousand leagues. You are likewise to understand that Malambruno told me, that when fortune should make me find out the knight who is to dissolve our enchantment—and that knight he held to be none other than the world-famous Don Quixote himself—he would send him a famous steed. It is managed by a wooden peg in its forehead, instead of a bridle, and flies as swiftly through the air as if all the devils in hell were switching him."

"Nay," quoth Sancho, "as for an easy pacer, commend me to my Dapple. Indeed, he is none of your high flyers, he cannot gallop in the air; but on the king's highway he shall pace ye with the best ambler that ever went on four legs."

At that moment, unexpectedly, who should enter the garden but four savages covered with green ivy, bearing on their shoulders a large wooden horse, which they set upon his legs before the company; and then one of them cried out, "Now let him that has the courage, mount this engine."

"I am not he," quoth Sancho, "for I have no courage, nor am I a knight."

"Madam," cried Don Quixote, "I will do it with all my heart, nor will I so much as stay for a cushion, or to put on my spurs, but mount instantly."

"That is more than I should do," quoth Sancho. "I am not in such a plaguey haste, not I; and if the quickset hedges on their snouts cannot be lopped off without my riding on that hard crupper, let these gentlewomen get some other barber."

Thereupon the duke reassured Sancho, and promised him the if he should now make this flight upon the wooden horse behind his valorous master, he should upon his return find himself the governor of a fair great island.

" Good, your worship, say no more," cried Sancho. " I am but a poor squire. But bang baseness; mount, master, and blindfold me, somebody; wish me a good voyage and pray for me. To horse, to horse: the tears of these poor bearded gentlewomen have melted my heart, and methinks I feel the bristles sticking in it."

Now, both being hoodwinked, and Don Quixote perceiving everything ready for their setting out, began to turn the pin; and no sooner had he set his hand to it, but the waiting women and all the company set up their throats, crying out, " Now, now, you fly aloft. See how they cut the air more swiftly than an arrow! Now they mount, and tower, and soar, while the gazing world wonders at their course! " " Sir," said Sancho, girding his hands about his master's waist, " why do they say we are so high, since we can hear their voices? " " Never mind that," answered Don Quixote; " for in these extraordinary kind of flights we must suppose our hearing and seeing will be extra-ordinary also. Come then, take courage; we make swinging way, and have a fair, merry gale." " I think so, too," quoth Sancho, " for I feel the wind puff as briskly upon me here, as if I do not know how many pairs of bellows were blowing wind in my tail."

Sancho was not altogether in the wrong; for two of three pairs of bellows were indeed levelled at him then, which gave air very plentifully.

Don Quixote at last feeling the wind, " Sure," said he, " we must be risen to the middle region of the air, where the winds, hail, snow, thunder, lightning, and other meteors are pro-duced; so that if we mount at this rate, we shall be in the region of fire presently, and, what is worst, I do not know how to manage this pin, so as to avoid being scorched and roasted alive."

At the same time some flax, with other combustible matter, which had been got ready, was clapped at the end of a long stick, and set on fire at a small distance from their noses, and the heat and smoke affecting the knight and his squire, " May I be hanged," quoth Sancho, " if we be not come to this fire-place you talk of, or very near it; for the half of my beard is singed already. I have a huge mind to peep out, and see whereabouts we are."

Now at last, resolving to put an end to this extraordinary adventure, which had so long entertained them successfully, the duke and duchess ordered one of their servants to give fire to the steed's tail; and the horse, being stuffed full of squibs, crackers, and other fireworks, burst presently into pieces, with a mighty noise, throwing the knight one way, and the squire another, both sufficiently singed. The Disconsolate Matron and the bearded regiment had disappeared from the garden, and the rest, counterfeiting a trance, lay flat upon the ground. When Don Quixote and Sancho got up, their wonder at being surrounded only, as they thought, by corpses, was diverted by the appearance of a large stake stuck in the ground with a scroll of parchment tied to it, bearing the message:

" The renowned knight, Don Quixote de la Mancha, achieved the venture of the Countess Trifaldi, otherwise called the Disconsolate Matron, and her companions in distress, by barely attempting it. Malambruno is fully satisfied. The waiting gentlewomen have lost their beards; King Clavijo and Queen Antonomasia have resumed their pristine shapes."

So ended the high adventure of the wooden horse. And now Sancho claimed his reward, the promised island. It happened that the duke, though he had indeed no island to bestow, was at that very time looking for a new governor for one of the townships of his domains. To this position, after he had made suitable arrangements for the sport, he now appointed the delighted Sancho.

Sancho, with a large equipage set forth on Dapple, leaving his master behind at the castle. No sooner had he arrived in the town, which, they gave him to understand, was the island of Barataria, than he was taken to the courts of justice, there to prove his fitness for the high position of governor by adjudicating in several vexed disputes between his subjects.

Sancho's native shrewdness overcame each knotty case that was brought before him. One old townsman plaintiff, wrangling about ten crowns borrowed from another, who affirmed he had not repaid it, declared he would be satisfied if his pretending creditor swore upon the rod of justice the account had not been settled. Handing him his staff for the plaintiff to hold, the other knelt down and performed the oath. Then the defendant took his staff again, and having made a low obeisance to the judge, was leaving the court.

Which, when Sancho perceived, reflecting on the passage of the cane, and admiring the creditor's patience, after he had studied a while with his head leaning on his stomach, and his forefinger on his nose, on a sudden he ordered the old man

with the staff to be called back. When he was returned,
" Honest man," said Sancho, " let me see that cane a little.
I have a use for it." Sancho took the cane, and giving it to the
other, " Now go your ways," said he, " for you are paid."
Then, seeing the old man's bewilderment, he ordered the staff
to be broken open in court, which was no sooner done but out
dropped the ten disputed crowns. All the spectators were
amazed, and began to look on their governor as a second
Solomon.

Yet, alas, Sancho soon found that the governorship of an
island was fraught with inconveniences he could ill bear. They
led him into the governor's palace, where a magnificent
collation was prepared for him. Beside his chair stood the
governor's physician. Half a hundred richly-prepared meat
dishes and all kinds of delicious fruits were brought to the
governor's elbow by the liveried servitors. But every time
Sancho tried to help himself, with a wave of his wand the
physician caused the dish to be taken away uneaten, saying it
was as much as his position was worth to allow any food that
might have an injurious effect to enter the precious govern-
mental stomach.

" If it be so," said Sancho, " let Mr. Doctor see which of
all these dishes on the table will do me most good and least
harm, and let me eat my belly full of that, without having it
whisked away with his wand. As I live, I am ready to die with
hunger; not to allow me to eat any victuals is the way to
shorten my life, and not to lengthen it." " Very true, my
Lord," replied the physician; " however, I am of opinion you
ought not to eat of these rabbits, as being a hairy, furry sort of
food; nor would I have you taste of that veal: indeed, if it
were neither roasted nor pickled, something might be said;
but as it is, it must not be."

And so, by order of the duke, were such pranks played upon
the new governor. At last, when he had been in his " island "
a week, governing with the canny wisdom of the simple country
soul, a mock attack upon the island was staged, in which poor
Sancho received such a battering and bruising, that after it
was all over he rose silently from his bed, where they had laid
him unconscious, and creeping along softly (for he was too much
bruised to go along very fast), he got to the stable, followed by
all the company; and coming to Dapple, he embraced the
quiet animal, gave him a loving kiss on the forehead, and, with
tears in his eyes, " Come hither," said he, " my friend, thou

faithful companion, and fellow-sharer in my travels and miseries; when thee and I consorted together, and all my cares were but to mend thy furniture, and feed thy little carcase, then happy were my days, my months, and years. But since I forsook thee and clambered up the towers of ambition and pride, a thousand woes, a thousand torments, and four thousand tribulations have haunted and worried my soul. I was not born to be a governor, nor to defend islands nor cities from enemies that break in upon them. I have neither won nor lost, which is as much as to say, without a penny I came to this government, and without a penny I leave it, quite contrary to what governors of islands use to do when they leave them."

And with that, taking no more for his journey than half a loaf of bread and half a cheese, he went back to serve his crackpate master, the Knight of the Ill-favoured Countenance.

Leaving the Duke's Court, after several day's riding, they approached the great Sierra Morena (or black) mountains, and as they wandered farther into the rocky paths, Don Quixote was transported with joy to find himself where he might flatter his ambition with the hopes of fresh adventures to signalize his valour; for this vastness made him call to mind the wonderful exploits that other knights-errant performed in such solitudes. Filled with those airy notions, he thought on nothing else: but Sancho was for more substantial food, and sitting sidelong, as women do, upon his beast, he slily took out from the provision panier he had filched from the barber's ass, now one piece of meat, then another, and kept his grinders going faster than his feet.

Thus occupied, they came to the foot of a high rock that stood by itself, as if it had been hewn out and divided from the rest; by the skirt of it glided a purling stream that softly took its winding course through an adjacent meadow. The verdant freshness of the grass, the number of wild trees, plants, and flowers that feasted the eyes in that pleasant solitude, invited the Knight of the Ill-favoured Countenance to make choice of it to perform an amorous penance.

When he had told Sancho his intention, "I design," he added, " that thou shalt set forward about three days hence. In the meanwhile thou shalt be a witness of what I will do for my lady's sake, that thou mayest give her an account of it, when thou deliverest her a letter I shall write."

" As for the three days you would have me loiter here to mind your mad tricks," replied Sancho, " you had as good make account they are already over; for I hold them for done, unsight, unseen, and will tell wonders to my Lady: wherefore write you your letter, and send me away with all haste."

"Well, be it so," answered the Knight of the Ill-favoured Countenance. "But since we have no paper, I must be obliged to write on the leaves or bark of trees, as they did in ancient times, and thou shalt get the letter fairly transcribed at the first village where thou can'st meet with a schoolmaster. It is no matter as to the hand in which the letter is written; for, as I remember, Dulcinea can neither read nor write, nor did she ever see any of my letters, nay, not so much as any of my writing in her life: for my love and hers have always been purely Platonic, never extending beyond the lawful bounds of a modest look; and that, too, very seldom, so strictly Lorenzo Corchuelo, her father, and Aldonza Nagales, her mother, have kept and educated her."

"Heigh-day!" quoth Sancho, "did you ever hear the like! and is my Lady Dulcinea del Toboso, at last, the daughter of Lorenzo Corchuelo, she that is otherwise called Aldonza Lorenzo?"

"The same," answered Don Quixote, "and it is she that merits to be the sovereign mistress of the universe."

"Udsdaggers," quoth Sancho, "I know her full well; she is a strapping wench, in faith, pitches the bar with e'er a lusty young fellow in our parish. By the mass, she is a notable, strong-built, sizable, sturdy, manly lass, and one that will keep her chin out of the mire, I warrant her. Body o' mine, what a pair of lungs and a voice she has when she sets up her throat! I saw her one day perched up on top of our steeple, to call to some ploughmen that were at work in a fallow-field: and though they were half a league off, they heard her as plain as if they had been in the churchyard under her."

"I have often told thee, Sancho," said Don Quixote, "and I tell thee again, that thou oughtest to bridle or immure thy saucy, prating tongue: for thou art but a dull-headed dunce, yet now and then thy ill-mannered jests bite too sharp."

"Sir," quoth Sancho, "unriddle my dull pate this: I dare-say the knights who did these penances you tell of had some reason to be mad; but what reason have you to be mad too? What lady ever sent you a-packing, or so much as slighted you?"

"Why, there is the point!" cried Don Quixote. "In this consists the singular perfection of my undertaking; for, mark me, Sancho, for a knight-errant to run mad upon any just

occasion, is neither strange nor meritorious; no, the rarity is
to run mad without a cause, without the least constraint or
necessity. There is a refined and exquisite passion for you,
Sancho! I am mad, and will be mad, until thy return with an
answer to the letter which thou must carry from me to my Lady
Dulcinea."

"There is no need," Don Quixote said when he had writ
his letter, "to set my name. Amadis of Gaul, I recollect,
never signed his letters."

"That's all one to me," quoth Sancho. "Now I intend to
set forth, without seeing any of your mad tricks; and I will
relate that I saw you perform so many that she can desire no
more."

"Nay," said Don Quixote, "I will have thee stay a while,
Sancho, and see me stark naked; it is also absolutely necessary
that thou shouldest see me practise some twenty or thirty mad
gambols."

With that, slipping off his breeches and stripping himself
naked to the waist, he gave two or three frisks in the air, and
then, pitching on his hands, he fetched his heels over his head
twice together; and as he tumbled with his legs aloft, discovered such rarities that Sancho even made haste to turn his
ass's head, that he might no longer see them, and rode away
full satisfied that he might swear his master was mad.

Then, taking the direct road to Toboso, the next day he
arrived at an inn. When he reached the door, two men happened to come out, and, believing they knew him, "Look,
master doctor," cried one to the other, "is not that Sancho
Pança, whom the housekeeper told us her master had inveigled
to go along with him?" "The same," answered the other.
Now these two happened to be Don Quixote's friends, the curate
and the barber.

The trusty squire presently knew them, and being asked
about his master, "I left him," he replied, "frisking and
doing penance in the midst of yonder mountain to his heart's
content." Then he gave them a full account of the business,
how he was then going from his master to carry a letter to my
lady Dulcinea del Toboso, Lorenzo Curchuelo's daughter, with
whom he was up to the ears in love.

The curate and the barber wondered more and more at the
increase of Don Quixote's madness, and they resolved to set
out forthwith in an attempt to bring the poor knight back home
again. Therewith they set about devising of a plan by which,

playing upon the very madness of the knight, they might inveigle him to cease his penance and return to La Mancha.

There happened to be staying at that inn two travellers, a young man of high birth, Don Ferdinand, and Dorothea, a young woman of as illustrious a parentage and exceeding beauty. They were lovers whom various mischances had for a while parted and fate had now happily reunited at this inn. To these two the barber and the curate did now tell the strange case Don Quixote was in, and after some talk conceived a design that was very well to their liking.

When they had done, they called Sancho to saddle his ass, for he must now accompany the barber and a noble damsel back to the Black Mountain. All this time Sancho had been sitting with the landlord, cramming his guts with his favourite dish of cow's heels; when he came in to the others and beheld the beautiful Dorothea, " Who is that fine lady? " he asked.

" She is," answered the curate, " the only heiress in a direct line to the vast kingdom of Micromicon: moved by the fame of your master's great exploits, that spreads itself over all Guinea, she comes to seek him out, and beg a boon of him; that is, to redress a wrong which a wicked giant has done her."

" Why, that is well," quoth Sancho, " a happy seeking and a happy finding. Now, if my master be but so lucky as to right that wrong by killing that son of a whore of a giant you tell me of, I am a made man."

After the curate had once more given Dorothea her cue, she and the barber, disguised in a false beard, set off with Sancho.

Thus they went on until they reached the Black Mountain and then, among the rocks, they spied Don Quixote, who had by this time put on his clothes, though not his armour. Immediately, Dorothea, understanding he was the person, alighted and advanced towards the knight, and, falling on her knees before him, in spite of his endeavours to hinder her: " Thrice valorous and invincible knight," said she, " never will I rise from this place till your generosity has granted me a boon, which shall redound to your honour and the relief of the most disconsolate and most injured damsel that the sun ever saw. Sir, the boon I have to beg of your magnanimous valour is, that you will be pleased to go with me instantly whither I shall conduct you, and promise me not to engage in any other adventure till you have revenged me on a traitor who usurps my kingdom, contrary to all laws, both human and divine."

" I grant you all this, lady," quoth Don Quixote, " and

therefore from this moment shake off all desponding thoughts and study to revive your drooping hopes; for, by the assistance of Heaven, and my strenuous arm, you shall see yourself restored to your kingdom, and seated on the throne of your ancestors."

Having gently raised her up, he embraced her with an awful grace and civility, and then called to Sancho for his arms.

And now the champion being completely accoutred, "Come on," said he, "let us go and vindicate the rights of this dispossessed princess."

The barber was all this while upon his knees, and had enough to do to keep himself from laughing, and his beard from falling, which, if it had dropped off, would have betrayed his face and the whole plot at once. Sancho, for his part, seeing his master in so fair a way of being next door to an emperor, many times congratulated himself on the speedy realization of his dreams; for he did not question that his master would marry that princess, and so be, at least, King of Micromicon.

While they rode back to the inn, Don Quixote entertained them with a long discourse, extolling the profession of chivalry above that of letters, bringing his oration to a close with an eloquent plaint about the cowardly modes of warfare in modern times: "Blessed were those happy ages that were strangers to the dreadful fury of these devilish instruments of artillery, whose inventor, I am satisfied, is now in Hell, receiving the reward of his cursed invention, which is the cause that very often a cowardly, base hand takes away the life of the bravest gentleman. This considered, I could almost say, I am sorry at my heart for having taken upon me this profession of a knight-errant in so detestable an age."

As they rode thus discoursing, they espied about a dozen men sitting on the green grass in the middle of a meadow. Near them they saw several spread sheets that seemed to cover something. Don Quixote rode up to the people and civilly asked them what they had got under that linen. "Sir," replied one of them, "they are some carved images that are to be set up at an altar we are erecting in our town." "If you please," said Don Quixote, "I should be glad to see them." So one of the men uncovered a figure that happened to be St. George. "This," said Don Quixote "was one of the best knights-errant the divine warfare or Church Militant ever had: his name was Don St. George, and he was an extraordinary protector of damsels."

After some other images of the Church Militant's knights had been uncovered and admired by Don Quixote, they showed a piece that represented St. Paul falling from his horse, with all the circumstances usually expressed in the story of his conversion. " This," said Don Quixote, " was the greatest enemy the Church Militant had once, and proved afterwards the greatest defender it will ever have."

Then Don Quixote, perceiving there were no other images, desired the men to cover those he had seen. " And now, my good friends," said he to them, " I cannot but esteem the sight I have had of those images as a happy omen; for these saints and knights were of the same profession I follow, which is that of arms: the difference only lies in this point, that they were saints and fought according to the rules of holy discipline; and I am a sinner, and fight after the manner of men. They conquered Heaven by force, for Heaven is taken by violence: but I, alas, cannot yet tell what I gain by the force of my labours! Yet by a happy change in my fortune, and an improvement in my understanding, I might perhaps take a better course than I do."

" Heaven grant it," quoth Sancho.

Shortly afterwards they returned to the inn, and the whole company having spent two days there, the curate and the barber thought out some device to carry home Don Quixote, without putting Don Ferdinand and Dorothea to the trouble of humouring his impertinence any longer. They first agreed with a wagoner that went by with his team of oxen to carry him home: then had a kind of wooden cage made, so large that the knight might conveniently sit, or lie, in it. Presently after, all the company of the inn disguised themselves, some with masques, others by disfiguring their faces, and the rest by change of apparel, so that Don Quixote should not take them to be the same persons. This done, they all silently entered his chamber, where he was sleeping very soundly: they immediately laid hold on him so forcibly, and held his arms and legs so hard, that he was not able to stir, or do anything but stare on those odd figures which stood round him. He instantly imagined himself to be enchanted and those frightful figures to be spirits and demons.

They lifted him out of his bed, and placing him in the cage, shut him in and nailed the bars of it fast.

In six days' time they reached the knight's village. It was about noon when they entered the town; and as it happened to

be on a Sunday, all the people were assembled in the market-
place, through the middle of which Don Quixote must of
necessity pass.   Everybody was curious to know what was in the
cage;   and the people were strangely surprised when they saw
and knew their townsman.   While they were gaping and
wondering, a little boy ran to the knight's house, and gave
intelligence to the housekeeper and niece that their master and
uncle was returned, stretched out at length on a bundle of hay,
in a wagon, and drawn along by a team of oxen.

The housekeeper and niece undressed Don Quixote and
put him to bed;   where he lay looking asquint but could not
imagine where he was.   And, indeed, whether it was by reason
of his exposure on the mountain or the frequent drubbings he
had received, Don Quixote was taken with a mortal fever.

He entered into a long swoon, and when he awaked, " Blessed
be the Almighty," cried he, " for this great benefit he has
vouchsafed to do me!   Infinite are his mercies; they are greater
and more in number than the sins of men.   My judgment is
returned clear and undisturbed, and that cloud of ignorance is
now removed which the continual reading of those damnable
books of knight-errantry had cast over my understanding.   I
find, niece and thou, good Sancho, that my end approaches;
but I would have it such, that though my life has got me the
character of a madman, I may deserve a better at my death."

" Woe's me, my dear master's worship! " cried Sancho, all
in tears, " do not die this bout, but even take my counsel, and
live on many years;   it is the maddest trick a man can ever
play in his whole life, to let his breath sneak out of his body
without any more ado, and without so much as a rap over the
pate, or a kick on the guts;   to go out like the snuff of a farthing
candle, and die merely of the mulligrubs or the sullens."

" Soft and fair, Sancho," replied Don Quixote.   " I was
mad, but I am now in my senses;   I was once Don Quixote de
La Mancha, but am now the plain Alonso Quixano, and I
hope the sincerity of my repentance may restore me to the
same esteem you have had for me before."

In short, Don Quixote's last day came and, amidst the tears
and lamentations of his friends, he gave up the ghost.   Thus
died that ingenious gentleman Don Quixote de la Mancha,
whose native place Cid Hamet, his historian, has not thought
fit to mention, with design that all the towns and villages in
La Mancha should contend for the honour of giving him birth,
as the seven cities of Greece did for Homer.

THE BROTHERS KARAMAZOV

By FYODOR DOSTOEVSKY

*" The Brothers Karamazov " is not only one of the greatest
novels ever written. It is also an attempt to survey the entire
life of civilized man in relation to his main problems—
religion, love, money, the future of society, etc., etc.
Obviously themes so vast cannot be dealt with in a brief
summary. Readers are strongly recommended to peruse the
book itself in order to form a true estimate of the amazing
range and grandeur of Dostoevsky's genius. What is
given below outlines the enthralling story of crime and passion
which is the foreground, as it were, to the author's magnificent tableau of all humanity groping towards the light.*

" IVAN, my dear boy, if only you'll go to Tchermashnya
and sell that property for me, I'll give you the sweetest
little wench in all Russia. She's running around barefoot, it's true, but she's a beauty. Don't despise these girls
from the slums; they're pearls of joy . . . he! he! he! "
tittered Fyodor Pavlovitch Karamazov, his beady old eyes
shining with delight as he poured out with unsteady hand
another glass of brandy.

Ivan glanced at his father with ill-concealed disgust. " Why
can't you go to Tchermashnya yourself? " he demanded.

" Because there's a very urgent matter here that requires—
he! he!—my *personal* attention."

Ivan exchanged a significant look with his younger brother,
Alyosha, who that evening had obtained special leave from
the monastery in order to visit his father.

An observer would have failed to notice any sign of the
relationship linking this strangely assorted trio—unless it were
the air of freedom, almost of wildness, in their demeanour,
which, according to local gossip, was said to mark all the
Karamazovs. Old Fyodor Karamazov was a wealthy landowner, whose long devotion to avarice, drink and sensuality
revealed itself in piercing little eyes, bloated and empurpled
cheeks, and full, slobbering lips. Ivan, who at twenty-four
had already made his mark as a brilliant journalist, had the
sharp, cold face, cynical manner and polished bearing of a man

of the world. Alyosha, four years younger than his brother, was preparing to become a monk, though any hint of asceticism or pride suggested by his cassock was belied at once by his fresh ruddy cheeks, merry eyes and expression of simple good-nature.

Alyosha and Ivan knew only too well why Fyodor Pavlovitch refused to go to Tchermashnya. They also knew that the " very urgent matter " which kept him at home would almost certainly involve their father and their elder brother, Mitya, in a conflict that might end in death.

Mitya Karamazov had been a lieutenant in the army until his dissolute life forced him to resign his commission. He had saved a general from disgrace, and out of gratitude this general's daughter, Katerina Ivanovna, become engaged to Mitya.

But the eldest Karamazov inherited in full measure the fever in the blood of his father. Mitya insulted Katerina abominably. He spent on carousals with prostitutes half the sum of three thousand roubles she asked him to send to her sister in Moscow. At last he abandoned her completely, and became madly infatuated with the lovely Grushenka, the former mistress of a Polish officer.

Then suddenly old Fyodor Karamazov himself had fallen a prey to the insidious charms of Grushenka. Perhaps the knowledge that she was already his son's beloved fanned the flame of his desire, but in any case he burned with unashamed torment to possess her. He had told Gruskenka that if she would come to him for just one single night he would reward her with three thousand roubles, waiting for her in an envelope under his pillow. Mitya, raging with jealousy, was watching his father's house night and day.

" I never thought a woman ugly in my life," said old Karamazov, between hiccoughs. " You can't understand that, eh, my boys, my little sucking-pigs. You've milk in your veins, not blood. Even *vieilles filles* can show you a trick or two that'll entrance you." Listen, I used to have some queer fun with your poor deceased mother. I'd crawl on my hands and knees and kiss her feet until she began to laugh, a tinkling little delicious laugh, you never heard anything like it, and a few minutes later it would have grown into hysteria and she'd be screaming as if she were in the throes of joy. I always had to take her to the monastery after one of those do's before I could bring her to her senses. The blessed Fathers prayed her back to reason. Religious wasn't the word for it with your poor mother; when the feasts of Our Lady were on, she wouldn't even let me into her bedroom. I'll knock the bloody mysticism out of her, thinks I one night. 'Here,' says I, 'you see your Holy Image? You believe it's miraculous? Then watch me spit on it, and you'll see nothing'll happen to me.' Good Lord, I thought for a moment she would kill me. But she only jumped up, wrung her hands, then suddenly hid her face in them, began trembling all over and fell on the floor . . . all in a heap, writhing and . . . Alyosha, Alyosha, what on earth's the matter? "

The old man sprang to his feet in alarm. Alyosha had jumped up from his seat exactly as his mother was said to have done, wrung his hands, hid his face in them, and fallen back in his chair, shaking all over in a paroxysm of violent, silent weeping.

"Ivan! Ivan! Water quickly!" cried old Karamazov. "It's like her, the spit and image of what she used to be in her religious fits, his mother. Spurt some water on him from your mouth; that's what I used to do with her. He's upset about his mother," he muttered.

"She was my mother, too, I believe," said Ivan icily. Points of fire glimmered in his dark, indolent eyes. The old man shrank back from him so hurriedly that he knocked over his chair.

"Your mother?" he mumbled uncertainly. "Was she? . . . Why, damn it, of course she was. Excuse me; why, I was almost thinking Ivan . . . he! he! he!" A drunken, half-senseless grin screwed up his lips.

At that moment a fearful clamour arose in the hall, there were loud shouts, the door of the dining-room was flung open, and a man burst into the room. He was about twenty-eight years old, of powerful build, but with pale, sunken cheeks. His thick black hair fell in disorder over his flushed forehead, and his large dark eyes shone with a gleam of madness as they met the terrified eyes of Fyodor Pavlovitch.

"He'll kill me! He'll kill me!" screamed the old man, flinging his arms around Ivan's neck. "Don't let Mitya get at me!"

Mitya rushed forward into the room. "She's here!" he yelled. "I saw her turn towards the house just now, but I couldn't catch her. Where is she? Where is she?"

He ran to the double door that led to the inner apartments. They were locked. Mitya seized a chair and smashed them open, then vanished into the corridor.

"Ivan! Alyosha!" quavered old Karamazov. "She's here! Grushenka's here! Mitya saw her go into the house himself." He smacked his lips noisily and lurched towards the double doors.

"Come back, you old lecher!" Ivan shouted. "He'll tear you to pieces. You've seen for yourself she hasn't come."

Mitya suddenly reappeared in the dining-room. He had found the other entrance locked, and also all the windows of the other rooms, so that Grushenka could neither have come in anywhere nor gone out.

"Hold him!" shrieked old Karamazov. "He's stolen the money from under my pillow." And, tearing himself from Ivan's grasp, he rushed up to Mitya. Mitya flung him with a crash to the floor, turned round, and heeled him savagely in the face. Ivan and Alyosha leapt upon him and strove to drag him away from their inert and moaning father.

"You've killed him," cried Ivan.

Mitya freed himself with an effort, and stared wildly at his brothers. "No such luck!" he gasped. "But I'll be back before long to finish the job." He glanced at Alyosha with imploring eyes. "Alyosha, you're the only one I can believe. Was she here just now, or not?"

"I swear she's not been here, and no one expected her," said Alyosha.

Without a word, Mitya turned and ran from the room, dashing aside two servants who had tried to hold him when he entered the house. Old Grigory, the butler, pressed a blood-stained handkerchief to his head as he came forward to his master. He was followed by a thin and pimply youth named Smerdyakov, who acted as Fyodor Karamazov's valet and cook.

Ivan and Grigory lifted their father to his feet and seated him in an armchair. His face streamed with blood. They bathed and dressed the wound, removed his clothes, and put him to bed. Suddenly the old man opened his eyes. "She's here! She *must* be here!" he wheezed. A hideous leer of ecstasy twitched his features. Then he lost consciousness again.

Ivan turned to Alyosha. "If I hadn't pulled Mitya away he'd have done for him," he said.

"God forbid!" cried Alyosha, shuddering.

"Why should He forbid?" said Ivan with a smile. "It would only have been a case of one reptile devouring another."

When Alyosha had done all he could to ensure his father was

comfortable, he left the house to return to the monastery. Ivan departed much later. Just as he was going out of the gate, he was stopped by Smerdyakov.

" Well? " snapped Ivan. He had always detested this sly and weedy youth, though everyone else pitied him, for he was a prey to epileptic seizures. Old Karamazov was very fond of him, perhaps because he had wonderful skill as a cook, perhaps because there was some truth in the popular rumour, impossible to prove or disprove, that Smerdyakov was his natural son.

" I'm in an awful plight, Mr. Ivan," muttered Smerdyakov. " Your brother, Mr. Mitya, and your esteemed father are both, saving your presence, quite crazy. Not a night passes but what the old man is roaming the house and worrying me every minute with ' Has she come? Why hasn't she come? ' And on the other side it's no better. As soon as it's dark, your brother comes up to me and hisses, ' Keep a sharp look-out, your dirty little soup-maker. If you miss her, or don't let me know the moment she arrives, I'll crush you like a fly.' Both of them are getting angrier and angrier. Sometimes I think I'll die of sheer fright. You see, whether Grushenka comes or not, Mr. Mitya is sure to murder the old man at the first opportunity, so that he can steal the money from his bedroom. Mr. Mitya hasn't a rouble left of his own, and he needs the three thousand to carry off Grushenka to some distant part of the country."

" What do you expect me to do about it? " rasped Ivan.

" Go to Tchermashnya to-morrow as your father wishes. Alyosha will be at the monastery. The old man wants you both out of the way when Grushenka comes."

" And I suppose you and Grigory will be more than a match for my rather impulsive brother? "

" No. Old Grigory would sleep through the Last Trump. As for myself, I shall have a bad attack of epilepsy to-morrow night that will last until dawn."

" How do you know that? "

" I can always tell when a fit's coming on."

" H'm. In that case it's certainly my duty to remain here and protect my father, instead of going to Tchermashnya."

" I beg you to reflect more carefully upon the position, Mr. Ivan. Your father has confided to me his intention to marry Grushenka in the near future. If he does so, his sons will, of course, be disinherited. But in the unfortunate event of his death before marriage, there would be forty thousand roubles for each of you."

Ivan's face hardened. "You've got everything weighed up, haven't you?" he said slowly.   .

"Then you will go to Tchermashnya, Mr. Ivan?"

"I'll think it over . . . you little rat," snarled Ivan, as he strode away into the darkness.

Next morning Ivan set out for Tchermashnya.

*   *   *   *   *

Grushenka lived with her maid, Fenya, in a small wooden lodge near the cathedral square. An hour after dusk had fallen on the following evening, Fenya was sewing in the kitchen when Mitya threw open the door, dashed into every room in the lodge in turn, then came back to Fenya and cried, "Where is she?"

Then, without giving the terror-stricken girl a moment to reply, he fell at her feet, sobbing, "Fenya, for Christ's sake, tell me, where is she."

"I don't know, Mitya Fyodorovitch, I don't know. You may kill me, but I can't tell you."

"You're lying," shouted Mitya. "Your guilty fear tells me where she is." On the table stood a mortar with a small brass pestle. Mitya snatched up the pestle and rushed into the street.

He crossed a square, ran down a long avenue, over a little bridge, and along a deserted lane, until he came to the high fence that surrounded his father's garden. He made a desperate leap, managed to grasp the top of the fence, and swung himself aloft.

"Yes, the old man's bedroom is lighted up. She's there all right," he muttered to himself. Without a sound, he lowered himself to the lawn, and crept slowly forward over the soft grass, listening to every tiptoed step he made. It took him five minutes to reach the lighted window. He tapped on it gently, then slipped into the shadow of a high elderberry bush.

The window opened with a jerk and revealed old Fyodor standing there brightly illumined by the slanting rays of a lamp inside the room. He was wearing a new striped-silk dressing-gown, open at the neck to show a clean, dandified shirt of fine linen with gold studs.

The old man thrust his head forward and began gazing in all directions. "Grushenka, is it you? Is it you?" he cooed in a trembling half-whisper. "Where are you, my dove? I've a little present for you."

"He means the three thousand roubles in the envelope," thought Mitya, and the vision of what he could do with the money ran like fire through his brain.

"But where are you?" whispered the old man hoarsely, leaning forward and almost climbing out of the window in his eagerness.

He was within arm's reach of Mitya. His father's low, receding forehead, hooked nose, slobbering lips, double chins and pendent Adam's apple were emphasized revoltingly by the light from the lamp. A surge of loathing whelmed Mitya's heart. He drew the pestle from his pocket. . . .

A red mist swam before his eyes. . . . For the next few minutes he knew no more until he was gasping and stumbling his way across the lawn. He reached the fence, sprang up, and had dragged himself nearly over it when he felt someone clutch his leg and heard the agonized, choking voice of old Grigory:

"Murderer!"

Mitya's arm flashed down like lightning. The old servant fell with a moan. Mitya stared at him for a moment, then dropped down beside him. Mitya suddenly realized he was holding a brass pestle in his hand; he looked at it in surprise, then flung it away from him.

He knelt down beside Grigory. The old servant's head was spattered with blood. Mitya pulled out his handkerchief and tried to staunch the flow. The handkerchief was soaked instantly. "I've killed him!" thought Mitya in a spasm of terror. He rushed to the fence, vaulted over, and sprinted madly down the lane and into the town. There was now only one glint of purpose in his soul—to see Grushenka once more before eternal chaos closed over him.

*   *   *   *   *

Fenya was sitting with her grandmother in the kitchen when Mitya ran in and seized her by the throat.

"Speak now or die!" he roared. "Where is she?"

Both women squealed. Fenya shrank back into her chair and her eyes bulged as Mitya's fingers closed inexorably round her throat. "Aie! I'll tell you!" she gasped. "Aie! you're choking me, Mitya darling. She's gone to Mokroe, to her officer."

" What officer? " snarled Mitya.

" Why, the Polish gentleman, the one that threw her over five years ago. Your friends Kalganov and Maximov are with her. They're all meeting at Trifon Borissovitch's place. Aie, Mitya, you look so wild; you're not going to murder her, darling? "

But Mitya was already outside the street and dashing across the square to Plotnikov's great store. " Get me horses and a cart at once," he yelled to the astonished proprietor. " And I want plenty of champagne—three dozen bottles. I'm going to Mokroe—there's twenty roubles for the driver if he can get there before midnight! " He pulled a sheaf of notes from his pocket. The proprietor noticed that some of them were stained with blood.

*   *   *   *   *

" Aie! " shrieked Grushenka, as Mitya entered the blue room of Trifon Borissovitch's hotel at Mokroe. She was a tall, blonde girl of twenty-two, with that soft fullness of beauty that blooms so early in Russian women and dies so young. Her face was peculiarly white and had faint pink tinges in the cheeks.

She was seated on a low chair. Facing her on a long sofa were Kalganov, a fair-haired and handsome student, Maximov, a middle-aged landowner, who had recently lost his fortune, and a sturdy little man, who looked very annoyed as Mitya came in. This was the Polish officer, Musyalovitch, for whom Grushenka had yearned so pitifully during the past five years. His companion, a huge dark man called Vrublevsky, was standing behind Grushenka's chair and leaning over her.

" Gentlemen," began Mitya in a loud voice, but stammering at every word, " I beg of you to let me remain here with you till morning. I'm—I'm a fellow-traveller . . . to eternity ! I—there's nothing the matter," he added, turning to Grushenka, who had shrunk back in her chair.

" Sir, this is a private party. There are other rooms," said the stout little Pole, removing the pipe from his mouth.

Mitya turned and addressed the two Poles. " Gentlemen, forgive my intrusion," he pleaded. " I wanted to spend a last night with my adored . . . my queen. Forgive me, gentlemen," he cried wildly. " I flew here and vowed. . . . Come, let's all be friends. I've brought floods of champagne. Look, the servants are bringing it in now. Let's drink to Poland! "

Trifon Borissovitch the innkeeper, followed by waiters, brought in Mitya's bottles and began pouring out champagne for the party. They clinked their glasses and drank to Poland.

" Open more bottles! " shouted Mitya. " And now we'll drink to Russia. Let us be brothers! "

The tall dark Pole raised his glass. " To Russia," he said ironically, " as she was before 1772."

Mitya flushed. " You've insulted my country," he cried.

" Silence! I won't have any quarrelling, do you hear? " said Grushenka imperiously. She stamped her foot.

" Gentlemen, forgive me," muttered Mitya. " It was all my fault. I'm sorry. Ah, you've a pack of cards. Come on, who'll take the bank? "

An hour later, Mitya had lost two hundred roubles to the Poles. Kalganov stretched out his hand and swept the cards from the table. " I won't let you go on playing, Mitya," he shouted drunkenly. " You've lost more than enough already."

" Why, damn you——" began Mitya.

Grushenka put her hand on his arm. " He's right," she said with a curious note in her voice. " Don't play any more."

A sudden inspiration came to Mitya as he saw the look in Grushenka's eyes. He rose to his feet and tapped Musyalovitch on the shoulder. " Come into the next room, my dear sir," he said, " I've something to say to you. Bring your body-guard, too," he added, with a glance at the big dark Pole.

He led the Poles into a room on the right. " Listen, my good sir," he said in a low, tense voice to Musyalovitch. " Take three thousand roubles from me and go to the devil. I'll get your coats, they'll harness the horses immediately, and you can clear off without anyone being the wiser."

The two Poles strode back into the other room.

" Grushenka," said Musyalovitch haughtily, " I have received a mortal insult. I came here to forgive the past——"

" You! " cried Grushenka, leaping from her seat. " You came here to forgive me! "

" Yes. I've always been soft-hearted. But I was astounded when you allowed your lover to join our party. And that isn't all. He has just offered me three thousand roubles to leave at once. I spat in his face! "

" What? He offered you money for me? " cried Grushenka hysterically. " Is it true, Mitya? How dare you? Am I for sale? Of course he refused it? "

" He took it! He took it! " yelled Mitya; " only he wanted

the whole three thousand at once, and I could only give him five hundred down!"

Grushenka sank down on her chair. "I see it all now," she said in a toneless voice. "He heard I had money, and so he came here to *forgive* me and graciously offer me his hand in marriage."

"Grushenka," thundered the red-faced little Pole, "I intended to forget the past and make you my wife. But now I find you a different woman—perverse, yes, and shameless!"

"Oh, go back where you came from," said Grushenka dully. "I've been a fool, a fool, to have tormented myself for five years over a creature like you. You're so old and fat you might be your own father. Where on earth did you get that wig from? My God, and I used to adore you! I've been crying my eyes out for five years. And all the time it was Mitya I loved, but I was so stupid I never realized it until now. Yes, he is the only man in the world for me. Forgive me, Mitya. I have tortured you beyond endurance. But now I throw myself at your feet. I will devote the rest of my life to you. I shall love you for ever. We are going to be so happy, *happy*!"

There was a sharp knocking at the door. Kalganov rose to his feet and opened it. A tall, stout man in the uniform of a police captain walked into the middle of the room.

"Mitya Fyodorovitch Karamazov," he said sternly, "I arrest you for the murder of your father."

* * * * *

"He is innocent," said Alyosha.

"What proof have you?" asked Ivan.

"He told me so himself," answered Alyosha, who had just returned from a visit to Mitya in prison, "and I believe him. Ivan, when they arrested him he did not even know our father had been murdered. He thought they must have mistaken Grigory for father. He was terribly worried about Grigory until they told him the wound was not serious and he would recover."

"How is Smerdyakov?"

"Very ill indeed. The fit went on until dawn and left him completely exhausted. Then the awful news——"

"I'll go along and see him," interrupted Ivan.

"He's at Maria Kondratyevna's house. There was no one left to look after him at father's," said Alyosha.

The two brothers arranged to meet the following day.

Ivan set off for Smerdyakov's apartment in the home of Maria Kondratyevna.

Smerdyakov was lying on an old sofa in his dressing-gown. He looked wan as a spectre. His eyes were deep-sunken and had blue pouches under them.

" I am sorry to find you so ill," began Ivan.

Smerdyakov gazed at him in surprise. " You don't look at all well yourself," he murmured. " You've gone paler—and your hands are trembling. Why are you so uneasy, Mr. Ivan? Is it because the trial begins to-morrow? Go home, go to bed and sleep in peace. There's nothing to be afraid of."

"I don't understand you," said Ivan, astounded. " Why should I be afraid? "

" I won't say anything about you," Smerdyakov whispered. " There are no proofs at all. . . . I say, how your hands are quivering! Go home and sleep and don't be afraid. Nothing will happen to you."

Ivan sprang to his feet and seized him by the shoulders. " Tell me everything, you cur, tell me everything! "

Smerdyakov riveted his eyes on Ivan with insane hatred. " Well, it was you who murdered him, wasn't it? " he hissed.

Ivan sank back on his chair with a mirthless laugh. " You mean because I went away to Tchermashnya and left the old man without a defender? "

Smerdyakov's eyes opened wide. " What's the use of keeping up this farce with each other? " he muttered. " Are you trying to throw it all on me, and to my face at that! *You* are the real murderer. I was only your instrument, your faithful servant, and it was following your words I did it."

Ivan's blood turned cold. " You . . . did . . . what ? "

" Why, bashed his head in, of course. Look! " Smerdyakov fumbled inside his dressing-gown, pulled out a bundle of notes and flung them on the table. Ivan saw there were three packets, each containing ten hundred-rouble notes.

" How did you do it? " asked Ivan mechanically. His face had gone white as a sheet.

" At eight o'clock last night I fell down the cellar steps in a fit—a sham one, naturally. Grigory carried me to my bed, which, as you know, is separated from his own by a partition. I dozed a bit and awoke to hear the master shouting, ' Mitya's been. He's run away! He's killed Grigory! ' I dressed and ran out into the garden. I found Grigory lying senseless near the fence. ' Now's my chance to finish off old Karamazov' I thought. 'Mitya's done one job, everyone'll think the other's his as well.'

"I hurried back to the master's room. He was standing by the open window. 'Grushenka's here,' I whispered. You should have seen his face. He looked as if he would fall over himself with excitement. 'Where, where?' he gabbled. 'Why, in that bush,' I said; 'she's laughing at you; can't you see her?' He leaned right out of the window. I picked up the iron paper-weight from his table—you know the one, it weighs three pounds—and crashed it down into his skull. He didn't even cry out. I hit him twice more to make sure. Then I had a good look at myself. Not a spot of blood on me anywhere. I wiped the paper-weight and hid it where no one'll ever find it, don't you worry. Then I grabbed the money. Mitya would never have found it. I was the only one besides the old man who knew the envelope was hidden behind an old ikon in the corner. I ripped open the envelope, took out the notes, and threw the torn envelope down on the floor——"

"Stop!" cried Ivan. "Why did you throw down the envelope?"

Smerdyakov grinned. "To put the detectives off my trail, of course. Everyone was aware I knew all about the envelope, that I myself had put the notes inside, and sealed and addressed it for the lazy old scoundrel to 'My darling Grushenka'. The detectives would reason that if I had stolen the envelope I would have put it straight into my pocket without opening it, because I knew what was inside it. But Mitya only knew about the envelope by hearsay; he'd never seen it; and if he took it, he'd be sure to tear it open at once to make sure the money was inside, and afterwards throw the envelope down, without having time to think how it would become evidence against him."

Ivan jumped up and paced restlessly up and down the room for several minutes. Then he stopped and looked at Smerdyakov as if he could kill him.

"Listen, you fiend," he said. "I'm taking these notes straight to the police, and I'm going to tell them everything."

Smerdyakov yawned. "Save yourself the trouble," he said. "No one knew the numbers of the notes; they might belong to anybody—yourself, for instance. As for the story I've told you, there isn't the least shred of evidence to confirm it."

" What did you do after you left my father's room? "
demanded Ivan, his eyes gleaming.

" I undressed and went back to bed. Grigory found me
there when he staggered in from the garden."

" Ah, I've got you now," cried Ivan triumphantly. " Grigory
must have seen you were shamming. No one on earth can
imitate an epileptic fit for so long as that."

" True," admitted Smerdyakov. " But when I got back
into bed, a real attack came on. It must have been because of
all the excitement, I suppose."

Veins stood out on Ivan's forehead. For some moments he
struggled vainly to speak. Then he yelled at Smerdyakov,
" You haven't won yet! I'll bring the police here and by
Christ we'll gouge and batter the truth out of you somehow! "

Smerdyakov laughed thinly. " I shouldn't do that if I
were you. It would be quite useless—and so unpleasant—for
both of us. I'm sure you don't want Katerina Ivanovna to
know the true reason why you went to Tchermashnya. Oh
yes, I know you love her. You've been to see her every day
since Mitya abandoned her. Well, now, I'll tell you something to cheer you. She loves you too. She told me so when
she called to see me this morning. So go home, dear Mr.
Ivan, and enjoy a nice deep sleep. Happy dreams! "

A tornado of conflicting emotions racked Ivan as he left
Smerdyakov's flat and made his way through the streets.
Katerina loved him. Mitya was innocent . . . but he deserved
to die all the same, the worthless scoundrel. Nevertheless it
was his duty to save his brother, even at the cost of his own
life. Ivan paused irresolutely outside the police-station. At
last he shrugged his shoulders, and set off for his lodging.

He strode up and down his room for hours in a dementia of
indecision. Suddenly there was a rap at the door. He
opened it. Alyosha stood outside.

" Are you alone? " he asked.

Ivan stared at the pure and ingenuous face of his younger
brother as if he had never seen it before in his life. Suddenly
he burst into a peal of hysterical laughter.

" No, the devil is with me! " he cried.

Alyosha gazed at him compassionately. " You're ill, Ivan,"
he said. " I must look after you. You're quite feverish.
I've brought you some grave news. Smerdyakov has just
hanged himself."

*　　*　　*　　*　　*

The court was packed to overflowing long before the judges made their appearance. Visitors had come from many distant towns, including Moscow and Petersburg. There were many fine ladies among them; Mitya's reputation as a conqueror of female hearts had spread far and wide. Gradually the confused murmur of voices subsided, and when the trial began there was a hush in which one could have heard a pin drop.

Ippolit Kirillovitch, the thick-set, aggressive prosecuting counsel, built up a damning chain of evidence. Mitya's hatred of his father, his assault upon him the day before the crime, his dire need of funds to carry off Grushenka, his presence in the garden at the time of the murder, Grigory's testimony, the bloodstained pestle, the torn envelope—all these and many other circumstances told heavily against the accused. One factor alone puzzled the counsel for the prosecution. Mitya, when arrested, had only a few hundred roubles on him. Even allowing for his extravagance at Mokroe, he should have had at least two thousand.

"What did you do with the remainder?" demanded Ippolit Kirillovitch. "Did you hide it somewhere in Trifon Borissovitch's inn?"

"I tell you for the hundredth time I never took the money," answered Mitya stiffly. He wore a brand-new frock coat, immaculate black kid gloves and exquisite linen, and even in this gravest crisis of his life seemed aware of the effect his fine appearance was creating among the women in the court. "I had fifteen hundred roubles when I set out for Mokroe— all I had left from the three thousand Katerina Ivanovna entrusted to me." He lowered his eyes as if ashamed.

"Where did you keep the money?"

"In a little cloth bag which hung from a cord round my neck."

"What did you do with the bag?"

"I threw it away in the market-place at Mokroe."

Ippolit Kirillovitch glanced round at the court with an ill-suppressed grin of triumph and resumed his seat. The counsel for the defence, Fetyukovitch, rose to his feet. He was a tall, spare man, with a thin, clean-shaven face, and an air of tireless suavity.

A whisper ran round the court. "They say he's diabolically clever." Then a woman's voice murmured, "Yes, but he hasn't a chance of destroying such a case as Ippolit Kirillovitch's."

D'Artagnan, the swaggering Gascon

A scene from " The Three Musketeers "

David meets Aunt Betsy Trotwood

A scene from " David Copperfield "

Fetyukovitch recalled each of the witnesses in turn and questioned them closely. At first the court failed to perceive the drift of his interrogations. After a time, however, it was realized that Fetyukovitch's subtle analysis was establishing the argument that, while the chain of evidence against Mitya was indeed formidable, not a single link in it would bear separate examination. He completely destroyed the testimonies of several witnesses, unmasked Trifon Borissovitch as a lying rascal, and made Grigory a laughing-stock through his self-contradictions and stupidity. Finally, he created a sensation by unexpectedly calling Alyosha to the stand.

It was the prosecutor, of course, who examined him first.

" Do you believe your brother killed your father? " asked Ippolit Kirillovitch.

" On the contrary, I *know* he is absolutely innocent," said Alyosha loudly and clearly. " It was not he who committed the murder."

A buzz of excitement ran through the court. Everyone loved and respected Alyosha. Everyone knew he would never tell a lie in any circumstances.

The prosecutor flushed with rage. " Why are you so completely persuaded of your brother's innocence? " he rasped.

" I know he would not lie to me. I saw from his face he wasn't lying."

" Only from his face? Is that all the proof you have? " asked the prosecutor, with a sneer.

" I need no other proof."

The prosecutor snorted and sat down. From any other witness the declaration of Mitya's innocence would have been worthless. But Kirillovitch knew only too well that Alyosha's calm words had produced a tremendous impression upon the jury.

Fetyukovitch had another blow waiting for the prosecutor. He rose to question Alyosha about the bag round Mitya's neck containing Katerina Ivanovna's money.

" I never saw the bag," said Alyosha. " But the day before Mitya went to Mokroe, I remember he struck himself on the breast, over and over again, and said ' I have here all the means I need.' At first I thought he was striking himself over the heart, then I realized that the place was much too high— just below the neck, in fact. It might well have been the little bag he was indicating."

"Exactly," cried Mitya from his seat. "That's right, Alyosha. It was the little bag I struck with my fist."

Though this evidence too would have appeared ludicrous from any other witness, Alyosha's surmise was obviously accepted by the court. A stir of whispering arose. "He'll be acquitted, after all," said someone quite audibly.

* * * * *

Ivan was called to the stand. He was deathly pale. Once he closed his eyes, swayed a little, and might have fallen had he not grasped the rail in time.

The prosecutor rose to question him. But before he could utter a word, Ivan pulled from his inside pocket a roll of notes and flung them on the table on which lay the "material evidence" of the torn envelope, the bloodstained pestle, etc.

"They belong in that envelope," he shouted. "I got them from Smerdyakov, from the murderer, yesterday. . . . I was with him just before he hanged himself. It was he, not my brother, killed my father. He murdered him and I incited him to do it. Unfortunately, there's no record of the numbers on those notes. They might have belonged to anyone. Funny, isn't it? Oh, damnably, hellishly funny!" He burst into hoarse and uncontrollable laughter.

"Are you in your right mind?" broke involuntarily from the President of the Court.

"I should think I am in my right mind . . . in the same nasty mind as all of you . . . as all these . . . hideous faces." He turned and faced the body of the court. "My father has been murdered and you pretend to be horrified," he snarled. "Liars! If there hadn't been a murder, you'd have gone home in a huff. It's a cheap thrill you're all after. *Panem et circenses*. Have you any water? Give me a drink, for Christ's sake!" He clutched at his head.

Alyosha sprang to his feet and cried, "He is ill. Don't believe him. He has brain fever." A dark-haired woman, with a lovely, impassioned face, rose from her seat, and, rigid with horror, gazed fixedly at Ivan. She was Katerina Ivanovna.

"Don't disturb yourselves. I am not mad. I am only a murderer," Ivan began again. "You can't expect eloquence from a murderer."

The prosecutor approached the President in obvious dismay. The two other judges communicated in hurried whispers. The President leaned forward.

"Witness, your words are incomprehensible. Calm your-

self if you can and tell your story.   How can you confirm what
you have said? "

" That's just it.   I haven't an atom of proof.   That viper
Smerdyakov won't send you proofs from the other world . . .
in another envelope! I've no witnesses, either . . . except
one, perhaps." He smiled thoughtfully.

" Produce your witness? "

" He has a tail, your excellency, and that would be highly
irregular.   The devil doesn't exist—in law." Ivan began to
whisper, as if confiding a precious secret.   " He's here somewhere, your excellency, perhaps under that table with the so
very material evidence.   I told him I wouldn't hold my tongue,
so he's come along with me to deny all I say.   Oh, how
stupid is all this foolery.   I'm your man, not Mitya.   I didn't
come here for nothing.   Well, what are you waiting for?   Why
don't you seize me?   Why is everyone so infernally stupid? "

The court usher grasped Ivan by the arm.   Ivan turned,
stared into his face, then took him by the shoulders and hurled
him violently to the floor.   An instant later Ivan was surrounded by police, who carried him, kicking and screaming,
outside the hall.

The whole court was on its feet, people were shouting and
waving, and it was several minutes before order could be
restored.   The President began to address the court.   Suddenly
his words were interrupted by a piercing cry from Katerina
Ivanovna.   She was overcome by an attack of hysteria.   She
sobbed and shrieked, pleaded with the ushers not to remove
her, and at last managed to shout to the President:

" There is more evidence I must give at once . . . at once.
Here is a document, a letter . . . take it, read it quickly.
I received it the day before the murder.   It's a letter from that
monster . . . that man there . . ." she screamed, pointing
at Mitya.   " It was he who killed his father.   But the other
one is ill; he is ill, he is delirious," she cried over and over
again.

The letter was read aloud—

FATAL KATYA,
        To-morrow I will get the money and repay your three
thousand, then farewell! If I can't borrow it, I give you my
word of honour I shall go to my father and break his skull and
take the money from under his pillow—if only Ivan has gone.
If I have to go to Siberia for it, I'll give you back your three

thousand. Katya, pray to God that someone will give me the money. Then I shall not be steeped in blood.

MITYA.

As the clerk finished reading the letter, Grushenka rushed forward to the dock before anyone could prevent her. Her face was stained with tears, her heavy ash-blonde hair tumbled in disorder over her shoulders.

" Mitya," she wailed like a stricken creature. " That serpent has destroyed you." Ushers seized her and dragged her away. She fought like a wild cat to get back to Mitya. Mitya uttered a cry and struggled to get to her. He was overpowered.

The evidence had been heard, the jury filed out for discussion, and there was little doubt now in the court as to the verdict. An hour later, a bell rang and the jury came back to their seats.

The President, speaking in a deathlike stillness, asked, " Did the prisoner commit the murder? "

The foreman of the jury answered in a clear, ringing tone, " Yes, guilty! "

Mitya stood up and cried in a heart-rending voice, " I swear by God and the dreadful Day of Judgment I am not guilty of my father's blood! Katya, I forgive you! Brothers, friends, have pity on the other woman! "

DAVID COPPERFIELD

By CHARLES DICKENS

*This, the best-known and, by its author, best-liked novel,
appeared originally in 1849–1850 It contains a great deal
of autobiographical material, but all of it has been subtly
transmuted into the basic framework of fiction.*

ON the day that I was born my eccentric Aunt Betsy
suddenly arrived and asked my widowed mother what
was to be the name of the girl?
" I don't know that it will be a girl," said my mother.
" I have a presentiment that it must be a girl. Don't
contradict. I intend to be her friend and godmother, and
you'll call her Betsy Trotwood Copperfield. There must be
no trifling with her affections, poor dear."
But when, later, the doctor announced that I was a boy, my
aunt said never a word. She took her bonnet by the strings,
aimed a blow at the doctor's head, put it on bent, and, vanishing like a discontented fairy, never returned.
Looking back I can remember, standing out by themselves
from a confusion of things, my mother and Peggotty, my
nurse. My mother was pretty, loving, but weak. My nurse
was fond of me; sometimes she would throw her arms wide,
take my curly head within them and give it a good squeeze.
But she was so plump that such a little exertion might cause
the buttons to fly off the back of her dress.
One day Peggotty and I answered the bell of the garden-
gate, and there was my mother, looking very pretty, and with
her a gentleman with beautiful black hair and whiskers, who
had walked home with us from church last Sunday. Jealous
that his hand should touch my mother's, I refused to offer
him my right hand. So I gave him the left hand, which he
shook and went away. At this minute I can see him turn
round in the garden and give us a last look with his ill-omened
black eyes.
Mr. Murdstone came again, and I liked him no better than
at the first meeting. One day he took me for a ride, and I
heard a friend of his refer to my mother as " the pretty little
widow ".

"Take care, if you please," said Mr. Murdstone. "Somebody's sharp."

Soon after this I was sent for a holiday to Peggotty's home at Yarmouth, a black superannuated boat from which an iron funnel smoked cosily; if it had been Aladdin's palace I could not have been more charmed with the romantic idea of living in it. When I returned I felt something was wrong, because my mother was not at the gate to meet me.

"Master David," said Peggotty, in a breathless sort of way, "you have got a pa."

I trembled and turned white and said, "I don't want to see him." I knew even then that Mr. Murdstone could mould my mother's pliant nature into any form he chose. As soon as I could I crept upstairs and wept.

Mr. Murdstone soon introduced his sister into the house, and the two began to exercise over me the rigid firmness they said I needed. My mother was too weak to prevent them. Shall I ever forget their dismal lessons and gloomy theology which made all children out to be a swarm of little vipers?

The presence of the Murdstones during my studies prevented me from learning, and so I was warned that I must be flogged. Mr. Murdstone caught my head in a vice and caned me heavily; and in the same instant I bit his hand right through. It sets my teeth on edge to think of it.

In revenge he beat me as though he would have beaten me to death, leaving me presently fevered and hot and torn and sore and raging in my puny way. I was kept prisoner for some days and not allowed to see my mother, and then packed off to Salem School, Blackheath, where I was ordered to pin to my back and wear continuously a placard which read: "Take care of him. He bites."

What I suffered from that placard nobody can imagine. I always fancied somebody was reading it. I positively began to have a dread of myself as of a wild boy that did bite. The greater part of the boys could not resist pretending that I was a dog, and patting and smoothing me lest I should bite, and saying, "Lie down, sir," and calling me Towzer. But on the whole it was much better than I anticipated.

Of the boys who became my friends, one was Traddles, who wore a tight sky-blue suit that made his arms and legs look like German sausages, and was always being caned; the other was Steerforth, a person of condescending power, noble bearing and high spirits.

" You haven't a sister ? " asked Steerforth of me.

" No," I answered.

" Pity," said he. " If you had, I think she would have been a pretty timid little bright-eyed sort of girl. I should have liked to know her."

The headmaster was Mr. Creakle, a man with a little nose, a large chin and a fiery face. He tugged my ear and announced that he was a Tartar. But there was one advantage in Mr. Creakle's severity. He found my placard in his way when he came up or down behind the form on which I sat, and wanted to take a cut at me in passing. For this reason the card was soon taken off, and I saw it no more.

During my second term at this school of terror I was informed that my mother had died. I went home and did not return.

* * * * *

As my home was so unhappy, I spent my holidays with Peggotty's people in the old boat at Yarmouth, the inhabitants of which comprised my nurse's brother, Mr. Peggotty, his nephew Ham, Mrs. Gummidge, a lorn lone woman, and Little Em'ly, a distant relative whose father, said Mr. Peggotty, had been " drownded ".

Of course I was in love with Little Em'ly. I am sure my fancy raised up something round that blue-eyed mite of a child which made a very angel of her. Little Em'ly was spoiled by all, and by no one more than by Mr. Peggotty himself, whom she could have coaxed into anything by laying her cheek against his rough whisker.

When I told this family about my school experiences and developed my favourite theme of praise for the generous protection I had received from the noble Steerforth, I saw Little Em'ly's face, bent forward over the table, listening with the deepest attention, her breath held, her blue eyes sparkling like jewels and the colour mantling in her cheeks.

Em'ly was confused by our observing her, and hung down her head, her face all covered with blushes. Gazing up presently through her curls and seeing that we were all looking at her still, she ran away, and kept away until it was nearly bedtime.

* * * * *

The carrier who brought me to Yarmouth was a silent, close-fisted man named Barkis who, however, managed to convey a message through me to my nurse Peggotty. It was to the effect that Barkis was willin', which news Peggotty received with blushing surprise. Yet she encouraged his strange and mostly silent wooing, and presently she became Mrs. Barkis. The bride assured me that there would always be a welcome and a bed for me whenever I visited her house.

I am glad to think there were two such guileless hearts at Peggotty's wedding as little Em'ly's and mine. Ah, how I loved Em'ly! What happiness if we too were married and were going away to live anywhere among the trees and the fields, children ever rambling hand in hand through sunshine!

Instead I was sent by my black-whiskered step-father to work in his wine-merchant's warehouse in London. Though I had been educated as a son of a gentleman, my work was to wash empty bottles and to paste labels, or fit corks, to full ones, which I did with secret agony of soul. Too young to undertake the sole charge of my existence, I would buy stale pastry at the half-price shops, and so squander the money I should have saved for a good dinner. Once I took my own bread under my arm into a beef-shop and ordered some meat to go with it. What the waiter thought of such a strange little apparition coming in all alone I don't know; but I can see him staring at me and bringing up the other waiter to have a look. I gave him a halfpenny for himself, and I wish he hadn't taken it.

I was lodged at the house of a stoutish middle-aged person named Micawber. He had no more hair on his head than there is on an egg. His face was extensive, his clothes shabby, but he wore an imposing shirt collar, had a confident roll in his voice and carried a jaunty sort of a stick. About him was an indescribable air of the genteel.

At his house in Windsor Terrace I met his wife, a thin and faded lady with a baby, one of twins, at her breast. Hardly ever did I see both the babies detached from Mrs. Micawber at the same time; one or the other was always taking refreshment. Always in financial difficulties, Mr. Micawber had a blind faith that one day something would turn up. But the only visitors to his house were creditors, one of whom used to edge his way in by seven o'clock in the morning and awaken Mr. Micawber with "Come, you ain't out yet, you know," and demand payment of debts.

Poor Mrs. Micawber! Though her husband went to a debtors' prison, took himself to any part of the country in the vain hope of something turning up, though he concealed things from her, pawned her property, " Yet," she said, " I never will desert Mr. Micawber ! "

I visited him in a debtors' prison, whereupon he warned me to observe that if a man had twenty pounds a year and spent nineteen pounds nineteen shillings and sixpence, he would be happy ; but that if he spent twenty pounds one, he would be miserable. After which he borrowed a shilling from me, gave me a written order to Mrs. Micawber for the amount, and put away his pocket-handkerchief and cheered up.

* * * * *

Having watched the Micawber family depart for Plymouth, and feeling very forlorn and romantic, I made up my mind to say farewell to my unpleasant work at Murdstone's, and find my Aunt Betsy, who had so unceremoniously vanished in dudgeon on the day of my birth.

After a five-day journey on foot I reached the bare, wide downs of Dover. I was minus a waistcoat and jacket, which I had pawned on the way to buy food. Having slept under haystacks—one night I passed outside my old school of Salem —I was not a presentable sight as I entered a shop and in-quired of the man behind the counter where Miss Trotwood lived.

" My mistress," said a maid who was being served. " What do you want with her ? "

" To speak to her, if you please."

" To beg of her you mean," retorted the damsel.

She told me I could follow her, and we came to a neat cottage with cheerful bow-windows.

" This is Miss Trotwood's." With which the maid hurried into the house.

With a strong consciousness of the plight of my appearance, I waited to introduce myself to my formidable aunt, who at that moment came stalking out of the house carrying a great knife.

" Go away," she said, making a distant chop in the air with her knife. " No boys here." She began to dig up a root.

" If you please, ma'am," I began.

She started and looked up.

" If you please, aunt, I am your nephew."

" Oh Lord ! " said my aunt, and sat flat down in the garden path, staring at me until I began to cry, when she got up in a great hurry, collared me and took me into the parlour.

There she unlocked a tall press, brought out several bottles, and poured the contents of each into my mouth. I think they must have been taken out at random, for I am sure I tasted aniseed, anchovy sauce, and salad dressing.

She rang the bell and told the maid to go upstairs and tell Mr. Dick that she wanted to speak to him.

A half-witted gentleman entered and squinted at me.

" Come," said my aunt, " I want some advice. This is David Copperfield. What shall I do with him? "

Mr. Dick looked vacantly at me and said:

" I should wash him! "

" Janet," said my aunt, " Mr. Dick sets us all right. Heat the bath! "

Janet was a pretty, blooming girl, one of a series whom my aunt had taken into her service expressly to educate her to renounce men, and who had generally complied by marrying the baker. My aunt was married to a ne'er-do-well who bled her white.

Mr. Dick was a protégé whom my aunt had saved from an asylum. He was a friendly soul; he made kites, and I helped him to fly them; he also spent much of his time writing a Memorial that was never finished because he could never square his own birthday with the date on which King Charles the First lost his head.

My aunt wrote to Mr. Murdstone and told him I was at her house, and he and his gloomy sister, riding on donkeys, called to see her and me.

" Shall I be given up to him? " I faltered.

" I don't know," said my aunt. " We shall see."

My aunt was a little more stern and imperious than usual, but I saw no other token of her preparing herself to receive the dreaded visitors. She told Mr. Murdstone that his late wife was an unworldly and unfortunate baby whose life was worn away in being taught to sing his notes.

" She was a loving baby, and through that weakness of hers you gave her the wounds of which she died. You tormented this poor child so that now the sight of him brings a disagreeable remembrance. Ay, you needn't wince. I know it's true."

As the two were departing in anger, my aunt gave Miss Murdstone the warning that she must not ride her donkey over the green before the house or she would knock her bonnet off and tread on it.

"Very good," said my aunt, turning from them. "That's settled. We will call you Trotwood Copperfield."

Thus I began my new life in a new name with everything new about me.

* * * * *

To finish my education my aunt sent me to school at Dr. Strong's, Canterbury, where I was splendidly treated. As there was no room there for boarders, a home was found for me at the house of Mr. Wickfield, my aunt's lawyer, who was cared for by his daughter, Agnes, a happy, capable girl with whom I was soon the best of friends.

Here I met Uriah Heep, a cadaverous, red-haired youth with hardly any eyebrows and no eyelashes; his red-brown eyes were so unsheltered that I wondered how he went to sleep. Uriah sat late at night improving his legal knowledge so that he might one day become a solicitor. As he read, his lank forefinger followed up every line, making clammy tracks along the page like a snail.

He told me that he was the 'umblest person going, that his mother was also a 'umble person, and he had a way of writhing when he wanted to express enthusiasm. One day he confided to me that his rascally purpose was to make himself so indispensable to his master that he would become not only partner in the firm but the husband of the sweet Agnes, who loathed him. I felt like running a red-hot poker through his false body. Once, when he strove to incriminate me in a piece of rascality, I struck him a blow on his lank jaw. His retaliation was to ask how I could do such a thing, to say that he had always liked me, Copperfield, and that he forgave me. His eyes, as he looked at me, seemed to take every shade of colour that could make eyes ugly.

"You forgive me!" I said disdainfully.

"I do, and you can't help yourself," said Uriah. "I will be a friend to you in spite of you."

I let him know that I should expect from him what I had always expected, the worst, and left him. But he knew me better than I knew myself. If he had openly exasperated me it would have been a relief and a justification; but he had put me on a slow fire, on which I lay tormented half the night.

* * * * *

My aunt sent me to town for a holiday. There I saw Steerforth, who took me to his home, a genteel red-brick house in Highgate, where I met his mother and her companion, a strange creature named Rosa Dartle. Rosa had black hair, eager black eyes, a scar on her lip, and she was very thin. I asked Steerforth if Miss Dartle was clever, and he said that she was " all edge ".

" What a remarkable scar that is upon her lip."

Steerforth looked uncomfortable, and then admitted that he had done it; as a young boy Rosa had exasperated him, and so he threw a hammer at her. " A promising young angel I must have been."

Mr. Peggotty's name came up, and Steerforth recalled meeting " that bluff fellow " and his nephew Ham when they visited me at school. I mentioned the very pretty niece of Mr. Peggotty, Little Em'ly, and Steerforth thought it might be a good thing to run down and meet " that sort of people in their boat and make one of them ".

" Are they really animals and clods and beings of another order? " asked Rosa Dartle.

" There's a pretty wide separation between them and us," said Steerforth with indifference.

Arrived in Yarmouth, I heard that Little Em'ly was now articled to the dressmaking. Mr. Omer, her employer, told me that she had an excellent taste.

" Believe me," said he, " she has such a pretty face of her own that half the women of this town are mad against her."

Before we visited the boat I called on my old nurse, Peggotty, who welcomed me heartily and took me to her husband's sick-room. The old carrier received me with a slow, rheumatic smile and said that he did not regret having been willing to marry Peggotty. Then he bade his wife get me a good dinner, turned us out of his room, and endured unheard-of agonies by crawling out of bed to produce a guinea from his hiding-place, with which to pay for my entertainment. Peggotty whispered to me that the carrier's illness had resulted in his becoming a little more " near " than before.

When Steerforth and I arrived at Peggotty's boat we heard a murmur of voices and clapping. Little Em'ly saw us first. She was in the very act of springing from the arms of the great, bashful, lumbering, kindly Ham into those of Uncle Peggotty, who was beaming with delight. In a moment we were all shaking hands together

I thought I had never seen Ham, the boat-builder, grin to anything like the extent to which he now grinned at us, while Mr. Peggotty explained how Little Em'ly and he had just become engaged. I felt it affecting to see such a sturdy fellow as Ham trembling in the strength of what he felt for the pretty little creature who had won his heart. But it was Steerforth who touched the prevailing chord of the moment with a skill impossible to me.

Em'ly said little all the evening, but she looked and listened, and her face got animated, and she was charming. Steerforth told us stories, and Little Em'ly laughed until the boat rang with her musical sounds. I could not satisfy myself whether it was in her own tormenting way, or in maidenly reserve before us, that she kept quite close to the wall and away from Ham all the evening.

"A most engaging little beauty!" said Steerforth to me as we left. But he added: "That's rather a chuckle-headed fellow for the girl."

He had been so hearty with them that I felt a shock. We stayed for more than a fortnight in that part of the country, but I had no idea where Steerforth spent much of his time while I was busy visiting the old scenes round my home.

Once he said to me rather cryptically:

"David, I wish I had had a judicious father, then I could have guided myself better!"

There was a passionate dejection in his manner that quite amazed me. He informed me that he had bought a boat to sail hereabouts and that he was going to have it re-christened.

"By what name?" I asked.

"The *Little Em'ly.*"

We saw Little Em'ly herself just then with Ham the boat-builder.

"Upon my soul," said Steerforth, "he's a true knight. He never leaves her."

Em'ly blushed as she gave her hand to Steerforth and me, and the two went on. Presently there passed us—evidently following them—a young woman, haggard, flaunting, poor and dressed in black.

"That is a black shadow to be following that girl," said Steerforth, standing still. "What does it mean?"

She was a woman of the town named Martha, who had once known Little Em'ly, and was seeking help, which, with the aid of Ham, Em'ly was able to give.

"Oh, Ham!" said Em'ly, "I know I am not so good a girl as I ought to be. I try your love too much. I know I do."

" I am happy all day long in the thoughts of you, my dear," said he.

* * * * *

My aunt now had me articled to a proctor in Doctors Commons, for which privilege she paid my principal, Mr. Spenlow, a thousand guineas. When my aunt lost her money I made an effort to cancel the articles, but Mr. Spenlow said that his partner, Mr. Jorkins, was a hard man, who would not agree to any such proposal. I approached Mr. Jorkins, and found him, on the contrary, a very timid, weak fellow who would have readily met my request had he not been under the thumb of his partner, Mr. Spenlow.

Meantime I had been taken home by my principal, and had fallen madly in love with his daughter, the adorable Dora, who unhappily was in the care of the dragon of my youth, Miss Murdstone.

I loved Dora to distraction. She was more than human to me. She was everything that everybody ever wanted. I could think of nothing but the captivating, bright-eyed, lovely Dora. What a form she had! what a face she had! what a graceful, variable, enchanting manner! I don't remember who was present, except Dora. I have not the least idea what we had for dinner besides Dora. My impression is that I dined off Dora entirely and sent away half-a-dozen plates untouched.

I never saw such curls. How could I? For there never was such curls as those she shook out to hide her blushes. Dora told me that Miss Murdstone was a tiresome creature, a vexatious companion. This she proved to be when she laid my love-letters before Mr. Spenlow, who ordered me to think no more of his daughter from then onwards, an order which I refused to obey.

I now became secretary to my old tutor, Dr. Strong, and I began to write. Great was the labour, priceless the reward. Dora must be won. I learned shorthand and induced my friend Traddles, now studying for the Bar, to recite the Parliamentary debates, that I might take them down as he spoke. The inconsistency and recklessness displayed by Traddles, as he obliged me, were not to be exceeded by any real politician.

* * * * *

I visited Steerforth again at his home before setting out once more to see my friends at Yarmouth.

"David," said he before retiring "if anything should ever separate us, you must think of me at my best, old boy."

In the dull dawn I looked into his room again. He was now lying fast asleep. The time came when I wondered that nothing troubled his repose. . . . I left him. Never more, O God forgive you, Steerforth! to touch that passive hand in love and friendship.

Arrived at Yarmouth, I called on my old nurse and her husband, and was told that the sick Barkis was mute and sense-less—" a-going out with the tide ".

" People can't die along the coast except when the tide's pretty nigh out," said Mr. Peggotty.

" Barkis, my dear," said his wife, introducing me.

" No better woman anywhere," Barkis cried faintly. He opened his eyes, and I was about to ask him if he knew me when he said with a pleasant smile:

" Barkis is willin'! "

And, it being low water, he went out with the tide.

*   *   *   *   *

There was news to come of a greater loss.

I was sitting with Mr. Peggotty in the old boat when Ham came in.

" Where's Em'ly? " said Mr. Peggotty.

" Mas'r Davy," said Ham, " will you come out for a minute? "

I saw that Ham was deadly pale.

" Ham! What's the matter? "

" Mas'r Davy! " Oh, for his broken heart, how dreadfully he wept!

" My love, Mas'r Davy—her that I'd have died for, and would die for now—she's *gone*! "

" *Gone !* "

" Em'ly's run away! Oh, Mas'r Davy, think *how* she's run away, when I pray God to kill her sooner than let her come to ruin and disgrace! "

Mr. Peggotty thrust forward his face, and never could I forget the change that came upon it if I were to live five hundred years. I remember a great wail and cry and we all standing in the room, I with a paper that Ham had given me, a blotted letter from which, in the midst of the silence of death, I read:

" When you who have loved me so much better than I have ever deserved, even when my mind was innocent, see this, I shall be far away . . . it will be never to come back unless he brings me back a lady. If even you, that I have wronged so much, that can never forgive me, could only know what I suffer."

" Mas'r Davy," exclaimed Ham, in a broken voice, " it ain't no fault of yours—but his name is Steerforth, and he's a damned villain ! "

Mr. Peggotty uttered no cry, but he took down his coat from the corner, and Ham asked him where he was going.

" Anywhere. I'm going to sink his boat where I would have drownded him, and I'm goin' to seek my niece through the world ! "

I happened to glance at Ham, and a frightful thought came into my mind; not that his face was angry, for it was not; there was an expression of stern determination—that if ever he encountered Steerforth he would kill him.

*　　*　　*　　*　　*

I received a note from Mr. Micawber, written in his char-acteristically lofty style, that contained surprising news; at last something had turned up. My old friend had been given a post as clerk to Uriah Heep. The news was followed by a mysterious communication from his wife which said that her husband felt he had sold himself to the devil, with the harrowing consequence that one formerly so domesticated was becoming alienated from her. On the slightest provo-cation, it would seem, he now expressed a wish for a separa-tion. Such was the influence upon her unfortunate husband of being in the employ of the 'umble Uriah.

Mr. Micawber came to see me and in a state of great agita-tion burst out with :

" What is the matter ! What is *not* the matter ! Villainy is the matter; baseness is the matter; deception, fraud, con-spiracy, are the matter, and the name of the whole atrocious mass is—HEEP."

At his request my aunt, Traddles and I called upon Heep, and Micawber made his accusations : Uriah had deluded and plundered his kindly employer, the father of Agnes, in every conceivable manner, forged his signature, falsified the accounts, misappropriated my aunt's property, and even induced his master to make over the business to him. ;

Mr. Micawber's dramatic denunciation had the beneficial result of making Heep and his mother quit Canterbury hurriedly to escape detention in Maidstone Gaol. Later

Uriah became implicated in a bank robbery and was sent to prison. The governor was Mr. Creakle, who came to regard the 'umble Uriah as a most promising subject for his odd scheme of prison reform, which was nothing more considerate than solitary confinement.

* * * * *

My wedding-day came and Traddles arrived with the licence. Dora had become so fond of Agnes that she even held her hand during the wedding ceremony and, as we drove away, hurried back to give Agnes her last kisses and farewells.

It seemed an extraordinary thing to have the sweet Dora always at home. At first I laughingly wondered why she wished me to call her " Child-Wife ". Yet it was soon evident. For Dora was incapable of running a home, of managing servants, of dealing with tradespeople who always robbed us. She could not understand figures nor my literary work. She admitted that she was " a little goose ", and told me that it was useless for me to try and make her wise. And she hid her face on my shoulder in a profusion of tears and curls. So I gave up the attempt to fit her for the control of my home, and never afterwards remonstrated with her for her lack of system and her untidy ways.

Yet I loved my wife dearly, and I was happy, but she was incapable of sharing my whole life, and so with me there was always something wanting. In time I came to know that my own heart was undisciplined when it first loved Dora. Yet she was truly fond and proud of me. When she heard of my growing reputation as an author she had tears of joy in her bright eyes as she said I was a dear old clever famous boy.

The shadow between us deepened. My pretty Dora was never very strong. I had hoped that a baby-smile upon her breast might change my child-wife into a woman. But it was not to be. I began to carry her downstairs every morning and upstairs each evening. Sometimes I felt that she was lighter in my arms, as if I was approaching some frozen region that would numb my life.

Towards the end she whispered to me that it would have been better if we had loved each other only as a boy and girl, and forgotten it. " I have begun to think I was not fit to be a wife," she said.

Through my tears I told her that she was as fit as I was to be her husband. " We have been very happy, my sweet Dora."

" Is it lonely downstairs? " she asked me.

" Very! very! "

" Don't cry! Is my chair there? "

" In its old place."

" Oh, how my poor boy cries! Hush! hush! Now send Agnes up to me and let no one else come. I want to speak to her—quite alone."

* * * * *

After the death of Dora I went away from England for three years, and it was some time after my return that I sought out Agnes. I clasped her in my arms.

" I loved Dora—fondly, Agnes, as you know——"

" Yes," she cried earnestly, " I am glad to know it."

" Even then my love would have been incomplete without your sympathy. I had it, and it was perfected. And when I lost her, Agnes, what should I have been without you still? I went away, dear Agnes, loving you. I returned home, loving you."

" There is one thing I must say," she replied.

" Dearest, what? "

She laid her gentle hands on my shoulders and looked calmly in my face.

" I have loved you all my life! " she said.

And Agnes laid her head upon my breast and wept, and I wept with her, we were so happy.

* * * * *

In London I met Mr. Peggotty, who had news. Little Em'ly had written asking him to relent towards a miserable girl. I asked him how Ham was keeping, and he said that Ham had never been heard to complain, but the blow had cut him deep. Later I saw Mr. Peggotty again, and he had more news. Em'ly was alive, and information could be found about her from Martha, the girl of the town whom she had once befriended. She guided us to a room in a sombre street near Golden Square, where we interrupted Rosa Dartle denouncing Little Em'ly for flaunting her charms before Steerforth.

" Mercy on me! " cried Little Em'ly. " I believed him, trusted him, loved him."

Rosa Dartle, with a face of malignity disfigured by passion, struck at the poor girl.

" *You* love him, *you*! " she cried.

She broke into a laugh. "*She* love!" she derided.
"That carrion."

Mr. Peggotty rushed into the room.

"Uncle."

I looked in and saw him supporting Little Em'ly's insensible
figure.

"Mas'r Davy," he said, "I thank God my dream's come
true. He has guided me to my darling."

Little Em'ly had been taken away to the Continent and
then deserted. She had returned to London, and would now
be cared for, as she had been of old, by Uncle Peggotty,
though not in the old boat.

I saw Ham and asked him if he had any message for her.
He begged me to say something which would ease her
sorrowful mind and yet not let her think as he could ever
marry, for it was not possible that anyone else could be to him
what she had been: and that his prayers were for her who
had always been so dear.

I pressed his manly hand and told him that I would do this
as well as I could. That night at Yarmouth the wind was low
and had a solemn sound. I thought of the blue-eyed child
who had enchanted me; I thought of Steerforth; and a foolish,
fearful fancy came upon me of his being near at hand, and
liable to be met at any turn.

Little Em'ly sent me an answer to the letter I sent to her on
behalf of Ham: "How can I thank you?" she wrote, "for
your good and blessed kindness to me. When I find what you
are, and what Uncle is, I think what God must be, and can
cry to Him."

*   *   *   *   *

I had been in Yarmouth when the seamen said that it blew
great guns, but I had never known the like of the storm which
blew on the night following the receipt of Em'ly's letter.

When daylight came a schooner, laden with wine, was seen
wrecked close in and the lifeboat was unable to go to her.
I heard that Ham was going to try to take a rope to the ship.
His look out to sea—exactly the same as that on the night
after Emily's flight—awoke me to the knowledge of his danger.
But I might as hopefully have entreated the wind.

"Mas'r Davy," he said, cheerily grasping me by both
hands, "if my time's come, 'tis come. If 'tant, I'll bide it.
I'm a-goin'."

He reached the wreck, but as he did so the ship sank.

Consternation was in every face. They drew Ham to my very feet—insensible—dead.

Presently another body was brought ashore. And on that part of the coast where Little Em'ly and I had looked for shells as children, I saw him lying with his head upon his arm, as I had often seen him lie at school—Steerforth, whose last word to me had been, " Think of me at my best! "

I took the news to his mother and Rosa Dartle at Highgate. Rosa turned suddenly on the stricken mother and told her, " proud mother of a false son ", to mourn for her nurture of him, her corruption of him.

" Oh, Miss Dartle, shame! " said I.

" I will speak," she returned. " Have I been silent all these years, and shall I not speak now? I loved him better than you ever loved him," she cried fiercely.

I mentioned his faults, and she turned on me again.

" Faults! Who dares malign him? He had a soul worth millions of the friends to whom he stooped. A curse upon you! " she cried in mingled rage and grief. " A curse upon you. Go! "

*   *   *   *   *

Uncle Peggotty and Little Em'ly, with Martha and the Micawbers, emigrated to Australia. I advanced to fame and fortune in the world of literature. Then one day Mr. Peggotty called and told me how my friends had fared on the other side of the world.

The news of Steerforth's end and the death of Ham in trying to save him had changed Emily much. But she had come through. She might have married well.

" But, uncle," she had said to Mr. Peggotty, " that's gone for ever."

" Cheerful along with me," said he, " retired when others is by; fond of going any distance to tend a sick person or to do some kindness to a girl's weddin'; patient; liked by young and old—that's Em'ly."

" And Mr. Micawber? " I asked.

Mr. Micawber had flourished in Australia. He was now a Magistrate.

THE THREE MUSKETEERS

By ALEXANDRE DUMAS

*This sparkling novel was first published in 1844 and founded,
with its sequels " Twenty Years After " and " Le Vicomte
de Bragelonne ", a whole school of cloak-and-dagger romance.
A warning to the reader might perhaps be issued about the
historical accuracy of the plot. Dumas was never afraid of
altering history if it failed to accord with his designs for
his characters.*

SON of illustrious ancestors and bound for Paris to seek
his fortune at the Court of Louis XIII, D'Artagnan, tall,
handsome, and reckless, clattered through the town of
Meung.

There was a more than outward resemblance between
the high-spirited, dashing young Gascon and the legendary
Don Quixote. True, D'Artagnan was no freak, but his
accoutrements were strange and shabby and his horse a
mere caricature of orange-coloured skin draped upon the
skeleton of a Béarnese pony. Don Quixote took windmills
for giants and sheep for armies; D'Artagnan took every smile
for an insult and every look for a provocation.

At an open window of an hotel was a gentleman; he made
some light remark which provoked his listeners to laughter.
This was enough for the fiery Gascon; none might laugh at
him. He sprang from his horse.

For a moment he registered the face which laughed cynically
into his: pale, dark, hooked nose, cruel mouth. D'Artagnan
drew his sword.

He was not, however, destined to avenge the jeering laughter.
The unknown man's servants set about him and he fell unconscious from loss of blood.

When he recovered, ·he sought out the pale-faced man, but
found him mounted and about to depart. In spite of his
wound, D'Artagnan leaped boldly forward.

" Base coward! False gentleman! " he cried. " But before
a woman you will not dare to fly! " For he had seen a fair
companion in a coach, to whom the unknown spoke.

" Remember," said Milady, leaning into the sunlight so

that her golden curls shone and the colour was shown in her languishing blue eyes. "Remember that the least delay may ruin everything."

The unknown bowed swiftly, and the coach careered wildly off in one direction, whilst the man galloped away in the other. D'Artagnan leaped after the man, but collapsed after a few paces, crying out weakly, "Coward! coward!" And then he added, "Ah! But *she* was fair!"

D'Artagnan valued above all his ancient lineage. But he bore a treasured possession with him in the form of a letter to M. de Tréville, captain of the King's Musketeers, which renowned company D'Artagnan hoped to join. With what horror did he learn that the unknown man had searched his clothes whilst he lay unconscious, and had stolen the letter!

Paris, and the whole of France was ruled by Louis, called The Just. But almost as powerful was Cardinal Richelieu, who kept as great state as the King and had much control over the policies of the country. M. de Tréville had formed for the King the bodyguard known the world over as the King's Musketeers; the Cardinal followed suit with his own Musketeers. This rivalry between the King and the Cardinal was imitated by their respective followers. But actually, on the Cardinal's side, this friendly competition in greatness was but a mask for his ambition to control the destinies of France.

At the Hôtel de Tréville D'Artagnan was well received, but M. de Tréville explained that none but seasoned soldiers could enter the Musketeers. However, satisfied of D'Artagnan's bona fides in spite of the loss of the letter, de Tréville offered him free tuition at the Royal Academy.

During his interview D'Artagnan saw an encounter between their commander and three of his Musketeers which fired him still further. What was his ill-luck but to bang into Athos, the wounded member of this trio, and his hasty apology not being accepted, he was forced into a rendez-vous for a duel. Still pursuing the pale man from Meung whom he saw from a window, a second encounter with another of the three Musketeers resulted in an appointment for a second duel. In an effort to make himself agreeable to Aramis, the third of these men, he was involved in a third duel!

Athos rose at the appointed place when D'Artagnan arrived and apologized for the lateness of his seconds.

"For my part, I have no seconds," replied D'Artagnan.

"Since I arrived in Paris only yesterday, I know no one but M. de Tréville."

"Well, but then," hesitated tall, handsome Athos, "if I kill you, I shall have the appearance of a boy-slayer."

D'Artagnan flushed at this reference to his youth. "You do me the honour to draw a sword with me whilst suffering from a wound," he replied with a sweeping bow.

They talked, and so pleasant and gallant was the youth that Athos wished that it was not incumbent upon him to kill so agreeable an adversary.

When his seconds turned up, naturally they proved to be Porthos and Aramis! "And now you are all assembled," cried D'Artagnan with considerable aplomb, "permit me to offer my apologies."

At these words the faces of The Three Inseparables fell. So agreeable a youth, so gallant and tactful, so altogether of their spirit and calibre . . . to apologize!

"Do not misunderstand me," went on D'Artagnan. He explained that his apology was merely in case he was dispatched before all of them could be revenged for his insults. Then, with a flourish, he drew his sword.

Hardly had the rapiers clashed than some of the Cardinal's guards appeared. The King's Musketeers caught at the forbidden duel, and by their deadly enemies!

The Three Inseparables were undecided. To submit was unthinkable, yet they were but three, and one of them wounded, against five picked swordsmen.

"But we are four," said D'Artagnan. "En garde, Messieurs!"

Our hero proved himself a brilliant, if unorthodox, swordsman, and dispatched the redoubtable Jussac himself. The King's men triumphed, three against five, and marched off in triumph to report the affair to M. de Tréville. D'Artagnan, as a result, was placed under M. d'Essart, brother-in-law to M. de Tréville, and was promised a place in the Musketeers at the earliest opportunity.

The Cardinal's rage knew no bounds, but he swallowed his mortification in anticipation of a far greater triumph which he planned. He believed that the Queen had shown her considerable favours, if no more, to the Duke of Buckingham, when he visited the Court as Ambassador.

By a strange coincidence, Madame Bonacieux, landlady of D'Artagnan's apartments, was involved in the Palace intrigue.

The Queen had indeed had conversations alone with my lord of Buckingham, and pretty Constance Bonacieux was an accomplice. The Cardinal managed her arrest, but before she could be tortured, D'Artagnan had rescued her. He not only found himself in the thick of a plot in which his mysterious unknown man was involved on the opposite side, but also deeply enamoured of Constance Bonacieux, in whom the amorous feeling was reciprocated.

He assisted in admitting the love-crazed Buckingham to the Queen in the Louvre itself.

"You love me, Madame; that is enough for me," sighed the Duke for the third time.

"Oh my God, my God!" cried the Queen, beautiful Anne of Austria. "I know not whether I love you or not, but what I know is that I will not be perjured nor dishonour France. Depart, my Lord, I implore you."

"Give me, then, some pledge of your indulgence, some gift that may remind me that I have not dreamed . . . something you have worn!"

She returned in a moment with a rosewood casket on which was her cipher encrusted in gold. "Keep this in memory of me," she murmured and allowed him to kiss her hand.

It was not long before the Cardinal had news through his spies of this gift. He instructed Milady, his tool in many of his nefarious plots, to secure one of the diamond studs from the set which the Queen had so foolishly given away. Milady was still in England . . . Buckingham was speeding thither with the studs, a gift of the King himself to his Queen!

Meanwhile the Cardinal allayed the King's jealousy. His time would come when he had *proof*; he assured the King that Buckingham's repeated visits to France were purely political. The Cardinal knew that this was the truth, as far as it went, for Buckingham was intriguing with Spain and Austria to secure his, Richelieu's, downfall. Once one of those studs were in his possession, he would so disgrace Anne that Louis would finally break all alliances with Austria, her country, and Spain, ruled over by her brother.

He managed to get the King to have the Queen's papers searched for a letter he suspected was to Buckingham. It was concealed upon her, and the man-at-arms forced her to yield it up. What was the Cardinal's chagrin to discover it was in truth political, to her brother! He was forced to placate the Queen, and suggested that the King give a grand ball in her honour.

"And tell Her Majesty," said the wily Cardinal, "that you wish her to wear the diamond studs which you recently presented to her."

Imagine the Queen's dismay on hearing this order. Constance undertook to recover the studs in time, and D'Artagnan offered to go to England to see the Duke.

M. de Tréville granted him the necessary leave of absence. "And if this secret concerns the very safety of the Queen," said the older man sternly, "one man is not enough. For one to arrive safely, four must set out. Tell Messieurs Athos, Porthos, and Aramis that I grant them leave also." There was a note of sadness in his voice at the thought that he might lose some of his gallant men.

By this time D'Artagnan had become a boon companion to Athos, Porthos, and Aramis and they were well known in Paris together as inseparable friends. The four set out together. If one fell, the others must drive forward, to the last man. The letter *must* reach Buckingham safely, and in time for him to act.

Three fell by the wayside in various encounters, and D'Artagnan set sail for England uncertain in what straits he might have abandoned his friends.

Arriving in a strange country, D'Artagnan traced the Duke from his castle to Windsor, and finally saw him out hunting with the King. A few words, and the Queen's letter, explained the situation and, with a swift apology to his sovereign, the Duke and D'Artagnan galloped back to the castle. Before a portrait of the Queen lay the box which contained the studs. Reverently he opened the lid.

"All is lost," shouted the Duke, with a terrible cry. "Two of the studs are wanting . . . they have been stolen on the Cardinal's behalf. The ribbon which held them has been cut."

His jeweller, hastily summoned, said he required eight days to copy them. "Eight days!" roared the Duke. "They must be in Paris in five days!"

He promised the jeweller double the price he asked if the studs could be ready, and, the jeweller agreeing to work night and day, he was locked into a secret room where none could molest him or further damage the precious jewels.

Meanwhile the Duke's couriers set out for France to arrange

relays of horses for D'Artagnan's return, and at last the diamonds
were ready.   So perfectly were they matched that the jeweller
himself could not tell the copies from the originals when they
were mixed together.

*   *   *   *   *

As the Queen finished her robing, trembling with fear in
spite of Constance's assurances, D'Artagnan clattered into
Paris, flogging his fourth exhausted thoroughbred.   Through
a day and a night he had ridden, leaving horses behind as they
fell steaming in the stalls;   all had been made easy and, with
the password on his lips, he entered the Louvre.

Court formalities kept the King at such a distance from the
Queen that he was unable to examine her jewels until after the
elaborate ballet which followed a lengthy dinner.   Finally
he came to her side, followed closely by the Cardinal, eager
for her downfall.

The King held out two glittering studs on the palm of his
hand.   "How, Sire?"   cried the Queen, feigning delight.
"You are giving me two more, then?"

Together the King and the Cardinal counted the glittering
diamond studs.   The Cardinal was the first to recover his
composure.   "I was desirous of presenting Her Majesty
with these two studs," he said to the dumbfounded King,
"and did not dare to offer them myself."

The Queen smiled, completely at her ease.   "And I
am the more grateful to your Eminence, since I suspect that
these two studs alone have cost you as much as all the others
cost His Majesty!"

D'Artagnan had received from the Queen a diamond
ring, and fervently pressed a kiss upon the hand which presented it to him.

His heart was heavy indeed on learning from M. de Tréville
that none of his friends had returned to Paris; he determined
to set out to seek them first thing in the morning.

"Why not to-night?" asked M. de Tréville, and he confessed he had an assignation—with Constance.

"Trust a mistress less than any friend," warned the older
man sagely, for women were a favourite tool of the Cardinal's.
"You have gained a thrice dangerous enemy in Cardinal
Richelieu.   Take the road to-night and seek your friends . . .
and sell that ring."   And he pointed to the diamond glittering
on D'Artagnan's finger.

When he protested that it was a gift from the Queen, de

Tréville insisted all the more that he get rid of it, since it might be recognized. Then added, seeing the young gallant's natural hesitation, " Then at least wear it turned inwards ! "

D'Artagnan set out to his rendez-vous with Constance in spite of the fact that he learned that a spy of the Cardinal's had read her note appointing the meeting-place.

But he waited in vain for his love; finally to learn that she had been abducted by the same pale dark stranger who seemed destined to cross his path!

M. de Tréville promised to appeal to the Queen for protection for Constance Bonacieux, and D'Artagnan set out to find his friends. After many adventures they all returned to Paris, within the time of their leave, to find that a campaign was to open in May and they were to be ready for war.

As preparations went forward, and there was no news of her, the thought of Constance dimmed in D'Artagnan's mind. Besides, he had chanced to meet Milady in circumstances which rendered her in his debt. She was French, but had been married to an Englishman, brother of Lord de Winter, and was the most bewitching creature he had ever met. Whilst trying to fascinate another young man, she encouraged D'Artagnan in his amorous desires; she had a shrewd suspicion that he had foiled her over the diamond studs and might find some opportunity to pay back this old score. And D'Artagnan, blinded by this new love, paid her assiduous court.

Kitty, Milady's maid, fell deeply in love with this handsome Musketeer of whom her mistress would have nothing, and tried to warn him of Milady's dangerous gifts and her power with the Cardinal. Finally Kitty betrayed her mistress by letting D'Artagnan see some of the passionate letters Milady was writing to another man. D'Artagnan planned to be revenged upon her and, through Kitty's unwilling assistance, he presented himself in her darkened bedroom under the pretence of being the young noble whom she had invited.

As he left her bed in the dim, rosy dawn, she pressed upon him a rich sapphire ring. What was his astonishment, on showing it to Athos, for him to proclaim that it was none other than a family heirloom. . . . D'Artagnan knew something of Athos's distinguished ancestry and of the tragedy which led him to conceal his identity, but he could get no information from him regarding Milady.

Intrigued by the mystery, he wrote to Milady, in his pretended character, and told her that he was tired of her. Infuriated, she tried to persuade D'Artagnan to fight a duel against such a treacherous lover. His reward for the youth's death should be a night with Milady!

For the second time D'Artagnan saw the light of dawn break from her sumptuous couch. "I have a confession to make," he said, having pleaded for her admission that she did, really, truly and deeply, love him, and no other.

"The Comte de Wardes of Thursday night and D'Artagnan of to-day are the same person." With a cry she sprang from the bed, and in his effort to detain her, her nightdress was torn from her shoulders.

With inexpressible horror D'Artagnan recognized, on her beautiful shoulder, the criminal's brand of a *fleur de lis*, burned by the common executioner!

He escaped from her fury, and her hastily summoned servants, through the faithful Kitty's room. Naturally Milady would allow no one to live in possession of her shameful secret, if she could help it, so the swaggering soldier found himself escaping in woman's attire.

Athos then admitted that Milady must be his wife, who had been branded for stealing the sacred vessels from a church, as well as other crimes. He had believed her dead, having seen her hanged, and could not believe her still alive.

"She is a fiend—a tigress! If she can rise from the dead, what can she not do to you—to both of us?" cried Athos. All along D'Artagnan had realized that she was as dangerous as an adder, but in the wild circles in which he moved, playing with fire was not only fascinating, but also fashionable.

Cardinal Richelieu commanded D'Artagnan's attendance upon him; it was a summons that could not be disobeyed. All four of the Inseparables were fearful of the outcome, but D'Artagnan interviewed the notorious Cardinal and found him a gallant enemy. He wished D'Artagnan to take a commission in his own Musketeers for the forthcoming campaign. The Cardinal persisted, for he was anxious to win D'Artagnan to his side; he knew every move D'Artagnan had made since he came to Paris, including his journey to England. When D'Artagnan finally refused, he warned him that after the campaign he would seek his revenge.

Meanwhile the plans for the campaign were not moving to the Cardinal's liking, and he sent for Milady. He had sufficient facts about the Queen and Buckingham to put him in a strong position. She was to see the Duke and persuade him that England must remain neutral—otherwise the Queen would be exposed. If the Duke refused, she must not hesitate, even at arranging his assassination.

Milady showed herself a willing tool, even for murder. All she demanded was the Cardinal's safe conduct and the promise of a life in return for the life she would take—D'Artagnan's life!. ' The Cardinal agreed.

Athos was fortunate enough to overhear part of this conversation, and cornered Milady afterwards, alone. Pale as a corpse, she cowered away, like a horrid image of terror. This was her husband, whom she had considered dead all the years since her remarriage. He roughly demanded the Cardinal's safe conduct and let her go . . . a woman who had been killed once, somehow it was unthinkable he should try to kill her again. . . .

Milady set out swiftly for England; to try to see the Cardinal again would result in her exposure as a branded criminal. Grinding her teeth, she vowed vengeance upon her three enemies: first Constance Bonacieux, then Athos, her husband, and finally, and most horribly, upon D'Artagnan. But for the moment the death of Buckingham. . . .

By now the four Inseparables were at the siege of Rochelle and D'Artagnan had been received into the Corps of Musketeers. Together they adventured into a bastion under the enemy's guns and discussed their plans, afraid that anywhere else the spies of the Cardinal might overhear them.

They decided that a message must be sent to England, to warn the Duke of his danger. Aramis undertook, through his Court connections, to get a message to the Queen of the dangers threatening Constance Bonacieux. More they could not do.

Their messenger reached England before Milady, and she found herself taken before de Winter on her arrival. He soon showed her that he knew of her plans upon his own life, that she might inherit his fortunes; of her designs upon Buckingham, through the Cardinal; finally of the *fleur de lis* and that, her husband still being alive, her marriage to his brother was invalid. But he was not able to guard her himself in his castle, so he sent for his faithful lieutenant, John Felton.

"Look at this woman," said de Winter; "she is possessed of all earthly seductions, but she is a monster. She has been guilty of as many crimes as you could *read of* in a year. You are my trusted friend—and you owe your life itself to me." Grimly John nodded; he loved de Winter as a father. "Swear,

John Felton, by your hopes of salvation "—Felton trembled; he was a religious fanatic—" swear you will keep her safely for the chastisement she has merited."

But fourteen days is a long time, and a woman with the skill of Milady soon began to break down John Felton's resistances by pretending to a religious devotion as deep as his own. Finally she had him completely in her power.

With lies and seductions she persuaded him that Buckingham was the cause of her misery and, after assisting her to escape, Felton presented himself to Buckingham. Lord de Winter arrived too late to prevent his love-crazed friend from stabbing the Duke to death.

Buckingham expired with the name of Anne on his lips, and through the window John saw Milady's ship sailing for France an hour and a half before the time appointed!

The four Inseparables had learned where Constance was, in a Convent under the Queen's protection; but time was drifting on, and they were unable to get leave to rescue her. Milady also knew where she was, and might be returning from England at any moment. At last their promised leave came through and they set out.

But Milady was ahead. On arrival at the Convent she asked accommodation temporarily, and soon made herself friendly, by lies and trickery, with Constance. Her plans were well laid for Constance's abduction, for she was a valuable capture for the Cardinal, but D'Artagnan and the Musketeers arrived at the moment she and Constance were about to leave.

Milady saw their horses from the window and dashed back to Constance. She emptied the contents of a ring into a glass of wine and pressed it upon Constance. As the unhappy girl sank to her knees, Milady stood gloating over her.

" This is not the way I wished to avenge myself," she hissed, " but we do what we can! "

Constance lived only long enough to name her murderer, and expired in D'Artagnan's arms. At that moment there was the clatter of another arrival, and Lord de Winter arrived, bent on revenging himself on Milady.

Athos, as her husband, claimed the right to order the methods of her death and, in a lonely house where she had taken refuge, the five men, with a masked and cloaked sixth, confronted her.

" I defy any of you," cried the terrified woman, " to prove who I am, that I have been branded, that I am any of the wicked things you claim."

The masked figure came forward and revealed himself. "No! No! It is an infernal apparition!" There was a terrible silence and she went on: "The executioner from Lille!"

He then told her the charges of which *he* accused her, many of them unknown even to Athos, and then the charges which Athos preferred, finally the murder of Buckingham. Each of the men, solemnly, when asked, pronounced her punishment as death.

Athos faced her, and it was as though they were alone. "Charlotte, your crimes have wearied men on earth and God in Heaven. If you know a prayer—say it, for you are condemned and you shall die!"

* * * * *

Some months later D'Artagnan at last came face to face with his unknown man. He hastened to draw.

"I am the Chevalier le Rochefort," said the stranger, bowing, "equerry to the Cardinal. He wishes to see you."

D'Artagnan again confronted the Cardinal. Richelieu was anxious to revenge Milady's death, but D'Artagnan told him of the trial and condemnation, and of the host of crimes she had committed.

"You are a brave youth, and a loyal one to France," said the Cardinal. He wrote a few lines and handed them to D'Artagnan; it was an officer's commission in the King's Musketeers. He then made le Rochefort and D'Artagnan promise eternal friendship.

D'Artagnan pressed Athos to fill in the blank name in the commission. "For Athos, this is too much," was the reply. "For the Comte de la Frere, it is too little."

Porthos refused because he was to retire and marry. Aramis had finally decided to enter the church, his secret longing for many years. So perforce D'Artagnan accepted the commission himself.

When Athos took the paper and wrote his friend's name in the vacant space, D'Artagnan broke down. "I shall have no more friends," he cried, "only bitter recollections."

Athos looked upon the young, tear-stained face. "You are young," he replied, "and your bitter recollections have time to change themselves into sweet remembrances."

THE MILL ON THE FLOSS

By GEORGE ELIOT

Mary Ann Cross, alias George Eliot, created something of a social disturbance by her " union without legal form " with George Henry Lewes from 1854 till his death in 1878. Her work, however, needs no association with so dead a scandal to be remembered. It stands on its own merits as sterling fiction, revealing a profound sense of pathos and humour, as well as a conviction of the purifying effect of suffering upon the human soul.

" WHAT I want is to give Tom a good eddication; an eddication as 'll be a bread to him." Sitting by a bright fire in the left-hand parlour of Dorlcote Mill, so spoke Mr. Tulliver, master of the mill, to Bessie, his wife—blonde, comely, and rather stupid.

A school was needed where, in his father's words, Tom could learn to know figures, and write like print, and learn to wrap things up in words as weren't actionable. To this, as to the suggestion that Tulliver should consult Mr. Riley, the valuer, Mrs. Tulliver assented; for, as usual, she agreed with her husband—as she did even when he ended by saying, " But what I'm afraid on is as Tom hasn't got the right sort o' brains for a smart fellow. He takes after your family. The little 'un takes after my side."

The " little 'un " was nine-years-old Maggie, at that moment wandering by the banks of the Floss, watching the ships with their cargoes of grain and coal and fir-planks as they sailed by to St. Ogg's. Maggie's straight black hair, which refused to curl, her brown skin, and her wilful, determined ways were the despair of her mother. Bessie would have preferred a pretty, docile child, such as her sister Deane's Lucy, to this turbulent little girl who read every book in the house and, to her mother's shame and her father's secret admiration, made disconcertingly sharp remarks to various visiting uncles and aunts.

The thirteen-year-old Tom was Maggie's brother—and hero. Holidays were doubly enjoyable, because then she could walk with Tom round the mill and in the river-meadows.

Tom, unlike his mother, was not for ever dreading that she would fall in the stream and be " drownded ". Tom was sensible; Tom was brave; Tom was . . . Tom was . . . Tom—Tom—Tom. . . .

Mr. Riley came. He agreed to approach the Rev. Mr. Stelling, an Oxford man who might tutor Tom for a hundred pounds a year. This decision taken, a family gathering had to be called that the news might be imparted. All such gatherings expected—and were given—pies, jellies, cheese cakes, plum cakes: all those delicious confections which, two days after Tom's return for the Easter holidays, Tom's mother set about making.

During those two days Maggie's heart rocketed from heights of joy to depths of despair, and then back to the heights. The very first evening had brought her need to confess that all Tom's rabbits had died, because she had forgotten to feed them. Her hero's anger had sent her flying to the attic, where she could sob unobserved. Then there was the morning of the party. She hadn't understood him about some jam puffs, and he had called—had called her " a greedy ". For hours he had left her lonely and wretched, while he went with Bob Jakin, the bird-scarer.

Oh, that misery! And then, oh, this other joy! The long morning spent with Tom, fishing with the new rod and line which he had bought her! She had early got a bite—a fine big tench her hook had brought wriggling up. And oh, Tom's exclamation at the sight of it—she'd never forget that! " Oh, Maggie, you little duck! empty the basket."

Aunt Glegg and her husband were the first to arrive at the party. Always the most formidable of the aunts, she had scarcely arrived when she was deploring the extravagance of Mrs. Tulliver's preparations with allusions to Mr. Tulliver's expensive fondness for litigation: " With your husband likely to spend his fortin' i' going to law, as he 's already spent yours," she said emphatically, " a plain pudding with a spoonful o' sugar, and no spice, 'ud be far more becoming."

Aunt Glegg was followed by two more aunts, both sisters of Bessie and herself. A four-wheeler brought Mrs. Pullet, accompanied by her husband, the gentleman farmer. Tall and good-looking, it was evident that she was a lover of dress. After Aunt Pullet, Aunt Deane. With her were her husband and Lucy, her young daughter, whose blonde curls showed the brown-skinned Maggie to such disadvantage. Poor

Maggie! Aunt Glegg disapproved of her from top to toe; Aunt Pullet thought she had too much hair and that this accounted for her too-brown skin. Even her father said that it should be cut, adding, however: "There's red wheat as well as white, and some like dark grain best." With only this to comfort her, Maggie had to obey her mother's command: "Go and get your hair brushed—do for shame!"

Tom followed his sister upstairs. He came down alone, smiling. They were half-way through the meal before Maggie, unable to stay longer away from the apricot pudding and the cowslip wine, made her second appearance.

Mrs. Tulliver gave a scream. Uncle Glegg exclaimed, "Heydey! what little gell 's this? Why, I don't know her. Is it some little gell you've picked up in the road, Kezia?"

"Why, she's gone and cut her hair herself," said Mr. Tulliver. "Did you ever know such a little hussy?"

When disapproving remark was added to disapproving remark, Maggie, unable to bear it longer, flung herself into her father's arms, sobbing loudly and yet hating her sobs. "Never mind," he comforted her, "you was in the right to cut it off if it plagued you; father 'ull take your part."

With the children sent off to the summer-house, Mr. Tulliver told their elders of his intention to send Tom to Mr. Stelling. One after the other the relations doubted whether this was wise. Aunt Glegg grew shrewish, as she made shrill references to the loan she had granted her brother-in-law. Mr. Tulliver's anger simmered, started to boil over, boiled over, and ended by exploding in words that drove Aunt Glegg from the house:

"My family 's as good as yours and better, for it hasn't got a damned ill-tempered woman in it."

Next morning Mr. Tulliver, pressed for money as usual, rode over to his sister, wife of struggling Farmer Moss, telling the couple that he must call in his loan of three hundred pounds. Riding home again, he reflected that, if he were hard on his own sister, so later Tom might be hard on the little 'un. He returned to the Moss's farm, comforting his anxious sister with the words: "Don't you fret—I'll make a shift without the money."

It was a kind act. Yet it put him into a tight corner; for even if Aunt Glegg did not call in the money, he was resolved to repay her. She did not call it in. Influenced by her sister Pullet's pleadings, Aunt Glegg decided to set an example, and not to behave ill because folks behaved ill to her.

Things went badly with Maggie on the day following the party. Tom was out of temper with her all day. It was this that, during their afternoon visit to Aunt Pullet at Garum Firs, drove Maggie to disgrace herself—and her mother—by pushing Lucy into the pond. When the carriage was called to take the children home, Maggie was missing. Mrs. Tulliver's old fear returned. "Drownded—she's got drownded."

Maggie had, in fact, run away to the gipsies. She would educate them and be their queen: it was an old idea of hers. Returning home late that night, her father was astonished to meet a Romany on a donkey, who was bringing back the wearied and frightened little girl to the mill.

His wife's account of her visit to Garum Firs angered Mr. Tulliver. Sister Pullet to speak for him indeed! Within a fortnight he had borrowed the five hundred pounds on bond from a client of Lawyer Wakem, that he might repay Aunt Glegg.

* * * * *

Tom's first half at Mr. Stelling's was neither happy nor easy. Not only had he to learn Latin, but an entirely new pronunciation of English. Proud as he was, he was often near to tears as he thought of the mill and Yap and Maggie. When Maggie came to stay with him for a fortnight during that half, misery became joy. He even accepted his sister's longing to learn from Mr. Stelling. That was like Maggie!

The Christmas holidays came. At home Tom felt that something was slightly wrong. It was not the meals: they were as splendid as ever. Yet his father was angry, always shouting about his wrongs.

Mr. Tulliver was about to go to law again. He intended to stop this man Pivart's irrigation scheme higher up the Floss. If he could, that was. But Wakem was behind Pivart, and the miller was convinced that all his wrongs could be traced to Wakem.

During Tom's second half Wakem's son, Philip, a clever and sensitive boy, made even more sensitive by his deformed back, came to join Tom at Mr. Stelling's. It was not until Maggie's second visit to the tutor's that the two boys became sympathetic. Maggie felt greatly drawn to Philip, and was especially kind and loving to him; while Tom's former antagonism to his companion was temporarily lessened. An accident helped this. Tom cut his foot with the sword he had borrowed from the drill sergeant in order to impress and frighten Maggie. With Tom in bed, Maggie grew still more close to Philip. Before she left, with all the ardour of her nature, she promised to kiss him whenever they should meet.

More than two years went by; Tom's last half at Mr. Stelling's was nearing its end. A day came when, as he was thinking pleasantly of what he would do when he had left school, he was summoned to the study, where his sister was waiting for him. Maggie herself had been hurriedly brought home from her finishing school because of her father's illness. Her news was dramatically grave. Their father had lost his lawsuit with Mr. Pivart; he had fallen off his horse.

Maggie was white and trembling as she whispered, " He seems to have lost his senses." Then, bursting forth, she cried: " Oh, Tom! he will lose the mill and the land and everything. He will have nothing left."

* * * * *

When Tom and Maggie reached home, they found a coarse, common, dingy man sitting in their father's chair, smoking a pipe of strong tobacco. He had a jug and glass beside him. The truth came to Tom in an instant. The bailiff! To be sold up was part of the disgrace and misery of failing. His father had " failed ".

The children went in search of their mother. They found her in the storeroom, with all her precious best things and her linen spread around her. The poor woman was crying and fingering her treasures: " They're all to be sold. And my silver teapot too I bought wi' my own money."

" Don't fret, Mother," Tom said tenderly. " I'll get a situation of some sort."

Next day Mr. Tulliver still lay insensible in his darkened room. With the exception of Mr. Deane, away on business, the aunts and uncles had arrived. The mortified Tom and Maggie heard them tell their mother what a disgrace to the family this selling up was; how they had always known that she would come to want; how, but for them, she would now have to go to the workhouse. As usual, only Mr. Glegg was kind. " What's done, can't be undone," he said. " We shall make a shift among us to buy what's sufficient, though, as Mrs. G. says, they must be plain and useful things."

Tom waited till they had all their say. Then quietly and respectfully he said in a shaking voice, " Aunt Glegg, if you think it's a disgrace to the family to be sold up, wouldn't it be better to prevent it altogether? And if you and my Aunt Pullet think of leaving any money to me and Maggie, wouldn't it be better to give it now, and pay the debt we're going to be sold up for, and save my mother from parting with her furniture?"

The company considered for a while. "But it's no use to pay off this debt and save the furniture, when there's all the law debts behind," Mr. Glegg said at last. Trembling with indignation Maggie got to her feet.

"Why do you come, then," she shouted, "talking and interfering with us and scolding us, if you don't mean to do anything to help my poor mother? Keep away from us. Tom and I don't ever want to have any of your money."

Immediately after this outburst Mrs. Moss arrived. She went straight up to Tom. "Oh, my poor children!" she said. "You've no call to think well o' me; I'm a poor aunt to you. We've three hundred pounds o' my brother's money— and yet we must be sold up to pay it."

Tom turned to Mr. Glegg. "Uncle, I don't think it would be right for my Aunt Moss to pay the money, if it would be against my father's will. He said to me some while ago that he would rather lose it than think of distressing Uncle Moss for it."

After much argument it was decided that Tom and his Uncle Glegg should look for the note for the three hundred pounds in Mr. Tulliver's room. While searching among the deeds, Mr. Glegg dropped the heavy lid of the safe-box. The reverberating crash penetrated the sick man's coma, and for a few minutes he recovered consciousness. Before relapsing into stupor, he directed that Mrs. Moss should not be pressed for the money, and also that Luke his miller should be repaid the fifty pounds which he had put into the business.

The family conference over, Tom visited his Uncle Dean to ask his help in finding a situation. At an humiliating interview Tom was made to feel that his expensive schooling had been of very little value. Eventually, his uncle did find Tom a post in his warehouse, arranging for him to have evening lessons in book-keeping. Tom would have been cheerful enough but for the bitter knowledge that his father would be able to pay only twelve shillings in the pound.

Meanwhile, unknown to any of her family, Mrs. Tulliver had visited Lawyer Wakem, and begged him not to bid for the mill and the land at the sale. She told him that Guest and Company, Mr. Deane's firm, were thinking of buying it and of keeping on her husband as manager. Wakem had not previously entertained the idea of bidding for the mill. But he now determined to purchase it.

The day came at last when Mr. Tulliver was helped downstairs by Luke. It grieved him to see the familiar rooms half-stripped of their belongings. This was not the worst. When told that Wakem had bought up everything and had offered to keep him on to work the mill, the intolerable news made him sink trembling into his chair.

"You may do as you like wi' me, Bessie," he said to his wife. "I've been the bringing of you to poverty. It's no use standing up to anything now."

Even so, the miller's old spirit had not wholly left him. With all of them present, he bade Tom write in the family Bible that he, Mr. Tulliver, would stay under Wakem to make amends to his wife, and because he wished to die in the place where he had been born; that he would serve the lawyer as an honest man, but that—he wished evil might befall Wakem. Finally, he turned to Tom, saying: "Now read it out!"

Tom obeyed.

"Now write—write as you'll remember what Wakem's done to your father, and you'll make him and his feel it, if ever the day comes. And sign your name Thomas Tulliver."

"Oh, no, Father, dear Father!" said Maggie, almost choked with fear. "You shouldn't make Tom write that."

"Be quiet, Maggie!" said Tom. "I *shall* write it."

* * * * *

In their changed circumstances the Tullivers' household was not a happy one. His business over, Mr. Tulliver hurried away from market, and refused all invitations from his friends. He could not be reconciled to his lot; his wife, bereft of most of her treasures, became worn in body and mind as she wandered aimlessly and restlessly about the half-furnished house; Tom was weary and abstracted during the short periods he spent at home; while Maggie felt crushed beneath the sadness of those she loved. Now that adversity had come, uncles and aunts paid short visits and were glad to return to their own prosperous homes.

On an afternoon when Maggie was sitting, sad at heart, in the garden, she saw Bob Jakin coming up the path. The boy who had scared birds and killed rats was now a packman, glorying in the sealskin cap and blue plush waistcoat which he wore. Out of kindness and for old acquaintance' sake he had brought a parcel of books as a present for Maggie. Among these was a copy of the *Imitation of Christ*: in the dark times to come Thomas à Kempis was to give Maggie much comfort and support.

Bob was not Maggie's only friend. Philip Wakem had loved Maggie since the days at Mr. Stelling's and, on his return from abroad, quickly made an opportunity of meeting her again. He saw her first in the Red Deeps, where the Scotch firs stood erect and beautiful. This older Maggie was beautiful also—far more beautiful than he had remembered. They continued to meet—in secret because open friendship was impossible.

Such was Maggie's preoccupation during the following year; Tom's was with his schemes for paying his father's debts. In these Bob Jakin shared, for it was Bob who had suggested the private trading which, thanks to a loan from his uncle Glegg, had made him a hundred and fifty pounds.

At the end of that twelvemonth, Philip and Maggie confessed their love for one another. Their joy was short-lived; for Tom, discovering their secret, forced Maggie in his presence to take farewell of Philip.

It was Tom's championship of his father that made him hurt his sister thus. Three weeks later, the miller and his son were once more talking of the debts to be repaid. In the tin box were one hundred and ninety-three pounds. Looking mournfully at the money, Mr. Tulliver said: "There's more nor three hundred wanting. . . . I must trusten to you to pay 'em. . . . But you're like enough to bury me first."

"No, Father," Tom said. "You will live to see the debts all paid—and with your own hand."

Tom, as his father now realized, had the money already. Almost stunned with emotion, the miller began to talk of the future, the creditors' meeting that Tom had called; and then, wiping away his tears, of how he would get from under Wakem's thumb.

At the creditors' meeting Mr. Tulliver looked almost his old self. His boy, his Tom, had found most of the money. But then, he'd spent a deal on his eddication, the father proudly told his friends.

Riding back alone, the miller came face to face with Wakem, with whom he at once picked a quarrel. He ceased to flog

the lawyer unmercifully with his riding-whip only when
Maggie rushed out of the house and clung to him, shouting
for help.

"I feel ill—faintish," he said. "Help me in."

He was put to bed. The doctor came, but could do nothing.
He was dead before morning.

*   *   *   *   *

Mr. Tulliver's death broke up the household. Tom went
to lodge with Bob Jakin, now a prosperous boat-owner, down
by the river. Maggie secured a teacher's post, although her
various aunts looked upon this as "being in service" and said
so, scathingly. Mrs. Tulliver, after the death of her sister
Deane, went to Park House in St. Ogg's, where she acted as
housekeeper for Lucy and her brother-in-law

After two years in the school Maggie came to Park House
for a holiday. She found the leisurely life with her cousin
exceedingly pleasant after those long months of struggle and
privation. Philip Wakem was a frequent visitor at Park House,
as was his friend, Stephen Guest, all but engaged to Lucy.

Since she was sure to meet Philip, at the beginning of her
stay Maggie went to Tom's lodgings, asking him to absolve
her from the promise she had given.

"Very well," Tom said coldly. "But if you think of
Philip Wakem as a lover again, you must give me up."

On her way back Maggie had comforted herself by reflecting
that Tom's coldness had lessened before they parted.

When at last the one-time lovers stood, face to face and
alone, in Lucy's drawing-room, their agitation was great.
They leaned forward; they clasped hands, but they knew
sadness as well as contentment.

"There is nothing to hinder our being friends, Philip,"
Maggie murmured. "I shall go away soon—to a new
situation."

"Is there no alternative, Maggie? Is that life away from
those who love you the only one you will allow yourself?"

"Yes, Philip," she answered, looking pleadingly at him.

Philip Wakem was not alone in yearning for Maggie. For
Stephen Guest, despite his efforts to control his feelings, soon
found himself deeply in love with her. Maggie's own love
went out in return, but loyalty, both to Philip and to her
cousin Lucy, made her repulse him when he first declared
his love. This was at a ball at Park House, but Stephen
was not to be so easily discouraged. For, although Maggie

took refuge with her Aunt Moss for a few days, Stephen
followed her. In the Basset lanes he renewed his pleading.
Maggie listened to him in great distress of mind. When he
begged her for one kiss—the first and the last—before they
parted, she gave him his desire. Yet, although she loved him,
although his arm was around her waist and the "Dearest"
he had whispered still in her ears, she said sadly but firmly:
"But, even if Lucy did not exist, I have other ties."

"You are engaged to Philip Wakem?" asked Stephen.

"I consider myself engaged to him; I don't mean to
marry anyone else."

Lucy, unaware of the conflicting emotions known to Philip,
Stephen and Maggie, went quietly on with her schemes for
their happiness. She knew that Tom's greatest wish was to
get back the mill. She thought that Philip might persuade
his father to sell.

In this Lucy showed her astuteness. After an angry scene
in which Philip confided to his father his desire to marry
Maggie, the lawyer at last consented to help his son and to
allow Tom to buy back the mill. Another scheme of Lucy's,
equally innocent, had far-reaching consequences. She planned
that Philip should take Maggie out for a whole morning's
rowing on the river. When the day arrived, Philip, sick with
torturing thoughts of Stephen and Maggie, sent to his friend,
asking him to take Maggie in the boat, as he was too ill to go.

"Oh, we can't," Maggie said, when Stephen had explained.
"Lucy did not expect. . . . She would be hurt." (Lucy had
gone for a morning's shopping with her Aunt Tulliver.)

But Stephen persisted. "Let us go," he entreated. Falter-
ingly, Maggie allowed herself to be helped into the boat.

For a long time they glided deliciously in the bright sun.
Suddenly Maggie cried:

"Oh, we have passed Luckreth—where we were to stop!"

"Yes. Let us never go home again—till no one can part
us; till we are married."

They glided on. Each dreaded to leave the other. When
a Dutch vessel came in sight, Stephen hailed her. They were
taken on board. With Stephen sitting by her side, Maggie
slept all night on the poop. In the morning the young man
saw that she was resolved to go back.

* * * * *

Her brother watched her approach; his expression was
harsh.

"Tom," his sister said faintly, "I am come back to you. I am come back home—for refuge—to tell you everything."

"You will find no home with me," he answered with rage. "You have disgraced us all. You have been base, deceitful. I wash my hands of you for ever."

Tom's attitude was but a foretaste of what St. Ogg's had in store for her. In her riverside lodgings with Bob and his wife, henceforward she had but one friend to support her. This was a priest, a widower, who gave her a post in his household as governess to his children. Yet even he, almost a saint though he was, after a while felt obliged to ask Maggie to find a post away from the town; for, as he gently explained, his championship of her was a source of discord between himself and his parishioners. Within the family circle, surprisingly enough, Aunt Glegg had stoutly refused to take the common view of Maggie; she had even offered her a home— if Maggie would be humble.

It was at this time that Maggie received a long letter from Philip in which he said that he had never doubted her; that it was he who was to blame for having urged his feelings on her.

Sitting disconsolately in her room one evening, Maggie was startled to see Lucy. Her cousin had stolen away from her sick room for a short while. The two girls clung together, each comforting the other.

That visit of Lucy's brought Maggie a measure of consolation. Yet soon she was once more fighting the old familiar battle. It was on a wild September evening of that year in which Dr. Ken had asked her to leave his house, that Maggie received the letter from Stephen which urged and implored her to marry him. "Write the one word 'Come '," he said, "and in two days I shall be with you."

In her loneliness and her sorrow the temptation was severe. It was many hours before she was able to put it from her. She fell to her knees in prayer. Soon she started up, feeling cold dampness about her knees. Instantly she knew the significance of this. The flood!

With great calm she wakened Bob and his wife, then hastily got into one of the boats, and started to row with all her strength across the fields. Her one thought was to reach the mill that she might rescue Tom.

For hours, as it seemed, she battled with the fierce waters; she beat her way against the turbulent wind. At last she was able to get the boat opposite the middle window. Tom looked out, astonished.

It was not until they were far down the stream that Tom, now wielding the oars, was able to realize how almost miraculous had been his sister's achievement in reaching him. The tears came into his eyes as he said the old childish word of endearment, " *Magsie !* "

They rowed on—it was their intention to get to Park House to give Lucy the help she might need. Suddenly there was a great crash: some wooden machinery had given way on one of the wharves. The great drifting mass came swirling towards them. From a nearby boat men shouted in horror. Tom put all his strength into his rowing. But the current was too strong; they could not escape.

" It is coming, Maggie," he cried hoarsely. He loosed the oars and clasped her to him. That was at one moment. At the next the boat was no longer to be seen upon the waters. The huge mass went hurrying on in hideous triumph.

The boat reappeared, but brother and sister had gone down in that last embrace, never to be parted.

TOM JONES

By HENRY FIELDING

*This immensely long work, in eighteen "books", each
with its introductory chapter, represents the English
eighteenth-century novel at its best. Published in 1749, it
has had many imitators, but none has ever succeeded in
capturing that boisterous enthusiasm that is part of the
elusive secret of Fielding's success.*

SQUIRE ALLWORTHY had an agreeable person, a sound
constitution, a solid understanding, a benevolent heart
and one of the largest estates in Somersetshire.

Here he lived in retirement with his sister, Miss Bridget.
This lady was now somewhat past the age of thirty, and was
so far from regretting her want of beauty, that she often declared
the charms of any woman were no better than snares for herself,
as well as for others. Yet so discreet was she in her conduct,
that she might have been thought to apprehend all the traps
ever laid for the most enchanting of her sex.

Mr. Allworthy had been absent a full quarter of a year on
business in London when he returned very late one evening
to his home. He enjoyed a light supper with Miss Bridget,
then made his way, much fatigued, to his chamber. Having
spent some minutes on his knees, he was preparing to step
into bed, when, upon turning back the clothes, he beheld a
child wrapped in linen, in a sweet and profound sleep, between
his sheets.

Miss Bridget would perhaps have evinced more kindness
for the foundling placed in her care had not her affections
strayed into another course. The object of her regard was a
certain Captain Blifil, who had been a guest for some months
in the squire's house. The gallant captain was far from
indifferent to Miss Bridget, being one of those wise men who
regard beauty in the other sex as a worthless and superficial
qualification; moreover, he was so greatly enamoured of the
squire's mansion, lands and hereditaments, that he would most
probably have contracted marriage with them even if he had
been obliged to take the witch of Endor into the bargain.

The captain's advances upon this citadel of virtue were

made with discretion, and it was not until some days after the sensible pair were privily wedded, that Mr. Allworthy learnt of its surrender. He readily forgave the deception, on the ground that his sister was now at an age when she knew her own interests best, and welcomed the captain as a brother-in-law.

Eight months after the nuptials, Mrs. Blifil was delivered of a boy so perfect in appearance that no one heeded the objection of the midwife that he was born a month before his full time.

Though the birth of an heir by this beloved sister was a source of great joy to Mr. Allworthy, yet it did not alienate his affections from the little foundling, to whom he had been godfather, and given his own name of Thomas. Strangely enough, Mrs. Blifil, too, early began to share this predilection, and revealed a fondness for Tommy's company and a cold indifference to Master Blifil's, that could not fail to arouse her husband's annoyance.

Indeed, this and other matters of discord exacerbated the captain's anger to such a pitch as to carry him off one sunny afternoon with a fit of apoplexy—a bereavement endured with remarkable fortitude by Mrs. Blifil.

She now began to devote herself to the foundling, and her preference for Tom Jones to her own child became so marked as to incite the disapprobation of all except Mr. Allworthy, who continued to treat the boy with every kindness. It was a wonder (so ran the universal censure) that the squire should allow such a lad to be educated with his nephew, lest the morals of the latter should be corrupted by his example. For Thomas early betrayed a propensity to many vices, especially theft, and even before he reached the age of sixteen had been denounced for robbing an orchard, stealing a duck out of a farmer's yard, and picking Master Blifil's pocket of a ball. Master Blifil, on the other hand, was sober, discreet, and pious beyond his age; qualities which endeared him to everyone who knew him.

The only servant in the family who showed any friendship for Tom Jones was the gamekeeper, a fellow of a loose disposition, called George Seagrim, who frequently allowed the boy to accompany him about the manor.

One day they were a-shooting together when they happened to spring a covey of partridges, which fled into the estate of Squire Western, Mr. Allworthy's neighbour. The gamekeeper had been ordered by his master never to trespass, on pain of dismissal, but over-persuaded by Tom, he entered the estate and shot one of the partridges.

Squire Western himself was riding near by, and, hearing the gun go off, immediately made towards the place. The gamekeeper hid in a furze-bush, but Tom was caught by the gentleman, who quickly found the partridge he concealed beneath his coat. He at once rode off to complain to Mr. Allworthy, who sent for Jones and asked the lad who was with him. Tom stoutly maintained he had been alone, but Master Blifil revealed that George Seagrim was the other culprit. Mr. Allworthy immediately dismissed the gamekeeper, and reprimanded his godson, albeit not too sternly, for he was aware of the boy's nice honour in shielding his accomplice.

Meanwhile, Tom had grown very intimate with Mr. Western. He had so greatly recommended himself to that gentleman by his prowess on horseback that the squire roundly declared after a drinking-bout that he wished he himself had a son of such parts. He was now a welcome guest at Mr. Western's table, and everything the squire held most dear—namely his guns, dogs and horses—were at Tom's command.

Tom therefore resolved to make use of this favour on behalf of his friend the gamekeeper, whom he hoped to introduce as a servant into Mr. Western's family. For this purpose, he decided to enlist first the support of the squire's only daughter.

Sophia Western was a girl of the middle height, of delicate and yet comely shape. Her hair, which was black, was so luxuriant that it reached her middle, before she cut it to comply with the modern fashion; and it was now curled gracefully in her neck. Her eyebrows were full, even, and arched beyond the power of imitation. Her black eyes had a lustre in them, which all their softness could not extinguish. Her nose was exactly regular, her cheeks of the oval kind, and in her right she had a dimple which the least smile discovered. Moreover, she had a remarkable sprightliness in her temper, which was greatly increased whenever Tom was in her company. Such, however, was her innocence and modesty, that her heart was lost to him before she suspected it was in danger.

Tom was far from proof to her allure, but the truth was that he felt himself committed to another woman. This was no other than Molly Seagrim, the gamekeeper's youngest daughter, who by the vehemence of her passion, and her forward behaviour, had already triumphed over his virtuous resolutions.

Matters were in this stand, when Tom one afternoon, finding

Sophia alone, began, after a short apology, and with a very serious face, to acquaint her that he had a favour to ask of her. She had no reason to suspect he was about to make love to her, yet some idea of that kind must have intruded itself, for her colour forsook her cheeks, her limbs trembled, and her tongue would have faltered had Tom stopped for an answer, but he proceeded to solicit her interest on behalf of the gamekeeper.

Sophia presently recovered from her confusion, and with a smile full of sweetness, said, " Is this the mighty favour you asked with so much gravity ? I will do it with all my heart."

In the weeks that followed, Tom hunted almost daily with the squire and came home with him to dinner, where Sophia levelled upon the youth the full battery of her charms. Insensibly, he began to return her affection, though now and again a sense of compassion for Molly Seagrim's plight would remind him that his heart should be engaged elsewhere.

Mr. Western, too, began to find Sophia so attractive that even his beloved dogs began to give place to her, but as he could not prevail on himself to abandon these, he insisted upon his daughter going hunting with him.

One day, as they were returning from the chase, her horse fell suddenly to prancing and capering. Tom Jones, a little distance behind, immediately galloped to her assistance, leapt from his own horse, and seized hers by the bridle. The unruly beast reared himself on his hind legs, and threw his lovely burden from his back, and Jones caught her in his arms. In that moment it came to him for the first time that he would know no peace until he had made Sophia his own.

He was further encouraged in this ambition by Mrs. Honour, Sophia's maid. " If you knew all," she observed to him one evening, " you would look a little higher than such trumpery as Molly Seagrim."

Feverish with a passion he dare not confess, our hero began to roam the fields on solitary walks, in which he often made plaint of his unhappy lot. " Oh, Sophia," he cried one afternoon, " would Heaven give thee to my arms, how blest would be my condition! Curst be that fortune which sets a distance between us."

From her observations of Sophia's languid air and distraught behaviour, Mistress Western was convinced the girl was in love, and that the object of her passion was Master Blifil. She communicated her suspicions to her brother.

" I was never more rejoiced in my life," cried Squire

Western, " for nothing can lie so handy together as our two estates, which are in a manner joined together in matrimony already."

But a few days later, Sophia revealed to her aunt that her heart was in the possession of—Mr. Jones. Squire Western at once went in a towering rage to Mr. Allworthy.

Mr. Allworthy calmed him, assured him he would never consent to such a match, and agreed to the squire's proposal that Sophia should marry Mr. Blifil. When the squire had left, Mr. Allworthy sent for his nephew, who told him about Jones's profligacy with Molly Seagrim.

Already incensed by the foundling's presumption in aspiring to the hand of Sophia, Mr. Allworthy could find no words strong enough to condemn the abandoned wretch. He sent for Jones, gave him some money, and told him to leave the house immediately and never return.

With a heart almost bursting with grief, Jones set out on the road to Bristol. He had lost his benefactor and his love, and little cared now what should happen to him.

He put up for the first night at a public-house, where he fell in with a company of soldiers, and stood treat to them. The bottle went round, and soon all tongues were loosened.

When it came to Jones's turn to give a toast, he could not refrain from mentioning the name of Sophia Western. " I knew one Sophia Western," cried a certain Ensign Northerton, who had seen the young lady with her aunt at a ball. " Her father had a great estate in Somersetshire, and she herself was lain with by half the young fellows at Bath."

" You are one of the most impudent rascals upon earth," shouted Jones, in an access of fury. He had no sooner spoken the words when the ensign discharged a bottle full at his head, which brought him unconscious to the ground.

For some days after the company had left the inn, Jones lay delirious with pain in his bed, attended by a surgeon daily. This was no other than the Partridge who had been dismissed his post by Mr. Allworthy. He was a man of many parts, for besides his book-learning, he was an excellent barber, and had also much skill in medicine. Now, like Jones, he was wandering the roads. When the youth had recovered of his wound, they set out together for Gloucester, and from thence to Upton.

As they neared Upton, they were startled by violent screams from a wood. Jones rushed into the wood, and beheld a woman stripped half naked, under the hands of a ruffian who was trying to hang her to a tree. Without more ado, Jones attacked this scoundrel with his cudgel, and saw to his amazement that it was Ensign Northerton, who, after a few lusty blows had been interchanged, took to his heels and disappeared among the trees. Jones unfastened the hapless woman and assisted her to a nearby inn.

Mrs. Waters—for such was her name—thanked him tenderly as soon as she recovered. She was a middle-aged lady of fascinating appearance, and quickly betrayed, by many arch glances, that she was by no means insusceptible to her handsome deliverer. From a sergeant at the inn, Jones learnt she was the wife of a Captain Waters, and had eloped with Ensign Northerton. Mrs. Waters privily confessed this amour to Jones, adding that the ensign had persuaded her to run away with him solely in order to murder her in some lonely place and then decamp with her jewels.

The flame that had arisen in the breast of our hero at the sight of her beauty was fanned now by pity and indignation; she in turn showed herself gratified by his ardour, and it was resolved between them that he should visit her room that night.

Meanwhile the unhappy Sophia had reached an extremity of suffering. Not only had she lost her beloved Jones, but she had to endure the assiduous court of Mr. Blifil, whom she loathed almost to nausea. "Father," she implored, seizing the brusque squire by the hand, "I cannot live with Mr. Blifil: to force me into this marriage would be killing me." "Then die and be damned," he cried, spurning her from him. "I am decided upon this match, and unless you consent to it, I will not give you a groat; no, though I saw you expiring with famine in the street."

A few days later, Sophia said dully to her maid, "Honour, I am determined to leave my father's house this very night. There is a lady of quality in London, a relation of mine, and I make no doubt of being very well and kindly received by her." After darkness had fallen, mistress and maid set out on foot along the road. By uncommon chance they encountered a fellow who had shown Jones the way to Bristol, and on knowing this, Sophia gave him a guinea to set her in the same direction. Steadfast inquiries aided her to trace our hero to the very inn at Upton where he was staying with Mrs. Waters, and here Sophia and her maid arrived in the early hours of the morning. Honour fell into talk with the landlady, who gave her such an encomium upon the beauty of a strange young man at the hostelry, that the maid had no doubt but it must be Mr. Jones. " Yonder is the squire's friend," said the landlady, pointing to Partridge, who was enjoying a pint of mulled ale in the parlour. Honour went up to Partridge, who informed her that Mr. Jones was indeed staying at the inn, but had retired to his bed. " Then wake him at once," said Honour; " my lady would speak to him, and I am sure Mr. Jones would be highly delighted." " Another time perhaps he might," answered Partridge, " but one woman is enough at once for a reasonable man." He accompanied this remark by a wink so expressive as to send Honour scurrying in alarm to her mistress.

" I can never believe this," Sophia interrupted her maid's torrent of abuse for Mr. Jones. She sent for the servant-girl, who revealed, in exchange for a guinea, the history of Mr. Jones's passion for Mrs. Waters. Sophia handed the girl her muff. " Take this to Mr. Jones's chamber," she said curtly, " and if the bed is empty, place it on it."

When Mr. Jones at length regained his bed—" Oh heavens," he cried out so loudly that Partridge rushed into the room, " how came this muff here? " " I saw it on the arm of one of two women who would have disturbed you," replied Partridge, " if I would have suffered them." " Where are they? " shouted Jones. " Many miles off, I believe, by this time," said Partridge.

Jones thereupon yelled at the poor fellow, now frightened out of his wits, to run downstairs and order him horses. Our hero dressed with the utmost dispatch, flew down the stairs, and was racing across the yard when he was gripped by the arm and swung round to find himself gazing into the empurpled face of Squire Western, who roared: " We have got the dog fox, I warrant the bitch is not far off."

Jones had some difficulty in protesting his ignorance of where the lady was, but at length the squire released him with a hearty curse, and, ordering horses for himself and his parson, Mr. Supple, who had accompanied him, set off in pursuit of his daughter.

Learning from an hostler that she had crossed the Severn, he likewise sped over the bridge, vowing the utmost vengeance against poor Sophia. After about two miles he pulled up in bewilderment at a crossroads.

The parson tried to console him. " Pogh! damn the slut! " answered the squire. " I am lamenting the loss of such a fine morning for hunting." As if fortune had decided to pity him, scarcely had he uttered the words than from a nearby field came the melodious choir of a pack of hounds in full cry. The squire's horse and its rider pricked up their ears. "She's gone, she's gone!" cried the squire, and without a moment's hesitation clapped spurs to his willing beast, and dashed into the field, hallowing and whooping.

The hounds ran very hard, and the squire pursued over hedge and ditch, completely forgetting his daughter. At length, after a few hours' riding, he arrived at the kill, and was invited to dinner by the master of the hunt. Squire Western was no match for his host that night, and after three bottles, retired to his bed "whistle drunk". In the morning he was soon persuaded to abandon the hopeless chase after his daughter, and returned to Somersetshire.

Jones had better fortune in the quest. He travelled post, allowing Partridge no time for sleep, and scarcely paused for food in his haste along a trail that led through Coventry, Daventry, Stratford, Dunstable, and St. Albans, where he found, to his dismay, that Sophia had taken the London road. He went on, however, to the metropolis, in faint hope of discovering her in one of the great houses of the fashionable quarter. These he visited daily, undaunted by the reproofs of haughty footmen. He also began to frequent the shows and public assemblies of the town, in the hope of discovering her.

His beauty of person was soon the talk of society, and many a fine lady revealed to him in that language of eyes that declares so much more than words that his attentions would not be rejected by them. Mr. Jones strove valiantly against such temptations, until one evening at a masque he met the ravishing Lady Bellaston, who persuaded him to court—and obtain— her favours in the privacy of her home.

One evening he called much earlier than she had expected. Mr. Jones was shown into a drawing-room to await her ladyship. Judge of his amazement when he saw, standing before a glass at the far end of the room, the vision of his lovely Sophia! Yes, it was indeed she, for the woman of quality she knew in the town was this very Lady Bellaston, who had received her into her home, and was projecting to marry her to a young and wealthy lord infatuated with her charms.

"Oh, my Sophia," cried Jones, falling upon his knees, "let me beseech your pardon." "My pardon," she exclaimed, recovering from her confusion. "Sure, sir, after what is

passed, you cannot expect, after what I have heard——"
" I scarce know what to say," interrupted Jones. " By
heavens! I scarce wish you should pardon me. Oh, my
Sophia, henceforth never cast away a thought on such a
wretch as I am! Let the remembrance of Upton blot me for
ever from your mind! "

Sophia stood trembling all this while. Her face was whiter
than snow and her heart was throbbing through her stays.

" To have my name traduced in public," she went on in a
low voice, " in inns, among the meanest vulgar! to have any
little favours that my unguarded heart may have too lightly
betrayed me to grant, boasted of there! nay, even to hear
that you had been forced to fly from my love! "

Nothing could have equalled Jones's surprise at these words
of Sophia. By adroit questioning, he presently found that her
supposing him guilty of so shocking an outrage against his love,
and her reputation, was entirely owing to Partridge's talk at
the inns before and including the one at Upton. He had no
very great difficulty in persuading her that he was entirely
innocent of an offence so foreign to his character, but she had a
great deal to hinder him from going instantly to his lodging and
putting Partridge to death, as he swore to do. This point
being cleared up, they soon found themselves so well pleased
with each other, that Jones let fall some words that sounded
like a proposal of marriage

" Oh, sir," she replied, " did not my duty to my father
forbid me to follow my own inclinations, ruin with you would
be more welcome than the most affluent fortune with another
man."

They arranged a further meeting, and Jones left the house
for his lodging. He was staying with a Mrs. Miller, a gentlewoman in modest circumstances, who lived on a small annuity
from Mr. Allworthy. Indeed, it was on this account that
Jones had recommended himself to her. Now, however, she
informed him that Mr. Allworthy had written to say he was
forthwith coming to London and would require the lodging.
Mrs. Blifil had lately died, and the good squire was anxious to
recover from his grief amid a change of scene. He would
bring with him young Mr. Blifil.

Squire Western had begun to despair of finding his truant
daughter, when he received one morning a letter from a distant
relation, who frequented the society in London. Her name
was Mrs. Fitzpatrick. She was a close friend of Lady Bellaston,

and through her visits to the house had discovered all the history of Sophia and Jones. Mrs. Fitzpatrick had become infatuated with our hero, and sought by her communication to the squire to remove her rival from the sphere of his affections.

Her efforts to entice Jones from his allegiance, though in vain, were nevertheless sufficient to awaken the suspicions of her husband. Mr. Fitzpatrick accosted Jones on the street, swords were drawn, and our hero ran the challenger through the body. He was instantly arrested, and dragged off to prison, there to await trial for murder.

Such was the news that greeted Mr. Allworthy upon his arrival at Mrs. Miller's lodging. The good man was perturbed beyond measure, but could only shake his head and say that a rogue so depraved must always end on the gallows.

But Mrs. Miller refused to believe in the guilt of our hero. She adored Jones for his many acts of kindness to her children. Determined to seek the truth of the case, she made inquiries far and wide. Jones swore that Mr. Fitzpatrick had attacked him first, and that he had drawn only in defence. Two seafaring men, however, who were passing at the time, declared Jones to be the aggressor.

Matters were at this pass, when Mrs. Waters, who had been Jones's mistress at Upton, called upon Mr. Allworthy with the revelation that the foundling he had turned from his door was his own nephew! "You doubtless remember, sir," she explained, " that Mr. Summer, the son of your friend, educated at your expense, who, after living a year in the house as if he had been your son, died there of the small-pox. Mr. Summer was the father of Mr. Jones, and his mother was no other than your sister, Miss Bridget. Just after your departure for London, Miss Bridget came to the house of my mother, and took me into her confidence. Mrs. Wilkins was sent away to a distant part of Dorsetshire to inquire into the character of a servant, and I alone attended Miss Bridget during the pains of her childbirth, returning immediately afterwards to my mother's home.

" Nor is that all. Your lawyer, Mr. Dowling, came to me a few days ago, and, mistaking me for Mr. Fitzpatrick's wife, told me I should be assisted with any money I wanted to carry on the prosecution of his murderer, by a worthy young gentleman, who had already persuaded two sailors to bear witness to the crime."

Mr. Allworthy thereupon sent for his lawyer, who at once

admitted he had bribed the witnesses at the instigation of Mr. Blifil. "Perhaps you would have acted otherwise," said Mr. Allworthy, "had you known that Mr. Jones is my nephew." "Indeed, sir, I did know it," replied Mr. Dowling, "but I thought, since you had said nought about the letter, you wished the matter to remain concealed." "What letter?" demanded Mr. Allworthy in amazement.

"Why, sir," answered Mr. Dowling, "the letter your sister gave me as she lay a-dying. She took me by the hand and said, ' Give this to Mr. Allworthy and tell him Mr. Jones is his nephew.' I delivered the letter and the message to Mr. Blifil, who said he would carry them both to you, which he hath since told me he did."

Mr. Allworthy stood aghast at this perfidy for some moments. Then he sent for his nephew, who, white-faced and trembling, was forced to admit the charge. Mr. Allworthy then told him he would make provision for him, but that he desired never to see him again.

Mr. Fitzpatrick was declared by the surgeon to be out of danger. As soon as he recovered sufficiently, he confessed that he had been the first to draw his sword, and Jones was instantly set at liberty.

Squire Western, who had recently arrived in town and taken his daughter into his lodging, was astounded by the news that Jones was Allworthy's nephew. He at once sought the young man out, and went up to him crying, "My old friend Tom, I am glad to see thee with all my heart! all past must be forgotten."

Together they made their way to the squire's lodging, Western slapped Jones on the back and told him to go into Sophia's room, and give him a hail as soon as all was settled. After a few minutes, however, Western's patience being at an end, he burst into the room, shouting, "Well! what, is it all over? Hath she appointed the day, boy?"

"What would my papa have me do?" cried Sophia. "What would I have thee do?" said Western, "why, gi'un thy hand this moment."

"I will be obedient to you, sir," cried Sophia. Jones fell on his knees in an agony of joy, while Western began to caper and dance about the room. Presently he stopped and roared, "Where the devil is Allworthy?" He rushed out of the room in quest of him, leaving the lovers to enjoy the first minutes of a bliss that was to endure for the rest of their lives.

MADAME BOVARY

By GUSTAVE FLAUBERT

Flaubert's greatest novel is a study of a certain type of woman so accurate that her name has been added to the nomenclature of psychology. "Bovaryism" is the term applied to the almost maniacal self-deception practised by numerous women who spend their lives dreaming of what might happen, what ought to happen—but which seldom does. But the novel is not a case-history. It is a vividly real story of life in a French provincial town whose uneventful background throws into stronger relief the violence of its protagonists' emotions.

IN the road opposite the farmhouse a man was standing. As he watched the shutters of the kitchen window, his heart beat fast and his whole body trembled.

Suddenly there came a clatter, and the window was flung open. So, after all, his dreams were being fulfilled: the arranged signal told Charles Bovary that Emma Rouault agreed to be his wife.

Emma wanted a midnight wedding by the light of torches, but old Rouault, the farmer, arranged for the traditional country ceremony; he invited forty-three of his friends.

The next day the couple went to Charles's home at Tostes, where he had a doctor's practice. He had mended old Rouault's broken leg and thereby gained a local reputation of being a first-rate doctor. Neither Emma nor her father knew the fracture was of the simplest kind.

Charles's cup of happiness was full. Dinner together, an evening stroll, her hands raised to smooth her dark hair, a glimpse of her straw hat hanging beside the window, made up a perpetual round of happiness for him.

For up till now, what had he got from life? At school he had been immured among companions richer or cleverer than himself who laughed at his country accent and jeered at his clothes. Afterwards, during his medical studies, lonely again, for he had never even been able to treat a shopgirl to an evening out. He had never had a mistress. Then he had married, a widow chosen for him by his mother, whose feet in bed were cold as icicles. She had left him a widower after fourteen months of marriage.

And now he possessed for life this beautiful, adorable creature. The universe did not extend for him beyond the circumference of her petticoat, and even so he reproached himself with not loving her as she deserved.

As for Emma, with arms kissed from finger-tips to shoulder, she pushed him away from her, half pleased, half vexed, as if he had been a clinging child.

Before their marriage, she thought she loved Charles. But when, afterwards, she missed the happiness that should have come, it seemed to her she must have been mistaken. More and more she wondered about the meaning of words that had seemed so beautiful to her in books, " felicity ", " passion ", " rapture ".

At thirteen, her father had sent her to a convent in Rouen. At first she enjoyed the life there among the good mild nuns; the enchanted quiet; moods of mystic languor induced by the exhalations of the altar-incense. Then, Confession; it was so much to her liking that she would draw it out by inventing peccadilloes. The preachers' mystic comparisons, " betrothed ", " bridegroom ", " eternal marriage ", starting from their context, stirred within her soul wells of unsuspected sweetness.

An old woman, who came to do their mending, secretly smuggled in novels for the older girls: tales about ladies swooning in pavilions, deeds in dark forests, vows, sighs, tears, courtiers valiant as lions and tender as lambs. She devoured them all. Her heroines were Mary Stuart, Joan of Arc, Heloïse, illustrious unfortunates.

But when her father came to fetch her away, she was, after all, not sorry to leave the convent; the Church appealed to her only because of the lily-laden mysticism it exhaled; sermons, prayers, and the disciplined regimen she found irksome.

When she got home, she amused herself at first ordering the household, but she quickly tired of the narrow daily round, and began to pine for the convent. When Charles first visited them, she already thought of herself as a disillusioned woman with nothing more to learn, nothing left to feel. The presence of Charles in the house altered all this, and she took the disturbance in her feelings for a sign that love, love she had up till now only read about, had come to her at last.

But Charles, she saw plainly now it was too late, in his black velvet frockcoat, long, narrow shoes and peaked hat, fell far short of her dream-husband. His conversation was as humdrum as a street pavement; it aroused nothing, emotion, laughter, or thought. And a man should understand everything, be an expert in all kinds of activities, be able to guide you safely over the raging ocean of passion, initiate you into all the refinements of life, unveil all its mysteries. But this man taught nothing, knew nothing, wished nothing. He thought the easy calm of the life he offered her was his gift to Emma; but it was one she resented.

She tried to make herself in love with him. On moonlit nights she took him into the garden, recited passionate poems and sang languishing airs to him; but neither poetry nor music dispelled the frightful *ennui* in her, or seemed to affect the complacency in him. She did not find it difficult to persuade herself that Charles's passion for her was not an extravagant one.

And then, at last, something happened: she was invited to a ball given by the Marquis D'Andervilliers at Vaubyessard.

Recalling that ball to mind became an absorbing occupation for her. She would wake up and immediately remind herself: " Ah, I was there a week—a fortnight—three weeks ago! " Gradually, the faces became confused; she forgot the tunes of the quadrilles; but while the details escaped her, the nostalgia remained.

In the early days of their marriage Emma would occupy herself and delight Charles by sketching and playing the piano. She was careful about her appearance, and even tried to introduce a dress reform in the rustic Charles. She used to be busy about the house, priding herself on keeping it trim. But with time her habits changed; she neglected her hobbies, left all household duties to the servant. She languished all day in her room, neither reading nor sewing, often not bothering to dress.

She became " difficult ", capricious; a pallor came into her cheeks, and she suffered from palpitations. Moods of feverish chatter alternated with torpid silences. She was always complaining about Tostes, and at length Charles decided to leave the village. It was not an easy decision to make; during the four years he had lived there he had built up quite a respectable practice.

After a good deal of reconnoitring, he picked on a large market town in the Neufchâtel arrondissement, Yonville-L'Abbaye.

When they left Tostes, Madame Bovary was pregnant.

It was dark when they reached their new home. This was the fourth time she had slept in a new place: there had been the first nights at the convent, Tostes, Vaubyessard. Each of those nights had marked the beginning of a new phase in her life. She did not believe the same things could happen in the same way in different places; therefore, so it seemed to her, since the days behind had been bad, those ahead would be better.

The change of residence brought many worries to Charles. Patients were slow to arrive, and lately he had spent a good deal of money on Emma's clothes; then there had been the expense of moving. But when he looked at Emma he was filled with joy and pride in the child she was to give him. His gratitude and the overwhelming tenderness he felt for her put all other thoughts out of his mind. At first Emma was bewildered with her condition; then this feeling changed into eagerness to know what it felt like to be a mother.

She wanted a son, dark and strong. This male child would be the condign recompense for all the vain, ineffectual days of her past life. But she bore a daughter.

She chose the name Berthe, remembering that was what a young woman she had admired at the ball had been called. The godfather, in default of old Rouault, who couldn't make the long journey, was the town chemist, Homais, proud son of his rationalistic age and busybody of the place. With this chemist there lodged a young solicitor's clerk, M. Leon, who was serving his articles before completing his studies for the Bar in Paris. At their first meeting Emma felt she was in the presence of a congenial spirit. He, too, had a nostalgia for the Paris boulevards and despised the country folk and their boorish ways; he loved poetry, where his taste coincided with hers—sentimental German lyrics; and the world of his choice, like hers, was made up of actors and music, rich clothes and refinement.

Life in the provincial town bored him to distraction; the arrival there of that romantically beautiful woman, so different from the others he knew, marked a red-letter day for him.

He visited the Bovarys several times, but when it appeared that Charles didn't particularly take to him, he was at a loss how to proceed between fear of being indiscreet and a desire of a seemingly impossible intimacy with Emma.

However, he had opportunities of meeting her nearly every

evening in the chemist's parlour, where Charles and Homais would foregather to play dominoes, and while they played and afterwards dozed off in stuffy complacence, Leon and Emma sat talking by the fire, reading poems together out of women's fashion papers, comparing notes on novels. In this way a bond grew up between them, formed from the constant interchange of romances they had read. M. Bovary, who was not given to jealousy, was not perturbed by the ripening friendship.

All at once Emma realized she had fallen in love with the young man. He was beautiful, she thought, with his pale languor and large blue eyes, with the lobe of his ear showing under a romantic lock of hair. She believed her love was reciprocated, and the age-old plaint welled from her heart, " If it had only been the will of Heaven ! " But then, why not? What was to prevent it?

The consciousness that she was in love brought a strange alteration in her. She gave up music altogether so that she could devote herself entirely to the house, took charge of Berthe, who had been looked after by a nurse since birth, lavished every attention on her husband. Outwardly, she was gentle, calm, reserved. But she was consumed with rage and hatred, and all her pent-up passion of resentment was directed against Charles, Charles who seemed oblivious of her anguish. If only he would have beaten her and given her a right to hate him, to revenge herself on him! Sometimes her thoughts surprised and terrified her, they were so monstrous.

She turned for a refuge to the Church. But the poor parish priest, overworked and harassed, had neither the time nor the perspicacity to take in the veiled hints she gave.

Her virtue seemed so unassailable to Leon that he gradually gave up hope of possessing her. He renounced her, and by so doing glorified her—the inaccessible Madonna. After that, life became impossible for him in Yonville, and he made up his mind to leave for Paris.

The departure of the lodger was a great event in the chemist's household, and gave occasion for a world of wise saws about the capital's temptations to young men. As for Emma, the parting filled her with an apathetic melancholy. Absence imparted to Leon an even greater attractiveness; he seemed in her memory taller, handsomer, more *distrait*, more charming then ever. He was present everywhere to her, his shadow haunted the walls of her house. She bitterly reproached herself for not making opportunities for him to possess her. She was seized with a desire to follow him to Paris, throw herself into his arms, crying, "It is I—I am yours!" But the difficulties of the project restrained her, and the frustration made her longings greater still.

The sad state of affairs at Tostes began all over again. Only, now she imagined herself to be unhappier by far, for she knew certainly that her grief would have no end. It seemed to her that a woman whose life was such a martyrdom was justified in some indulgence of her whims. She grew extravagant, spending large sums on frocks, toilet preparations, knick-knacks of all sorts. She determined to learn Italian, bought a whole set of dictionaries, grammars, courses, and never looked at them. She had frequent fainting fits and began to spit blood, but her only answer to Charles's anxiety was, "What does it matter?"

Wednesday was Market Day in Yonville, and Emma liked to watch the crowd from her window. Then one morning she noticed a gentleman in a green velvet coat and yellow gloves. It happened that one of his servants wished to be bled and he brought him along to see Charles. Emma acted as nurse and exchanged a word or two with the gentleman. She found out that he was Rudolf Boulanger, squire of the neighbouring estate of Houchette.

Rudolf left the doctor's house deep in thought. Madame Bovary appealed to him; he found her very pretty; he admired her fine teeth, her black eyes and her neat ankle; and her figure was slim and graceful as a Parisienne's. What a contrast to the husband! The doctor was certainly very stupid, and, besides, his nails were dirty and he hadn't shaved for three days at least. Easy to guess she must be tired of him, bored stiff. Her rightful place was Paris, where she should be dancing polkas, poor little woman! She must be gaping for love, like a carp on a kitchen-table does for water. Three words of gallantry and she would be his, no doubt about it. And what a tender, charming mistress she would make! The difficulty would be—getting rid of her.

Rudolf was thirty-four, brutal in temperament, with a good deal of astute common sense. He foresaw a number of difficulties that might embarrass intimacy with her. But those eyes! they pierced his heart like a gimlet. And she was pale; he adored pale women.

Before Rudolf got home, his mind was made up: he would possess her.

Their next meeting was at the Agricultural Show. And while the crowd listened to speeches from the mayor and aldermen, he led her to an empty room in the town hall from where, he told her, they could get a better view. He had gauged her to a nicety, and spoke to her of his anguished soul, the prey of dreams, fantasies, desires; of the tedium of his daily round and the longing for the woman of his dreams (here he looked expressively at Madame Bovary); of the insignificance of a man-made moral code compared to the eternity of passion, the most beautiful thing on earth and the source of heroism, enthusiasm, poetry, music—in short, of everything.

He was sitting at Emma's feet, on a low stool, arms clasped round his knees, face lifted towards hers, his body close. She was conscious of two things: tiny golden beams in his eyes radiating from black pupils; the perfume of his hair pomade—the same perfume her viscount dancing-partner at Vaubyessard had used. ?

She felt faint; it seemed to her she saw the coach that had taken Leon from Yonville. She thought she saw Leon himself, at her feet. And now it was that almost-forgotten waltz air that possessed her.

Yet, all through, she was conscious of that pervading perfume: Rudolf's hair pomade.

When his fingers found hers, she did not resist. Their lips were dry with a supreme desire. Their fingers intertwined naturally, forerunners of their desires.

It was not until six weeks afterwards that Rudolf called again at her house. He saw Emma go pale when he came in; knew he had judged things correctly by not returning too soon. He asked Charles casually if it might not be possible that riding would improve Madame Bovary's health. Charles, at his wit's end how to banish his wife's alarming symptoms, jumped at the idea.

But Emma didn't want to go riding. She protested vehemently. Her last line of defence was that, anyhow, she couldn't go riding without a habit. "You must get one made," Charles said. That decided it.

On their first ride together she let him take her.

At home, her room became a perpetual sanctuary where she could commune with her face in the mirror. She marvelled at the transfiguration in herself. Never before had her eyes held those still depths, so wide, profound. " I have a lover," she kept murmuring, " a lover ! " She marvelled, for it was as though a second puberty had come to her. The dam had burst and love rushed forth joying. She allowed herself to be carried on the flood, exulting in the freedom, at last.

They kept up a daily correspondence in secret; but she always found his letters too short. One morning, early, she felt she must see Rudolf. Charles had left the house before daybreak. She stole out over the fields, hurrying on without one look behind. She arrived all drenched with dew, and cast herself on her lover's bed.

All through the winter, two or three nights a week, Rudolf came into their garden. She waited in an anguish of expectation until Charles had gone to bed. Their love nest was the old arbor with its rickety seat, where formerly Leon had sat and adored her on summer evenings. She never thought of Leon now.

There were times when Rudolf thought she was growing rather too sentimental, with her insistance of an exchange of miniatures and locks of hair. She asked him once for a real wedding ring. Still, she was lovely; and he had possessed few women so ingenuous in love. Love like theirs, without debauchery, held the piquancy of novelty; it flattered his pride and fed his sensuality. The enthusiasm with which she abandoned herself, though it shocked his bourgeois good sense, charmed him in his heart of hearts because he was the object of it. And then, sure of being loved, his attitude gradually changed. His tender words and passionate caresses were things of the past; he scarcely concealed his indifference.

Emma repented. She went so far as to wonder why it was she detested Charles, and if it wouldn't be better to try to love him. If she couldn't do that, then perhaps she could admire him for his efficiency as a doctor?

It happened that the chemist had for some time been trying to persuade Charles to experiment with a new operation on the club-footed errand boy at the hotel. Now, with Emma's encouragement added to the pestering of the chemist, much against his will, Charles decided to risk it. The operation was a complete failure; the poor boy's leg had to be amputated. Overcome with humiliation, Emma bought him a most expensive wooden leg. Ever afterwards the sound of that artificial limb creaking and clumping along the pavements made Charles turn and fly for fear of meeting his victim.

Emma's disillusionment had reached its limit. She flung herself with renewed ardour, fed with all her hatred and resentment, into her adulterous liaison. Now she threw all discretion to the winds, defied appearances, and often left her lover's house in broad daylight. She lavished expensive presents on him, and when she could not pay for them established credit with the town's ill-famed pawnbroker, M. L'Heureux. Once she went so far as to intercept the settlement of one of her husband's bills.

Then she had a frightful scene with Charles's mother, who had come to live with them. Mme. Bovary was anxious about her son's happiness, and Emma's behaviour shocked her more and more.

The result was that Emma made up her mind she could not live with her husband any longer. She implored Rudolf to take her away to a far country where they could live in unhampered enjoyment of their love.

Rudolf had no intention of agreeing to that, but he was at a loss to give satisfactory reasons. So he allowed Emma to make all the preparations, and then, on the eve of their planned departure, he sent her a carefully-couched letter in which he told her of his great renunciation in not allowing her to accompany him and embark on an adventure she must sooner or later bitterly repent.

They only just managed to prevent Emma throwing herself out of a window. A desperate attack of brain-fever followed, and the Last Sacrament was administered.

Charles lived through a period of hell. It seemed on the one hand that his beloved wife, the life of his life, was going to leave him for ever. At the same time bills he had no funds to meet poured in upon him. Emma's illness, the extravagant purchases she had made for Rudolf, drove him into the clutches of M. L'Heureux, the usurer. He had to borrow to pay his debts, and he knew he could never make the loans good.

But Emma did not die. Slowly, by imperceptible degrees, she recovered. When she was able to go out, Charles, to distract her, took her to Rouen to hear a famous tenor. In the opera house they met Leon.

After completing his studies in Paris, he had accepted a clerkship in the office of a Rouen solicitor. He had matured a little, for his escapades with Paris shop-girls and harmless debauches with his fellow-students had given him at least an air of outward confidence. But he was still shy, really.

Leon, all through, had preserved an image of Emma. She had represented for him as it were a vague promise, suspended in the future like a golden fruit depending from some exotic tree.

He easily arranged for Charles to persuade Emma to stay over in Rouen for the next day's performance. Then, waiting his opportunity, he found her alone in her hotel room and forced himself to tell her of his love, his dreams during his unhappy absence from her. "I always suspected it," she told him.

Leon's shyness was more dangerous for her than the bold approaches of Rudolf.

All the same, that evening she wrote him an interminable letter, saying all was over between them, and they must not for their happiness' sake meet again. But she did not know his address, and so in order to deliver her letter she had to go to the cathedral, where they had fixed a meeting-place the previous day.

Leon hailed a cab. She would not get in. But when Leon told her it was done in Paris, she yielded.

And during the drive she became his mistress.

Once more, it was Charles himself who opened the way to his wife's guilty passion. By this time, M. L'Heureux had them both completely in his power. Conceiving that the best, the only, way to get his money back was to concentrate on Emma, he proposed to her that she should get a power of attorney to settle the matter in her husband's name. She had no wish to be made responsible. But then she realized that this was a legal matter and required expert advice. She told Charles she did not know whom to consult. And he, poor man, fell into the trap: Leon was the very man, he thought.

So she went to Rouen to consult Leon. She stayed there three days, their " honeymoon ".

On her return, she seemed to be consumed with a musical fervour. The trouble was, her fingers had grown stiff through want of practice and she had forgotten the scales. Charles suggested she should take lessons in Rouen.

They rented a hotel room in Rouen and called it their " home ". Inside, moving amongst the faded upholstery of the furniture, they really did feel at home there.

At Yonville, her domestic life returned full cycle. The " Rudolf time " began there again. She was charming and attentive to her husband, who thought himself the happiest of men.

As time went on, Emma felt more and more need to resort

to external aids to keep passion alive. For, though she was for ever promising herself ineffable felicity at the next journey's end, she had always to confess to herself, returning in the train, that she had not felt anything out of the ordinary. These disappointments seemed to engender new hopes, for she would go back to her lover on the next trip more eager and impassioned than ever. She would undress brutally, tearing herself open. She tiptoed, barefoot, to the door, to see if it was really shut. Then, pale and serious, without speaking a word, she would throw herself with one movement on Leon's breast, shuddering.

Leon did not wish to question her, but seeing her like that, so expert in all the artifices of passion, he could only suppose she had passed through the whole gamut of love and pain. That was all to the good; but what he resented was the increasing absorption of his personality by hers. Hers was a constant victory, and he begrudged it. It was he who was her mistress. Besides this, his employer, who had found out about the liaison, warned him more than once of the dangers he was running of ruining his career for a woman.

And Emma, too, was not satisfied. She puzzled over the insufficiency of life, how everything she turned to for support crumbled beneath her. All life's promises turned into lies. Each smile hid a yawn, there was a curse gnawing at every joy, and satiety lurked unseen in every promised pleasure; love's sweetest kisses left on your lips the bitterness of yearning for unattainable delight.

One night when she returned home from Rouen there was a letter waiting for her, written on grey paper; her eye picked out phrases in it, " In virtue of the seizure in execution of judgment "—" within twenty-four hours without fail "—" to pay the sum of eight thousand francs." The vastness of the amount reassured her. It must be just another of M. L'Heureux's tricks.

But the fact was that in one way and another, running up accounts, borrowing and then renewing her loans, she had ended up by owing the usurer such a neat little sum that he needed it at once for an important investment.

The truth came to her at last, and with it panic. Charles would see the bailiffs seize upon his effects, dismember his house; his career would be ruined, and all because of her.

She tried to melt the heart of M. L'Heureux, even went on her knees to him. It was no good. Then she tried Leon. But the magnitude of her debts staggered him. Perhaps a thousand, he muttered, but made no effort to raise even that. Then she tried the solicitor in Yonville, but when he replied that he expected a repayment in kind, she ran from his office.

She went to Rudolf, oblivious to the fact that she was offering herself up to a prostitution precisely similar to that which she had rejected in horror at the solicitor's house.

But Rudolf could not help her either.

Emma knew then there was only one way out. She stole into the chemist's house and swallowed some arsenic.

When he came home Charles found her writing a letter. She seemed quite calm. Then she lay down on the bed. She slept and woke up with a bitter taste in her mouth. Curiously, she studied her reactions. No, she was not suffering. She could hear the fire crackling, the ticking of the clock, Charles's breathing at the bedhead. Only she was thirsty, so thirsty. She asked for water, and suddenly vomited.

Softly, almost as if he were caressing her, Charles stroked her stomach. She uttered a sharp cry. He recoiled, terror-stricken.

Her face turned blue, oozed drops of sweat. Her teeth began to chatter and she looked vaguely around. Once or twice she smiled. Then her moaning increased and suddenly she shrieked aloud.

They sent for two doctors. But there was nothing to be done. She began to vomit blood. Brown spots broke out all over her body. She shrieked out in agony. Her pulse slipped between the fingers like a harp-string taut to breaking-point.

The priest came and administered the extreme unction.

Soon afterwards she died.

It was Charles's wish that she should be buried in her wedding-dress, with white shoes and a wreath. They spread her hair over her shoulders, and laid her in a triple coffin of oak, mahogany and lead.

Emma's death was the end for Charles, too. He never went out, saw no one, refused to receive his patients. Passers-by caught glimpses of him in his garden, ragged, unkempt, wild, weeping aloud as he paced his garden.

One evening his daughter found him dead in the arbor, with a long strand of black hair in his hand.

THE VICAR OF WAKEFIELD

By OLIVER GOLDSMITH

Four important omissions in this digest are the incidental poems: " The Hermit", " Edwin and Angelina", " Elegy on the Death of a Mad Dog ", and " When Lovely Woman Stoops to Folly ". These charming verses, which should be read, help to alleviate an atmosphere of misery and misfortune that very nearly becomes comic to modern eyes. Nothing is allowed to come right with the unfortunate vicar until the very end of the book. In spite of this artificiality, however, Goldsmith's limpid yet polished English transforms a nearly-ridiculous parable into a masterpiece.

I WAS ever of opinion, that the honest man who married and brought up a large family, did more service than he who continued singly and only talked of population. I thus set an example to my parish, early marrying a good-natured, well-read, housewifely woman; rearing a family in the path of affection and duty. Our eldest son was named George, after his uncle, who left us ten thousand pounds. The second child, a girl, was called Olivia, and the next Sophia. Following Sophia came Moses, and after an interval of twelve years, we had two sons more. My happiness in the bosom of my family was exceeded only by that of my wife, for we loved each other tenderly, and our fondness increased as we grew old. Olivia, now about eighteen, possessed a luxuriant beauty, whilst her sister Sophia was soft, modest, and alluring. George was bred at Oxford, as I intended him for one of the learned professions, whilst Moses, whom I designed for business, received a sort of miscellaneous education at home.

My eldest son, just upon leaving college, became engaged to Miss Arabella Wilmot, the beautiful daughter of my old friend and neighbour, who was a dignitary of the church, and in circumstances to give her a large fortune. I had composed a tract, in defence of my favourite monogamist principle, which in the pride of my heart I showed to Mr. Wilmot, feeling assured of his approbation, but too late I discovered that he was most violently attached to the contrary opinion, being at that time actually courting a fourth wife. As may be expected, this produced an acrimonious dispute between us, which was interrupted by one of my relatives. "The merchant in town," said he, "in whose hands your money was lodged has gone off to avoid a statute of bankruptcy, and is thought not to have left a shilling in the pound."

It would be endless to describe the different sensations of both families at this piece of news; misfortune had us in its grip, but what others felt was slight to what the lovers appeared to endure. Mr. Wilmot, nothing loth, determined by this to break off the match. With the remains of my lost fortune I purchased a small farm of twenty acres, and a fortnight later removed thence some seventy miles, first despatching my eldest son to seek his fortune in London, where his address would stand him in good stead.

About the beginning of autumn, on a holiday—for I kept such intervals as relaxation from labour—as we sat outside, the girls forming a small concert with voices and guitars, a stag bounded nimbly past, which by its panting seemed pressed by the hunters, who also ere long passed swiftly by. A young gentleman, however, of genteel appearance, stopped short, and having first regarded us, gave his horse to a servant in attendance, and approached us with a superior, careless air. Saluting, he let us know that his name was Thornhill, owner of the estates which lay for some extent around us, and nephew to that renowned, though eccentric, philanthropist, Sir William Thornhill. His easy address and fine clothes found no repulse from us; indeed, the whole family seemed earnest to please him. At the approach of evening he took leave, requesting permission to renew his visit, which, as he was our landlord, we readily agreed to.

As soon as he was gone, my wife said, "Tell me, Sophy my dear, what do you think of our visitor? Don't you think he seemed to be good-natured?" "Immensely so, indeed, dear mamma," replied she. "I think he has a great deal to say upon everything, and is never at a loss; and the more trifling the subject, the more he has to say." "Yes," cried Olivia, "he is well enough for a man, but, for my part, I don't much like him; he is so extremely impudent and familiar, and on the guitar he is shocking." This I interpreted by contraries; that Sophia internally despised, as much as Olivia secretly admired him. I was not prepossessed in his favour, and said so, admonishing my womenfolk against fortune-hunting, when I was interrupted by a servant from the 'Squire, who, with his compliments, sent us a side of venison, and a promise to dine with us some days after. I was silenced, but reflected that virtue which requires to be ever guarded is scarce worth the sentinel.

Whilst part of the venison was being prepared for supper, who should appear but Mr. Burchell, known in our neighbourhood as the " Poor Gentleman ", and whose acquaintance we had made on our journey hither.

He supped, and spent the night with us, the next morning rising early to assist at saving an aftergrowth of hay. At which occupation, however, I could not help noticing his assiduity in helping Sophia in her part of the task, but I had too good an opinion of her understanding, and was too well convinced of her ambition, to be uneasy about a man of broken fortune, be he but yet scarce thirty.

All was bustle and preparation on the day when we entertained our young landlord, who arrived in company with two friends and his chaplain. He politely ordered his servants to the next alehouse, but my wife insisted on entertaining them all, for which, by the by, our family was pinched for three weeks after. The evening passed pleasantly enough, in good-humoured dispute and discussion, but as Mr. Thornhill directed his looks and conversation almost entirely to Olivia, it became no longer a doubt that she was the object that induced him to be our visitor.

The day following we were again visited by Mr. Burchell, and although he more than repaid our hospitality with his toil and lightheartedness, I began to be displeased with the frequency of his return. We were all reclining in the field round a temperate repast, when Mr. Thornhill's chaplain appeared to inform us that his master had provided music and refreshments, and intended that night giving the young ladies a ball by moonlight on the grass plot before our door. From this entertainment Mr. Burchell excused himself, and he had scarce taken his leave, ere Mr. Thornhill arrived with a couple of under-gentlemen, and two ladies richly dressed, whom he introduced as women of very great distinction and fashion from town. Chairs being short, he proposed that every gentleman should sit in a lady's lap, but to this proposal I strongly objected, notwithstanding a look of disapprobation from my wife. My neighbour Flamborough's daughters appeared, flaunting with red top knots, and the evening passed merrily; the moon shone bright and our music consisted of two fiddles, with a pipe and tabor. Some awkwardness was caused when Mr. Thornhill said, "My fortune is pretty large; love, liberty, and pleasure are my maxims; but curse me, if a settlement of half my estate could give my charming Olivia pleasure, it should be hers; and the only favour I would ask in return would be to add myself to the benefit." I answered this thinly disguised base proposal with dignity and spirit, but was soon sorry for my warmth when the young gentleman, grasping my hand, swore he commended my spirit though he disapproved my suspicions. At last the two fashionable ladies, apprehensive of catching cold, moved to break up the ball, one expressing herself in a very coarse manner, observing, "that by the living jingo I am all of a muck sweat". Such lapse we excused with our own ignorance of high life, for indeed they talked of but little else, save such as pictures, Shakespeare, taste, and the musical glasses.

We accepted neighbour Flamborough's invitation to celebrate Michaelmas Eve with his family, and Mr. Burchell, who was of the party, organized the games with his usual address. "Hunt the slipper" was in riotous progress, when, confusion on confusion, who should enter the room but our two great acquaintances from town, Lady Blarney and Miss Carolina Wilhelmina Amelia Skeggs! They had been to our house to see us, and, finding us from home, came after us hither. To every remark they made, Mr. Burchell, who sat with his face to the fire, cried out, "Fudge," an expression which displeased us all, and damped the rising spirit of the conversation. It transpired that both the Peeress and her friend were needing a companion, one wishing to pay thirty pounds a year, and one twenty-five guineas, as salary.

My wife, first studying my countenance for approval, then petitioned a plea on behalf of our daughters, eloquently describing their accomplishments, and indeed I could not help being of the opinion that two such places would fit them exactly, and the money be useful. The ladies agreed to consider the proposal, and left us in a high state of conjectural excitement, for it would mean the girls going to London, where my wife anticipated them meeting all sorts of acquaintances of taste, eligible in the matrimonial market.

I now began to find that all my long and painful lectures upon temperance, simplicity, and contentment were entirely disregarded. The distinctions paid us by our betters awaked that pride which I had but laid asleep. My wife and daughters now proposed to sell our Colt, and buy us a horse that would carry a single or a double upon occasion, and make a pretty appearance at church, or upon a visit. They overbore my scruples, and a fair but little distant happening upon the following day, my son Moses departed for it, mounted upon the Colt, with a deal box before him to bring home groceries in.

He was scarce gone when a footman arrived with a card for my daughters, importing that the two ladies had received such pleasing accounts from Mr. Thornhill of us all, that after a few previous inquiries they hoped to be perfectly satisfied. After noon Mr. Burchell arrived with various small presents, and we could not avoid communicating our happiness to him. After reading the note he shook his head, observing that an affair of this sort demanded the utmost circumspection. His diffidence angered my wife, who ranted at him with more abuse than wit, that I was fain to change the conversation, when Moses returned. He came slowly on foot, and sweating under the deal box which he had strapt round his shoulders like a peddler.

" I have sold him," he cried, " for three pounds five shillings and two pence." " Well done," returned his mother. " I knew you would touch them off. Between ourselves, three pounds five shillings and two pence is no bad day's work. Come, let us have it then."

" I have brought back no money," replied he. " I have laid it all out in a bargain, and here it is. A gross of green spectacles, with silver rims and shagreen cases."

At first she seemed faint, then flew into a passion, " You have parted with the Colt," she fumed, " and brought us back nothing but a gross of green paltry spectacles. A fig for the silver rims, I dare swear they won't sell for above half the money at the rate of broken silver, five shillings an ounce." " You need be under no uneasiness," I said, " about selling the rims, for they are not worth sixpence. I perceive they are only copper varnished over."

It was found that our remaining horse was useless for the plough without his companion, so it was decided that as my daughters must be equipped for their journey to town, which according to Mr. Thornhill was certain, I should visit the fair myself to prevent imposition, and dispose of him. This was the first mercantile transaction of my life. Arrived at the fair, so many came up and crabbed the poor beast, that I became ashamed of him myself. Alas, I did no better, indeed worse, than Moses. I met an old and devoutly learned man, whose venerable aspect filled me with respect. Even more so when in conversation it transpired he knew and admired my few writings. There's no limit to the amount of flattery an author can swallow. I showed him the horse and, in fine, we struck a bargain. He produced, and asked me to change, a thirty-pound note. I was unable to do so, so the old gentleman, saying he was an old friend of my neighbour Flamborough, offered me a draft upon him, payable at sight. A draft upon my neighbour was to me the same as money. The draft was signed, and Mr. Jenkinson, the old gentleman, his man Abraham and my horse old Blackberry, trotted off well pleased with each other. Imagine my chagrin, when I called upon Mr. Flamborough on my way home, to honour the bill, to find that it was spurious and that I had been robbed by Ephraim Jenkinson, the same rascal that sold the spectacles to Moses yesterday. I was greatly mortified, returning home in fear and trembling, but alas! the family were no way disposed for battle. The London trip was off, some malicious person had given iniquitous reports of us to the ladies, who had that day set out for the town.

Perplexity as to our ill-wisher was still in our minds, when one of our little boys brought in a letter-case, found whilst he was playing on the green. It was quickly known to belong to Mr. Burchell, and amongst other things was a sealed note, superscribed, " the copy of a letter to be sent to the ladies at Thornhill Castle "! Although I was against it, at the joint instigation of the family I broke the seal, and read as follows :—

LADIES,

I am informed for a truth, that you have some intention of bringing two young ladies to town, whom I have some knowledge of, under the character of companions. As I would neither have simplicity imposed upon, nor virtue contaminated, I must offer it as my opinion, that the impropriety of such a step will be attended with dangerous consequences. Take, therefore, the admonition of a friend and seriously reflect on the consequences of introducing infamy and vice into retreats where peace and innocence have hitherto resided.

Our doubts were now at an end; although there was much applicable to both sides, the malicious meaning was obvious.

The author appeared just as I finished reading, and I resolved
to tackle him directly. I fixed my eye steadfastly upon him.

" And how could you," said I, " so basely, so ungratefully
presume to write this letter? "

" And how came you," replied he, with look of unparalleled
effrontery, " so basely presume to open this letter? Don't
you know now, I could hang you all for this? All that I
have to do is to swear at the next Justice's that you have
been guilty of breaking open the lock of my pocket-book,
and so hang you all up at his door."

This piece of unexpected insolence raised me to such a
pitch, that I could scarce govern my passion. I bade him
be gone; threw him his pocket-book, which he took with the
utmost composure, and left us quite astonished at the serenity
of his assurance.

After his departure the visits of Mr. Thornhill became more
frequent and prolonged. His behaviour avowed his passion
for Olivia, but he adroitly parried all my wife's wiles to bring
him to declare an honourable love. One there was who did,
however. Mr. Williams, a farmer in easy circumstances,
prudent and sincere, bespoke me for her hand. I consulted
with her, and, without forcing her preference, she agreed to
marry him in four weeks' time, unless the 'Squire should
declare in his turn. He made no effort, however, to restrain
her nuptials, until, within four days of the appointed time,
as my little family at night were gathered round a charming
fire, little Dick came running in crying, " Oh, papa, papa,
my sister Livy is gone off with two gentlemen in a post-
chaise ! "

Consternation, amazement, and confusion shook us to the
marrow at this piece of news. Passion seized me, as I reached
my pistols to go in search of her betrayer; but the admonitions
of my son, and the tears of my wife restrained me. The
night passed in misery; and next morning I set forth to
find her, armed but with my Bible and staff. My suspicions
fell first upon our young landlord, but making my way to his
seat, I fell in with one of my parishioners, who said he saw a
young lady resembling Olivia in a post-chaise with a gentleman, whom by the description I could only guess to be Mr.
Burchell, and that they drove very fast. I determined to
find out for certain and continued my way.

After some two hours walking, I fell in with a strolling
player whose cart contained scenes and other theatrical

furniture; he was proceeding to the next village in advance, the company following the next day. We discoursed upon the theatre very pleasantly, until such time as we reached his destination, where I resolved to spend the night. In the common room of the inn we were accosted by a well-dressed gentleman, whom I set down for a parliament-man at least. He insisted the Player and I sup with him at his house, and after a short walk he ushered us into one of the most magnificent mansions I had yet seen. An elegant supper was brought in; two or three ladies in easy dishabille were introduced, and the conversation began with some sprightliness. Politics engaged our attention for some time, when suddenly a footman rapped upon the door, and the ladies cried out, "As sure as death, there is our master and mistress come home!" It seems that our entertainer all this time was no less than the butler, borrowing his master's shoes; nothing could exceed my dismay upon seeing the gentleman and his lady enter, when whom should I next see enter but my dear Miss Arabella Wilmot, who was formerly designed to be married to my son George, but whose match was broken off as before related. She was delighted to see me, and on hearing my name, Doctor Primrose, her aunt and uncle welcomed me with cordial hospitality. They prevailed upon me to stay some days, and the day following we went to see the players perform in a barn converted to a theatre. We were sat in the front row, when let parents think of my sensations by their own, I recognized my own son George acting Horatio. He was about to speak when he perceived Miss Wilmot and me, and instead stood speechless and immovable. Miss Wilmot, pale and trembling, desired me to conduct her back to her uncle's, who, when he heard our story, at once sent his coach and an invitation for him. Mr. Arnold gave him the kindest reception, and I received him with my usual transport; for I could never counterfeit false resentment. Supper over, he told us his adventures; of his misery as an unsuccessful writer in London; his acting as familiar dependant and fighting a duel on his employer's behalf; an attempt at teaching languages in Holland; wandering across France as a minstrel; a visit to Spain, then walking and working his passage home, and finally his joining the troup of actors in which we saw him. As he concluded his recital, Mr. Thornhill was announced. He seemed rather taken aback at seeing my son and me, but after a short time his presence increased the general good humour. He told me that he left my family well, and was surprised I had no news of Olivia.

We continued here a week, the attentions of our landlord being most marked to Miss Wilmot, who seemed to hear them rather in compliance with the will of her aunt than from real inclination. Mr. Thornhill's kindness reached its height when he informed me that he had procured an ensign's commission for my son; the fee of three hundred pounds he had got reduced to one hundred, and he offered to advance me this amount. This was a favour we wanted words to express our sense of; I readily therefore gave my bond for the money and testified as much gratitude as if I never intended to pay. The next day George departed to take up his commission; neither the fatigues and dangers he was going to encounter, nor the friends and mistress—for Miss Wilmot really loved him—he was leaving behind, in any way damped his spirits. I gave him all I had, my blessing.

The day after I also left the good family that had been so kind to me, and returned towards home, despairing of ever finding my daughter more. Within twenty-five miles of home I put up at an inn for the night, and whilst conversing with the landlord overheard his wife loudly upbraiding a female lodger upstairs. "What, you strumpet," screamed the virago, "to come and take upon an honest house without cross or coin to bless yourself with! Come along, I say!" "Oh dear madam," cried the stranger, "pity me, pity a poor abandoned creature, for one night, and death will do the rest!" I instantly recognized the voice of Olivia, and flew to her rescue. She told me that in all good faith she was married to Mr. Thornhill, but that after the ceremony, which was performed by a Popish priest, she found it not to be binding, for he had been married already six or eight times by the same priest. Indeed, he introduced her to two unhappy women, whom he had similarly deceived, and now lived in contented prostitution. He proposed the same life to her, which she resisted, finally fleeing from the house when offered by him to a young baronet.

It was near midnight the next night, silent and still, when I knocked with happiness upon my own door, but suddenly the house burst out in a blaze of fire, every aperture red with conflagration. The family awoke at my cry, and came running out, naked, and we stood looking on helplessly. With a shock I realized that my two babes were still within, and dashing into the inferno, I caught them both in my arms and snatched them through the fire as far as possible, while just as I got out, the roof sank in. Their mother laughed and wept by turns, whilst I found that my arm to the shoulder was scorched in a terrible manner. My goods, amongst which were the notes I had reserved for my daughters' fortunes, were entirely consumed. The goodness and charity of our neighbours furnished us with necessities; and we moved into one of our outhouses, a wretched dwelling enough, but yet home to the pious and cheerful heart.

My wife received Olivia but coolly, for women have a much stronger sense of female error than men, and the poor girl seemed devoid of all spirit. She told us that Mr. Burchell, far from being the knave I had suspected, had done all in his power to dissuade her from her designs, and been responsible, by what unseen power she knew not, for the rapid return to town of the two great ladies, who were not great at all, but women of the town in the employ of Mr. Thornhill. That gentleman himself called on us with the most barefaced effrontery and assurance, saying there had been nothing criminal in his conduct, and that if Olivia had sense enough a proper husband could soon be found, whilst he would be most happy to remain her lover. This base proposal called forth bitter and angry reproaches from me, whereat he changed his tune, threatening to call upon the bond he gave me for my son, and claim the rent due, which owing to my present misfortunes I had not.

We soon found he had not threatened in vain. His steward called for the rent, and not receiving it appraised my cattle, and sold them for half their value. The day after, the ground heavily laden with snow, two officers of justice arrived, made me their prisoner, and bade me prepare to go with them to the county gaol, eleven miles off. I felt weak and ill, with a fever from my burns, but they were adamant. My family expeditiously packed our few belongings, and within an hour we set forth slowly on foot. Some hours before night we reached the mean town. I was allowed to sup with my family at an inn, and then attended the officers to the prison, which consisted of one large apartment, strongly grated and paved with stone, common to felons and debtors alike at certain hours, whilst all prisoners had separate cells where they were locked for the night.

As I sat in a corner apart, feeling far from cheerful, I was joined by a fellow-prisoner, who, finding I had made no provision for a bed and that I was like then to sleep only upon the straw allowed, offered me half of his bedclothes. Touched by his generosity, I thanked him. He then began to discourse in a seemingly learned manner upon the world, but " I ask pardon, sir," cried I, " for interrupting so much learning; but I think I have heard all this before. Did we not meet at Wellsbridge Fair, and is not your name Ephraim Jenkinson? " Yes, sir," returned he, " I bought your horse, but forgot to pay for him. Your neighbour Flamborough is the only prosecutor I am afraid of at the next Assizes, for he intends to swear positively against me as a coiner. Ah, sir! had I but bestowed half the pains in learning a trade that I have in learning to be a scoundrel, I might have been a rich man at this day. But rogue as I am, still may I be your friend, and that perhaps when you least expect it." We were interrupted by the roll call, after which I was locked in my cell. After my usual meditations, and having praised my heavenly corrector, I laid myself down, and slept with the utmost tranquillity.

Thus several weeks passed. The execrations, lewdness, and brutality of the prisoners disgusted me, and I endeavoured to reform them by reading and exhortation; at first I met nothing but ridicule, but later earned some success. My wife and family endeavoured to persuade me to let Mr. Thornhill know that I would not oppose his marriage to Miss Wilmot, but this I positively refused to do whilst I had breath in my body. Olivia's health declined; my soul was bursting from its prison to go to her assistance, when news came that she was dead! I was at length persuaded that, in the interests of my own health, as well as my family, there was now no longer any need to disapprove the marriage.

My son Moses took my letter of submission, but returned with a message that it was too late and unnecessary; that Mr. Thornhill had heard of an application I had made to his uncle, and that all future applications should be addressed to his attorney. " Well, sir," said I to my fellow-prisoner, " you now discover the temper of the man that oppresses me; but I shall soon be free in spite of all his bolts to restrain me. As I draw daily nearer to an abode which looks brighter as I approach, my only thoughts are for my orphans." Just as I spoke my wife appeared with looks of terror, accompanied by another woman, who informed us that as my wife and daughter

Sophia and herself were walking in the great road a little way out of the village, a post-chaise and pair drove up to them and stopped. Upon which a well-dressed man, not Mr. Thornhill, got out, clasped my daughter round the waist, forced her in, bidding the postilion drive on, so that they were out of sight before my wife and family had time to collect their wits. This was a cruel blow, but another sorrow followed fast upon this one's heel. We were lamenting Sophie's abduction when the door of my cell flew open amidst much noise, and a man entered, bloody, wounded, and fettered with the heaviest irons. Compassion changed to horror when I recognized my son George. He explained that he received a letter from my wife written in the bitter ness of anger, in which she described our woes, and requested him to avenge our cause. Immediately he sent a challenge to Mr. Thornhill, which he answered not in person, but by sending four of his domestics to seize the challenger. A fight ensued in which my son desperately wounded one, but was captured by the others. " The coward," continued George, " is determined to put the law in execution against me; the proofs are undeniable; I have sent a challenge, and as I am the first transgressor upon the statute, I see no hope of pardon. But you have often charmed me with your lessons in fortitude; let me now, sir, find them in your example." With the fall of night George was removed to a stronger cell; I therefore laid me down, and one of my little ones sat by my bedside reading; we were disturbed by the gaoler, a kindly man, who informed me, with haste and looks of pleasure, that my daughter was found. Moses came running in a moment after crying out that his sister Sophie was below, and coming up with our old friend Mr. Burchell. She told us that in her struggles with her captor she succeeded in breaking the canvas of the chaise, and having entreated several passing vehicles in vain for help, she at last espied Mr. Burchell. At her cries he ran up by the side of the horses, and with one blow knocked the postilion to the ground. The horses stopped, and the ruffian leapt out, sword in hand, but Mr. Burchell shivered this to pieces with his staff; he then pursued the man for some distance, but he was a great runner and escaped.

I expressed my gratitude to her deliverer, and apologized for the way in which we had previously misjudged him. He graciously accepted all I said, but sternly rebuked my son George for his behaviour. I hastened to explain my wife's imprudent letter, to which he replied with great dignity.

We now found to our surprise that our poor, harmless, and amusing Mr. Burchell was none other than the celebrated Sir William Thornhill, to whose virtues and singularities scarce any were strangers. Sophia, who a few moments before thought him her own, perceiving the immense distance to which he was removed by fortune, was unable to conceal her tears. He then asked Sophia if she could describe the man who abducted her, so that he could advertise for him; Mr. Jenkinson, who was standing by, thought he knew him by her description, and offered, by Sir William's permission, to go and fetch him with two gaolers. He departed as we sat down to dinner ordered by the baronet, who first wrote a prescription to relieve my arm, which continued very painful. Ere we had finished, Sir William sent for his nephew, who entered, as usual with a smile. He stated his case clearly and simply. "I appeared, sir," he said, "with Doctor Primrose's daughter at some places of public amusement; thus what was levity, scandal called by a harsher name, and it was reported I had debauched her. I waited on him in person, willing to clear the thing to his satisfaction, and he received me only with insult and abuse. As for the rest, if he has contracted debts, it is the business of my attorney and steward to proceed as they have done; and I see no hardship or injustice in pursuing the most legal means of redress. I defy him to contradict a single particular. As for his son, I have two witnesses to prove his challenge, and one of my servants wounded dangerously. I will see public justice done!" Our attention was called off by the entrance of Jenkinson and the two gaolers, with a tall man exactly answering the description given by my daughter of the ruffian who had carried her off. The moment Squire Thornhill perceived Jenkinson and his prisoner, he shrank back with terror, and would have left, had not Jenkinson detained him. "What 'Squire," cried he, "are you ashamed of your two old acquaintances Jenkinson and Baxter?" This Baxter immediately gave us an account of his actions; he was supposed to be the man so wounded by my son George; he was paid to abduct Sophie; he was the procuror of ladies for Mr. Thornhill's pleasure—in short, a fine villain. "All his guilt is now too plain," exclaimed Sir William, "and I find his present prosecution dictated by tyranny, cowardice, and revenge. Mr.

Gaoler, set free this young officer; I'll set the affair in its proper light to the magistrate. But where is the unfortunate Olivia? Let her appear to confront this wretch." "Ah, sir," said I, " I was once indeed happy in a daughter but,"— another interruption stopped me, for who should enter but Miss Arabella Wilmot, who was next day to have been married to Mr. Thornhill. Out of the goodness of her heart she had come to see me, and was astonished to see the baronet and his nephew with us. Sir William quickly enlightened her as to the character of her betrothed; she seemed like to swoon as she said, " O goodness, how I have been deceived! Mr. Thornhill informed me for certain that Captain Primrose was gone off to America with his new married lady." My wife thereupon expatiated upon the sincerity of her son's passion for Miss Wilmot, and as she spoke he came in, cleansed and rehabilitated in his regimentals; and without vanity (for I am above it), he appeared as handsome a fellow as ever wore a military dress. As glove fits the hand, so she flew to him; they renewed their vows of constancy, whilst my son Moses ran to fetch her father. He no sooner arrived but he gave them his blessing. Mr. Thornhill then removed his mask, and showed himself to be a barefaced rascal; he insisted that under the marriage settlement he retained Miss Wilmot's fortune, and Sir William, who had assisted the drawing up of the document, had to agree. " Hold, sir," cried Jenkinson, " can the 'Squire have this lady's fortune if he be already married to another? " " Undoubtedly not," replied the baronet. Jenkinson departed with his usual alacrity, and returned—amazement fails me—with my daughter Olivia! " There she is," cried he, " your own honourable child, and as honest a woman as any in the whole room. As sure as you stand there, 'Squire, this young lady is your lawful wedded wife, and here is the licence by which you were married. You will remember commissioning me to secure a false priest and false licence? Well, to my shame I confess it, but I went and got a true priest and a true licence, so that I could keep the licence and let you know I could prove it upon you, whenever I wanted money. And, sir," continued he, addressing me, " I thought the only possible means of freeing you from prison was by your submitting to the 'Squire's new marriage. This you had vowed never to do whilst your daughter was living, so I prevailed upon your wife to join in the deceit that she was dead."

Happiness expanded on every face; except Mr. Thornhill's, who fell on his knees before his uncle, imploring compassion. Sir William was going to spurn him, but at my request, he raised him saying, " Thy vices, crimes, and ingratitude deserve no tenderness; a bare competence shall be supplied thee to support the wants of life, but not its follies. Thy wife shall be put in possession of a third part of that fortune which once was thine, and from her tenderness alone art thou to expect any extraordinary supplies for the future." Before he could reply he dismissed him, bidding him choose one of his former domestics only to wait upon him. Whilst joy was on every countenance, Sir William claimed my daughter Sophia for his own. " I have for some years," said he, " sought for a woman who, a stranger to my fortune, could think that I had merit as a man. How great at last must be my rapture, to have made a conquest over such sense and such heavenly beauty," and he caught her to his breast with ardour.

After supper, as my spirits were exhausted by the alternations of pleasure and pain which they had sustained during the day, I withdrew; and leaving the company in the midst of their mirth, as soon as I found myself alone, I poured out my heart in gratitude to the Giver of joy as well as sorrow, and then slept undisturbed till morning. When I awoke, I found my eldest son sitting by my bedside, who came to increase my joy with the news that my merchant who had failed in town was arrested at Antwerp, and there had given up effects to a much greater amount than what was due to his creditors. This unexpected good fortune delighted me. I went down to find the whole company as merry as affluence and innocence could make them. Sir William produced the marriage licences, and hoped I would not refuse my assistance in making them all happy this morning.

After the double ceremony we returned to the inn, where my old neighbour Flamborough, who agreed to withhold his evidence against Jenkinson, and his daughters had arrived in the coach which I had despatched for them. We all sat down to table, and it is impossible to describe our good humour. I can't say whether we had more wit among us than usual; but I am certain we had more laughter.

TESS OF THE D'URBERVILLES
A PURE WOMAN

By THOMAS HARDY

The tragic epic of Tess Durbeyfield is the story of a " well-meaning " man's misguided cruelty to the woman he believed he loved. Yet it is far more than that ; for in the tale of adorable Tess the milkmaid, with her pure, warm heart and her eager human impulses, we discern, with growing horror, the bitter thread of destiny weaving—weaving and tightening as time passes, until at last it closes round her young throat on the scaffold.

To appreciate fully how Hardy has wrought a thing of wonder and beauty from this story of ignorance, seduction, heartache and violence, the book must be read in its entirety. It is hoped that the following condensed account will stimulate the desire to do so.

" Good night, Sir John," said Parson Tringham, an antiquary, half jocularly to ignorant, beer-loving Jack Durbeyfield, local haggler (carrier) in the village of Marlott, which lay, remote from the world, in the green, fertile valley of Blackmoor. And he went on to tell the bewildered Jack that he was actually the lineal descendant of the noble and ancient family of D'Urbervilles, now deemed extinct and with their possessions scattered.

Deeply impressed, the simple countryman hastened home to boast to his wife and large young family of this sudden elevation to rank. Meanwhile his eldest daughter Tess, beautiful and unselfish, was gazing with shy, longing eyes at handsome Angel Clare, a vicar's son, who had paused briefly during a walking tour with his brothers to dance with the village girls during their maytime revels on the green. She wished he had danced with her.

At home : " What good will it do us, being gentlefolk, mother ? " she asked wonderingly, when told the news.

Joan Durbeyfield, kindly natured, but as shiftless and irresponsible as her husband, was already eagerly planning.

" There's a rich lady named D'Urberville out at Trantridge.

You go and claim kin with her, Tess, and she'll put 'ee in the way of helping us all, and marrying a gentleman!"

So, to please her mother and in the hope that she might help to provide for the younger children, Tess went to Trantridge, where Alec D'Urberville received her and arranged for her to be engaged as poultry-maid by his blind mother. "But mind, no nonsense about D'Urberville; Durbeyfield only, you know —quite another name."

"I wish for no better, sir," said Tess with dignity.

Alec D'Urberville had, in truth, less claim to the ancient name than Tess herself. The son of a deceased merchant who had taken the name, he was struck by her beauty and bent on seducing her. From the first he tried to take liberties with her; Tess, mortified and indignant, repulsed him, hurting his vanity and increasing his ardour. But she felt she could not go home and face her parents' reproaches; besides, Alec was skilfully pressing his suit by helping her family, giving her father a new cob and sending toys to her young brothers and sisters.

Divided between uneasiness and a hope that she was acting for the best, Tess applied herself diligently to her work among the fowls and managed to keep Alec's advances at bay. But his strategy was too much for her; when his chance came, as it did one September evening, he did not scruple to take it.

Having rescued her from a slight brawl in which some local villagers had involved her as they walked back from the market town, D'Urberville took her on his horse to a remote wood. While he pretended to be searching for their whereabouts, Tess, weary from a long day's work, fell asleep, a tear on her cheek. And so Alec found her. He knelt and bent lower, until her breath warmed his face.

Darkness and silence ruled everywhere around. But where was Tess's guardian angel?

Some weeks later, remorseful, disillusioned, and unhappy, Tess crept home to her parents' house. It was her wish; Alec D'Urberville half contemptuously let her go. At their parting: "I didn't understand your meaning till it was too late," she reproached him. He shrugged.

"That's what every woman says. You are absurdly melancholy, Tess. Show your beauty to the world before it fades. And good-bye, my four months' cousin!"

Joan Durbeyfield's reproaches were hard to bear. She told Tess that she should have been more careful if she hadn't meant to get Alec to marry her.

"Oh, mother!" cried Tess, agonized. "I was a child when I left this house four months ago! Why didn't you tell me there was danger in men-folk? Ladies read novels that tell them of these tricks; but I never learnt that way, and you did not help me!"

Subdued, Joan wiped her eyes. "Well, we must make the best of it. 'Tis nater, after all, and what do please God!"

Through its changing seasons the year wore on, and the following August found Tess a mother. Paler than before, and with her girlish exuberance restrained, she worked in the fields, binding the sheaves of wheat with dock-like regularity, avoiding the company of the other women.

"She's fond of that there child, though she mid pretend to hate en," said one woman, watching her suckle her baby which a younger sister, 'Liza-Lu by name, brought to the field at midday. "'Twas a thousand pities it should have happened to she—but 'tis always the comeliest; the plain ones be safe as churches."

But Tess, with her flower-like mouth and large tender eyes, adored her child, and wished only to keep it in life and health. When she reached home one night and learned that it was seriously ill, she was plunged into misery, deepened by the realization that her child was not baptized. Her darling about to die, and no salvation!

"I must get the parson!" she cried, but her father, drunken and obstinate, said he would not permit any prying into his house and affairs, and locked the door.

The night wore on; the infant was rapidly sinking. Distracted, she murmured incoherent prayers; then, awaking the younger children, she lit candles, arranged the washstand as a font, and stood by it with the baby in her arm. To her sister next in age she gave the Prayer-Book, bidding her hold it open before her at the service of baptism, as she had seen the clerk do it in church for the parson. A name suggested by a phrase in the book of Genesis came to her.

"Sorrow, I baptize thee in the name of the Father, and of the Son, and of the Holy Ghost." She sprinkled the water. "Say 'Amen', children."

She completed the service, the tiny voices piping "Amen" in obedient response. In the blue of the morning poor Sorrow, that fragile soldier and servant, breathed his last, and when the other children awoke they cried bitterly, and begged Sissy to have another pretty baby.

Almost at a leap Tess thus changed from simple girl to complex woman. The year wore on as, wrapped in her deepening thoughts, she worked at home, plucking fowls, cramming turkeys and geese, making clothes for her sisters and brothers, out of finery D'Urberville had given her, and she had put by with contempt. Apply to him she would not.

Was once lost always lost really true of chastity? she asked herself. 'She might prove it false if she could veil bygones. Surely, if she could get away she might annihilate the past.

Her chance came in early May; a dairyman with whom her mother had once put her in touch wrote offering her work. She accepted gladly, and set out on a thyme-scented, bird-hatching morning to journey to Talbothays, set in the valley of the Great Dairies, where the green leas were so thickly speckled with white-coated cows as to dazzle the eye.

And here, among the friendly, sturdy, slow-speaking dairy-folk, she found a young man she had seen once before. He wore the ordinary white pinner of a dairy-farmer when milking, but beneath it was something educated, reserved, subtle, sad, differing.

He was the passing stranger, Angel Clare, who had attracted her that May day long ago, on the village green at Marlott, during the dancing.

" He's learning farming under Mr. Crick, but he's quite the gentleman born," explained Izz Huett, one of the milkmaids. " His father is the Reverend Mr. Clare at Emminster, a very earnest clergyman. All his sons, except our Mr. Angel Clare, he made pa'sons too."

Angel Clare had disappointed his father deeply by his refusal to take holy orders. He wanted to start farming in the colonies, which struck Tess as a strange ambition for a bookish, musical, thinking young man of good education. He was an intelligence to her rather than a man—at first. To him, she was new experience, a visionary essence of woman. He called her Artemis, Demeter, half teasingly. " Call me Tess," she said, confused by her own ignorance, and hungering for his good opinion. At night, in the great attic room she shared with the three other milkmaids, she heard them discussing him. Angel Clare had all their hearts in his keeping—their honour too, as Tess realized from their whispered, blushing avowals. And she admired and respected him for what she considered his self-controlling sense of duty, lacking which more than one simple heart might have gone weeping on her pilgrimage.

In the hot, scented summer days her passion grew, and Clare's also. They were thrown together at work, now that milking was done in the meadows for coolness. One day, moved by her sweetness and vital warmth, he put his arms about her. "Forgive me, Tess dear!" he whispered. "I love you, dearest, in all sincerity."

Tess's excitable heart beat against his by way of reply; the sun slanted down on the blue veins of her temple, on her naked arm, and her neck, and her hair. She was as warm as a sunned cat. She looked at him as Eve at her second waking might have regarded Adam.

"Will you marry me, Tessy?"

"I cannot—I love you—but I *cannot* marry you!"

He pressed her for a reason, but she evaded him. The struggle was fearful; but she had come to Talbothays with a made-up mind. Never could she agree; her conscience had decided for her when her mind was unbiased, and it ought not to be overruled now. She almost wished that someone would tell him about her past, to settle the matter. But no one did. No one seemed to know.

Clare would not leave her alone. Continually he implored her to consent to marry him. He gave her a week to decide; but meanwhile he wooed her in undertones like that of the purling milk—at the cow's side, at skimmings, at butter-makings, at cheese-makings, among broody poultry, and among farrowing pigs—as no milkmaid was ever wooed before by such a man.

She knew she must break down. She loved him so passionately, and he was so godlike in her eyes.

She struggled to make her confession.

"There is—is something very unusual about it—about me. I—I was——" Her breath quickened. He urged her gently. "Yes, dearest?"

"I—I—am—not a Durbeyfield, but a D'Urberville—a descendant of the family who owned that old house we passed——"

"A D'Urberville? Indeed? And is that all the trouble, dear Tess?"

"Yes," she answered faintly.

"Well—why should I love you less after knowing this?" he asked. "And why are you crying?"

"I—oh—I vowed I would die unmarried!"

"Tess—you say you care for me—prove it in some way!"

She clasped his neck in a distraction of tenderness, and for the first time Clare learnt what an impassioned woman's kisses were like upon the lips of one whom she loved with all heart and soul, as Tess loved him.

" Do you believe now? " she asked, flushed.

So she consented. The " appetite for joy " which pervades all creation was not to be controlled by vague lucubrations over the social rubric.

She dismissed the past—trod upon it and put it out, as one treads on a coal that is smouldering and dangerous.

The wedding was arranged for New Year's Eve. A week before, as they waited in an inn parlour after doing some Christmas shopping, a man stared at her—a Trantridge man. He turned to his companion and made a slighting remark about her, referring to the affair with D'Urberville. Angel Clare, overhearing him, struck him and was prepared to fight. The man then took back his words, apologizing for having mistaken Tess for another woman.

The lovers drove home. " Could we put our wedding off for a little? " asked Tess in a dry, dull voice.

" No, my love. Calm yourself." He dismissed her suggestion with a laugh, telling her not to have fancies.

That night she wrote out a full confession and slipped the letter under his door. The next morning she sought his face anxiously; it was unmoved, and he kissed her as warmly as ever.

The wedding day dawned. And then, when it was too late to do anything, something moved her to slip into his room—to stoop to the threshold of the doorway. . . .

The letter was still there, for in her haste she had slipped it under the carpet that ran to the door.

Feeling faint, she took the letter and destroyed it.

The marriage service was over; she was now Mrs. Angel Clare. But had she any moral right to the name?

That evening, as they sat after supper by the wood fire in their lodgings, Angel said abruptly: " I want to make a confession to you, Love." And Tess, who had just resolved that, come what might, *she* would tell him all, here and now, welcomed his words with gladness and relief.

He then told her of an incident in London when, tossed like a cork on the waves of doubt and difficulty, he had plunged into eight-and-forty hours' dissipation with a stranger.

" Do you forgive me? " he asked at last.

She pressed his hand tightly. " Now let me confess," she said; and pressing her forehead against his temple, she told him without flinching about her acquaintance with Alec D'Urberville.

" In the name of our love, forgive me! " she whispered with a dry mouth. " I have forgiven you for the same! "

He broke into horrible laughter, as unnatural and ghastly as a laugh in hell.

" I cannot—stay—in this room—just now . . ." And he left her.

They lived through a despairing day or two, more widely apart than before they were lovers. One night Clare, sleepwalking, bore Tess across the fields to a ruined abbey and placed her in an empty stone coffin, murmuring: " My poor Tess—my wife—dead, dead! " And this was what he felt, that the pure, sweet, virginal girl he had adored was no more—and there remained only another woman in her shape.

He decreed that they must part and gave her a sum of money. Tess, sick at heart, returned to her mother, only to meet fresh reproaches for her folly, as Joan saw it, for having confessed her past.

Clare went to visit his family, and while there made arrangements to go abroad. He evaded his father's and mother's questions about his wife, and a few weeks later sailed for Brazil.

Things went hardly with Tess during the next year. Unable to stay with her parents, she found intermittent work at dairies and farms, hoping always that her husband would return, or write to her to join him in Brazil; but no letter came. She was not to know that Angel lay ill of fever in the clay lands near Curitiba. Meeting Marian, one of her companions from Tolbothay days, she went with her to work at Flintcomb-Ash Farm, hacking swedes. " 'Tis a starve-acre place," said Marian. But Tess set to work. Patience, that blending of moral courage with physical timidity, was now no longer a minor feature in Mrs. Angel Clare; and it sustained her.

Driven to desperation by Angel's silence, she went to visit his parents one Sunday. But as she approached the vicarage she overheard a slighting remark by one of Angel's brothers, as to his " ill-considered marriage to a dairymaid ". She turned back, tears running down her face.

Pausing, exhausted, to rest and drink some milk which an old cottage woman offered her, she learned that there was preaching going on in an adjacent barn.

And as she presently passed the barn, the preacher's voice

was heard. "Oh foolish Galatians, who hath bewitched you, that ye should not obey the truth?" And he went on to say that once he had been the greatest of all sinners, wantonly associating with the reckless and the lewd. But the day of awakening had come. . . .

Startled, Tess recognized the voice as that of Alec D'Urberville. She entered the barn and gazed at the man who had been her seducer, and whom she had not seen since her departure from Trantridge. His face was transfigured; sensuousness had given way to devotional passion.

Alec caught sight of Tess; his lip trembled. Later he overtook her on her homeward way, and told her that his conversion had been brought about by old Mr. Clare.

She let him know of her first great trouble—the only one that related to him. D'Urberville was struck mute.

Shortly afterwards he came to Tess, as she worked in the fields, with a proposal. He wished to make amends for the wrong done to her: would she marry him and accompany him to Africa, where he wished to work as a missionary? Tess confessed that she had married another man. "He is far away. Because of you. He found out——"

Alec's desire for Tess was not dead; the sight of her had revived it and he neglected his preaching to see her. As time passed, his very appearance changed; the original *Weltlust* had come back and he was the jaunty, slapdash admirer again. "You've knocked my faith out of me—so be willing to share my backsliding, and leave that mule you call husband for ever!"

Passionately she swung her leather glove at his mouth, drawing blood. His temper rose. "Remember, my lady, I was your master once! I will be your master again!"

In her wretchedness Tess wrote a pitiful letter to Angel, begging him to come to her. She ended: "Save me from what threatens me!—Your faithful heartbroken Tess."

By degrees her hope died. Fresh troubles came—her father died—when Lady-Day came, Widow Joan and her children had to leave the cottage and go elsewhere. Tess, on the evening before they all had to go, knelt in the window-bench watching the drizzling rain. She reflected bitterly that her return had made matters worse; her mother might have been permitted to stay on had she, Tess, not lost her reputation.

When Alec D'Urberville appeared and offered to take care of them all at Trantridge, empty since his mother's death, she refused his proposal stormily. That night she addressed her first reproach to Angel, scribbling: " O why have you treated me so monstrously? I do not deserve it! You are cruel, cruel indeed! I will try to forget you. T."

Meanwhile her loyal friends, Izz and Marian, were also writing to Angel Clare. " Honour'd Sir," ran their appeal, " Look to your Wife if you do love her as much as she do love you. For she is sore put to by an Enemy in the shape of a Friend. . . . From Two Well-Wishers."

It was evening at Emminster Vicarage when Angel Clare came home. His parents were shocked to see him; his sunken eye-pits were of morbid hue, and the light in his eyes had waned.

They gave him two letters: the last one, brief and heartbroken, from Tess, and the poor plain missive just come from Marian and Izz Huett. Reading these, and the earlier letter which had reached him in Brazil, Angel set out to seek Tess.

Her mother faced him with embarrassment. " She isn't here. I—don't know exactly where she is staying——"

" Please tell me her address—in kindness to a lonely wretched man!' "

In a low voice Joan said, " She is at Sandbourne."

Inquiries brought Angel to the door of a villa in the fashionable watering-place. He was shown into the front room. Tess appeared, her beauty enhanced by her attire—a cashmere dressing-gown with slippers to match.

Her eyes shone unnaturally. " It is too late! " she said. " I waited and waited for you—and he kept saying I was foolish—he was very kind to me, and to mother and all of us—he is upstairs—I hate him now! Oh, go away—please! "

His face grew cold and shrunken; and then he found himself alone. Leaving the house, he walked along he did not know whither.

Later, breathless and quivering, Tess overtook him. " I have killed him! Will you forgive me my sin now? " A pitiful white smile lit her face as she spoke.

At last, tenderness was absolutely dominant in Clare.

His kissed her endlessly with his white lips and said, " I will not desert you! I will protect you, my dearest love! Whatever you may have done! "

They walked on together, taking refuge at last in an empty house in the depths of the New Forest. In an upper room was a great four-poster bedstead with crimson damask hangings.

So five days passed in absolute seclusion, with the birds of the New Forest their only company.

Then, feeling it was wise to move on, they left the house. "Happy house, good-bye!" said Tess. "My life can only be a question of a few weeks. And—I do not wish to outlive your present feeling for me. I would rather be dead and buried than feel you despise me."

"I cannot ever despise you, Tess, dearest love."

They came to a great wind-raked place, with huge stone pillars uprising. "It is Stonehenge!" said Clare. "The heathen temple. Older than the centuries; older than the D'Urbervilles!"

She lay down on a fallen stone slab, warm and dry.

"I am so sleepy, Angel."

"I think you are lying on an altar." He knelt and put his lips on hers.

As she slept, he watched her; and then, behind him, he heard the brush of feet. A man appeared—then another, and another. . . .

She started up.

"Have they come for me, Angel?"

"Yes, dearest. They have come."

"I'm—almost glad," she murmured. "This happiness was —almost too much. . . ."

"I am ready," she said quietly.

      *   *   *   *   *

The July sun beat down on the lovely old city of Wintoncester. It was eight o'clock. Hand in hand two young people climbed the long hill that led to a building with short barred windows— a frowning building with an ugly tower. To the eyes of Angel and 'Liza-Lu, the young sister of Tess, nothing was visible but this blot on the city's beauty. Slighter than Tess, a spiritualized image of her, but with the same beautiful eyes, 'Liza-Lu clung to the man whose steps dragged beside hers. To his care Tess, in her last days, had committed her young sister, asking him to marry, guard and teach her.

Upon the cornice of the tower a tall staff was fixed. Their eyes were riveted on it. A few minutes after the hour had struck something moved slowly up the staff, and extended itself in the breeze. It was a black flag.

"Justice" was done. The D'Urberville knights and dames slept on in their tombs unknowing. The gazers bent in prayer; the flag waved silently. When they had strength they arose, joined hands again, and went on.

NOTRE DAME

By VICTOR HUGO

Victor Hugo (1802–1885) was born at Besançon, the son of a French general. He produced his first literary work, a tragedy, at the age of fourteen; his last, when he was over eighty. The great historical romance " Notre Dame de Paris" was published in 1831. An intensely dramatic story of Paris in the late fifteenth century, it revealed the author as a French Walter Scott. But that was only one side of Hugo. He was greater as a poet than as a novelist. He was also a dramatist, a philosopher, an historian, and a politician. "Notre Dame" has probably enjoyed a greater success in English-speaking countries than any other French literary work.

FROM an early hour on the 6th of January, 1482, Paris had been in a turmoil. It was a double holiday, being the Day of the Kings, otherwise known as the Epiphany, and also the Feast of Fools. The people were eagerly anticipating the great event of the day, the performance of a mystery play at the Palace of Justice. The representation of the mystery was to be followed by the election of the Pope of the Fools, and the distinguished Flemish Ambassadors who had arrived in Paris two days previously were to witness the play.

The mystery was to be performed on a lofty wooden platform erected on a colossal marble table that stood at one end of the great hall of the Palace. The actors had for dressing-room the space under the platform, which was shut in by hangings of tapestry, and the only means of communication between the platform and this room was a rough ladder placed in full view of the audience.

The people had been good-humoured for several hours after they had first assembled in and around the hall, amusing themselves by shouting, singing, and exchanging rude jokes with each other, but as twelve o'clock—the hour at which the Flemish Embassy was to arrive and the mystery was due to begin—drew near, sections of the crowd began to show signs of irritation. Their tedium was temporarily relieved by the arrival of the rector and other dignitaries of the university, who were greeted with the facetious remarks of the crowd.

Hardly had the rector and his company reached their places before the clock struck twelve. The crowd suddenly became silent, and every face was turned expectantly towards the gallery reserved for the Flemish Embassy. The minutes passed, but no ambassadors appeared. The crowd became restive, and again angry voices were heard.

When it began to appear that nothing could restrain the mob from violence, the curtains of the dressing-room were thrown back and one of the players, dressed for the part of Jupiter, advanced to the edge of the marble table, there to announce that the play would begin as soon as His Eminence the Cardinal arrived. The crowd allowed the man to speak, but began to shout again as soon as he had finished, threatening the most terrible acts of vengeance on all concerned should the mystery not be started immediately.

Then a handsome young man in threadbare clothes advanced towards Jupiter from the shadow of one of the pillars.

" Begin immediately, Jupiter," he said. " I undertake to make it all right with the Bailiff and the Cardinal."

The player hesitated no longer, but shouted at the top of his voice, " Citizens, we shall begin this moment." His announcement was greeted with wild cheers, which had hardly died down before four players mounted to the platform.

The play was very dull, and the only thing that gripped the attention of the audience was the weird attire of the players. There was but one person in the hall who followed the speeches: Pierre Gringoire, he who had so luckily intervened after Jupiter's reference to the Cardinal. His interest was due to the fact that he had written the piece.

Hardly had the players got properly into their stride before the Cardinal, the Flemish ambassadors, and a numerous train of attendants entered the hall. The players stopped short, and every eye turned towards the reserved gallery.

The people were at first awed by the appearance of the visitors, but, quickly recollecting that, since it was the Feast of Fools, they were at liberty to behave as they pleased, they started to crack offensive jokes at the expense of the Cardinal and his retinue.

Fifteen minutes after the entry of the visitors, one of the Flemish envoys, a tall, jolly-faced man, stood up and addressed himself to the audience. He demanded that the play should be discontinued, and that the people should proceed immediately to the election of the Pope of the Fools.

"We have our own Pope of Fools at Ghent," he went on. "We elect him in this way: we assemble a crowd, such as there is here, and then anyone who likes, sticks his head through a hole and grimaces at the others, and the man who succeeds in making the ugliest face is chosen Pope. I propose that you follow the fashion of my country here and now."

The citizens received this suggestion with enthusiasm. It was decided that the little chapel opposite the marble table should house the competitors.

Candidate after candidate protruded his ugly countenance through the window of the chapel and grimaced at the delighted mob. So many revolting images were presented that it seemed it would be impossible to decide upon the ugliest. But suddenly a thunderous roar of applause rent the air. The Pope of the Fools had been unanimously elected.

No one present had ever seen such an incredibly ugly face as at that moment displayed itself. The mouth was horseshoe-shaped; the nose tetrahedronal; one eye was overshadowed by carroty bristles, the other buried beneath an enormous wen; the teeth were irregular, and one of them protruded, tusk-like, through the horny lips. When the body to which the face belonged appeared, the admiration of the crowd knew no bounds. An enormous bump on the shoulders was counterbalanced by a prodigious swelling of the stomach; the hands and feet were gigantic; the legs horribly misshapen. It was Quasimodo, the bell-ringer! Quasimodo, the hunchback of Notre Dame! Quasimodo, the one-eyed, the bandy-legged.

The pasteboard tiara and the mock robe of the Pope of Fools were fetched and placed upon the exultant hunchback. He was then requested to sit upon a coloured litter, which was immediately hoisted on to the shoulders of twelve officers of the fraternity of fools. A procession was formed and a tour of the streets of the city was begun.

*   *   *   *   *

Only a small handful of people was left in the hall to witness the still-hopeful Gringoire's last effort at getting the mystery finished.

Suddenly someone shouted, "La Esmeralda! La Esmeralda in the Square," and all rushed to see who La Esmeralda might be.

Gringoire's last hopes were shattered. Cursing the stupidity of the Parisians, he too rushed out into the street. After wandering about for a long time he came to the Place de Grève and, having espied a bonfire, made his way towards it.

There was a circle of people around the fire, watching with fascinated eyes a young girl dancing. At sight of her, Gringoire forgot his troubles. Dark-complexioned, slim, finely shaped, her black eyes flashed fire as she twirled round on her toes with her exquisitely shaped arms held above her head. It was obvious that she was a gipsy.

Among the hundreds of faces that were turned upon her there was one that wore a sinister look—a look expressive half of ecstatic pleasure, half of horrified loathing. Its owner was not more than thirty-five years of age, but he was already bald, and his brow was furrowed with wrinkles. His dress could not be seen.

The girl stopped dancing and, bending down, called to a little white goat that had been lying near her. The animal jumped up and, obeying orders given by his mistress, began to perform tricks so cunning that the people were astounded.

"There is sorcery in this!" said the harsh voice of the bald man. The crowd drowned his words with cheers, but the little dancing-girl shuddered and turned away to continue the performance.

A little later a woman's voice was heard screaming from a dark corner of the square, "Wilt thou begone, Egyptian grasshopper?" There was venom in the cry, and it was followed up with others even more unpleasant. Just then the procession of the Feast of Fools came in sight and all else was forgotten. Seated high above the ranks of the ruffians who owed him, as Pope of Fools, allegiance, sat Quasimodo, a look of pride upon his face.

As Quasimodo was borne past the Maison-aux-Piliers, the bald-headed man darted out from the crowd and snatched from his hands his gilt-wood crosier, the mark of his office. Gringoire recognized the man as Claude Frollo, the archdeacon. The crowd held its breath, expecting to see the Herculean hunchback tear the priest limb from limb; but, to the amazement of all, the Pope dropped on his knees before him, and remained in that posture while the priest pulled off his tiara and stripped him of his tinsel-cope.

The outraged Fraternity of Fools would have thrown themselves upon the priest, had not the hunchback, after rising from his knees, placed himself before his dethroner and gnashed his teeth like a wild animal as he made a way for him through the crowd.

Gringoire watched the strange pair disappear and then, catching sight of the dancing-girl, he set off to follow her through the streets.

The night was far advanced, and there were but few people in the back streets and alleyways along which the girl and her goat were making their way.

She turned a corner and was momentarily lost to sight. Immediately afterwards Gringoire heard her give a shriek and, running up, saw her struggling in the grasp of two men. One of the men, whom he recognized as Quasimodo, dealt him a fearful blow which sent him flying into the gutter.

When it seemed that Quasimodo had only to bear the girl off, a horseman, followed by about a dozen archers, dashed out from a side street and wrenched her from his grasp. The hunchback was seized and bound, while his companion quietly slipped away. The dancer turned to the horseman and inquired his name.

" Captain Phœbus de Châteaupers, at your service, my dear," replied the officer.

" Thank you," she said; and then, while he was twirling his moustache, she turned and disappeared into the night.

By the time Gringoire had recovered his senses the street was deserted. Wandering disconsolately in search of a bed, he strayed into the dreaded Cour des Miracles, the haunt of thieves, prostitutes, rogues, and murderers. He was seized by a crowd of ruffians and brought before their King, who decided that unless he could induce one of the women of the Cour des Miracles to take him as her husband, he should be immediately hanged. By far the greater number of the women turned from him in disgust without giving him a second glance, and the rogues were about to put his head through the noose when they were interrupted by the cry " La Esmeralda! La Esmeralda! " Gringoire turned to behold the dancing-girl.

" Do you propose to hang this fellow? " she asked the King.

" Yes, sister, unless you wish to marry him," replied he.

The dancer pouted her lower lip and then said, " I will have him! "

Their wedding-night was as unlike the normal as it could possibly have been. Gringoire attempted to make love to her. Her reply was to whip out a knife and threaten to murder him. They slept in separate rooms, and poor Gringoire did not even have a bed.

*   *   *   *   *

Squire Allworthy finds Tom in his bed

Tom rescues Mrs. Waters from Ensign Northerton

Scenes from " Tom Jones "

Drake, playing bowls, is warned of the Armada's approach

An illustration to "Westward Ho!"

At the time of the events recorded above, Quasimodo, the hunchback, was twenty years of age. Sixteen years earlier he had been exposed as a foundling in the church in which he was now bell-ringer. A crowd of old women had gathered round his cradle, and so horrified were they by his ugliness that they concluded he was the offspring of the devil and that it would be well if he were placed upon a burning faggot. He would almost certainly have been burned had not Claude Frollo, a young priest, intervened.

Pushing aside the group of garrulous old hags, he approached the cradle and extending his hand over it pronounced the words, " I adopt this child." The priest then wrapped the boy in his cassock and bore him away. The women were astounded at his action, and one of them whispered, " Did I not tell you that Claude Frollo is a sorcerer? "

The priest was no ordinary man. His austere countenance, his piercing gaze, his complete devotion to his vocation, marked him off from his fellow-priests. Before he took over the hideous Quasimodo, the sole object of his affections was his younger brother Jehan, whom he had adopted as an infant.

When the hunchback grew up, the priest, who had by then become an archdeacon, gained him the post of bell-ringer at the Cathedral. Thereafter Quasimodo lived for two things only: his bells and his foster-father. On both he lavished a passionate affection. As if to cut him off even more completely from the world, the great bells had deafened Quasimodo with their thunderous chimes, so that he could hear no human voice.

All the warmth of the priest's heart was reserved for his brother. Jehan proved a bitter disappointment, for instead of following in Claude's footsteps and devoting himself to religion and learning, he frequented taverns and gaming-houses, spending money like water and gaining a great reputation as a profligate. All the reproofs and remonstrances of his brother were in vain; so, to forget his misery, Claude locked himself in his library and made himself master of the occult sciences. Hence his reputation as a sorcerer, for to the illiterate populace deep learning and magic were often indistinguishable.

* * * * *

After having been arrested by Captain Phœbus and his archers, the unfortunate Quasimodo was hailed before the magistrate; charged with causing a nocturnal disturbance, assaulting a lewd woman, and resisting the King's guard. He was sentenced to be flogged and placed in the pillory of the

Place de Grève, where the day before Gringoire had been fascinated by the beauty of La Esmeralda.

The reader will remember that La Esmeralda's performance had been rudely interrupted by the bitter screams of a woman. This woman, known as Sister Gudule, had for precisely sixteen years been locked up in a penitent's cell beside the pillory of the Place de Grève.. She had not been placed in the cell by the officers of the law, but had herself chosen this form of penance.

Extremely beautiful as a young girl, she had given herself over to a life of pleasure and dissipation. By the age of twenty the last of her lovers had deserted her because her charms were beginning to fade, and she was left alone with a baby girl, upon whom she lavished all her affection.

One day, when the infant was about a year old, she slipped out of the house, leaving it asleep inside. When she returned the cradle was empty, the only sign of her beloved child being a tiny slipper that the kidnappers had accidentally let fall. A band of gipsies had been in the neighbourhood that morning, and so it was assumed that it was they who had stolen the infant.

Later the same day, when the mother returned to the house after a vain search for her child, she found crawling about the floor a little monster, one-eyed and lame. This hideous wretch was to take the place of her beautiful daughter. The mother crazed with grief and rage, took the road to Paris, clutching the slipper the kidnappers had dropped. Thinking that the tragedy which had overtaken her was a punishment from God for the sins of her youth, she locked herself up in Madame Rolande's cell in the Place de Grève, and had remained there ever since, subsisting on scraps of food thrown into her cell by the charitable. Everyone called her Sister Gudule, but her real name was Paquette la Chantefleurie.

As for the misshapen brat that had been left in her house, the Archbishop carefully took the devil out of him, and had him sent to Paris to be exposed as a foundling in Notre Dame.

The cell in which the crazed Gudule had confined herself was within sight of the pillory at which Quasimodo had been condemned to undergo his punishment.

The poor deaf wretch, ignorant of his sentence, and therefore of his terrible fate, allowed himself to be bound to the wheel of the pillory without protest. It was only when he caught sight of the metal-loaded leather whip with which he was to be flogged that he realized his fate. He struggled vainly when the first lashes struck his naked, deformed back, but thereafter suffered inert and in silence. He was flogged until the blood streamed down his body, and then placed in the pillory, there to remain for an hour, and endure, besides physical pain, the jeers of a depraved mob. In the very Place through which he had the day before been triumphantly borne as Pope of Fools, poor Quasimodo was now being tortured.

Some little while after he had been placed in the pillory, Quasimodo saw a priest riding across the square upon a mule. At the sight of him, the hunchback's gruesome countenance assumed an expression of gentleness—almost of pleasure. It was as if he expected to be delivered from his torment. But as soon as the priest realized who the sufferer was, he turned the mule about and rode quickly away. Thus was Quasimodo deserted by the only human creature he had ever loved—and by the author of his present misfortunes, because the priest it was who had ordered him to seize La Esmeralda and who had accompanied him when he made the attempt.

After Claude Frollo had passed by on the other side, the hunchback, broken now in spirit as well as in body, and experiencing a terrible thirst, cried out "Water! water!" The mob responded to his piteous appeal by hurling at him stones and filth out of the gutters.

After repeating his cry a third time, Quasimodo observed a young girl approaching the pillory. She was followed by a goat, from which circumstance the hunchback recognized her as the damsel whom he had attempted to abduct. Assuming that she was approaching to strike him while he was bound and defenceless, his eyes blazed with rage and he vainly writhed to avoid her. But, instead of lifting her hand against him, the dancer loosed a gourd of water from her girdle and presented it to Quasimodo's parched lips. Tears started from the hunchback's bloodshot eyes as he drank greedily.

The attention of the mob was distracted from this touching scene by a bitter exclamation from Sister Gudule, who had been watching from her cell. The sight of the dancer, whom she knew to be a gipsy, had excited her to a paroxysm of rage.

"Cursed be thou, spawn of Egypt!" she cried. "Cursed! Cursed! Cursed!"

And as La Esmeralda descended the steps of the pillory, the crazed penitent screamed, "Get thee down! Get thee down, Egyptian child-stealer! Thou wilt have to go up again one of these days!"

* * * * *

Quasimodo went back to Notre Dame, there to ring his bells, but with much less enthusiasm than formerly. Whereas before he was placed in the pillory he thought only of the Cathedral and of the Archdeacon, his mind was now engrossed with memories of the angelic creature who had repaid his attempt to abduct her by an act of kindness.

Thoughts of the same creature monopolized the attention of the Archdeacon, who spent long hours alone in a secret chamber in Notre Dame. He had found out about Gringoire's virgin marriage to the dancer, and he had also discovered, by careful questioning of the young playwright, that La Esmeralda's thoughts were concentrated upon a certain Phœbus, though who this Phœbus was he had been unable to determine.

La Esmeralda continued to perform in the streets, attended now by Gringoire as well as by her goat. She and Gringoire appeared to be fonder of the goat than of each other. The dancer remained with the playwright merely because she had covenanted to do so to save his life; he with her, because she provided him with board and lodging.

Several weeks after La Esmeralda had been rescued by Captain Phœbus, she accidentally came in contact with him again, and arranged to meet him at night in a disreputable lodging-house.

One of Phœbus' drinking companions was young Jehan, the Archdeacon's brother. Before setting out to keep his appointment with La Esmeralda, Phœbus spent several hours in a tavern with his friend. The two young men were followed by the Archdeacon, who overheard Phœbus telling Jehan of his assignation.

After Phœbus had left Jehan dead drunk in the gutter, the priest followed the Captain to the lodging-house, and by a series of cunning tricks managed to gain entrance to a room next door to that occupied by the two lovers. For some minutes he watched through a crack in the wall as they made love; and suddenly driven crazy by jealous rage, he burst into their room and savagely stabbed the amorous Captain. La Esmeralda fainted, and when she came to she was surrounded by soldiers of the watch. Phœbus was lying in a pool of blood, but there was no sign of the priest. He had escaped through a window that opened on the river.

*   *   *   *   *

The dancer was brought to trial on the charge of having, with the assistance of the devil and of a spectre monk, killed Captain Phœbus de Châteaupers. The fact that the gallant

Captain was making a good recovery did not worry the court. La Esmeralda at first refused to admit her guilt, but torture was applied, and she then confessed to sorcery, magic, incontinence, and murder done upon the Captain's body. She was sentenced to do penance before the great porch of Notre Dame, and then to be taken to the Place de Grève and there hanged by the neck on the gallows of the city.

After sentence had been passed, the unhappy girl was thrown into a dark dungeon under the Palace of Justice. She who in the streets of Paris had symbolized gaiety, freedom, and light was now weighed down with chains and immured in a lightless cell. They had told her that Phœbus was dead, and she therefore no longer desired anything for herself but death.

The priest visited her in the dungeon. He confessed his love for her and also the part he had played in the attempt to abduct her, and in the attack on Phœbus. He said that if she would agree to go away to the country with him, he would enable her to escape from prison and from death. She indignantly rejected his offer, telling him that she would rather die than have anything to do with him; and so he left her to her fate in baffled rage.

On the day appointed, La Esmeralda was brought to the great porch of Notre Dame and there spiritually prepared for execution. The priest in charge of the services was none other than Claude Frollo, and, while he officiated, in low tones he made another appeal to the girl, telling her that he could yet save her. Her refusal was as unequivocal as before.

As she was being led away to the gallows, she happened to lift her eyes to the windows of a neighbouring house, and to her unbounded joy there observed the figure of Phœbus. She cried out to him, but he hastily retired with a woman who was standing beside him. At this, Esmeralda fainted.

The crowd gathered round Notre Dame had been too engrossed in watching the dancer to notice Quasimodo perched high up on the face of the church. Nor had they noticed that from him to the pavement hung a rope.

Hardly had La Esmeralda's body fallen to the ground before the hunchback slid down the rope like a raindrop down a pane of glass. In a flash he was beside the girl. Then, having felled her two guards with his enormous fists, he lifted the dancer and bore her swiftly within the porch of Notre Dame, crying " Sanctuary! Sanctuary! " Once inside the church the girl was safe from the arm of the Law.

Quasimodo carried her to a small chamber in the upper part of the edifice and, having given her food and bedding, he said, " During the day you must stay here, but at night you can walk about all over the church. But do not go outside either by day or by night, or they will kill you, and that will be the death of me." That same evening La Esmeralda found her goat in her cell.

Knowing that while the girl remained in the Cathedral, Quasimodo would take good care of her, the angry priest decided to devise a means of getting her away. He therefore sought out Gringoire and, telling the simple-minded poet that it was essential for Esmeralda's safety that she should be moved from Notre Dame, asked him if he could think of any means of accomplishing this. Gringoire agreed, after much argument, to induce his fellow-vagabonds, the inhabitants of the Cour des Miracles, to storm the Cathedral and liberate the dancer.

The next night, when Quasimodo was making his rounds, he observed an enormous crowd making its way towards the church. This was the army of the vagabonds.

The vagabonds attacked the great door with picks, crowbars, and other implements, but before they had had time to make any impression upon it a great beam, thrown by Quasimodo, came hurtling from above the porch and, landing in the midst of those gathered around it, killed a dozen of them.

Undaunted by the losses they had suffered, the attackers then seized the fallen beam and, using it as a battering-ram, returned to the assault. Quasimodo commenced to hurl down on their heads large blocks of stone that had been left by the masons who had been repairing the edifice. Fearful havoc was thus caused, but every time one vagabond fell another took his place, Quasimodo's ammunition was soon exhausted, but he was not yet beaten. He lighted great fires of faggots in the lead-lined gutters of the church, and thick streams of molten lead poured down on the attackers' heads.

But soon afterwards, Jehan, the priest's brother, approached with a ladder, which he and his comrades placed against the face of the church and started to ascend, with the intention of gaining entrance to one of the galleries, eighty feet up. No sooner had Jehan scrambled into the gallery, and before the next man had time to do so, Quasimodo approached and, using all his strength, flung the ladder backwards. It crashed into the mob below, killing many besides those who were climbing it. He then seized Jehan and sent him flying after the ladder.

Meanwhile the King's guard had been called by the alarmed citizens. Just as the vagabonds were preparing to place other ladders in position, they were taken in the rear by the soldiers —under Captain de Châteaupers—and quickly dispersed.

Having made quite certain that the attack had been defeated, Quasimodo rushed to find La Esmeralda, but when he got to her cell he found it empty. While the battle was at its height Gringoire and the priest had entered the church by a secret door that could only be gained from the river. The priest was disguised, and when he entered the girl's chamber along with Gringoire she did not recognize him.

La Esmeralda was terrified when the priest disclosed his identity. He again declared his love, and promised to save her if she would live with him. When she repeated her refusal he took her to the Place de Grève and, dragging her up to Sister Gudule's cell, said, "Gudule! Here is the woman you hate! Hold her till I fetch the sergeants." The crazy witch obeyed, and held the girl as in a vice.

While she held La Esmeralda, Sister Gudule gave the girl a wild account of her misfortunes. She finally showed her the infant's slipper that she had kept for sixteen years. When she did so, La Esmeralda tore open a locket at her breast and produced the slipper's fellow. Mother and child recognized each other at last.

Frantically Sister Gudule tore down one of the bars of her cage and pulled the girl inside, so as to hide her from the soldiers who were approaching. But all in vain. After a desperate struggle, in which the wretched mother was accidentally killed, La Esmeralda was dragged to the gallows and hanged.

After leading the soldiers to her, the priest had retired to an upper gallery of the Cathedral, from thence to watch the execution. As he was intently watching the girl's still-living body dangling in the air, Quasimodo came up behind him and sent him flying over the balustrade to crash to death on the pavement below.

Quasimodo was never seen again, but a few years later, when the vault in which La Esmeralda's body had been placed was opened, two skeletons were there found locked together. One was that of a young girl; the other that of a hunchback. As the vertebræ of the hunchback's neck had not been ruptured, it was evident that he had not been hanged. He must therefore have gone thither to die.

WESTWARD HO!

By CHARLES KINGSLEY

Kingsley, historian, social reformer, and naturalist, possessed in addition an admirable romantic prose style which is exhibited at its finest in this swashbuckling tale of adventure and intrigue in the reign of Queen Elizabeth. The book was first published in 1855, and was immediately popular.

AMYAS LEIGH had the salt of the sea in his blood from earliest boyhood. His native town, Bideford, in North Devon, was the great port of the West of England in Elizabeth's day. And if Frank, his elder brother, followed rather the gentler, learned way of their parents, the tastes of Amyas drove him ever to the waterside. There, while the ships of England sailed over the horizon to the unknown, he would watch the bronzed sailors ashore, listen unseen to their stories, and learn the uses of the web of cordage on every ship.

One evening in the year 1575, at a tavern in Bideford, John Oxenham, a bold sea-rover, was living again with his gunner the raid on Nombre de Dios, in which they had followed Drake to a daring success. Salvation Yeo, the gunner, passed round for inspection a great buffalo horn on which was engraved a map of the Spanish Main. Amyas was enthralled by it, and Oxenham could hardly believe the young giant was only fifteen years old when he offered to fight for the buffalo horn.

But he got it for nothing, and took it home to dream on, while Oxenham, who was recruiting for an expedition of his own, swore to be at supper that night at Burrough Court, Amyas's home.

He went, fully resolved to snatch the boy to sea, but Sir Richard Grenvile, the stainless chevalier of Elizabethan knighthood, was at supper, too. The plea of Amyas to go was granted, but only after he had grown older and finished his schooling. And, before the boasting Oxenham left Burrough Court, the wisdom of the decision was seen. For the adventurer saw a vision of a white bird that always appeared to an Oxenham soon doomed to die. And so Amyas Leigh went back to school, and Mr. Oxenham went his way to Plymouth again, and sailed for the Spanish Main.

A year after that, Amyas's father died, and the boy went straight to Sir Richard Grenvile and said,

"You must be my father now, sir." And it was so. Mrs. Leigh continued to live at Burrough, with Amyas growing to huge manhood under her eyes, while Frank tickled Elizabeth's fancy at Court with his cultured wit. And, all the time, Sir Richard Grenvile kept an eye on the young sea-hawk at Burrough. In due time Amyas went to sea.

He went first of all because of a schoolmaster's bald head and, secondly, because of a beautiful girl. Not caring to be flogged for drawing caricatures, Amyas broke his slate over the head of the schoolmaster, because, as he said, to Sir Richard:

"Oh, sir, if you had but seen his bald head, you would have broken it yourself!"

His other offence was to throw over the quay a man who said that Barnstaple could boast prettier girls than Rose Salterne of Bideford.

It was plain that Amyas had grown too big for school. His herculean frame needed harder work. So, remembering his promise to send him to sea, but also to send him to sea only with real men, Sir Richard Grenvile took him to Plymouth. And, under the wing of the stocky, tough mariner who was making England ring with his name—Captain Francis Drake—Amyas vanished for three years.

The whole of North Devon turned out to greet the Bideford men of the expedition when they returned. A great pageant had been arranged and all society was there. Famous names of Devon—Grenviles, Carys, Fortescues, Leighs, Stukeleys— were there. Frank Leigh came from London to greet his brother, dressed in dove-grey and with a flower behind his ear.

For Amyas, there were two jarring notes in the surging, laughing day, two things that spoilt a little the heartening warmth of his welcome. An old woman pleaded for news of her son, Salvation Yeo, who had gone on that ill-fated voyage with Oxenham. Amyas still remembered the sailor who had given him the engraved buffalo horn, but was forced to say that he had heard nothing of him in the Indies. But it hurt him still more to find that Rose Salterne, the girl he loved, was not in her rightful place in the pageant as the Nymph of Torridge. She was not to be seen even in the crowd.

The reason was simple enough. Her father packed her off to a relative at Kilkhampton as soon as he heard of the business.

He explained to Mrs. Leigh: " I am but a burgher, Mrs. Leigh, and you a lady of blood; but I am too proud to let any man say that Simon Salterne threw his daughter at your son's head."

The trouble was that Amyas was not the only gallant in the field. Will Cary, of Clovelly, his old friend, was another. And there were more as yet unsuspected.

But love was forgotten next morning when Frank and Amyas met their cousin, Eustace. Son of a man who had remained a Roman Catholic, Eustace had come under Jesuit teaching, and a narrow nature had been ill-trained. The brothers found him with two suspicious strangers in Appledore, and feared they were Jesuits in disguise. Sir Richard Grenvile met them while hunting with Will Cary, and scented them a mile off. He saw even farther, and knew them for agents of Irish rebellion as well as Roman bigots. For no man who was a true Catholic and, at the same time, a true Englishman, need be afraid to proclaim his faith at that time. The net result was that the beaches were watched night and day to stop any more such men landing.

But Eustace was in the power of the two who had already landed. He agreed to go to Clovelly beach the following night and get letters from an incoming boat. While he was being persuaded, Rose Salterne had visited an old woman who had a reputation for witchcraft. Unable to make up her mind whom to marry among all the gallants who pursued her, she sought occult advice.

That night, and the following night, were fateful times for all. Amyas talked far into the night of his love for Rose, only to find at dawn that his brother was his rival. Next day came an anonymous note hinting of dark doings on Clovelly beach at nightfall. Amyas and Frank watched together, and Eustace had his jaw broken before he gave up the letter he had fetched. Sir Richard Grenvile galloped to the home of Eustace's father, but the priests had gone. And so Will Cary rode like the wind to try and catch them at Marsland Mouth, the only place now unwatched. There Rose Salterne was bathing at midnight to see the face of her true love in the glass afterwards. So the witch woman had bade her, and stood by to see it done. And, pressed terrified into a small cave, Rose saw the escaping priests take boat and row away, and saw Will Cary leap from a foam-flecked horse—too late to stop them.

But the letter from Ireland had been dramatic. No less

than eight hundred Spaniards had landed there. As his unselfish way of leaving Frank a clear field with Rose Salterne,
Amyas asked permission of Sir Richard Grenvile, and was told
to go and serve with Winter in the Irish campaign. Before he
went there began a partnership that lasted for the whole of
Amyas's active life. Salvation Yeo came home, sole survivor
of Oxenham's tragic enterprise. The grim story of the expedition has no place in the life of Amyas except for one thing.
Before he was hanged by the Spaniards, Oxenham had found a
Spanish lady who had been his mistress years before. She
and their little girl had dared to go with him as he and his men
were hounded through the forests of the Main. When she
stabbed herself as the Spaniards caught them at last, Salvation
Yeo took the child and sought the woods again. But it was no
good. He was captured and separated from her, and now was
back home, dreaming only of returning to the West to find " his
little maid ". When he heard of Amyas going to Ireland, he
asked to join him at once, and was accepted.

There was one more important event before Amyas left for
Milford Haven and Ireland. Frank contrived to bring together in the Ship Tavern, at Bideford, all rivals for the hand
of Rose Salterne. Frank's silver tongue won them all from
thoughts of fighting each other, and the Brotherhood of the
Rose was formed. Each man swore to go away and seek honour
in war or at Court in the name of his lady. They were forced
to bring in Jack Brimblecombe, fat son of the schoolmaster
Amyas had once smitten. He had been listening, and gave
himself away by sneezing. But, as he, too, loved Rose Salterne
there was no harm done. And so they all parted.

Christmas came peacefully to North Devon while Amyas
waged fierce fight at Smerwick. Before the Spanish garrison
was put to the sword as a stern example to all invaders, Amyas
captured the commander, Don Guzman Maria Magdalena
Sotomayor de Soto. He went an honoured captive to Sir
Richard Grenvile's home at Bideford, while Amyas went deep
into the Irish bogs in pursuit of further honour and further
forgetfulness. And, because the Brotherhood of the Rose had
sent all its members overseas, save only fat Jack Brimblecombe,
the courtly Don Guzman had no rivals in the rapid suit he laid
to Rose Salterne's affections.

In Ireland, Eustace Leigh moved furtively on seditious
business, and Amyas talked long hours with Sir Walter Raleigh
on projects for colonizing in the West or for broaching its golden

secrets. They settled finally on a dash to find the fabled city of the Incas. Raleigh went home to England to persuade Mrs. Leigh to give her permission. It was given. Amyas sailed West without seeing either Rose Salterne or Don Guzman.

Soon after he had gone, there was a mighty feast in the great hall at Annery, such as had seldom been since Judge Hankford feasted Edward the Fourth there; and while every one was eating their best, and drinking their worst, Rose Salterne and Don Guzman were pretending not to see each other, and watching each other all the more. But Rose, at least, had to be very careful of her glances; for not only was her father at the table, but just opposite her sat none other than Messrs. William Cary and Arthur St. Leger, lieutenants in her Majesty's Irish army, who had returned on furlough a few days before. These two were both Brothers of the Rose.

Afterwards, Will Cary saw Rose in the Spaniard's arms, and was only restrained from fighting there and then by Lady Grenvile. But, the moment a chance came, he insulted Don Guzman, and the duel was fixed for the sands soon after dawn. Sir Richard stopped the fight at the first wound, and next day, as his ransom had come, the Spaniard vanished, leaving a bad impression on his knightly host and having roused the hostility that all England was beginning to feel towards his country.

Amyas came back from a fruitless voyage, but Sir Humphrey Gilbert, his leader, perished in a tremendous storm. Worn-out by privation, saddened by failure, Amyas received at Plymouth news that unmanned him. Don Guzman, his honoured prisoner, had left England. And with him had gone the peerless Nymph of Torridge, Rose Salterne. No trace but a footmark under her bedroom window remained of the love Amyas and the others had sworn ever to defend.

Will Cary was home and had slight news. The fugitives had been seen on Lundy Island, but, after that, all was blank. There was missing, too, the old witch woman, Lucy Passmore. Old Salterne prayed Amyas to take ship and seek his daughter. While Amyas posted to London, whither his mother had moved, Will Cary exchanged letters with Frank Leigh, telling him the heart-breaking news and receiving consolation. Jack Brimblecombe came out a fully militant member of the Brotherhood, and was ready to go anywhere in search of their lost maid.

One after another, they proved true to their vows. Even gentle, cultured Frank Leigh voted at once for an expedition to the West and obtained permission from both Queen and mother to go. Back in Bideford, all the work of fitting a ship began. Rose's father wished to pay all expenses, but the Brothers of the Rose would not have it.

The crew were picked men, the equipment of the *Rose* second to none. Amyas's old captain, Sir Francis Drake, was deep in peaceable matters, having been made mayor of Plymouth, but he sent his sailor's blessing on the venture. In the middle of November, 1583, the topsails of the *Rose* grew smaller in the West till her white sails faded away into the grey Atlantic mist, perhaps for ever. And Mrs. Leigh gathered her cloak about her, and bowed her head and worshipped; and then went home to loneliness and prayer.

They made landfall at Barbados, where Frank and Will Cary feasted their eyes on the tropic beauties of which they had heard so much. There was grimmer work off Grenada, where pearls were taken from a Spanish caravel after a stiff fight. Amyas had sworn, as a good subject of Gloriana, never to forget, even though he was on a private quest, that hurt must be brought to Spain as much as possible.

So, too, they heard that Don Guzman was Governor of La Guayra. There they hastened, only to find the haven full of Spanish warships. Their original idea to make an armed landing was hopeless, but Frank was determined at least to try and speak with Rose.

Amyas insisted on him having a companion, and the lot fell upon him. From a silent landing on the beach below the Governor's house, they crept up to the garden through brilliant shrubs. And then, to their astonishment and white anger, they found Rose outside the house in the company of their Catholic cousin, Eustace. That weak-willed creature was attempting to seduce Rose away from her Spanish husband, using horrible threats of the Inquisition.

Rose's shriek at the menace brought the guard tumbling out. Amyas flung himself at Eustace, but had no time to mete out the death he burned to give him. Frank had a few words with Rose, and then Amyas held the path while he dashed for the boat. But it was too late for easy going.

Gigantic Amyas fought like a lion, upheld by the knowledge that Rose Salterne was truly married and no mere plaything of the Don's. When Frank crashed to earth, knocked senseless by a great stone, he bore him through shot-torn water to the boat, only to lose his grip when he, too, was beaten down by the pursuing guard. Two men only of that tragic boatload returned to the *Rose*, Amyas and a seaman. Frank Leigh was in the clutch of Spain, the others died where they fought.

Next day came the great sea-fight of the *Rose*. Crazed by the loss of his brother, Amyas paced the deck all night, desperate for dawn and a chance to try a forlorn assault on La Guayra. But between him and the shore lay a great galleon and two galleys. Salvation Yeo looked to his guns. Will Cary and the others awaited their real baptism of fire. With trumpets braying and banners flying, the *Rose* bore down on the *Madre Dolorosa* as soon as it was light.

Drake had not wasted his teaching on Amyas. The young giant knew how much quicker an English ship could manœuvre and how deadly her low guns could be at close quarters. Holding off for a while, he went about suddenly and took the *Rose* across the Spaniard's stern.

"Now then!" roared Amyas. "Fire, and with a will! Have at her, archers; have at her, muskets all!" and in an instant a storm of bar and chain shot, round and canister, swept the proud Don from stem to stern, while through the white cloud of smoke the musket-balls, and the still deadlier clothyard arrows, whistled and rushed upon their venomous errand. Down went the steersman, and every soul who manned the poop. Down went the mizzen-topmast, in went the stern windows and quarter-galleries; and as the smoke cleared away, the gorgeous painting of the *Madre Dolorosa*, with her heart full of seven swords, which, in a gilded frame, bedizened the Spanish stern, was shivered in splinters; while the golden flag of Spain, which the last moment flaunted above their heads, hung trailing in the water. The ship, her tiller shot away, and her helmsman killed, staggered helplessly a moment, and then fell up into the wind.

The galleys were pounded and one was boarded. The other fled. Turning, Amyas took up the fight with the galleon again. But when finally the *Madre Dolorosa* sank slowly from sight, the *Rose*, too, was in sorry condition. Taking her a mile or two up-shore, Amyas entered a mangrove-bordered river to careen the ship and repair the shot-holes. In that eerie place, where alligators crawled in the stinking mud and lines of tall herons stood dimly in the growing gloom, yellow fever lurked. That night two-thirds of the crew were down with it.

Certain that only death would be their portion in the misty swamps, Amyas led his men into the hills, trying to march overland and capture a ship on the Pacific coast. Salvation

Yeo burned the *Rose* to put pursuers off the track. While their dreadful trials began, Frank and Rose lay in the Inquisition at Cartagena. Before long they were burned at the stake, together in death as they had never been in life.

For three long years the crew of the *Rose* wandered the forests of the Main, searching for the Golden City of the Incas, hoping for riches before they sought a ship. By the wooded banks of the Orinoco they searched, and at the head-waters of the mighty Amazon. Fire-spouting Cotopaxi saw them pass. The grim Rio Negro claimed five lives, the Andes two more. At last they stood on the Cordillera, and it was agreed that all should go down the nearest river till the sea be reached again.

Half-way down that raging stream Amyas found a canoe and, looking around to find an Indian who might guide them, found instead a tall, golden girl, shy, wild, and somehow unlike an Indian girl.

When her confidence was won, she took them all to her tribal camp, where she was worshipped almost as a god. Amyas and his men lived for months with them in peace and content, far above the city of Santa Fé. But, when an Indian came in with news of a Spanish gold-train, Amyas knew their chance had come. It was time to take the trail once more.

They ambushed that gold-train and captured it, going jubilantly on to the downward road through the forest. Ayaconora, the golden Indian girl, caught up with them, asking only to go with Amyas, whom she adored as a being beyond dreams. Twice she was sent back, and only Salvation Yeo saved her from suicide the third time.

After that, Amyas gave it up. All took a vow to treat her like a sister, and they came at last to the sea at New Granada. Near the shore lay the great galleon, the *City of the True Cross*.

In the luxurious saloon, the Lord Bishop of Cartagena talked idly with a friar. The guard slept. When night came, the silent approach of the boats of the men of the *Rose* gave them the galleon after a brief fight. Amyas, then, had no knowledge of the tragedy that act was to reveal.

From the bilges came a poor, demented old woman, mazed and fantastic in the lurid garment of the auto da fé. She shrank like a beaten spaniel before the Bishop of Cartagena, and one and all knew she had suffered at his hands and at those of the Inquisition. Grimmer things were to come. As kindness brought back glimmerings of sense to the woman, she was found to be none other than Lucy Passmore, the old witch woman who had vanished from Devon with Don Guzman and Rose Salterne. Out came the sad tale of the martyrdom of Frank and Rose. Black-browed and merciless, Amyas sent the Bishop and his friar to dangle and kick from the yard-arm and then, with a load of grief on his soul, squared the galleon away to the East and England.

But there was joy to come for at least one man in the crew. Ayaconora spent long hours with all, learning English, losing Indian ways. One day she took up and sang right through an English sea-song that Yeo was humming at his work. The old gunner was taken back many years by it. He questioned the girl. Bit by bit came other English words, long forgotten, scraps of memory that proved to everybody that Ayaconora was no Indian girl, but the daughter of John Oxenham and his Spanish mistress, the " little maid " that Salvation Yeo had lost so long ago.

Mrs. Leigh's weary vigil ended in February, more than four years after the *Rose* sailed so proudly from Appledore pool. Amyas dropped on his knees before her. He said, quite simply, knowing her thoughts: " I would have died to save him, mother, if I could."

Thrusting back grief at Frank's death, Mrs. Leigh filled her heart with love for the blond giant who had come home and for the shy girl who came with him. Old Salterne learned with tears of thankfulness that Rose had been truly married, then he quietly died. Rich and at peace, Amyas dwelt quietly for a year. Only the demoniac lust for revenge on Don Guzman still burned in his heart and embittered happy hours. But he remained faithful to his promise to his mother, and went no more adventuring. He was even proof against temptation from Drake, who asked him to go with him to Cadiz and " singe the King of Spain's beard ". He was content to ask his old chief to look out for Don Guzman, and then went on with his quiet life at home.

Into the serenity that was even then being disturbed by the mutter of Armada warnings, came Sir Walter Raleigh. He had been charged by Elizabeth to carry out his old project to colonize Virginia.

Amyas was given free leave to go by his mother, though it broke her heart to give it, and all the first months of 1588 were spent in preparation. All the time, too, Sir Richard Grenvile prepared the West Country against the threat from Spain. Drake had given the Dons a lesson, but still the masts multiplied at Lisbon and Cadiz. Ayaconora quietly became an English lady, studious to learn, sweet and dutiful to Mrs. Leigh, worshipping Amyas from afar. Amyas's mother saw clearly the way of things, but, when she talked of it to her son, his revenge-tortured soul was untrue to him. He raged:

" I mean this, that she is half a Spaniard, mother; and I cannot!—Her blood may be as blue as King Philip's own, but it is Spanish still! I cannot bear the thought that my children should have in their veins one drop of that poison."

Then came great events. Grenvile sent word that the Armada had sailed at last. The *Vengeance*, nearly ready for the Virginian voyage, was unloaded and filled again with the goods of war. Thinking himself happy once more, Amyas sailed south, treading the deck of his own ship and bent on war with Spain. He would not admit to himself that England's need was his own opportunity for revenge.

And, after the waiting at Plymouth, Amyas went into the terrific sea-fight in the Channel. Drake sent him word that Don Guzman commanded a galleon called the *Santa Catharina*. Straightway, Amyas forgot the great cause in which he fought, and quested solely for that one ship.

He hardly noticed the havoc wrought on the Armada by Effingham and Drake, Hawkins and Frobisher. Not till the fire-ships had cleared the Spanish fleet from anchor, not till the wind was gripping them after Gravelines, did the *Santa Catharina* lie under his guns.

Night robbed him of a finish even then. Don Guzman ploughed north in the teeth of the gale that finally dispersed the Armada. Amyas was on his heels all the time, frustrated by shoals and by gigantic seas and by nightfalls. So it continued.

The grim chase never closed till Scotland had been rounded and the *Santa Catharina* entered the Bristol Channel. Amyas took a hone from his pocket and, red-eyed, sullen, began ceaselessly to whet the edge of his sword. As Lundy Island loomed ahead, he knew the Spaniard was trapped.

Then once more came a furious north-wester. Unfamiliar with the Channel, Don Guzman was driven hard on Lundy's granite rocks. They saw the mighty ship heel over from the wind, and sweep headlong down the cataract of the race, plunging her yards into the foam, and showing her whole black side even to the keel, till she rolled clean over, and vanished for ever and ever.

Amyas hurled his sword far into the sea and cursed the God

who had taken vengeance from under his hand. In that same moment came a fearful lightning flash, and in that same moment, too, the giant was stricken blind.

When the first madness of his affliction was over, he asked to be taken to the cliff-tops of Lundy. There he fought with himself, learned the worth of his futile lust for revenge, and came down, calm and clear-minded, to the guiding hands held out to him.

It was not so easy back home. Familiar doors hurt him, corners of furniture jabbed viciously at him, old, loved books were shut for ever. He took an apple from a dish and idly turned it over and over in his hands as he pitied himself in thought. And then the apple dropped.

Groping for it, the helpless giant struck his head on a table. It was too much. Tears came to his exhausted soul. But the tears were dried and his heart lightened. For Ayaconora came warm and loving from the night surrounding him, and he knew that all he had lost was as nothing compared to all he had found.

UNE VIE

By GUY DE MAUPASSANT

*" Une Vie ", which appeared in 1883, was De Maupassant's
first full-length novel. A brilliant and moving account of a
woman's life, it is perhaps the greatest of this author's
works. Certainly no other novelist has written a finer study
on the same lines. His active literary life was very short :
he died in a lunatic asylum in his forty-third year, but he had
by then established himself as the world's greatest short-story
writer, and the passage of the years has only served to enhance
his reputation.*

JEANNE LE PERTHUIS DES VAUDS left her convent in 1819,
when she was seventeen years old. Her father, the Baron,
had kept her there, secluded from the world, for five years,
and when she returned to her parents she was completely
ignorant of what are called " the facts of life ".

The Baron, though an aristocrat, was by education and
temperament a philosophical radical. A whole-hearted disciple of Jean-Jacques Rousseau, he hoped to be able to make
his daughter happy and virtuous by " bringing her out "
amid the sights and sounds of the countryside round *Les
Peuples*, the old family seat on the cliffs near Yport.

Les Peuples was to become Jeanne's property. She was to
be married there, and there settle down for the rest of her
life, leading the quiet, healthy existence of the prosperous
country gentry.

She was radiantly happy during the first weeks at *Les
Peuples*. She wandered all alone about the countryside,
thrilled by the caresses of wind and sun, drinking in the
intoxicating scent of wild flowers.

Jeanne was young, beautiful, and wealthy; she had the
most charming estate in all France; her father was wisely
indulgent, and her mother fondly adoring. She wanted only
one thing more to make her life complete: a husband. Night
and day she dreamed of love, yearning for the day when she
would meet the man who had been predestined to make her
his own.

One Sunday, not many weeks after they had come to live

at *Les Peuples*, the priest introduced them to the Viscount de Lamare, who had recently taken up residence in the neighbourhood. The Viscount was not very rich, but he was young, handsome, and charming. The Baron and his wife both liked him and invited him to dinner. Soon he came regularly to the house. It was not long before Jeanne was head-over-heels in love with him. Her parents gently encouraged her, and almost before she realized what was happening, she was married.

On her wedding-day the Baron took Jeanne aside and, after some hesitation, spoke as follows:

" I have asked your mother to tell you about the facts of marriage, but she refuses to do so. It therefore devolves upon me to warn you that, upon marriage, things are revealed to women that have hitherto been kept secret from them. If no hint of these things is given to them beforehand, they sometimes recoil, shocked and frightened, from the harsh realities, and refuse to yield to their husbands. I cannot tell you more, but you must realize that you belong to Julian completely."

These words frightened Jeanne without, however, enlightening her. There was much that she knew instinctively, but only experience could teach her the nature of these " harsh realities ".

That night she shuddered with apprehension after her maid, Rosalie, had undressed her and put her to bed. She hid her head under the sheets when she heard her husband knocking on the bedroom door. He waited a little while and then knocked again, but, getting no reply, he came in and stood by the bed. She uncovered her head and, looking up at him fearfully, said:

" Oh, how you frightened me! "

" But were you not expecting me, then? " he asked.

She did not reply.

When he attempted to make love to her she shuddered and turned away, saying, " Oh, please, not yet."

A little later he made another attempt, but again she repulsed him. He then fell asleep, and in the morning behaved as if nothing had happened to disturb the harmony that existed between them. He seemed content to wait.

She had her first night of love while they were on their honeymoon in Corsica. She had dreaded it, but when it came all her fears were laid aside. The remaining weeks of

the honeymoon passed like a dream, made up of passionate
embraces and wildly exciting caresses.

But the dream was soon ended. When they returned to
Les Peuples, Jeanne felt flat and dispirited. She had looked
forward so much to the mystery of love, and now there seemed
to be not much in it. She had so much wanted to be married.
Now that this ambition had been achieved there seemed to be
nothing further to look forward to. Life stretched before her
empty and bleak, whereas only a few months before it had
seemed full of exciting possibilities.

Was she really in love with this man into whose hands she
had resigned herself, her fortune, and her home? She found
him physically attractive—yes; but was she really going to
like living with him? What had she in common with him
save a transient physical passion?

During the honeymoon she had discovered that Julian was
very careful about money—too careful, in fact. This horrified
her all the more because her father had always insisted that
the best thing to do with money was to spend it as quickly
and pleasantly as possible.

As soon as they returned to *Les Peuples*, Julian seemed to
lose interest in his wife. He left her to sleep by herself, pleading that he was tired. He also became very slovenly in habit
and appearance, going about in dirty old clothes with an
untrimmed beard. He took over the entire management of
the estate, and immediately instituted an economy campaign
which made him very unpopular with both peasants and
servants; the gallant, well-groomed lover had been replaced
by a mean and boorish husband.

*   *   *   *   *

During their first winter at *Les Peuples*, Rosalie, Jeanne's
maid, gave birth to an illegitimate child. She obstinately
refused to say who the father was, despite the combined
efforts of Jeanne, the Baron, and the priest to induce her to
divulge his name.

Julian wished to give Rosalie a little money and send her
away, but Jeanne insisted that the maid should be allowed to
stay on at *Les Peuples*, and that the infant should be taken
care of by a nurse.

One night, not many weeks after the child had been born,
Jeanne, finding herself unable to sleep because of the extreme
cold, got out of bed and ran upstairs to Rosalie's room with
the intention of sharing her bed. She was astonished to find

that the maid was not in her room and that her bed had not
been slept in.

Jeanne rushed downstairs again to waken Julian and, bursting into his room, found him in bed with Rosalie. Horror-
stricken, she rushed back into her own room, whither Julian
followed her. But the idea of having him near her or feeling
his touch and hearing his voice filled Jeanne with loathing,
and, in a frantic desire to get away from him, she ran out
into the snow-filled night. She ran wildly down the garden
and then across the moor towards the sea. When she reached
the cliff she crouched down on the grass, trembling like a sail
in the wind.

Visions of long-past happenings flashed through her mind,
and she bitterly recalled the romantic yearnings of her youth.
All was over now; nothing was left but weariness and despair.

Julian and the two men-servants had followed her tracks
in the snow. While she was still trying to gather courage to
take the fatal leap down on to the wave-lashed rocks, they
came up and caught her. She lost consciousness, and they
carried her home and put her to bed.

Thereafter she spent many delirious nights and days. At
last, one evening, her mind clear, she found herself alone
with the Baroness. She immediately told her mother how she
had found Rosalie in bed with Julian. But the Baroness,
thinking she was still delirious, would not believe her.

In the end the priest was sent for and Rosalie made to
confess her guilt before the priest in Jeanne's bedroom. The
maid revealed that Julian had seduced her before his marriage,
and that he had resumed illicit relations with her immediately
after the honeymoon. Worst of all, he was the father of her
child.

Jeanne was filled with a cold determination to leave her
husband for ever, and in this she was supported by her father,
who was boiling with indignation. But the good-natured old
priest, anxious that there should be the minimum of scandal
and unpleasantness, reminded the Baron that he had not
seldom been unfaithful to his wife, and urged that Jeanne
should forgive Julian. After much discussion the priest's
view prevailed. Jeanne agreed to continue to occupy the
same house as Julian; and it was arranged that Rosalie
should be given a farm and that a husband should be found
for her. Jeanne sullenly agreed to these proposals, black
despair in her heart.

A few months later she gave birth to a boy. During her confinement she had cursed God for bringing this terrible physical pain upon her after all the spiritual torment through which she had gone, but as soon as she was delivered of the child she was filled with inexpressible joy. Here, at last, after interminable months of anguish and disillusionment, was something to love her. Thereafter she lived only for Paul, her son. She no longer felt bitter towards Julian; she was completely indifferent to him.

*   *   *   *   *

There were several aristocratic families living in the neighbourhood, but the only local people with whom Julian cared to be on friendly terms were the Fourvilles. Gilberte, Countess de Fourville, was young, beautiful, and impetuous; her husband, big-bodied, great-hearted, and charming, was madly in love with her.

Julian was obviously very attracted by the Countess, but was a little cold towards her husband. Jeanne regarded the wife as her friend, and found herself in complete sympathy with the jovial Count.

One day Jeanne wandered into a wood in which Julian had made love to her shortly after they had first met. There she came upon two horses tethered together. She recognized them as those of her husband and Gilberte, but of their owners she could find no trace except a pair of woman's gloves and a pair of riding-whips. She waited in vain for twenty minutes, hoping they would come back, and then, quite suddenly, it dawned upon her that they were lovers. She fled back to Les Peuples, but decided to pretend not to know of their relationship.

*   *   *   *   *

Soon afterwards Jeanne's mother, who had long been ailing, died. To Jeanne, in her near-hysterical state, her death came as a terrible shock. After discovering about Julian's infidelities, Jeanne had begun to loathe anything to do with sexual passion, and she had turned eagerly towards her parents as towards persons who were above any suspicion of sexual irregularity. Her mother, in particular, she had come to regard as a pure and perfect wife and mother. The night after her mother's death, Jeanne began piously to go through her private papers. Among them she discovered evidence that her mother had been shamefully unfaithful not long after

her marriage. At first she could hardly believe her eyes, bu
the evidence was overwhelming, so she burnt all her mother'
letters lest the Baron should read them. This revelatio
almost killed Jeanne's faith in human nature.

When she had recovered from the double shock of he
mother's death and the destruction of one more illusion, sh
began to wish for another child to keep Paul company. Sh
was very perplexed as to how to achieve this end. Her hus
band had not shared her bed since the affair of Rosalie, an
she had, of course, no wish that he should. But her desir
for another child became so strong that she asked the pries
to convey to her husband that she wished to renew marita
relations with him.

Julian condescendingly obliged her, but he took good car
to prevent conception from taking place. In despair, Jeann
asked him outright to give her another child, but he flatl
refused. Then, prompted by the old priest, she resorted t
guile. One day she told Julian that she was with child
This was untrue, but he believed it, and thereafter took n
precautions. Soon, to her unbounded delight, she discovered
herself pregnant. She then locked her door against he
husband.

*   *   *   *   *

Soon afterwards the old priest, who had been in the parish
for sixteen years, was given promotion elsewhere. His place
was taken by a fanatical young Puritan called Tolbiac, who
came with the intention of cleaning up the parish. The old
priest warned him that the only way to keep his parishioners
pure was to chain them up, but he indignantly refused to
believe this.

Abbé Tolbiac soon found out about the illicit relationship
between Gilberte and Julian. He called upon Jeanne, told
her of his discovery, and demanded that she should either
force her husband to renounce Gilberte or leave him. She
refused to take either course, whereupon the priest departed
in a towering rage. On the following Sunday he denounced
Les Peuples from the pulpit, making veiled references to Julian's
love affair. Not long afterwards the spiteful priest was seen
leaving the Fourvilles' residence.

On a stormy afternoon in May, Count de Fourville came
running up to *Les Peuples* in a state of great agitation. He asked
Jeanne if his wife was with her, and when she replied in the
negative, he hesitated for a moment and then rushed away

towards the sea. Jeanne started to follow him, but he soon disappeared from sight.

Having reached the edge of the cliff, he turned to the right, in the direction of the deep valley of Vancotte. There he saw a shepherd's hut on wheels, and, tethered to it, two horses. He approached the hut and set the horses free. Then he applied his eyes to a crack in the wall of the hut. What he saw inside drove him into a frenzy.

He jumped up, shot the outside bolt of the hut door, and then, placing himself between the shafts, dragged the hut to the top of the slope. There he let go the shafts, and the hut rushed wildly down the hill, its guilty occupants screaming. When the hut reached the bottom, it was smashed to pieces and the two lovers were lifeless and horribly mangled.

That night Jeanne was delivered of a dead child—a girl. For three months afterwards she remained in bed. At times it seemed that she was at the point of death, but the unremitting care of the Baron and old Aunt Lison saved her life.

When she was well again her mind was haunted with bittersweet memories of the early days of her married life. She began to forget Julian's faults and to remember with sad gratitude the little happinesses he had given her. She pictured him as he had been when she had first given in to him in Corsica. But with the passage of time she thought less and less of him, devoting herself more and more completely to her son.

Young Paul, worshipped and attended upon by three people—Jeanne, the Baron, and Aunt Lison—was utterly spoilt. He was the supreme ruler of *Les Peuples*.

The family was completely estranged from the Church on account of Abbé Tolbiac's behaviour, and Paul was brought up in the agnostical tenets of the Baron. One day he announced to Aunt Lison, who had been surreptitiously attempting to pump some religion into him, that " God is everywhere except in church ".

At the age of fifteen Paul was sent to a boarding-school, at the Baron's suggestion. At first his mother had refused to let him go, but she gave in when the Baron pointed out that she was being thoroughly selfish instead of kind, as she thought.

During the years when Paul was at school, Jeanne lived only for the holidays. It horrified her when she noticed how quickly he was growing up, but she insisted on treating him like a child. She herself had aged so much that she might have been taken for her father's sister.

At the age of twenty Paul began to show signs of dissolute tendencies. He borrowed large sums of money, which he left his mother to repay, and he took to drinking, gambling, and loose women. Then one day it was discovered that he had gone to London with a woman of the streets. The only letters Jeanne received from him were appeals for money.

Shortly after this the Baron fell dead in his lawyer's office, and a few months later Aunt Lison died, saying that she would ask God to take pity on Jeanne.

After Aunt Lison's funeral, Rosalie, now a buxom and prosperous farmer's wife, arrived at *Les Peuples* to look after Jeanne. The latter allowed this woman, who had once been her maid, to take complete control over herself and over all her affairs.

Rosalie soon found that Paul's extravagances had dissipated the greater part of the family fortune. She made Jeanne sell *Les Peuples* and move into a little house on the high road, some miles inland. Jeanne had by now suffered so many calamities that she was too stunned to do anything except obey Rosalie. Acting on the latter's instructions, she ceased to send money to her son, but she let him know that he would always be welcome whenever he might choose to return home.

Jeanne still entertained the hope that Paul would return to her, but as the years passed she grew more and more apathetic.

One day in early spring Rosalie took her to *Les Peuples*. The new owner was away, and Jeanne was graciously allowed to enter her old home once again. She wandered from room to room with an agonizing pain in her heart. Every little bit of the house recalled some poignant memory.

That evening she received a letter from Paul. He said that the woman with whom he had been living was dying after having given birth to a child, and he asked Jeanne to take the infant, as he was penniless.

Rosalie was sent to get the child, and a few days later returned with it and handed it over to the now radiantly happy Jeanne. The mother had died the night before, and Paul was to return after the funeral.

As Rosalie sat watching Jeanne smothering the infant boy in kisses, she said, gently, " Life, you see, is never so good or so bad as people think."

THE CLOISTER AND THE HEARTH

By CHARLES READE

*This huge romance of the Middle Ages, first published in
1861, is the result of an exhaustive study of medieval life.
The hero's career is more or less based on available facts
concerning the father of Erasmus. The book reveals the
great narrative gifts of its author more clearly than in his
other work, where it is obscured by violent propaganda.*

IN the little town of Tergou in Holland there lived in the
fifteenth century a cloth merchant named Eli with his wife
Catherine. They had nine children, of whom but five
come into this tale: Cornelis and Sybrandt, lazy, deceitful,
and evil-hearted; Giles, a dwarf of amazing strength; Kate,
the gentle cripple; and Gerard, our hero. Gerard was
destined for the Church, and had been educated in a monastery.
He could write very beautifully—a rare accomplishment in that
age when calligraphy was a highly prized art. He could also
paint, and in the pursuit of these arts was encouraged by old
Margaret Van Eyck, sister of the famous painters.

One year the Prince of the Low Countries offered prizes in
open competition for various branches of the arts, including
manuscript-writing and illumination. Gerard went to Rotterdam to compete. On the way he met an old man and a beautiful girl half-fainting with hunger by the roadside. They were
an old doctor and his daughter, Peter and Margaret Brandt,
from the neighbouring village of Sevenbergen. Gerard shared
his food with them. The lovely auburn hair, white skin,
and deep violet eyes of the girl captivated Gerard, and almost
from the first glance he was in love with her.

In Rotterdam Gerard took a letter from Margaret Van
Eyck to the Princess Marie, heir to the throne of the Nether-
lands, and then but a child. Her mother was so charmed with
the young artist's modesty and sincerity that, on hearing he
was to be a priest, she promised him on her daughter's behalf a
benefice near his native town when he should be ordained.
But alas! a priest must give up all earthly ties, and Gerard was
in love. He was constantly at Margaret's house in Sevenbergen. He determined to give up his career as a priest.

But he had an enemy, the avaricious burgomaster, Ghysbrecht Van Swieten. Twenty years before, this man had wronged Peter Brandt and his daughter, and now he was mightily afeared that Gerard might discover his guilty secret. So he told Gerard's father, Eli, that Gerard was courting Margaret.

There was a terrible family quarrel. Gerard vowed he would ne'er be a priest while Margaret lived. On Dame Van Eyck's advice the lovers decided to marry at once in secret, and to flee to Italy, the land of the arts, where Gerard should make his name. They were formally betrothed, a ceremony in those days almost equal to marriage, and soon they were standing before a priest awaiting the final blessing.

But it was not to be. Gerard's idle brothers, Cornelis and Sybrandt, afraid that Gerard would lessen their share of Eli's wealth if he did not become a priest, were determined that he should not marry. Their sly cunning told them that the burgomaster Van Swieten also for some reason wished to prevent the match. A drunken man's babble informed the brothers when Gerard's wedding was to take place. They flew to tell the burgomaster. Before the betrothed couple could complete their vows they were torn asunder by the burgomaster's men, and Gerard was carried off to gaol, ostensibly for having disobeyed his father's will.

He was confined at the top of a tall tower. That night Margaret and a friend, an old soldier named Martin, came to Gerard's rescue. Martin shot an arrow, to which was attached a cord, through the prison window. Gerard pulled up the cord, to which a stout rope was fastened. He tied the rope to an old, heavy coffer in the cell, and in so doing accidentally opened the secret lock. A number of old documents fell out, which Gerard took with him down the rope to safety.

The lovers fled to Margaret's house at Sevenbergen, but the next night they found the house surrounded by Van Swieten's men. Ghysbrecht had discovered that Gerard had escaped with the very document which proved the burgomaster had cheated the Brandts. Gerard hid in a hole in the floor under Margaret's bed, and the soldiers never found him. Overcome with the fears of the night, the lovers spent the rest of the night in each other's arms.

Next day Gerard fled to Italy. He left behind for the burgomaster all the documents except one, on which he saw the name of Brandt. This he determined to read. Martin undertook to show him the road to the German border. Margaret was to go a short way with them. Scarcely had they started but the hue and cry was after them. The burgomaster's bloodhounds tracked them through the forest. After a terrible and thrilling chase Gerard escaped over the border into Germany.

Alone, on foot, Gerard made his way through a strange land where Dutch cleanliness and Dutch courtesy were alike unknown. At a filthy inn he met a jovial Burgundian soldier who cheered him with a motto he used on every conceivable occasion: " *Courage, mon ami, le diable est mort.*" An odd friendship grew up between the rough, good-hearted crossbowman, Denys, with his weakness for petticoats, and the young artist priest, with his single passion for one pure woman.

Many were the adventures which befell the two on their way. One day on the road to Dusseldorf they killed a bear cub. They carried the bleeding carcass with them for their supper. Later Gerard turned round to see a huge she-bear rushing down on them. She was mad with anger at the loss of her cub, and had followed the scent of the blood. She made for Denys, who leaped up the nearest tree.

Ill luck would have it that the tree was dead and short, without branches. Denys would certainly have been killed had not Gerard picked up Denys's crossbow and shot at the bear with desperate, unskilled hands. The bear abandoned Denys and pursued Gerard, who took refuge in another tree. But though Gerard was the more agile, the bear was relentless. Up she lumbered after him, mad for·blood. Out along a branch she pursued him, till Gerard had nothing behind and below him but a forty-foot drop, and in front of him the snarling she-bear. Then a bow twanged, blood spurted out of the bear's jaws, and it rolled to the ground, dead. Denys had saved him.

After an encounter with a bandit under a gibbet laden with the dangling corpses of his companions, Gerard and Denys reached Dusseldorf. There Gerard, whose leg had had a goodly piece taken out of it by the bear, fell ill with a fever. He was visited, unasked, by a physician, who so angered him with his pomposity and his quackery, that the invalid clinched the argument as to whether he should be bled or not, by throwing a bolster at the doctor and bringing him to the floor, robes, phials and all. Gerard, gentle youth though he was, had ever a hot temper.

Fearing the good physician's revenge, the travellers slipped from the town next morning, and hired a boat to take them down the Rhine. All at once two things occurred. They spied a posse of officers of the Law pursuing them down the bank, and the boatman's little boy pulled the plug from the bottom of the boat. In a few moments they were in the cold and rushing Rhine.

Gerard was a strong swimmer, but Denys was rendered helpless by the heavy crossbow slung across his back. Gerard was half-way to the bank when he heard a cry: " Adieu, comrade, adieu! " and there was Denys, fast sinking. In a moment Gerard was back at the spot where Denys had disappeared, and, by means of the same crossbow, hauled him to the surface, and presently towed him to the shore—the opposite shore to that where their pursuers were waiting for them.

Strangely enough, this sousing cured Gerard of his fever. The hunt was out after the pair, but they outwitted the pursuers, and that night lay safe at a monastery, where a healing poultice was laid on Gerard's leg. Gerard always felt happy in a monastery, and sometimes repaid the hospitality by doing copying for the monks. Poor Denys could not abide a monastery, and felt fifty times more at home sleeping in a cowshed, as they sometimes were obliged to do, or even in a tavern infested with robbers. But after his experiences in one monastery, where the young monks stole out at night to carouse in the crypt of the church, Denys owned that his opinion of the monastic life had risen. Poor Gerard was dreadfully shocked.

Soon the travellers came to Burgundy, Denys's beloved native land, of which he had never ceased to sing the praises all the while they sojourned in Germany. Here indeed the inns were much cleaner and the fare much better, and Gerard began to think that his friend had not over-rated the Burgundian virtues until they slept at a certain inn. Denys, seeing a buxom girl at the door, led the way in without further inquiry. The landlord made them pay for their supper in advance. Then he went out.

While supper was preparing, Denys, as was his wont, fell to courting the buxom serving-wench. They were alone in the yard, and, to his surprise, she began to weep. She said her sweetheart had been hanged. Denys tried to cheer her, but she would not be comforted. Then she seemed to take a great resolution and told him: " The landlord is gone to fetch the band."

" The band! What band? "

" Those who will cut your throat and take your gold."

It appeared that Manon's sweetheart had been one of the band before he was caught. In league with the landlord, they robbed and murdered the guests of the inn. Denys persuaded the girl to run to the town, which lay a league or two distant, to summon aid. It was a wild, stormy night.

When Denys went back into the house, he found seven villainous-looking men seated round the fire, and the landlord pouring them out neat brandy. To gain time, Denys paid for another bottle for the merry company, and, feigning to suspect nothing, went to join Gerard in their room and to prepare the defence.

The robber he feared most was a huge man they called the Abbot, who wielded an axe. It was useless to bolt the door, for the doorpost was false and swung outwards on a hinge. The two men concealed themselves on either side of the door. Presently the first assassin crept in, and was slain on the instant by Denys's dagger. They put the corpse in a chair facing the door, and Gerard adorned the face with phosphorus, and writ the word DEATH in fiery letters on the forehead.

Presently another came up to see what had happened to the first, saw this luminous apparition confronting him in the dark room, and ran howling down the stairs. Then came the Abbot. He gave a gasp on seeing the apparition, and Denys shot him in the mouth. It was his last arrow, and only wounded and maddened the Abbot. He kicked his dead comrade aside and came on, wielding his huge axe. An heroic fight to the death followed. Ere it was over, help from the neighbouring town had arrived. The Abbot, spitted on the two swords of Denys and Gerard, wrenched free, took a flying leap down the staircase and fell dead.

In the town, whither the two friends went next day to make their depositions, for the rest of the gang had been taken and were to be tried, another misfortune befell. While Denys was gambling with some fair ladies, who not only cheated him, but robbed him of his purse to boot, Gerard was arrested for sorcery for making of a luminous corpse. He was like to have been burned, had not the local curé come to his assistance, and, in return for a gift of the phosphorus, which he forthwith put to miracle-making uses, procured Gerard's release.

Scarcely had the friends left the town than they met a troop of soldiers led by the Bastard of Burgundy. They were bound northwards to quell a rising in Flanders. To Denys's surprise and horror, they seized him and forced him to go with them on pain of death. Soon after they were gone, Gerard was robbed of his purse by a nobleman's servants. So he was left, friendless and penniless in a strange land, and not half-way to his destination, Rome.

Meanwhile Margaret had struck up a friendship with Gerard's patroness, the Dame Van Eyck. To her she confided all her troubles except one, and that she told nobody. It grieved her sorely nevertheless, for Gerard had taken with him the written testimony of betrothal, which in those times was equal to marriage lines. One day by chance she met Catherine at Dame Van Eyck's house. Catherine was waiting to ask the old lady to read a letter she had received from Gerard, for Eli, the only member of the household who could read, was away from home. Margaret offered to read the letter, and Gerard's mother, not knowing the young lady, thankfully accepted. Emotion proved too strong for the poor reader, and she fell in a swoon at Catherine's feet. Then Catherine discovered two things: that the girl was Margaret Brandt, and that Gerard was to be a father.

A pupil of the Van Eycks, one Hans Memling, was then setting out for Rome. He was entrusted with a letter from Margaret Brandt to Gerard. He was good soul enough, but he loved the "nipperkin, canakin and brown browl" more than they deserve. In a tavern at Tergou he babbled out to Sybrandt that he was taking a letter to Gerard in Italy. Sybrandt told Cornelis, and then they both informed the burgomaster.

Ghysbrecht Van Swieten, knowing Gerard to have the fatal document in his hands, determined to prevent his return to Holland. Gerard was an escaped prisoner, with dire penalties hanging over his head. Only his love for Margaret, therefore, could make him risk a return. (Ghysbrecht did not know that the old soldier Martin had ere this obtained a pardon for Gerard from the Duke.) So Cornelis and Sybrandt and the burgomaster between them conceived the diabolical plan of making Gerard believe that Margaret was dead. To this end the burgomaster wrote a false letter, purporting to be from Margaret Van Eyck, to inform Gerard of Margaret's death. The brothers substituted it for the true one in Hans Memling's wallet.

Margaret and her father left Sevenbergen and went to live

Richard Cœur de Lion is surprised in Sherwood Forest

A scene from " Ivanhoe "

Napoleon meets Alexander I of Russia

An illustration to "War and Peace"

above a tailor's shop in Brede-Kirk Street, Rotterdam. For a short time all went well. Her father had begun to acquire a reputation as physician, when the old man was laid low by a stroke. From that time he was no more than a helpless child. Then Margaret stepped into his shoes, and soon was making a pretty living administering simples and herbs and common-sense remedies. Since her cures killed none, the professional physicians grew jealous, and she was like to have been prosecuted as a witch. She escaped with a heavy fine, however, and was forbidden to practise.

She now had her sick father and old Martin, who lived with them, to support, and a child coming. She took in washing from her old patients, and Martin carried the basket. One day she found a soldier talking to the girls at the well. " Courage," he cried, " the Devil is dead," and she knew him for Gerard's friend Denys. Thereafter he also came to live with her, and helped with the ironing.

One day an unexpected and unwelcome visitor came to the house. It was Ghysbrecht Van Swieten. He delivered a letter from Gerard, and went scowling away. Gerard had sent a letter by a Dutch ship from Venice; it had fallen into the burgomaster's hand, and, smitten by a pang of remorse, he had brought it, after tampering with the seal, to Margaret.

Eli was to set up Cornelis and Sybrandt in a shop in Rotterdam, and the whole family were now in that city. By a sad series of misunderstandings, a deadly feud was in progress between Margaret and Gerard's family. Only the little gentle-hearted cripple, Kate, was her friend. In his letter, however, Gerard bade Margaret read it to his family. Accompanied by Denys, therefore, she went to Eli's house, and there read the letter aloud. It detailed Gerard's adventures from the time Denys left him until his arrival in Venice.

First he was befriended by a master-beggar, by name Cul de Jatte, who took him as servant and travelled with him into Germany. From him Gerard learned much of the tricks and deceits then in practice among the goodly fraternity of vaga-bonds. He saw Cul de Jatte paint sores on himself, and tie up his limbs to look like deformities, and steal bones from the churchyard to sell as holy relics, and a hundred other tricks. Gerard steadfastly refused to help him in his deceptions, but turned a few pennies on his own account by playing ditties on a psaltery that the beggar had bought him.

After he and Cul de Jatte parted ways, Gerard was overtaken

by a nobleman on horseback, who insisted on exchanging clothes with him, setting him on his horse, and travelling with him as a servant. The nobleman was doing a penance that obliged him to change places with a poor man. So Gerard came to Augsburg, and there fell in with the great merchant Fugger, who was also travelling to Italy, and took on Gerard as his scrivener.

Gerard rode in the merchant's litter amid a vast armed caravan of travellers, and should have been safe from further peril. But one day he got down to walk, and presently lost the company. A storm came on, and spying an old windmill, he decided to take shelter in it. It seemed deserted, but he had not been inside long when a band of desperadoes came in and barred the door. The windmill was their headquarters; Gerard had little hope of leaving it alive.

He braved it out, explained his predicament, and asked for a bed. He was taken up a winding staircase to the very top of the mill, and shown a small room with a truckle bed. There was no bolt on the door. Fearing the worst, he lay down at the door with his sword drawn. Suddenly, with a loud clang, the bed disappeared into the floor. A trapdoor underneath it had opened, and, looking down, Gerard saw a yawning pit going right down to a well below the floor of the mill.

Knowing that the robbers would come up to find out why he had not fallen into their horrible trap, Gerard made a rope of some straw which was lying in the room and let himself out of the window. Then he sprang on to one of the sails as they revolved past him. From the sail he fell to the ground, and sprained one leg. He could hear the whole band thundering up the staircase to his room.

In desperation he hobbled to some barrels of spirit which were lying near the door of the mill, pierced them with his dagger, and threw them on to a pile of straw by the door. Then with his tinder he lit the pile and set fire to the mill. The assassins were trapped in the burning building. Gerard crawled back to the road, and by good luck met the caravan again. So, without further adventure, he came to Venice, and sent off his letter.

Gerard took ship for Rome. Between Naples and the Holy City he was shipwrecked in a terrible storm. The only people beside himself on the boat who did not give way to craven fear were a huge Dominican friar, who stood in the poop ignoring the elements and confessing the passengers, and a Roman woman with a babe at her breast. Gerard saved the woman by binding her to a wooden statue of the Virgin and lowering it like a boat off the ship. Then the gigantic monk helped Gerard to throw overboard a broken mast, and holding to this they were both brought to land. Next day Gerard reached the Holy City.

He had believed he could easily make a living by his skill at writing, but he found that a thick wall of fees, commissions, and chicanery stood between patrons of art and an unknown artist. However, he struck up a friendship with a painter who lodged in the same house and who found himself in like case, and they kept the pot boiling by painting playing-cards. Then it turned out that the landlady had a friend who was the very woman whom Gerard had saved from the shipwreck, one Teresa. She could not do enough for Gerard, and eventually introduced him to Father Colonna, a priest of the powerful and wealthy Colonna family, and himself a great patron of the arts.

From then on Gerard prospered. He received a commission to copy manuscripts in the Vatican. One day he was sent for to the Cesarini palace, and a young princess commanded him to write a letter for her. She fell in love with him, declared her love, and when, though perhaps tempted by her extraordinary classic beauty, he kept aloof, she all but had him murdered in her house. Fearing her vengeance, he decided to lie low for a little, and, having nothing to do, set himself to read the old document relating to the Brandts. The writing of it was so ill, that he had not before had the patience to decipher it. Now he discovered that Ghysbrecht Van Swieten was illegally holding land and rents belonging to Margaret and her father.

He determined to return to Holland at once. But the next day arrived the false letter by the hand of Hans Memling. Margaret, it said, was dead and buried. Struck down by the blow, Gerard fell desperately ill and all but died himself. When he recovered, his despair turned to reckless bitterness. He plunged into the wildest dissipation, drinking, gaming, wenching. One day the princess saw him in a wild company in a boat on the Tiber, and by his side what she thought to be a beautiful harlot (and was in reality a boy dressed up) who mocked her to Gerard's companions. Furious, she determined on her revenge.

She hired a professional assassin to murder Gerard. This

man was no other than the husband of Teresa. He followed
Gerard one night when, a prey once more to the blackest
melancholy, the heartbroken lover wandered down to the Tiber
full of thoughts of suicide. Seeing the assassin, Gerard went
up to him and, baring his breast, begged the man to kill him.
The assassin recognized him, and stayed his hand. With a
snarl of contempt Gerard rushed from him, and with one cry,
" Margaret ! " flung himself into the river.

That same night, Margaret gave birth to a boy, and in her
weakness and joy called on Gerard to come back to her.
Faintly, as if at a vast distance, she heard Gerard's voice
answer, " Margaret ! "

The assassin rescued Gerard and took him to a Dominican
monastery hard by.   Here his tortured soul passed to penitence,
and turned from the world, and Gerard became a monk.
Meanwhile in the tailor's house in Brede-Kirk Street one of the
greatest men of the century was being suckled, and weaned,
and was cutting his teeth.

Gerard was now Brother Clement, a Dominican friar.   In
the same monastery lived the gigantic monk who had braved
the elements in the shipwreck.   His name was Brother Jerome,
and he took Clement's spiritual welfare into his especial care.
Clement's zeal and his rare mastery of languages destined him
to become a travelling preacher.   Before going forth once more
into the world, however, he was subjected, under Brother
Jerome's stern tutelage, to a number of sore trials.

Jerome took him into the foullest prisons, made him officiate
at horrible executions, took him to where his erstwhile companions were roistering, and above all forbade him to frequent
his good friend Father Colonna, who, though a priest, in his
heart, put the ideals of the Greeks above the Christian Church.
At length Clement was ordered to England with Brother
Jerome.

On his way through Italy he met a motley company of
pilgrims, and among them a beautiful young lady of rank, who,
as a penance, came forward to wash his feet, as she did to every
travelling friar she met.   She wore a mask.   She confessed her
sin to him—that she had had a young stranger, whom she loved,
murdered by an assassin.   It was the princess.   The assassin
had never returned to her, and her spies had told her Gerard
was dead.

Clement listened with emotion to her tale, and then, as she
appeared so truly unhappy and penitent, he told her gently the

true facts, but as if he were another person. At the end she recognized him, and fell swooning at his feet. He bade her leave the pilgrimage and return to Rome to work out her penance in good deeds among her own people.

Gerard stayed for some time teaching in the University of Basle. His manner of life—deep study and self-mortification— were rapidly earning him a reputation of saintliness. After a twelve-month Brother Jerome came to fetch him to England. The two friars went preaching down the Rhine.

Meanwhile in Rotterdam Margaret was sorely distressed at Gerard's absence. His father had sent him a letter to Rome telling him that he was pardoned and begging him to return immediately. But the months had passed, and there was no sign from him. Margaret was having a hard struggle to make ends meet.

But conscience was working in Ghysbrecht Van Swieten. He was growing old, and remorse prayed upon him. Now Margaret sometimes found gifts of money mysteriously appear in her house. Catherine, who helped her with the baby, had sent Denys back to Burgundy. Old Martin was dead. Presently Margaret's father died also, but before he passed away he had a vision. " I see him," he cried, " in a boat; on a great river; coming this way."

Acting on this, as she felt, Heaven-sent sign, Margaret sent a young man who was in love with her, Luke, up the Rhine to a station where all the public boats put in, to look for Gerard. Brother Clement, however, had left the boat higher up, and was gone to rescue a runaway nun from a life of sin in an ill-famed tavern. Jerome went on to Rotterdam to bespeak a passage to England. He met Luke inquiring for Gerard, and told him: " He you seek will be here by the next boat, and if he chooses to answer to that name. . . ."

Clement, however, took a short cut on foot and joined the boat below the station, and arrived the same day in Rotterdam. Constantly during his journey he had been praying for Margaret's departed soul.

More and more distressed at Gerard's silence, Margaret at length went with a neighbour to consult a famous hermit at Gouda. Imploringly she asked: " Is he quick or dead, true to his vows or false? " The answer was a faint voice saying: " Send me a holy friar, I am dying."

When Clement reached Rotterdam he found that Brother Jerome had already taken ship for England, and had left a message saying that Clement would do better to stay in Holland and preach to his own folk. Clement withdrew to a monastery, where the prior appointed him to preach the next day in the great church of Saint Laurens. On his way thither Clement met a woman who asked him to go to the hermit of Gouda.

That day Margaret, who had not heard a sermon for many a day, decided to hear the new preacher. Before she found a seat in the church she stood against a pillar, and the sun lit up her beautiful auburn hair. Clement saw and started, awestruck. He thought she was a spirit. Margaret did not recognize the robed monk, but yet saw that he had for some reason recognized her. She determined to wait for him after the service.

Thinking that Margaret must be buried in the churchyard of Saint Laurence, since her spirit had appeared in the church, Clement inquired of the sexton for her grave. The sexton was Margaret's neighbour, and knew her well. He had also once been in the employ of Ghysbrecht Van Swieten. When he learned from the friar that Gerard (for Clement did not reveal himself but pretended to be Gerard's friend) believed Margaret to be dead, he told the friar how he had once heard the burgomaster and Gerard's two brothers Cornelis and Sybrandt talking about a letter which they were to put in place of another in the wallet of one Hans Memling, and how the burgomaster had given the brothers money to do it.

On hearing this Clement gave way to a most terrible wrath, and strode straight to his parent's house. Margaret, coming up to the sexton a moment after, heard the story and knew who the friar was. Fearing bloodshed (for she knew Gerard's hot temper), she rushed to Eli's house. Gerard had just gone, having burst in on the family at dinner and cursed Cornelis and Sybrandt with all the terrors of the medieval curse.

Gerard then went to Tergou to the burgomaster's house. Ghysbrecht Van Swieten was mortally ill. Gerard confessed him, and, without revealing his identity, made him promise to restore the stolen lands to Margaret. Then he went to the dying hermit, and, after comforting his end, buried him and took his place in the cave. The holy anchorite lived without ever showing his face to the world. People brought gifts to the mouth of the cave and asked blessing.

Margaret was now a rich woman, but still a sorely unhappy one, since Gerard had disappeared again. Meanwhile Gerard's other brother, the dwarf Giles, who was a favourite at Court, had reminded the young Princess Marie of her promise as a child to give Gerard a benefice. She forthwith gave him the vacant benefice of Gouda. . As, however, he did not come to claim it, at the end of six months it was about to be disposed of elsewhere. ,

But at last Margaret had found out that Gerard was the hermit of Gouda. She took her little boy one night and went to the cave. She went in alone. Gerard, who was very weak and feverish through the rigorous mortification of the flesh which he had undertaken in order to forget his love, thought she was sent by the Devil. He reviled her and fled from the cave. Then she put the little boy in the cave and went away. When she came back she saw Gerard, who thought the child a foundling, dandling him on his knee. Then she went in, and told Gerard that the child was his son.

The unhappy pair were reconciled, and at length Margaret persuaded the hermit to leave his cell that same night and go to the Gouda manse, which she and Catherine had made ready. Thus Gerard became vicar of Gouda. Margaret Van Eyck's late servant and companion (the old lady was now dead) became his housekeeper and married Margaret's swain Luke.

Margaret often visited the vicarage, and she and Gerard worked together for the poor of Gouda. Never, however, did she and Gerard pass the bounds of pure friendship. The little boy grew, and at nine years was sent away to school, where he astonished his masters by his prodigious aptitude for learning.

One day plague broke out in the town where the boy was at school. Gerard hastily went to take him away. He found Margaret there before him. She had put the child in safety, but herself had caught the fell disease, and was even then dying. She confessed to Gerard and died in his arms. He was broken-hearted. He took her back to Gouda and buried her in the churchyard. As the first clod fell on her coffin something snapped in his breast. He left the manse and entered a Dominican monastery, a dying man. Soon he too was laid in Gouda churchyard in the same grave as his Margaret.

The little boy, Margaret and Gerard's son, belongs not to Fiction but History. Over the tailor's house in Brede-Kirk Street is writ in Latin: HERE IS THE LITTLE HOUSE WHERE ERASMUS WAS BORN.

IVANHOE

By SIR WALTER SCOTT

This novel, published in 1819, was the author's first depar-
ture from Scottish themes and his most popular book. Though
dictated while Scott was suffering from illness, it has a
masterly sweep and power, and is among the first successful
attempts to recreate a " historical " atmosphere.

CEDRIC the Saxon, Thane of Rotherwood, sat in his ivory-
inlaid chair at his banqueting-table and scowled.
He had many things to disturb him, chief of which was
the conquest of England by the Norman adventurers. Yet he,
the descendant of the great Hereward, would do his utmost to
show these arrogant Normans the mettle of the Saxon race.

By the marriage of his ward the Lady Rowena, descendant of
King Alfred, with the noble Athelstane he would unite two
English royal houses, to whom would rally all his oppressed
countrymen.

" These Norman fools," he cursed, " think me old, but they
shall find that, alone and childless as I am, the blood of Hereward still flows in the veins of Cedric."

Then, in a lowered tone, he lamented that his son Wilfrid,
the Knight of Ivanhoe, had not ruled his unreasonable passion
for Rowena, for which he had been banished, leaving Cedric
in his old age like the solitary oak to withstand the full sweep of
the Norman tempest.

The blast of a horn stirred him from his musing.

" To the gates, knaves ! "

The warder returned with the news that Prior Aymer and Sir
Brian de Bois-Guilbert, commander of the Knights Templar,
sought lodgings for the night.

"Normans both," muttered Cedric. " But the hospitality
of Rotherwood must not be impeached."

When the repast was about to begin, the major-domo raised
his wand and said, " Forbear. Place for the Lady Rowena."
Cedric rose, went to meet his ward, and escorted her to the
elevated seat at his own right hand.

At sight of the Saxon beauty, Brian de Bois-Guilbert was
deeply stirred; she differed widely from the Eastern sultanas

with whom he was more acquainted. Rowena was tall and exquisitely fair, but the noble cast of her head prevented the insipidity which sometimes attaches to fair beauties. When she saw the Knight Templar's eyes bent on her with an ardour that gave them the effect of lighted charcoal, she drew with dignity the veil round her face to intimate that his glance was disagreeable.

Just then Oswald the cup-bearer whispered in his master's ear that another newcomer was without, a Jew calling himself Isaac of York.

Introduced with little ceremony and advancing with fear, hesitation and deep humility, a tall, thin old man approached the lower end of the Saxon's board. As none offered to make room for him, a Pilgrim, who sat in the chimney corner, asked the shivering, hungry Jew to accept his seat.

Discussion at the table turned on the Crusades. Bois-Guilbert declared that the English knights were second only to the Templars, but was unexpectedly interrupted by the Pilgrim with, " Second to none! " The interrupter recalled that he had once seen King Richard and five of his English knights challenge all comers in the lists and that each knight had cast to the ground three antagonists. Bois-Guilbert scowled when Cedric asked the names of the doughty knights who had so gallantly upheld the honour of England, but he was unprepared for the disconcerting reply.

The Pilgrim gave all the names, save one, " a lesser knight whose name dwells not in my memory. But Sir Brian de Bois-Guilbert well knows the truth of what I have told you."

Unaware of the special interest which his news would convey to his Saxon hosts, who were strangers, the Norman, stung by the Pilgrim's remarks, burst forth with :

" I will myself tell the name of the knight before whose lance fortune and my horse's fault occasioned my falling—it was the Knight of Ivanhoe ! Were he in England and durst repeat in this week's tournament the challenge, I would give him every advantage of weapons and abide the result ! "

The silence was broken by the voice of the beautiful Rowena, who said with unusual warmth :

" And I affirm that he will meet fairly any honourable challenge ! "

At mention of his banished son, and by Rowena's instant defence of him, Cedric the Saxon was both startled and disturbed. But he added :

"Were further pledge necessary, I myself would gage my honour for the honour of Ivanhoe."

* * * * *

The tournament at Ashby, opened next day by Prince John in place of King Richard, still believed to be a prisoner in Austria, was one of the most memorable in the history of chivalry.

Memorable too for the house of Cedric, which at first watched with despair the Saxon champions being overthrown by the confident Norman challengers, led by Bois-Guilbert. Then a young knight, styling himself the Disinherited, mounted on a black charger, came forth unexpectedly and, dipping his lance with supreme grace, saluted the Prince and the ladies.

Though few believed that the promised encounter could end favourably for the newcomer, the multitude applauded his youthful grace, dexterity and great courage as he rode straight to the central pavilion and, with the sharp end of his lance, struck the shield of Bois-Guilbert, leader of the challengers, until it rang again.

"Have you heard mass this morning," demanded the surprised and arrogant Templar, "that you peril yourself so frankly?"

"I am fitter to meet death than thou art," was the retort.

"Then this night thou shalt sleep in Paradise."

The two met in the centre of the lists with the shock of a thunderbolt, and their lances burst into shivers. Equipped with fresh weapons, they sprang again from their stations and charged. The Disinherited Knight reeled, but kept his seat, and his own lance went fair and true, hitting the proud Norman's visor, the point retaining its hold on the bars. The unseated Templar, stung to madness by his disgrace, drew his sword and waved it at the newcomer, who leapt from his saddle and drew his own sword. But here the fight was stopped, for the youth had fairly won, leaving the boastful Bois-Guilbert, to spend the rest of his day sulking in his tent.

"Sir Disinherited Knight," cried Prince John from the Royal Pavilion, "It is now your duty to name the fair lady who, as Queen of Honour and Love, is to preside over next day's festival. Raise your lance."

The knight obeyed, and Prince John placed upon its point a coronet of green satin, which the conqueror carried along the galleries of beauties until he deposited it—at the feet of the fair lady Rowena.

* * * * *

In next day's tournament about a hundred knights took the field in two companies of fifty, one led by Brian de Bois-Guilbert, the other by the Disinherited Knight.

After their numbers had been thinned in an exceptionally severe encounter, the Disinherited Knight found himself opposed by three determined contestants: Athelstane, who, though a Saxon, had joined the Normans, Front-de-Bœuf and Bois-Guilbert. At the most critical moment there dashed to the youth's rescue one of his own party, the Black Knight, who rolled Front-de-Bœuf to the ground and then knocked the slow Athelstane senseless. In the desperate combat that followed, Bois-Guilbert was again unseated by the Disinherited Knight, and only the arrival of Prince John to declare the tournament at an end prevented the discomfited Templar from being forced to yield to his enemy, sword at throat.

Acclaimed the champion of the day, the Disinherited was conducted to the foot of the throne of honour to receive from Lady Rowena the reward of a splendid chaplet. He was wounded, and was heard to protest against the marshals for removing his helmet. But they did so, and the well-formed but sunburned features of a young man of twenty-five were seen amidst a profusion of fair hair. His countenance was pale as death and streaked with blood.

As the Knight's helmet was removed Rowena uttered a faint shriek, and Cedric rushed forward to separate his son Wilfrid of Ivanhoe from the girl he had been forbidden to marry. But the marshals of the tournament had forestalled him.

* * * * *

During the tournament Prince John, catching sight of a beautiful Jewess in the crowd, had invited her and her father, Isaac of York, to take a seat in the box occupied by Athelstane, much to that worthy's indignation. It was Isaac and his daughter Rebecca who tended the wounded Ivanhoe after the tournament, and took him for nursing and shelter to their residence in Ashby. Here Ivanhoe was also struck by the lustrous beauty of Rebecca, and would not have dissented from the remark which Prince John had made concerning her when he exclaimed:

"By the bald scalp of Abraham, yonder Jewess must be the very model of that perfection whose charms drove frantic the wisest king that ever lived."

And yet, when Rebecca told Ivanhoe, as she nursed him, that she was a Jewess, she sighed internally to observe his glance of tenderness and respectful admiration for his bene-factress exchanged for a manner cold, composed, and collected as towards one of an inferior race.

The three, with Ivanhoe carried on a litter, set out from Ashby, but the Saxon guards deserted. Fearing attack from outlaws, Isaac begged permission to join Cedric's party return-ing to Rotherwood, but was curtly refused by Athelstane, smarting still from the snub administered to him through the Jew by Prince John, at the tournament.

Just then Rebecca, making her way through the attendants to the palfrey of the Saxon lady, knelt down, and in the Oriental way of addressing superiors, kissed the hem of Rowena's garment.

" It is not for myself that I pray this favour, nor is it for this poor old man. . . . But it is in the name of one dear to many, and even dear to you, that I beseech you to let this sick person be transported with care and tenderness under your protection. For if evil chance him, the last moment of your life would be embittered with regret for denying that which I ask."

The noble and solemn air with which Rebecca made this appeal for one whose identity she dared not disclose in the presence of a father who had disinherited him, gave it double weight with the Lady Rowena. So it was that, unknown to her, the man she loved joined her father Cedric's party, and was still with them when they were ambushed in a narrow pass by some of the Norman nobles from the tournament, led by De Bracy, of the Free Companions, who was an intriguer with Prince John against King Richard.

The Saxon captives were taken to Torquilstone, castle of the roystering Baron Front-de-Bœuf, where they were to be held for ransom, revenge, and still more sinister purposes.

*　　*　　*　　*　　*

The first unfortunate to be interrogated by his Norman captors was Isaac of York, into whose dungeon descended Front-de-Bœuf, with his torturers.

" Most accursed dog of an accursed race," said Front-de-Bœuf, and straightway ordered his wretched captive to send to York and bring back for him a thousand silver pounds.

" Holy Abraham," returned the Jew. . . . " Not within the walls of York, ransack my house and that of all my tribe, wilt thou find a tithe of that huge sum of silver."

" I am reasonable," answered Front-de-Bœuf, " and if silver is scant, I refuse not gold."

" Have mercy on me, noble knight! " exclaimed Isaac.   " I am old and poor and helpless."

" Old thou mayest be," replied the knight—" more shame to their folly who have suffered thee to grow grey in usury and knavery. Feeble thou mayest be. But rich thou art."

" I swear to you, noble knight . . ."

" Perjure not thyself," said the Norman.   " This dungeon is no place for trifling. Prisoners ten thousand times more distinguished than thou have died within these walls, and their fate hath never been known. But for thee is reserved a long and lingering death. . . ."

Whereupon Front-de-Bœuf ordered his Saracen slaves to light a fire under a bed of iron bars.

" Now choose between such a scorching bed and the payment of a thousand pounds of silver."

" It is impossible," exclaimed the miserable Jew.

" Seize him and strip him," commanded the knight.

The unhappy Jew eyed in vain their countenances in the hope of discovering symptoms of relenting.

" I will pay," he said.   " Let my daughter Rebecca go forth to York with your safe-conduct."

" Thy daughter! " said Front-de-Bœuf.   " I gave that black-browed girl to be handmaiden to Sir Brian de Bois-Guilbert."

The yell which Isaac of York raised at this unfeeling communication made the very vault ring. He threw himself on the pavement and clasped the knees of Front-de-Bœuf.

" Take all you have asked—take ten times more, reduce me to ruin and to beggary, if thou wilt, broil me on that furnace, but spare my daughter, deliver her in safety and honour."

" I thought your race loved nothing save their money-bags," said Front-de-Bœuf, relenting somewhat.

" Robber and villain! " hissed the Jew, " I will pay thee nothing unless my daughter is delivered to me in safety."

" Strip him, slaves, and chain him down to the bars."

But the torture was delayed by the sound of a bugle, twice-winded, without the castle.

*   *   *   *   *

While the unhappy Jew was undergoing his ordeal in the dungeon, De Bracy was paying his attentions to Rowena elsewhere.

" Sir Knight," said she coldly, " I know you not, and that no man wearing spurs ought thus to intrude himself into the presence of an unprotected lady."

" De Bracy's name has not been always unspoken when heralds or minstrels have praised deeds of chivalry," he retorted.

" But which of them," demanded Rowena, " shall record in song your conquest of this night over an old man followed by a few timid hinds, and its booty, an unfortunate maiden, transported against her will to the castle of a robber? "

" You are unjust," said the knight, in confusion. " Yourself free from passion, you can allow no excuse for the frenzy of another, although caused by your own beauty."

" Such language of strolling minstrels becomes not the mouth of knights or nobles."

" Proud damsel," said De Bracy, incensed at finding his gallant style procured him nothing but contempt. He added less hotly: " Thou art proud Rowena, and thou art the fitter to be my wife. By what other means couldst thou be raised to high honour and to princely place? "

" Sir Knight," said Rowena, " when I leave the Grange in which I was brought up, it shall be with one who has not learnt to despise its dwelling and its manners."

De Bracy, guessing her meaning, assured her that Wilfrid of Ivanhoe would never lead her to his footstool. " This rival is in my power."

" Wilfrid here? " said Rowena, incredulous.

De Bracy laughed. Not only was Wilfrid in the castle, but his host Front-de-Bœuf had only to recognize him, the knight who opposed his own claim to the fair barony of Ivanhoe, and he would destroy him.

" Save him for the love of Heaven! " exclaimed Rowena, suddenly frightened.

" I can, I will—when Rowena consents to be the bride of De Bracy."

*　　　*　　　*　　　*　　　*

While the foregoing scenes were taking place, Rebecca awaited her fate in a distant and sequestered turret, guarded by the daughter of one of Cedric's dead friends, an old Saxon hag Ulrica, who had been ravished by the Norman captors of this, her ancestral halls.

The hag scowled at the fair Jewess with the malignant envy which old age and ugliness, united with evil conditions, are apt to look upon youth and beauty. " There is no escape," said the hag, " but through the gates of death." She left the room as she spoke, her features writhed into a sort of sneering laugh.

Presently Rebecca trembled and changed colour when she heard a step on the stair, and a tall man dressed as an outlaw entered, as though for the execution of some deed of which he was ashamed. Anticipating his explanation, Rebecca unclasped two costly bracelets and a collar, which she offered him:

"Take these, good friend, and for God's sake be merciful to me and my aged father."

"Fair flower of Palestine," replied the man, "these pearls yield in whiteness to your teeth; the diamonds are brilliant, but they cannot match your eyes; and I prefer beauty to wealth."

"Thou art no outlaw," said Rebecca; "no outlaw has ever refused such offers."

"I am not an outlaw, then, fair Rose of Sharon," said Brian de Bois-Guilbert, dropping his mantle.

"Then what wouldst thou have of me?" said the alarmed Rebecca. "I am a Jewess. Our union would be contrary to the laws of Church and synagogue."

"It were so indeed," replied the Templar, laughing. "I cannot wed. It is against my vow as a Templar to love any maiden otherwise than as I would love thee. Thou art the captive of my bow and spear—subject to my will by the laws of all nations."

"Stand back!" exclaimed Rebecca. "I will proclaim thy villainy, Templar, from one end of Europe to the other. You will be held accursed for dishonouring the cross that thou wearest."

"Thou art sharp-witted," replied the Templar, "but loud must be thy voice if it is heard beyond the iron walls of this castle."

"I will not submit to thee!" cried Rebecca. "Thou, the best lance of the Templars—craven knight—forsworn priest! I spit at thee. The God of Abraham hath opened an escape for his daughter—even from this abyss of infamy!"

She threw open the latticed window and in an instant stood on the very verge of the parapet, with not the slightest screen between her and the tremendous depth below. Clasping her hands, she extended them towards heaven, imploring mercy on her soul before making the plunge.

The Templar, who never yielded to pity or distress, gave way to his admiration of her fortitude.

"Come down," he coaxed, "rash girl!—I swear by earth and sea and sky I will offer thee no offence."

"I will not trust thee, Templar," said Rebecca.

The sound of the bugle without summoned the Templar from the room.

*   *   *   *   *

The Norman conspirators had been summoned to consider a letter written by Cedric's jester Wamba, demanding the release of all the captives, failing which he and his comrades, none other than Robin Hood, his merry men, and the Black Knight, would besiege the castle and destroy it.

At news that there were at least two hundred men outside the castle Front-de-Bœuf became alarmed, and was counselled by the Templar to send at once to York or elsewhere for assistance.

As they had no messenger who would undertake this errand, the Normans hit upon the ruse of asking the besiegers to send in a priest who would reconcile the captives to God, for they were to be executed on the following morning.

But the priest who was sent into the castle was none other than Cedric's jester Wamba, disguised. Left unguarded in the presence of his master, the jester prevailed on Cedric to exchange clothes and escape from the castle.

Presently the unsuspecting Front-de-Bœuf led Cedric, habited in monk's garb, to the postern gate, urging him to do his utmost to bring Norman aid to their beleaguered friends.

"If thou wilt do mine errand and return hither, thou shalt see Saxon flesh as cheap as ever was swine's flesh in Sheffield market."

As the two parted, the baron thrust into Cedric's unwilling hand a piece of gold and warned:

"Remember, I will flay off both your monk's cowl and skin too if thou failest in thy purpose!"

"And full leave will I give thee to do both," answered Cedric, "if, when we meet again, I deserve not better at thy hand."

Turning back towards the castle, the old die-hard threw the piece of gold towards the donor, exclaiming, "False Norman, thy money perish with thee!"

Front-de-Bœuf heard the words imperfectly, but the action was suspicious. "Archers," he called to the warders on the battlements, "send me an arrow through yon monk's frock!

Yet stay—we must thus far trust him, since we have no better shift. I think he dare not betray me."

The Norman took a long draft of wine, then sought out his prisoners—and noticed something amiss. He struck Cedric's cap from the head of the Jester and, throwing open the collar, discovered the fatal badge of servitude.

"Fiends of hell!" shouted Front-de-Bœuf. "And thou," he said to the Jester. "I will give thee holy orders. Tear the scalp from his head and pitch him headlong from the battlements. Thy trade is to jest, canst thou jest now?"

"If thou give me the red cap thou propose," whimpered Wamba, "out of a simple monk you will make a cardinal."

"The poor wretch," said De Bracy, "is resolved to die in his vocation. Front-de-Bœuf, thou shalt not slay him. He shall make sport for my Free Companions."

But the demonstrations of the enemy outside cut off further talk.

* * * * *

The progress of the historic battle for Torquilstone was watched by Rebecca from the room of Ivanhoe, who had to lie like a bedridden monk while the game that would give him freedom or death was played out by others.

"What dost thou see, Rebecca?"

"Nothing but a cloud of arrows flying so thick as to dazzle mine eyes and to hide the bowmen who shoot them."

"The archery may avail but little against stone walls. Look for the Black Knight, fair Rebecca, leading his followers onwards."

"I see him not."

"Foul craven! Does he blench when the wind blows high?"

"He blenches not! He blenches not! I see him now; he heads his body of men close under the barbican. They have made a breach! They rush in—they are thrust back! Front-de-Bœuf heads the defenders! I see his gigantic form above the press! They throng in again! God of Jacob it is the meeting of two fierce tides!"

She uttered a loud shriek.

"He is down! He is down!"

"Who is down?" cried Ivanhoe; "for our dear lady's sake!"

"The Black Knight. But no, he is on foot again. His sword is broken. He snatches an axe from a yeoman. He presses Front-de-Bœuf with blow on blow. The giant stoops and totters like an oak under the steel of the woodman. He falls. He falls."

* * * * *

Front-de-Bœuf was taken to his room, and, in the interval of the fighting which followed, Bois-Guilbert and De Bracy discussed him.

" Yet a few hours," said the callous Templar, " and Front-de-Bœuf is with his fathers."

" A brave addition to the kingdom of Satan," said De Bracy.

" Lives Reginald Front-de-Bœuf? " demanded a broken and shrill voice by the bedside of the dying baron, who shuddered and asked :

" Who is there? "

" I am thy evil angel."

" Think not that I will blench from thee."

" Think on thy sins, Front-de-Bœuf. On rebellion, rapine, murder."

" Let me die in peace."

" In peace thou shalt *not* die," replied the voice. " Even in death shalt thou think on thy murders."

" Vile murderous hag, detestable screech-owl! " exclaimed the dying noble, now recognizing Ulrica, his former paramour.

" Ay—it is she who demands all that she has lost by the name of Front-de-Bœuf. Thou hast been my evil angel, and I will be thine till the very instant of dissolution! "

" Gods and fiends! Oh, for one moment's strength! "

" Think not of it, valiant warrior. Thou shalt die no soldier's death. Rememberest the magazine of fuel that is stored beneath these apartments. The flames are fast rising."

Outside, the voice of the Templar sounded above the din of battle.

" All is lost, De Bracy, the castle burns."

De Bracy led his men to the postern gate, but they were beaten back, and the vaulted passages rang with the encounter between De Bracy and the Black Knight, until the former was felled with a ponderous axe.

" Yield ye, De Bracy? " said the Black Champion.

" Not to an unknown conqueror."

Suddenly the Black Knight whispered his name and the startled De Bracy made his submission.

Rushing into the burning castle, the Black Knight bore out the wounded Ivanhoe in his arms. Rowena was saved by her father's servants, but Rebecca, carried off by Bois-Guilbert, filled the air with her departing shrieks.

Tongues of fire had now risen to the evening skies. Tower after tower crashed down. As the victors gazed with wonder upon the flames, in which their own ranks and arms glanced dusky red, they saw the maniac figure of the Saxon Ulrica outlined above, tossing her arms abroad with wild exultation, as if she reigned empress of the conflagration. Then the whole turret gave way, and she fell to perish in the flames that had consumed her tyrant.

* * * * *

One of the casualties of the battle of Torquilstone was Athelstane, the Saxon hope, who had been felled by a sword-blow.

Before saying farewell to the Black Knight, Cedric invited him to come to Athelstane's castle of Coningsburgh for the funeral celebrations.

The Knight came, attended by Ivanhoe, disguised, and immediately begged Cedric to grant him the boon promised for his share in the fight for the castle.

Cedric coloured, and protested that it was scarce fitting for a stranger to mingle in an affair concerning his own honour.

" Nor do I wish to mingle," said the Knight mildly, " except so far as you will admit me to have an interest. As yet you have known me only as the Black Knight of the Fetterlock. Know me now as Richard Plantagenet! "

" Richard of Anjou! " exclaimed Cedric, stepping backward.

" No, noble Cedric! Richard of England, whose deepest wish is to see her sons united to each other. . . . And now I require of thee, as a man of thy word, to give and receive to thy paternal affection the good knight Wilfrid of Ivanhoe."

" And this is Wilfrid," said Cedric, pointing to the disguised knight in attendance.

" My father! My father! " said Wilfrid, prostrating himself at Cedric's feet, " grant me thy forgiveness! "

" Thou hast it, son," said Cedric, raising him up. " Thou art about to speak, and I guess the topic. But the Lady Rowena must complete two years' mourning for her betrothed husband, Athelstane, before we can treat of a new union."

It seemed as if Cedric's words had raised a spectre, for at that moment the " dead " Athelstane appeared, very much alive, with the news that he had only been stunned by the sword that had struck him down.

" My ward Rowena, you will not desert her? " asked the alarmed Cedric, still hoping for a revival of Saxon England.

" Father Cedric," protested Athelstane, " be reasonable. The Lady Rowena cares not for me. Here, Cousin Wilfrid, in thy favour I renounce and abjure. . . . Hey! our cousin Wilfrid hath vanished! "

The gallant Knight of Ivanhoe had responded to a sudden appeal, made by his fair nurse Rebecca, to come to her aid at the Preceptory of Templestowe, to which she had been carried by Bois-Guilbert, and where, to save himself from the punishment of broken rules, he had admitted her to be a sorceress, the punishment for which was death, unless saved by a champion.

The judges had been two hours in the lists waiting when Ivanhoe arrived. The Templars' champion, Bois-Guilbert, looked fiercely at his old antagonist.

" Dog of a Saxon! " he blustered. " Take thy lance and prepare for the death thou hast drawn upon thee."

" Ha! proud Templar! Hast thou forgotten that twice before didst thou fall before this lance? "

The trumpets sounded, the knights charged each other, in full career, and . . . Bois-Guilbert fell in the lists, killed, not by his rival, but by his own contending passions.

*　　　*　　　*　　　*　　　*

On the second morning after the nuptials of Wilfrid and Rowena had been celebrated, Rebecca called on the Lady of Ivanhoe and, with head bent to the ground, kissed the embroidered hem of her tunic.

There was an involuntary tremor in Rebecca's voice and a tenderness of accent which perhaps betrayed more than she would willingly have expressed as she bade Rowena adieu.

She glided from the apartment, leaving Rowena surprised, as if a vision had passed her. The fair Saxon related the singular conference to her husband, on whose mind it left a deep impression. He lived long and happily with Rowena, for they were attached to each other by the bonds of early affection, and they loved each other the more from the recollection of the obstacles which had impeded their union. Yet it would be inquiring too curiously to ask whether the recollection of Rebecca's beauty and magnanimity did not recur to his mind more frequently than the fair descendant of Alfred might altogether have approved.

VANITY FAIR

By W. M. THACKERAY

*Described as the most successful novel of manners in the
English language, this shifting kaleidoscope of vivid
impressions retains for us even to-day its century-old drama
and passion. It is a story of human emotion set against a
background composed of brilliant details merged to one tone,
so that the principal characters are thrown into high relief.*

It was one sunny morning in June, in the first years of the last
century, that two young girls left the prim quiet of Miss
Pinkerton's Academy for Young Ladies in Chiswick Mall,
to drive forth into the great world, their schooldays over.

But there could be no greater contrast than between Amelia
Sedley, with her rosy cheeks, sweet smile, the bluest, most
guileless eyes in the world, beloved by all her schoolmates and
now returning to the bosom of her respectable and wealthy
family, and Rebecca Sharp, whose departure passed un-
regretted, though she made it memorable by throwing out of
the coach window that famous farewell gift to all their young
ladies—Johnson's Dictionary! It was to the dismay of the
gentle Amelia, who had never harmed a soul in her life and
certainly never imagined the feeling of hatred that possessed
Becky's soul in that moment against the Misses Pinkerton and
their genteel school.

At her companion's remonstrances the bitterness that she
had been forced to repress for so long came to a head, and she
poured it forth to Amelia, for, as she said, " Revenge may be
wicked, but it's natural. I'm no angel."

The world, indeed, had not been very kind to Rebecca.
Her father had been an artist, brilliant, careless, over-fond
of the bottle, whilst her mother—long since dead—was a
French opera girl. He had taught drawing at the Academy,
where, at his death, Becky, aged seventeen, went to teach
French and live as an articled pupil, none too happy a position
for the proud girl. Slight, pale, sandy-haired, with curiously
attractive greenish eyes, she had seen a seamy side of life that
the protected girls she now met could scarcely conceive. She
was filled with resentment at their ease and comfort, that

contrasted ill with her defenceless, poverty-stricken lot, but determined to learn what she could there to improve the only chance in life that she had—a position as governess in a noble family.

After a wordy battle with the autocratic elder Miss Pinkerton, that good lady heard of a post in Sir Pitt Crawley's family, and so Becky's future was settled.

Kind-hearted Amelia had befriended the orphaned girl, and, leaving school at the same time, invited her darling Becky to spend a week or so with her family in Russell Square, before embarking on her new venture.

Becky was charmed with everything on her arrival in Bloomsbury, and was especially solicitous in her inquiries about the only son of the house—Mr. Joseph, home on sick leave from India, where, as collector of Bogley Wallah in Bengal, he was a respected employee of the East India Company. Was he rich?, the artless girl inquired. Had he a wife and charming family?—and seemed quite surprised when the innocent Amelia informed her that her brother was quite fancy free.

No one could have called Joe Sedley handsome; though stout, vain, over-dressed, he believed himself so in his heart of hearts. But the sight of a woman always brought a terrible fit of shyness to the poor man, that he had never been able to conquer.

Even Rebecca's not too quietly whispered comments on his good look didn't restore his self-confidence. Needless to say, fancying himself as a man of the world, he did not live at home, but had rooms in a fashionable part of the city, and led the life of a man about town to the best of his limited ability. But he had few friends, and life was not really pleasant for the pompous little man.

Pressed by his father to stay to dinner on the evening of Amelia's return, and not unpleased by Rebecca's remarks, he agreed to do so, and her expressions of pleasure on tasting an Indian curry for the first time, gave him not a little enjoyment, though the poor girl, truth to tell, found it almost too hot to swallow!

She was a model of submissive gratitude during the days that followed and quite captured the whole Sedley family. Amelia was more than ever her dearest friend, whilst even Joseph gained a little confidence gradually in her presence. When his sister reminded him of a promised visit to Vauxhall, he was quite eager to go.

But it was necessary for both the young ladies to have escorts, so that the name of Mr. Sedley's godson, Lieutenant George Osborne, was mentioned by that elderly merchant, with ever so slight a twinkle at Amelia, as he pronounced that name.

The evening of the promised party brought a thunderstorm, and the four young people were forced to stay at home, but this gave a pleasant opportunity for *tête-à-têtes*. Amelia was delighted at seeing her handsome, dashing George again, whom she had known and adored since childhood, whilst Rebecca welcomed the opportunity of pursuing her campaign against Joseph, who found himself quite brilliantly talkative when alone with her, and was utterly charmed by her singing, which was indeed very pretty. It occurred to him that it would be pleasant to have such a modest, attractive, accomplished girl as a wife, even if she had not a penny to her name.

The very next day brought good weather, and the jaunt to Vauxhall was decided on. Becky felt sure that the night would see her victory, and Joseph at her feet.

George mentioned that he had invited his great friend, William Dobbin, to join the evening's party. Since their schooldays, when William had gone to defend young George in a quarrel with the school bully, they had been the firmest of friends. Dobbin, tall, ungainly, shy, though brilliant at his books, took delight in looking after the handsome, spoilt little boy, and even now thought the world of George, to whose regiment he had been appointed. Since those past days his father, a grocer, had become very wealthy and even acquired a title, but William was as modest and unassuming as ever.

On arrival at Vauxhall, the party soon split up into two couples, though they vowed to meet again at supper-time, whilst poor Dobbin was left to wander about on his own. What with the fireworks, the music, and thousand other delights of that charming place, Rebecca did not obtain the avowal she wanted. The bowl of rack punch at supper completed her defeat, for Joseph enjoyed it hugely and he completely lost his wits, singing, quarrelling, and calling her his " dearest diddle diddle darling," which made the party most conspicuous, so that if it had not been for Dobbin's timely arrival on the scene, the end of the evening would have been even worse. George took the two girls hurriedly away and left his friend to deal with Joe.

She was still hopeful the next day, though the time for her departure was drawing near, but she could not, however, reckon with the headache that follows too much punch, and the teasing remarks of George Osborne to poor Joseph as to his last evening's boldness towards Miss Rebecca, done in none too pleasant a manner, since that young gentleman did not fancy a penniless governess as a future sister-in-law.

But on his arrival at Russell Square, Becky realized something of what had passed, from his conversation, and George would have had quite a surprise if he had realized the bitterness that he had aroused.

When a note arrived from Joseph, telling of his immediate departure for Cheltenham, owing to illness, and apologizing for his behaviour, Rebecca knew the worst pang, as yet, of her life.

Not that she showed any sign of her feelings, and when the time came for her to go, thanked the family prettily, accepting with the best of grace the many gifts that Amelia made her.

Sir Pitt Crawley, Baronet, of Queen's Crawley, Hants, and Great Gaunt Street, London, was well known, if neither liked nor respected, in the great world, and it was to his house in town that Becky had to go, to accompany him down to his country estate, where he spent most of his time. It was for the two daughters of his plebeian second wife that she had been engaged, and she was full of anticipation as to the elegance and good manners that a baronet must surely possess, in such a contrast to the bourgeois atmosphere of the Sedley home.

To her surprise, the door of the house was opened by an elderly, bald-headed man with leering grey eyes, set in a red face, who led her into the gloomy old mansion, where she learnt, to her astonishment, that he was Sir Pitt himself, in spite of his rough country accent and shabby clothes. She was soon to learn that meanness was his reigning vice, and he possessed respect for no man—or woman.

In her letters to Amelia from Queen's Crawley, she described the great house with its faded, neglected mistress, quite incapable of living up to her position; the two insignificant little girls; their pious and solemn step-brother, Mr. Pitt, the heir; Rawdon, the younger son, away now with his regiment; and the air of decay that hung like a mist over the whole place.

Sir Pitt's brother, Bute Crawley, reigned at the rectory, and little love was lost between the two families, as the financial hopes of both were concentrated on the handsome fortune owned by Miss Crawley, Sir Pitt's half-sister, and the question of how she would dispose of the money was a source of anxiety to both.

It seemed to be Rawdon that had her favour, for she had even been known to settle his debts, when, as became a dashing young officer in the Dragoons, they became too pressing. Great was the fuss that was made of the old lady on her visits to Queen's Crawley, and the old house knew better meals and a general air of ease quite absent on other occasions.

Rebecca settled down in the household, adopting every method of pleasing that she thought fit. She did not press their school-books too rigorously on the two girls; she was respectfully admiring to Mr. Pitt; she played backgammon with his tipsy old father, and soon became of great help to him as a secretary, sorting out his innumerable papers and letters, for the old man was always engaged in some law-suit or other. He grew more and more dependent on her for advice, and little was done without consulting the young governess.

It was a great day when Miss Crawley decided on a visit to her relatives in the country, and everything was done to make her stay at the hall agreeable. The Bute Crawleys let their feud disappear in her presence, and one might even have thought the two families on good terms. The worldly old woman fully appreciated the situation and obtained a malicious satisfaction from the trouble her visit caused.

Rawdon arrived home especially for the occasion, and Becky wrote of him to her Amelia, describing him as a great dandy, adored by his aunt, who had an eye for a handsome man, especially a man of the world, ready to drink, gamble, fight a duel and make love to a pretty woman, and lead a life that she considered the height of manliness. Mr. Pitt she dismissed as a milksop, and he had taken the opportunity to be absent from home on his aunt's visit.

Nor did Miss Crawley stand aloof from Becky's pleasing ways, and made a great fuss of her upon every occasion. She prided herself on her liberal opinions, and vowed Becky was the only person in the whole countryside whose conversation had any vivacity or wit.

But neither his aunt nor Amelia heard of all her little encounters with Rawdon. The dragoon was slow of speech, and had no talent for pretty words, but Becky could see his admiration in his eyes, and kept him dangling after her, without sacrificing one whit of that delicacy and modesty that had been impressed on all Miss Pinkerton's young ladies, though she used her fine eyes and pretty voice with a subtlety that the Academy could never have appreciated.

But what of Amelia? She was busy adoring her wonderful George, who, truth to tell, found it quite a natural thing to be so loved. Indeed, he had been spoilt and adored all his life by his two doting sisters and proud father, and took the girl's worship as a matter of course.

Many were the pangs the poor child suffered when George was too busy to spare time for her. Gambling, playing cards, billiards, and entering into the doubtful enjoyments of many of his brother-officers, took much of his time, and little Emmy had to bear it with uncomplaining patience, though her pillow was often wet with tears.

Of late, her father had seemed very preoccupied, and the reason for this appeared one evening when George's father told him that he didn't like the look of old Sedley's affairs, and the less he saw of his daughter the better.

So while Emmy's little heart suffered all the pangs of love, Miss Crawley had returned to her house in Park Lane, accompanied by her dear Becky, who was to look after her for a while, as the good wine and elaborate dishes in her honour at Queen's Crawley had proved a little too much for her. Becky's arrival was much resented by the faithful Briggs, companion for many years to the old lady.

Captain Rawdon paid his aunt many a visit from his barracks close by in Knightsbridge, and no doubt he occasionally caught a glimpse of the fascinating Becky. Poor Lady Crawley, desperately ill in the country, received little attention from her family, but the rich old woman who had been made ill through her own greediness was another matter.

As Miss Crawley grew better through Becky's excellent nursing, many were the appeals that came from Sir Pitt for her return, but his half-sister did not want to part from her amusing companion, whose sharp wit diverted her, and so he was left fuming—missing her more than a little.

Amelia and Becky renewed their friendship, that of late had grown a little wan, since both girls were absorbed in their own affairs. Introduced at Park Lane, Miss Crawley approved of Emmy's pretty face and modest ways, and, as Rawdon knew George, invitations were dispatched forthwith for a little party. It proved quite a success, as George was flattered at being asked to the house of one of the nobility, though Rawdon did not much care for George's condescending attitude towards Becky.

News came of Lady Crawley's death, though none wept for

that unhappy lady. Sir Pitt, coming to town to deal with his numerous affairs, came himself to beg Miss Becky to return, and there was something unusual in his manner that agitated that usually self-possessed young woman. And when he begged his dear Becky to return—to come as Lady Crawley—she was deeply touched. The infatuated old rascal even fell on his knees to seal the bargain, and, to his astonishment, saw tears in her eyes, and indeed she had cause to weep at her predicament, for she had to confess, " Oh, Sir Pitt, I—I'm married already." Miss Crawley arrived then on the scene, none too pleased. But the old man recovered himself remarkably quickly, and departed chuckling, telling Becky she could at any rate count on him as a friend, and he'd be glad to see her back at Queen's Crawley.

It was a glittering prize that she had missed, but Rebecca was ever one to take life as she found it, and she confessed to the astonished Miss Crawley that, deeply as she was touched by the honour, an attachment elsewhere bound her. She did not say to whom, for she realized that in spite of the old woman's protestations as to her liberal mind, when she learned of the marriage of the penniless little governess to none other than her favourite nephew—Rawdon Crawley himself—she would be far from pleased.

That not very intelligent officer was utterly charmed by the clever girl, and speechless with admiration at her grace and wit.

The time had come now when their marriage could be kept a secret no longer, and one day a certain bedroom in Park Lane was empty when the maid entered it in the morning, though a note had been left for Miss Briggs, quite won over now by Becky, explaining what had happened and begging her to intervene on their behalf with Miss Crawley.

The anger of the old lady was only exceeded by the fury of Sir Pitt, when he arrived to fetch the girl back to Hampshire. In a tempest of wrath he cursed both her name and Rawdon's.

While Becky was endeavouring to advance her fortunes, the Sedley family had suffered a bitter blow. The state of affairs in Europe had affected the business, and Old Sedley was utterly ruined. The house in Russell Square and its contents were put up for sale. Becky and her husband visited the sale, and there was quite a tussle for a little piano, beloved by Amelia, until the hammer fell at last—and it came into the possession of a certain Captain Dobbin.

Its destination was a tiny villa in Fulham which was now the home of the broken old man; where his wife and Emmy managed on the allowance sent them by Joseph. But the fall of their fortunes was not such a blow to the poor girl as the thought she had had for months past that George was not quite the adoring lover that she cherished in her dreams. When a letter came from old Mr. Osborne declaring their marriage to be out of the question now, she took it with a deathly calm.

The very news that had caused her father's ruin intervened now still further in her life—Napoleon had returned from exile, and all Europe was in arms against him. George and William would perhaps be called abroad with their regiment.

Dobbin had found that young man one day with a note from Amelia releasing him from their engagement, and even that selfish, frivolous heart was touched by the sweetness of her words. As for Dobbin, he could scarcely conceal his feelings, for to him Amelia was the ideal of all that womanhood could mean and her happiness worth everything in the world to him, though he might not share in it. Together they recalled her gentle charm and goodness; a pang of unworthiness, of realization of the love that he had treated so carelessly came to George, and, persuaded by Dobbin, he went straightway to the little villa, to bring joy unimaginable to a simple, loving heart that had known only the bitterness of despair of recent months. It did not take long for the roses to return to Amelia's pale cheeks and the brilliance to her pretty eyes.

Meanwhile, life was not quite as Becky had planned it; his aunt had never forgiven Rawdon, and though they lived very comfortably still on credit, the day would come when that must end. Mrs. Bute Crawley was in charge now at Park Lane, and neglected no opportunity of pointing out Rawdon's wickedness and that of his cunning little wife. To be ordered abroad with his regiment might be the best solution to their difficulties.

Hearing news of George's renewed attachment to Amelia, his father—that hard-hearted old merchant—threatened to cut him off without a penny, and after a dreadful scene George walked out of the house, to which he was destined never to return.

With Dobbin's help a quiet wedding was arranged, and the couple went to Brighton for a few days, to be followed later by Joseph, still his fat, vain old self. Miss Crawley was enjoying the air of that delightful place, and so Rawdon and his lady were there too, in hot pursuit. Encounter with George and his bride was inevitable, and the little party was soon inseparable. Becky showed by her manner that any slight hostility between her and George was quite forgotten, and, indeed, exhibited this so plainly that poor little Amelia was quite left in the shade. She was outshone by Mrs. Rawdon's brilliance, which her husband seemed to appreciate so much.

One day Dobbin arrived hurriedly with important news for George: first that he had broken the news of the latter's marriage to his father, to Mr. Osborne's unbounded fury; and secondly, that the army had been ordered to Belgium, there to encounter the great Bonaparte.

Becky's sharp eyes soon saw what Amelia had not guessed, that George's kindly but awkward friend Dobbin was deeply in love with her. Between Becky and that gentleman, however, little love was lost.

Amelia and George left for London to settle their affairs, it being decided that the ladies should accompany their husbands to Brussels, with Joseph for company. It was not with regret that the little wife parted from the too attractive Rebecca.

All that they had from George's father was a sum of two thousand pounds due to him under a settlement, and not a penny more would the couple receive. There was no longer a place for his son in the Osborne household.

And so they set forth for Brussels, where the utmost confidence reigned: Napoleon would soon be settled by the unconquerable armies—and meanwhile, gaiety was the order of the day. Visitors flocked there as though to watch a play. Needless to say, that they should meet the Crawleys was inevitable, and Emmy watched her former friend's triumph in the social world into which she now entered. As for George—he was enslaved!

On the 15th of June the Duchess of Richmond gave a ball— one day to be famous in history—and in that brilliant assembly the wife of Rawdon Crawley was remarked on all sides; her toilette was supremely elegant, her manner as though she had moved all her life in such circles. But Amelia sat by herself, whilst George sought Rebecca, the centre of an admiring throng. After enduring agonies of humiliation, neglected, forlorn, the poor girl begged the faithful Dobbin to take her home.

Fateful news came with the dawn, and William went to find his friend. He was at the gambling-table, but the news Dobbin brought soon sobered him, and as he walked through the pale dawn, realized that he was going to an encounter from which

there might be no return.   He thought suddenly with bitter
regret of his hasty marriage—his unkindness to that gentle
loving creature, his wife—but there was no time now for
repentance.

The story of Waterloo and its glory is too well known to
repeat; but thousands lost their lives that Napoleon might
be defeated for ever—amongst them George Osborne.   Amelia
waited, her heart full of love and foreboding for his return,
all bitter thoughts long since forgotten in the anguish of war.
It was Dobbin who cared for her in her grief, who caused
George's father to know of her condition—she was going to
have a child.   But though he appeared in Brussels to visit his
son's grave, Amelia he hated, and refused to help her in any
way.

The money that George had was long since gone, for they
had lived extravagantly, and he had spared himself nothing
that he wanted.   Amelia never realized just how little she
had, nor just how much help she owed to Dobbin.   Being the
executor of his friend's will, he was able to do this.   Distracted
in her grief, money was of no importance to her.

With her son's birth, however, new hope came to Amelia—
a reason for living, now that her hero was gone for ever.
Motherhood made her blossom again; she had no thought in
life but for her child.   Brought back to England by the faithful
William, she settled down to a quiet life in the little villa in
Fulham, her existence dedicated to maternal love.   If her
parents noticed Major Dobbin's devotion, the presents he
showered on all the little household, his frequent visits, Amelia
did not; her being was wholly occupied.   When, one day, he
announced that he had been ordered to India, she regretted
the departure of a kind friend, but that was all.

In Paris, Becky, now herself the mother of a son, was leading
a life of fashion on the credit Rawdon could still command
there, and his skill in gambling further augmented their
fortunes.   But she saw no advancement for him, and they
decided to return to London, where influence might obtain
him an appointment worthy of an officer and a member of the
Crawley family.   His aunt was still obdurate, but Becky had
confidence in her wits to gain advancement for her husband.

So they moved into a charming little house in Curzon
Street, and when news came of Miss Crawley's death, were not
unduly surprised to hear that the major portion of it went to
his brother Pitt, who, now married, had managed to insinuate

himself into her graces.   Never at a loss, a tactful letter was
dispatched, congratulating Pitt on his good fortune and wishing
him every prosperity, asking after Lady Jane, and hoping little
Rawdon might one day have the happiness to meet his dear
relatives.

So was the way smoothed out for a friendly relationship
with his brother's family.

In Hampshire, the old baronet grew more and more eccentric
with increasing years, his taste for low company more pronounced, and his fondness for the bottle even stronger.   Rumour
said that Horrocks the butler's blowsy daughter had ambitions
to be Lady Crawley, and indeed she had no small power in the
neglected house.   But one night, after a stronger than usual
dose of rum and water, the wicked old man died—regretted by
no one, except possibly Miss Horrocks, who saw her position gone.

Pitt breathed a sigh of relief, for he could now set his ancestral
home in order.   The Rawdon Crawleys came down for the
funeral, of course, and Becky was the soul of tact, pleasing her
pompous brother-in-law by her admiration of his ability, and
captivating Lady Jane by her interest in the children, though it
cannot be said that little Rawdon ever saw signs of such
tenderness at home in Curzon Street.

On their return to town they plunged again into the life to
which Becky was such an ornament.   Everyone knew that at
Mrs. Crawley's house one could not fail to be amused, particularly the gentlemen!   One of the most frequent visitors to
her house was the great Lord Steyne—immensely rich, his
power and influence could open all doors to her.   That his
reputation was notorious in no way made him unwelcome, and
the friends he brought could gamble with Rawdon, who more
and more retired into the background. Mrs. Crawley's
husband cut a very poor figure, and the greatest joy of his life
was to go upstairs to the nursery to play with his little son.
Occasionally his lovely mamma went there, but the child had
but a few languid words from her, before she left him to go to
the opera, to the play, or one of the innumerable diversions
which took all her time.

Amelia lived her quiet life, quite contented with its simplicity, and if money was rather short, had she not the greatest
treasure in the world to guard, and was not that worth everything to her?   Dobbin in India had letters describing the
wonderful boy's progress, and he cherished them, as he did
everything that came from the woman he adored.

Old Osborne had news of his beautiful little grandson through his daughter, who had met the child at the Dobbins' house, where the Misses Dobbins delighted to invite him. The bitter old man drank in news of his grandchild with pitiful eagerness, and one day came the opportunity for which he had been waiting.

He had the temerity to offer the poor mother money if she would give up her claim to little George and allow him to be brought up as befitted a gentleman by his grandfather. Even Amelia's gentle spirit was roused to rebellion at the thought of sacrificing her darling, her only joy, in a life that was becoming increasingly burdened by poverty—her father squandering what little he possessed—until one day she realized it meant her boy would miss the chances in life that he deserved, and with many a bitter pang and secret tear, she let him go. But a proviso was made that the gentle widow should see her boy whenever she wished to do so, to which old Osborne had to agree.

The Sedley family sank deeper into poverty, her father having foolishly mortgaged even Joe's allowance; their creditors were pressing. Desperate to aid her parents, she thought for a moment of marriage—for even in their present circumstances she met with adoration, and the curate thought Mrs. Amelia his ideal of a wife—but she put that thought away. Whatever the temptation, George's memory was all-important to her. But the strain was too much for her mother, whose last years had seen so much of disappointment, and the poor old lady just faded out of a life that had grown wearisome. Amelia was left to comfort her father as she could and to dream of her George's wonderful future.

Whilst she suffered, Becky's plans were prospering, and the greatest triumph of her life came when her sister-in-law, Lady Jane, presented her at Court. Sir Pitt had been quite won over—more than his wife really cared to own, but she was a timid little woman and obeyed her husband's commands. As they rode in the coach she remarked on the beauty of Becky's diamonds and the exquisite lace that trimmed the rich brocade of her dress. The jewels, Becky assured her, were but hired, whilst the lace was a bargain that she had possessed these many years. Did she glance mischievously at Sir Pitt when referring to her jewels—fingering a diamond clasp that he had given her? Though, to be sure, those very diamonds never went back to the jeweller's, but were locked away in a little desk in which Becky kept all her treasures, including quite a store of bank-notes of which Rawdon hadn't the least suspicion.

But of what importance was that shabby officer, grown somewhat portly of late? The evening was his wife's. Even His Imperial Majesty was charmed, and Lord Steyne full of gracious compliments, eyeing those superb diamonds with a strange little smile at the corners of his sardonic lips.

There was nowhere now to which she could not gain an entrée, and even those ladies of spotless virtue who had looked askance at little Mrs. Crawley, welcomed her now. The aloof Lady Steyne was forced to give her hospitality. The little governess had progressed since the days of Miss Pinkerton. Yet in all this glory, from time to time she grew even a little bored: it was almost too easy a triumph!

Lord Steyne was seen more than ever at her house. After all, a woman of fashion is not expected to have a husband too much in evidence, and there was always the faithful Miss Briggs—now her *dame de compagnie*—to observe the proprieties. The latter was not always paid her salary; but, then, neither were the bills of many of the tradesmen who supplied luxuries for those famous little supper parties.

It was after Becky had appeared with great effect one night at some fashionable charades given at My Lord Steyne's residence, that Rawdon, after having seen his wife into her carriage, proposed to walk home with a friend. Out of the shadows stepped two men—rough men—whose mien he could not mistake. They were bailiffs, and escape was useless. He must endure enforced hospitality at Mr. Moss's house in Cursitor Street, until such time as kind friends would come to his aid and settle the debt for which he was immured. It was not the first time Rawdon had found himself there, and so he settled down, deciding to write to Becky the next day and get her to find what was necessary for his release.

In the morning he dispatched a note and looked forward to his release with pleasure, feeling certain that she would manage it for him that day, even if it meant pawning some of her trinkets. Time passed and no reply came. Towards evening came a note from his wife: such a sad little note—the thought of him being imprisoned at Mr. Moss's had broken her heart, and though she had been feeling far from well that day—the physician had been called to see her—she had got up and rushed out to see what could be done. But Mr. Nathan, at whose bequest Rawdon had been detained, was implacable: he must have the full sum or nothing.   On her imploring him, however, he had agreed to let her pawn her few jewels, and the money would be there to free him the very next day.   Meanwhile, his desolated Becky had returned to her bed with a fever.

Strange suspicions came to his heart on reading this note, suspicions that had visited him more than once of late.   Would she welcome this opportunity of his absence, and, if so, to whom would she turn for consolation?

He dashed off a note rapidly to his brother explaining what had happened to him and begging for his help.   An hour or so brought a visitor to see him.   For a moment he could not believe his eyes—it was Lady Jane; her tender heart had been touched by his predicament and she brought the money that he needed.   Tears came to his eyes at the sight of her—she had treated his little Rawdon with such sweetness, and represented a goodness that he had almost forgotten existed.

It was towards nine that he walked home, or rather ran, as some strange impulse seemed to urge him on.   At the sight of his house, ablaze with light, he paled and a fit of trembling overcame him.   For a moment he could not stir, then he entered the house silently.   There was no one about: the servants were absent, Miss Briggs had been sent away some time ago, the boy was at school.   He mounted the stairs to one of the upper rooms, from which came the sound of his wife's voice, singing as only she could sing.

When he opened the door it was to see Becky seated on a sofa, in a beautiful gown, blazing with diamonds, Lord Steyne bending over her hand, which he was kissing.   The dazzling smile on her face turned to a fixed stare as she saw her husband, but Steyne was enraged—he suspected a trap.   Endeavouring to make the best of it, he attempted a friendly gesture to Rawdon, but Becky understood the look in her husband's eyes. She threw herself at his feet, protesting her innocence, calling Lord Steyne to prove that this was so.   Convinced now that the pair had planned the *dénouement*, Steyne turned to her with a snarl, protesting that every jewel she wore was paid for by him, and God knows what else besides, and he wasn't going to be trapped by such a rascally pair.   With that he attempted to leave, but Rawdon struck him in the face.

For the first time, Becky respected her husband.   He turned to her then and tore the glittering jewels from her neck and arms and flung them on the floor—one struck Steyne on the forehead, and left a scar he was to bear until his death.

Now he demanded her keys to prove that Steyne's words were indeed true as to the money she had. The little desk she kept her treasures in was opened, and he found it crammed with notes—enough to settle their debts—some of which he took to make what reparation he could; then he left her—pale and dishevelled—a ruined woman!

Never at a loss, she sought Sir Pitt's help the following day, but Rawdon had been there before her, and Lady Jane had told her story. It was too late! By the irony of fate, news of the governorship that Becky had begged Steyne to obtain for her husband appeared in that morning's paper. It was in the tropics, and thither Rawdon went, to die an exile.

In the humbler world of Amelia, her chief joy was still her boy, who was growing up into a handsome little tyrant, nothing being spared him by his doting grandfather. One day at school a tall, brown-faced stranger called to see him, and it did not take him long to recognize his father's friend, Major Dobbin, of whom his mother had often talked. They were soon the greatest of friends.

As for Dobbin, no one could guess his joy at the sight of his sweet Amelia, his love for her burning as brightly as ever in that devoted heart. Joseph, too, had arrived home, shocked to find his family in such straits, and carried them off to pleasanter surroundings. Emmy bloomed again as life grew easier, but her father did not long survive their happy change of circumstances, in spite of her devoted nursing.

Young George made the Major his hero, and his mother was overjoyed to see so much of their devoted friend. But the mention of his love brought back memories of her dear dead husband, and she could but offer him a friend's regard, with which he had to be contented. The little woman scarcely realized the worth of the precious jewel that she was offered.

A trip abroad was proposed, and Joseph, the Major, Amelia, and George set forth on a leisurely tour of Europe. One night in the gambling-rooms at Baden Baden, Joseph was surprised to be addressed by a strange lady in a mask—for it was carnival time—whose voice was still charming, though her dress was shabbily smart and her face a little over-rouged. Then he realized that it was Rebecca—but how sadly changed! Many were the continental towns that had seen Becky's vagabond progress, a rather lonely, sad one, as nowhere could she escape the breath of scandal.

It was a pitiful tale of wronged innocence that she told Joe, enhanced by the appeal of a still very handsome pair of eyes and round white arms. Quite convinced, he went straight to Amelia, whose heart was instantly touched. William was very sceptical, and said the woman brought misery wherever she went. He implored Emmy not to see her again, and the subject led to a bitter quarrel, in which she spurned the friendship that she had taken so easily all these years. At last, stung by her injustice, the faithful William told of his years of love and longing, saying that an end had come to his patience, he could no longer be at the beck and call of a woman who was not worthy of a strong, deep love.

After Emmy's victory, and William's departure, why was it that life seemed so flat that the tears would come to her eyes? Her rosy cheeks grew pale, her manner quiet and sad; the gaieties of the town lost their savour.

But a pretty, rich young widow—old Osborne at his death had left her richly provided for—was obvious prey for the adventurers that abound in all cities, and the approaches of two friends of Becky's filled her with horror. Desperate, her pride gone, she wrote a letter one day and sent it to London.

Becky saw very well what had happened, and in a moment of generosity decided to intervene. She told Amelia clearly that she had thrown away a love any woman would be proud to gain, for a memory that was not worth a thought. Emmy protested that no one should speak so of her dear George. But Becky described him as he really was—conceited, weak, and vain, and, as her crowning proof, produced a note he had written her on that fatal eve of Waterloo, begging her to run away with him. The revelation did not work such havoc as she had expected. It was almost a release for Emmy's troubled heart—she could now let it love where it had so longed to do.

As for Becky, she disappeared from their simple, happy life, and remained abroad to comfort Joe, who liked a continental existence. It was not long before he was completely under her thumb, and when William tried to rescue him he refused to leave her. At his death it was found that he had left little but a life insurance, to be divided between Amelia and his dear Mrs. Crawley.

In time Becky's son inherited the estate, but would never see his mother, though he made her a liberal allowance. She returned to England at last to indulge in good works at Bath, and was an ardent church-goer—in fact, a model member of the community.

WAR AND PEACE

By COUNT LEO TOLSTOY

" The union of a great moral conviction and realistic details," says the Oxford Companion to English Literature, " and an immense imaginative vision, combine to make him one of the great European writers." This gigantic panorama of Russian life during the war with Napoleon (published in 1860) is one of the most astonishing tours de force ever written, combining as it does the historical and the philosophical, and sublimating the former through the latter so that it becomes symbolic of the whole activities of mankind. No digest can do more than give the barest of outlines. To be appreciated fully the book must be read in its entirety.

"So you too are enlisting for the war?" said Anna Pavlovna Scherer.

"Yes . . . General Kutuzov has been good enough to take me as an aide-de-camp," replied Prince Andrey Bolkonsky with an air of embarrassment. He was an extremely handsome young man, and his clear, incisive features were seen at their best advantage by his hostess, for his face was in profile to her as he scanned, through half-closed eyelids, the *élite* of Petersburg society who had gathered in her brilliantly lighted salon on this sultry evening in July, 1805.

"And your wife?"

"She is going to my father's place in the country."

"But surely you wouldn't rob us of our darling little Lise?" persisted Anna Pavlovna.

Just then the young Princess Lise Bolkonsky passed by them on the arm of the Vicomte de Montemart, an *émigré* from the French Revolution. "Oh, Andrey," she cried, "the vicomte has told me such an amusing story about Bonaparte and an actress in Paris."

Prince Andrey scowled and did not answer. He was annoyed by the coquetry with which she always addressed him in public—as if they were still lovers, and not husband and wife. And he positively detested the way her short upper lip, faintly darkened with down, lifted up appealingly whenever she was unusually gay.

He had even begun to wonder of late why he had married her. " I must have been bewitched by her pretty face," he reflected savagely, " for she's easily the most stupid and helpless woman in Petersburg."

If Prince Andrey had looked more closely into his own heart, he might have seen that it was not really his wife he had grown to dislike, but rather the way of living—the interminable round of *soirées*, balls, concerts, and assemblies—in which she took such obvious delight and which had begun to arouse in him a vague yet profound loathing. He might have seen that the life of fashionable society had become a prison to him. Instead, he saw only that Lise had the mind of a spoilt and happy child, that she was naïve and frivolous and rather vain, and that if he did not escape from her soon he would go mad.

Suddenly Prince Andrey's face lightened with a smile. He had just caught sight, in the middle of the room, of a fat young man in spectacles, with close-cropped head, and foppishly attired in a brown silk coat, lace ruffle and brown silk breeches. He had a good-natured grin on his face, and his manner was benign almost to the point of inanity. He was the illegitimate son of old Count Bezuhov, a celebrated *roué* of the day, immensely wealthy, and now dangerously ill in Moscow.

Young Pierre Bezuhov was making his début in society. Sent abroad as a child of ten to complete his education, he had returned to Russia only a few months ago. He seemed blissfully unaware of the importance of the news which most of the illustrious guests were discussing in hushed tones—the news that Russia had decided to join Britain and Austria in the war against Napoleon.

Pierre was chatting gaily with Prince Vassily Kuragin and his beautiful daughter, Ellen, when he saw Prince Andrey smiling at him. Prince Vassily and his daughter linked arms with young Bezuhov and went across to Andrey and Anna Pavlovna.

" Why, it's you, Pierre," said Andrey ironically, " and in high society, too! "

Prince Vassily inclined his bald and shining head towards Anna Pavlovna. " See what you can do with this shy young bear," he said. " He's been staying with me for weeks and this is the first time I've managed to lure him into the open. Nothing'll bring him on so quickly as the friendship of a clever woman."

As Prince Vassily and his daughter moved away, Pierre gazed after Ellen with rapturous, almost frightened eyes. She had the allure and poise of an acknowledged beauty. Her snow-white shoulders, glossy hair, and diamonds gleamed as she passed between the men, who moved aside with instinctive awe to make way for her.

"Very lovely," said Prince Andrey.

"Very," murmured Pierre. He was silent for a few moments. Then he said to Andrey in an undertone. "I'm coming to you for supper—afterwards. May I?"

"No, quite impossible," answered Andrey, laughing, and giving Pierre's hand an affectionate squeeze that belied his words.

Prince Vassily had left his daughter, and was crossing to the other side of the great drawing-room, when he felt a pressure on his arm, and looked down into the imploring·eyes of an elderly lady with a kindly and care-worn face. She was Princess Anna Drubetskoy, of one of the oldest families in Russia, but she was poor and had outlived all the influential relations at Court who might have promoted the career of her son Boris in the army.

"My dear Prince," she said nervously, for this was not the first time she had pleaded with him, " I have never reminded you of what my father did for you. But now I beg of you, for God's sake, say a word to the Emperor, and get Boris transferred to the Guards."

Prince Vassily's policy was never to ask favours for other people from the powers-that-be, in case the time should come when he would be unable to ask them for himself. But just now he was in such a high good-humour that he forgot this rule.

"Very well, *chère* Anna Mihalovna," he said gently. " I will do the impossible. Your son shall be transferred to the Guards."

An hour later the guests began to depart. Pierre was one of the last to go, not because he had enjoyed himself, but merely because he knew even less about getting out of a drawing-room than getting into one. Awkward, stout, and abnormally tall, he lumbered dreamily to and fro among the vanishing throng.

He set out on foot for Andrey's house, where he found the prince waiting up for him; Lise had gone to bed. After supper they sat and smoked in Andrey's study.

"This war against Napoleon," observed Pierre suddenly. "If it were a war for freedom, I could have understood it, I would have been the first to go into the army. But to help England and Austria against the greatest man in the world—that's not right."

Prince Andrey shrugged his shoulders. "If everyone would fight only for his own convictions, there'd *be* no more war."

"Well, why are you going to the war, then?" asked Pierre.

"Why? I—I couldn't say offhand. Because I have to. And besides, you see, I'm going"—he hesitated "—I'm going because my life here is getting on my nerves."

He leaned forward and said hoarsely to Pierre, "Never, never marry, old man; take my advice; don't marry until you've done all you've set out to do in life, until you no longer love the woman you have chosen, or you'll make a mistake that can never be put right, and everything worth while in you will be squandered away on trifles. . . ."

It was after one o'clock when Pierre left his friend's house. He had promised Andrey during their talk that he would give up the life of dissipation with which, merely for want of something to do, he had been whiling away his nights in Petersburg. The leader of his "set" was Anatole Kuragin, the scapegrace son of Prince Vassily, who lived at the Horse Guards' barracks.

"Women and wine I can understand," Andrey had said. "But Kuragin's women and wine!" He shuddered.

Pierre got into a hired coach, and, without thinking, ordered the driver to take him to the Horse Guards' barracks. It was pleasant to ride like this through the moonlit empty streets. . . . Suddenly Pierre remembered his promise.

"Ah, well," he soothed his conscience, "just one more night, and then *finis*!"

He jumped out of the coach and ran up the steps into the barracks. The ante-room was deserted; empty bottles, cloaks, shoes, were strewn around pell-mell. From above came a wild burst of cheering.

Pierre went upstairs into a brilliantly-lighted room. Eight young men were crowded round the open window. Three others, reeling drunk, were struggling to hold back a young bear on a chain.

"Here's the bottle, Dolohov," cried Anatole Kuragin, a tall young man, strikingly handsome, with his cavalry shirt open over his chest. He forced his way to the window, followed by Pierre.

Outside, on the sloping window-ledge of this third-storey room, sat a young infantry officer with curly hair and ice-blue eyes.

"Dolohov is going to drink a bottle of rum straight off without touching the ledge with his hands," explained Anatole to Pierre.

The young officer took the bottle and held it to his lips, bent his head back, and held his free hand upwards in a perilous attempt to keep his balance.

"It's madness," screamed a voice; "he'll be killed."

Pierre shut his eyes. When he opened them again, Dolohov's head was so far bent back that his curls touched his shirt collar, and his free hand was outstretched and trembling in an extremity of effort. The bottle was nearly empty. Suddenly Dolohov made a shuddering movement with his spine that almost threw him from the ledge, his clutching fingers grasped frantically at the window-frame and missed. . . . Pierre shut his eyes and felt he would never open them again. Then he heard a shout of laughter and glanced up. Dolohov, his face white and merry, was swinging himself through the window into the room again.

"I'll do it, too," roared Pierre, pounding a table with his fist. "Give me a bottle of rum!"

Anatole stared at him thoughtfully. "Listen, old man," he said slowly, "you can try it to-morrow. But now we're all going out for some more vodka. Come on!"

"Yes, come on, come on!" shouted Pierre. "And we'll take the little fellow along, too." And he caught hold of the bear and began waltzing round and round the room with it.

* * * * *

Soon after Anna Pavlovna's *soirée*, old Princess Anna Drubetskoy went to stay with her rich relatives, the Rostovs, in Moscow. It was with this family that her darling Boris had been living for years, until he recently joined a regiment of the line. Now, thanks to Prince Vassily's influence, he had been transferred to the Guards as a sub-lieutenant, and would very shortly be leaving the Rostovs and Moscow and his beloved mother for the campaign in Austria.

Countess Rostov was a thin, sallow woman of forty-five, and her deliberate mode of speaking and moving, really due to enfeebled health, gave her an air of pronounced dignity. The count, on the other hand, was a vigorous and fussy little man, nervously eager to please his guests.

The conversation veered to the main item of news in Moscow that morning, the grave illness of wealthy old Count Bezuhov, who had once been so admired for his personal beauty by the ladies of Moscow.

"I am very sorry for the dear old count," said Princess Anna, wiping her eyes: "his health in such an uncertain state and now Pierre's goings-on; it'll be the death of him. This is what comes of modern education!"

"Why, what has Pierre been doing?" asked Countess Rostov in alarm.

"He and Anatole Kuragin and a young man called Dolohov —the son of Marya Dolohov, you know, such a respectable woman—they're perfect ruffians! The three of them got hold of a bear from somewhere, put it in a carriage with them, and were going with it to some actress's. The police tried to stop them. They seized the police officer, tied him back to back on the bear, and dropped the bear into the river. The bear swam ashore with the police officer on him."

"A lovely sight he must have looked, *ma chère*," cried Count Rostov, shaking with laughter.

Princess Anna gazed at him primly. "They have had to suffer for it," she said. "Dolohov has been degraded to the rank of a common soldier, and Bezuhov's son has been banished to Moscow. As for Anatole Kuragin . . . his father, Prince Vassily, managed to hush it up somehow, but he too has had to leave Petersburg."

Countess Rostov sighed. "How handsome old Bezuhov was!" she murmured. "A finer-looking man I never saw."

"Yes, we all know his reputation," said Princess Anna meaningly. "He had lost count of his own children. . . . But this Pierre was always his favourite. Of course, the direct heir is Prince Vassily, through his wife, so that no one can tell, if he dies (and he's so ill that it's expected any moment), whom that vast property will come to, Pierre or Prince Vassily. Forty thousand serfs and millions of roubles!"

Just then there was a scuffle outside the door, which was suddenly flung open, and a laughing, red-faced girl of thirteen rushed in, hugging a doll to her tightly in her slender bare arms. Almost immediately afterwards there appeared in the open doorway a tall, fair-haired young officer.

"Boris says he's going to take Mimi away to the war with

him," cried the little girl, then went off into a peal of ringing laughter as she tried to hide the doll in her arms.

"Well, I've known her since she was a baby," said the young officer, staring hard at the doll, "and I still love her with all my heart, even if her nose is broken and she has a crack across the top of her skull."

"Don't let him take her, mother," cried the little girl, burying her face in Countess Rostov's blouse and trying to stifle her mirth.

"There, now, Natasha, enough of this nonsense; run along, dear," said the countess, pushing her away with a pretence of anger.

The dark-eyed little girl, rather plain, but full of life, sprang up and flew out of the room as fast as her agile legs could carry her, narrowly missing her elder brother, Nikolay, who was entering the room with their cousin, Sonya. They were followed at a distance by the youngest Rostov, little four-year-old Petya, a plump and solemn youngster, who took his station by his mother's chair and mutely surveyed the company.

Nikolay was a curly-headed youth of eighteen, handsome, and with a frank but irresolute air. Sonya, the countess's niece, who had been brought up with the family, was a slender brunette, with gentle eyes heavily shaded by long lashes, jet-black hair twisted in two coils round her head, and a pallid skin. There was something in the quiet reserve and slyness of her manner that reminded one of a kitten. Though she rarely looked at Nikolay, it was manifest to the most casual observer that the entire power of her being was drawn to him.

"Yes, _ma chère_," Count Rostov was saying to old Princess Drubetskoy, "here your son Boris has received his commission as an officer, and Nikolay is so fond of his friend that he doesn't want to be left behind, and is giving up the university and his poor old father to go into the army. And there was a place all ready for him in the archives department. He's going into the hussars. There's friendship for you!"

A few weeks later, the Rostovs held a ball to celebrate Natasha's fourteenth birthday. In the interval, Sonya disappeared. Natasha searched for her in vain until she was inspired to visit the lumber-room.

Yes, Sonya was lying face downwards, crushing her gossamer pink frock on a dirty old striped feather-bed, and sobbing as if her heart would break.

"Why, Sonya, what is it? What's the matter with you?

. . . Ooh-ooh! " And Natasha's big mouth dropped open
at once and she wailed loudly as a baby, the tears streaming
down her flat cheeks.

" Nikolinka's going off to that horrid war in a week . . .
his . . . paper . . . has come," gasped Sonya, shaking from
head to foot. " And he's my cousin, and we can never marry;
and besides, auntie would never let him marry me—she'd say
I was spoiling his career, and she wants him to marry the
Countess Julie! "

Natasha lifted her up and hugged her, smiling through her
tears. " Sonya, darling, I never heard such nonsense. Don't
you remember how we talked it over with Nicky that night in
the divan-room, and settled it once and for all? Why, uncle
Shinshin's brother is married to his first cousin, and we're only
second cousins, you know. And Nicky's simply dying of love
for you—he's said so over and over again—and he never gives
a thought to that stuck-up creature Julie! "

" Do you think so? Honestly now? " said Sonya, smoothing
her frock and her hair.

Natasha solemnly drew her finger across her throat, and
they both laughed gleefully. " Let's hurry back," whispered
Natasha, patting a stray wisp of hair on her friend's head, " I've
promised the next dance to Boris."

*   *   *   *   *

While the guests in the Rostovs' hall whirled to and fro in
the sixth *anglaise* of the evening, at the other end of the town,
in one of its largest mansions, old Count Bezuhov lay in the
throes of his sixth stroke.

The doctors had announced there was no hope of recovery.
The dying man had already received absolution and the
Sacrament, preparations were being made to administer
extreme unction, and throughout the great house reigned a
thrilling hush. Prince Vassily, who was the direct heir through
his wife, and the Count's three daughters, were in constant
attendance at the bedside.

Pierre arrived at the mansion in a carriage which had been
sent to his lodging by Prince Vassily. Somewhat to Pierre's
surprise, the carriage drew up outside the back entrance to
the mansion. Pierre got out, walked slowly upstairs, and was
escorted by a whispering, tiptoeing bevy of servants, doctors,
and nurses, into the immense bedchamber, divided by columns
and an arch, and carpeted by Persian rugs.

People were busy for several minutes around the high bed.

When they moved away, Pierre felt a touch on his arm. He turned and saw old Princess Anna Drubetskoy, who murmured to him, " Come along." Pierre approached the bed and gazed at the old count's magnificent face, with its broad and lofty brow, proud cold eyes, and fine, though sensual mouth.

The old count groaned. A servant hurried forward to turn him on his right side, so that he would be more comfortable. It was no easy task to move the heavy body, with its massive shoulders and tremendous arch of chest One of the count's arms dragged helplessly behind, and he made a vain effort to pull it after him. The count noticed Pierre's look of pity during this struggle, and a smile appeared on his lips—a feeble and anguished smile, contrasting strangely with those powerful features. At the sight of that smile, Pierre felt his throat go hard and there was a tickling in his nose he could not endure and tears were suddenly wet and cold on his cheeks.

The old count moaned and closed his eyes. Pierre sat and looked at him. He was lying very still. Pierre began to wonder what he ought to do next.

Pierre felt a touch on his arm. " He is. . . . Let us go," whispered Princess Anna. Pierre followed her out of the room.

Two days later, when the will was read, Pierre learnt he was sole heir to Count Bezuhov's huge fortune and many estates, which included some of the largest in Russia.

* * * * *

" Moscow talks of nothing but the war. The Guards are already starting on their march to the frontier. Heaven grant that the Corsican monster who is destroying the peace of Europe may be foiled by the angel whom God in His mercy has given us as our Tsar.

" This terrible conflict has robbed me of one of my heart's dearest allies—I mean Nicholas Rostov, the young man I spoke to you of in the summer, who has left the university and joined the army. Some day I will tell you all we said to each other in parting, but as yet the sweet pain is too fresh in memory. Ah, dearest Marya, how lucky you are to know nothing of such joys and sorrows, both so poignant as scarcely to be borne!

" Let me hear all about the arrival of your brother Andrey and his darling little wife. I embrace you as I love you.

JULIE."

" P.S.—Why are we not together again on the blue sofa in your study, the *confidential* sofa? Why cannot I draw new hope and comfort from your divinely beautiful eyes? "

She flatters me, thought Princess Marya Bolkonsky sadly, as she put down the letter on her dressing-table and glanced with a sigh into the mirror. The glass reflected a plain and sickly face and a thin, ungainly figure. But Countess Julie had not flattered her friend in the least. The young princess's eyes were so large and expressive and luminous, so alive with intelligence and fine emotion, that they made the plainness of her face more attractive than any beauty.

Princess Marya sighed again, then, with a guilty start of recollection, looked at her watch. She was five minutes late for her geometry lesson. Almost panic-stricken with fear, she rummaged in a drawer until she found a tattered exercise-book, then hurried from her boudoir along the corridors leading to her father's room.

Old Prince Nikolay Bolkonsky, once a commander-in-chief, had grown weary of life at Court and retired to his estate at Bleak Hills, where he lived with his daughter, Princess Marya, and her French companion, Mademoiselle Bourienne. He planned his days with military exactitude, and save during meals, which had to be served to the minute, spent every waking moment at work.

Princess Marya knocked timidly at the door and entered. Her father glanced round, then went on turning a snuff-box on a lathe. The great room was full of objects manifestly in constant use—high bookcases with their glass doors open and their contents in wild disorder, tables strewn with maps and plans, an escritoire with a closely-written manuscript pad, carpenters' tools lying all over the floor, half-finished chairs and cupboards.

The old prince was a shrunken but vigorous litttle man. After a few more turns he took his foot from the lathe and went up to his daughter.

"You're late," he said curtly, offering her an unshaven cheek. "Never mind, sit down!" He drew up a chair to an empty table, pulled a text-book from a drawer and began, "Now, madam, these triangles are equal; kindly observe, the angle ABC . . ."

As the lesson went on, a scared look appeared in the princess's eyes, and unsightly red blotches spread over her face. It was obvious that she did not understand a word, and that she was too afraid to ask for explanations. At length the old man thrust back his chair with a loud grating noise and jumped to his feet.

" Your head must be made of wood ! " he yelled. He paced angrily to and fro. " Mathematics is a grand subject," he muttered. " Patience, patience, that's all you need ! You want to be something better than these silly modern girls, I hope ! "

Suddenly he came back to her, laid his hand on her hair, and gazed at her with piercing tenderness. " It won't do, it won't do," he said gently. " But there now, run along. And if your brother Andrey and that wife of his come before dinner, remember I'm not to be disturbed."

Princess Marya was in the divan-room struggling with her daily practice on the clavichord when Prince Andrey and Lise arrived. The little princess entered the room first ; Marya rose from her stool with a cry of delight and clasped Lise in her arms. Lise had grown stouter, she thought, but her short upper lip, with its faint down and valiant smile, still rose as gaily as ever when she spoke. The two women kissed rapturously.

After dinner, the old prince took Andrey back with him to his study. " Well, my fine warrior," he said, " so you want to fight Bonaparte, eh ? Mind you beat him, or we Russians'll all be his slaves. But come, tell me how we're planning the Austrian campaign."

Andrey had to explain in full to the old man how the Russian troops were to link up with the Austrians in time to confront Napoleon with a superior force before he could take Vienna. The moment of farewell drew near.

" Father," said Prince Andrey haltingly, " I've brought you . . . my wife . . . with child. . . . I'm ashamed as it is to leave her on your hands, but . . ."

" Don't talk nonsense. Say what you want."

" When my wife's confinement is due, send to Moscow for an accoucheur. . . . And let him stay here ! "

The old prince stared at him.

" I admit that out of a million cases, only one goes wrong," said Prince Andrey, his voice breaking, " but they've been telling her things ; she's had a dream and she's frightened."

" H'm . . . h'm," muttered the old prince. " All right. She's pretty. Well now, good-bye." He gave his son his hand to kiss and embraced him. " Remember, if you are killed it will be a grief to me in my old age. . . ." His voice rose almost to a scream. " But if I learn that you have not behaved like the son of Nikolay Bolkonsky . . ."

Prince Andrey smiled. " You needn't have said that, father," he said affectionately.

They stood facing each other. The old man's fierce eyes were fixed on his son's eyes.

" Well, what are you waiting for ? " cried the old man suddenly. " We have said good-bye. Get along." He flung open the study door. " Get along ! " he roared, his loud and angry voice echoing and re-echoing down the corridor.

Lise glanced up anxiously when her husband entered the drawing-room, where she was talking with Princess Marya and Mademoiselle Bourienne.

" I must leave now," he said, looking at her, and there was almost a sneer in the " now ", as if it meant, " Now hurry up and go through your little performance."

" Andrey? At once? " said the little princess. She turned pale and gazed at him in anguish. He put his arms round her, then felt her go suddenly limp. Very gently and carefully he carried her to a low chair, glanced into her face, and kissed her bloodless lips.

Then he turned to his sister. " Good-bye, Masha," he said quietly. They kissed each other's hands; Prince Andrey walked swiftly out of the room.

* * * * *

By the middle of October, 1805, the first Russian troops were occupying the towns and villages of eastern Austria. They had expected orders to move on as quickly as possible to effect a junction with General Mack and his Austrian army at Ulm. But there were incomprehensible delays; orders and counter-orders succeeded one another with bewildering rapidity. The men were not sorry to rest for a while, many of them were exhausted by the series of forced marches over a stretch of more than a thousand miles. They were short of food, clothing, and equipment, and would remain so until the transport columns caught up with them.

One of these regiments arrived at Braunau late one evening, bedraggled and dirty, with torn and buttonless uniforms and boots that gaped with holes—only to learn that there would be a general inspection an hour after dawn by the Russian commander-in-chief and an Austrian general. The general in command of this regiment was almost beside himself with fury at the news. His men had marched twenty-five miles that day, and now they must sit up all night mending and cleaning and polishing !

Just after dawn he had the fall-in sounded. When the men were assembled and at attention, he strutted anxiously to and fro before them, agreeably surprised by their neatness—the torn boots were a pity, but couldn't be helped, of course.

The aide-de-camp who had brought the instructions from the commander-in-chief approached the general and whispered something in his ear. The general's grey whiskers bristled and his mottled red jowls swelled dangerously. Turning to a major, he snarled, "A fine mess we've made of it. Why didn't you realize that the words ' in marching order ' meant wearing their greatcoats?" He advanced nearer the regiment and bellowed hoarsely, " Change into your greatcoats, lads, and for God's sake be quick about it! "

Captains and sergeants bustled to and fro among the ranks, and instantly the regiment became a heaving mass of men straggling apart and shouting and laughing as they ran backwards and forwards, stooping to remove their knapsacks over their heads, taking out their grey greatcoats, and thrusting their arms into the sleeves.

It was half an hour before the men were in position again. The general's nerves were raw. He walked before the regiment again with his dithering strut, and scanned it with merciless eyes.

Suddenly he halted and the purple veins of his face and neck stood out like cords. A man in the second rank had on a blue greatcoat instead of a grey one. The general turned to the captain of the company and, pointing with his finger, yelped :

" Who's that dressed up like a bloody Hungarian? "

" That's Dolohov, Your Excellency, the degraded officer."

" Degraded to what? A private or a field-marshal? You'll be dressing your men in petticoats next." He strutted angrily up to Dolohov, who, with an impudent grin on his hard white face, gazed straight into the eyes of the general.

" What are you doing in a blue coat? " barked the general. " Sergeant, rip it off the dirty b——."

" General, I am here to obey orders—— " began Dolohov.

" Silence! " roared the general.

" —but not to endure insults! " went on Dolohov in a clear and ringing voice.

The general stared at him in astonishment. Then he growled, " Get him into a grey greatcoat," and strode angrily away.

A few minutes later, old Prince Kutuzov, the commander-in-chief, accompanied by an Austrian general, arrived in a coach from Vienna. Kutuzov, stout and grizzled, seemed already overcome by the weariness of age. He walked slowly and listlessly through the ranks, stopping now and then to exchange a friendly word with officers and soldiers. Looking at their boots, he often shook his head dejectedly, and pointed them out to the Austrian general. Behind Kutuzov followed his suite; nearest of all to the commander-in-chief was his handsome adjutant, Prince Andrey Bolkonsky.

After the review, Kutuzov and the Austrian general retired to the commander-in-chief's private room. Kutuzov sent Andrey to get some documents. Outside the room he met Kozlovsky, the adjutant on duty.

" No news from Mack? " asked Kozlovsky.

" No."

" I suppose if he'd been beaten, the news would be here by now."

" Very likely," said Andrey, and was moving towards the door, when it was flung open, and a tall stranger, wearing the long coat and Maria Theresa order of an Austrian general, and with a black kerchief tied round his head, lurched unsteadily into the room.

" Commander-in-chief Kutuzov? " he demanded in a harsh German accent.

" He is engaged," answered Kozlovsky, rising and hurriedly barring the way to the commander-in-chief's room. " Whom shall I announce? "

But at that moment Kutuzov himself opened the door, and at the sight of the stranger, his jaw dropped stupidly.

The general with the bandaged head stumbled coweringly forward, as though fleeing from some awful danger.

" You see the unfortunate Mack," he groaned brokenly.

A scowl appeared on Kutuzov's face, then vanished almost at once, and with a look of pity he threw his arm round the Austrian general, helped him into his room, and closed the door.

The fateful news spread like wildfire among the Russian troops. General Mack had been outwitted by Napoleon at Ulm and surrendered the main Austrian army. He himself had only escaped capture by a miracle.

The plight of the Russian army during the weeks that followed became perilous in the extreme. Pursued by French forces of a hundred thousand men, commanded by Napoleon himself, Kutuzov's army of thirty-five thousand beat a hasty retreat to the lower ground about the Danube. Here they were overtaken by the enemy, and fought rear-guard skirmishes, avoiding all engagements save those needed to secure the withdrawal of artillery and baggage. Desperately, they turned and stood at bay, at Lambach, Amsteten, and Melk, but the only results of these actions was to accelerate the already rapid retreat.

Near Schöngraben they were lured to a halt by the false promise of a truce from Marshal Murat. Before they realized their deception, they found themselves trapped on their hillside position by a strong force rushed to the scene by Napoleon.

The French were advancing so swiftly up the hill that Prince Andrey could soon discern clearly their sashes and red epaulettes. The Russian front line had formed with infantry on the right flank, artillery in the centre, and cavalry on the left. Prince Bagration, general in command of the right flank, rode round the ranks of infantry, then dismounted, and gave the reins of his horse to a Cossack. He advanced a few paces before the centre of the line of infantrymen, bent and stretched his legs like a jockey, and straightened his cap. The French column came into sight round a bend in the hill. Prince Bagration turned for a moment to the front line and called out in a resolute voice:

" With God's help, lads! "

Then, with the awkward, lumbering pace of a man rarely off horseback, he walked downwards over the uneven ground, Prince Andrey at his side, and the men a little to the rear. Suddenly there was a crack of a shot from the French, then another . . . and then firing rang out steadily and wisps of smoke puffed from all along the climbing enemy line.

Several Russians fell. The snapping of shots from both sides was now so rapid as to make it impossible to hear the shouts of the officers. Nearly every soldier's face was now comically smudged with powder as he plugged with his ramrod, got charges out of his pouch, or fired his musket.

By the time Andrey got down to the hollow at the foot of the hill the air was so dense with the white and acrid smoke that he could see only a few yards around him, and every other sound was muffled by the continuous roll of musketry. Two soldiers passed him dragging a third up the hill; his head was covered with blood and he was coughing and gasping.

Suddenly Andrey felt his arm gripped, and found himself

staring into the excited face of Prince Bagration. "Send down the two battalions of the Sixth Chasseurs!" he yelled. Prince Andrey nodded. As he made his way back up the hill, the reeking smoke cleared. He could hear now not only the whiz of bullets but the low hum of cannon-balls and grenades. A ball tore into the earth quite near him, throwing up the soil with stupendous force. He gave the order to the commander of the Sixth Chasseurs, and reported to Kutuzov, who asked him to ride at once to the battery in the centre and see how things were faring.

Andrey rode to the battery and dismounted by the end one of its four cannons. Directly facing the battery on the skyline of the opposite hill could be seen the village of Schöngraben, the French headquarters, and amid the smoke Andrey observed three masses of French troops advancing. The battery was under the command of a red-haired, freckled little captain named Tushin, who kept up its fire so briskly that the French thought the main Russian forces must be concentrated there, and twice had attacked in strength and been driven back with heavy slaughter by the grapeshot from its four cannons.

Just as Andrey reached the battery, Tushin had managed to set fire to Schöngraben. At the sight of the merry blaze, the gunners danced like children, then, without waiting for Tushin's instructions, began aiming all four cannons at it.

"That's the idea," they encouraged one another gleefully as the fire rapidly spread; "give 'em another to fry their bacon."

In revenge, the French stationed ten cannons on the right of the village and pounded away heavily at Tushin's battery. Within a few minutes the balls were falling among his cannons, knocking over two horses and tearing the foot off a gunner.

An hour later seventeen of the forty gunners were dead. But Tushin, a frail little man, still ran to and fro amid the smoke and the deafening racket, shuddering from head to foot at each boom of the cannon, chirping "Smash away, lads!" in his weak falsetto, aiming the guns, estimating the charges, pleading now here now there for "just one more pipe for that stroke."

Andrey rode back to Kutuzov, who told him to order Tushin to retreat at once. One cannon ball after another flew over Andrey's head on the return journey, and in spite of all his efforts he was seized by an uncontrollable shivering. "I mustn't be afraid," he thought, and deliberately rode into the midst of the shell-torn battery before dismounting.

Among the four cannons and their perspiring gunners now raged a din that seemed to come from all sides, from under the earth, from the sky. Horses and men lay inextricably mingled in a blood-strewn welter of harness and wheels. Tushin was arguing with a staff-officer as Andrey came up, and from time to time glancing with delight at number one gunner of the second cannon, who was riotously drunk and toiling like a madman.

"Here comes another of their mothballs," squeaked Tushin to the drunken gunner, as a cannon-ball thudded into the earth beside him. "Mind you throw it back, Ivan."

"Are you mad?" shouted the officer. "You've been ordered twice already to retreat."

"Why pick out me?" said Tushin timidly, looking with alarm at the superior officer.

The officer ducked smartly to avoid a cannon-ball. He was about to speak again, when another ball rushed past him. He turned his horse's head, applied his spurs, and galloped away.

"Retreat! Everyone must retreat!" he shouted from a distance.

A hoarse roar of laughter went up from the gunners.

Prince Andrey gave a stern order to Tushin, then helped the gunners to move the two cannons that were undamaged down the safe side of the hill. "Good-bye till we meet again," he said to Tushin, then held out his hand.

"Good-bye," said Tushin, tears streaming down his cheeks.

* * * * *

Meanwhile, on the left flank the Pavlograd regiment of hussars were suddenly ordered to repulse a surprise attack, and young Ensign Nikolay Rostov had scarcely time to swing into the saddle before the command rang out to form in order.

Sabres clinked out of their sheaths.

"Forward, quick, gallop!" yelled the commander.

The horses' haunches in the front line moved away from Nikolay. Shots rattled in the distance. On the right Nikolay could see the line of hussars, advancing, as it seemed to him, incredibly slowly.

"Quicker," snapped the word of command along the line, and Nikolay felt his horse's hindquarters sink as he settled into a gallop. Far ahead he could see a dark, moving band. That must be the enemy, he decided; well, I'm ready for him; and he could feel already the exhilarating downward slash of his sabre. The thrill of the dash through the cold keen air made his pulses beat like hammers. He applied the spurs, and his horse sped forward in an easy and powerful rhythm, outstripping the line with a speed as unreal as a dream.

Nikolay saw the French uniforms clearly now advancing across the field. All at once a humming as of a myriad of bees swept over Nikolay: the other horses were catching up with him and passing him; another hussar crashed into him and turned round with a face red with fury as his horse pounded on, and suddenly Nikolay knew that the line had gone by and left him behind.

"What's the matter? I'm not moving, I'm falling, I'm killed," he said to himself. His horse sank to his knees, and Nikolay was alone in the middle of the field. Blood spurted from the horse's head. Nikolay tried to get up, dragged his left leg from under the horse, then fell down again.

His sabretache was entangled in the saddle. He pulled it free, and stood up. His left arm had gone numb and the wrist and hand felt as if they did not belong to it. He examined his hand carefully for spots of blood.

" Thank God, here's someone to help me," he said to himself, noticing some men running towards him. The leader of the men wore a queer-looking shako and a blue coat and had a swarthy face and a hooked nose. Behind him came many more, running swiftly, and in their rear two men were holding up a Russian hussar; he must be wounded, too, thought Nikolay.

The advancing soldiers had lowered their bayonets and were now running so swiftly and intently towards Nikolay that a quiver of fear passed through him. " Can they be French? " he wondered. "And are coming to kill me? _Me_, whom everyone loves . . . mother . . . Natasha . . . Sonya . . . Julie? Impossible."

The man with the hook nose was now so near that Nikolay could see a breathlessly eager stillness in his face. Nikolay snatched up his pistol, but instead of aiming and firing it, he found himself unable to do more than fling it at the Frenchman. Then he turned and set off running across the field as fast as his legs would carry him, jumping over hedges, darting and spurting with the panic verve of a hare escaping from dogs.

Whenever he looked back, a chill of horror ran down his spine; they were gaining on him. A hundred yards in front was a wood he knew to be occupied by Russian infantry, but he was exhausted, and his left arm seemed to weigh a hundred pounds. He glanced round; the man with the hook nose had dropped on one knee and was taking aim at him. Nikolay moaned, he could run no farther, he ducked as the bullets whizzed by and over him. Then, clutching his left hand in his right, he made a last despairing effort; stumbling and gasping he reached the wood just as a volley of musketry crackled from the Russian sharpshooters' line at its edge, putting the band of Frenchmen to flight.

By nightfall the French had been driven back far enough to allow the Russian army to escape from the trap and continue its retreat in safety. All along the road, wounded men were begging for seats on the cannons, but the gunners had been ordered to refuse all " lifts " so that the artillery could be got away as quickly as possible.

A white-faced young ensign of hussars, nursing a bandaged arm, approached Tushin's battery and implored the freckled little captain for a seat. " Captain, for God's sake, I've hurt my arm," he said beseechingly. " For God's sake, I'm done up, I can't walk another step." It was evident from his piteous tone he had been everywhere refused.

" Let him get on, let him get on," said Tushin. He turned to a gunner. " But where's the wounded officer? "

" We took him off, he was dead," said the gunner.

" Then you can take his place, my dear," said Tushin to Nikolay Rostov. " Sit on Mrs. Gobolov," he added, indicating the cannon from which they had removed the dead officer.

" Where are you wounded? How did it happen? " asked Tushin.

" It's only a sprain," stammered Nikolay, shamefacedly.

" But there's blood on the cannon," said Tushin.

" That was the dead officer stained it," said an artilleryman, carefully wiping away every speck of blood from the shining cannon.

* * * * *

Pierre had led a very lonely, idle, and carefree life before he became Count Bezuhov and one of the richest men in Russia. Now, however, he found himself so beset by visitors, so occupied with affairs, that he never managed to get a moment to himself unless he stayed in bed. He had to sign countless papers, appear at meetings of lawyers, hold long consultations with the stewards of his many estates, and in general take control of all sorts of business about which he knew nothing and cared even less. Moreover, hundreds of people who had hitherto been quite unaware of his existence now rarely let him alone if they could help it.

Prince Vassily was by far the most assiduous of all these well-wishers, and no trouble was too great for him in his efforts to accustom the awkward young man both to the dignities and the pleasures of his important new station. He obtained for him an appointment as gentleman of the bedchamber, insisted on his staying with him at his mansion in Petersburg, and introduced him everywhere into the best society.

Pierre found, to his no small gratification, that the lovely Ellen appeared to share her father's liking for his company. He became her constant escort at the many balls, assemblies, and concerts of the season, and more than one interested observer noticed his naïve admiration of her beauty.

" She's exquisite, isn't she? " Anna Pavlovna Scherer whispered in his ear one evening. " And how she carries herself! Such grace and perfection of manner! Happy will be he who wins her. Even the most insignificant man would take a brilliant place in society as her husband."

Pierre walked over to the corner where Ellen was seated with Anna Pavlovna's aunt. Ellen looked round smiling at him, and made room for him at her side on the divan. She leaned forward. Her dress was cut very low both in front and behind, her bosom was revealed in all its allure to his short-sighted eyes, and her neck was so close to his lips that he could have kissed it almost without moving. He breathed the intimate fragrance that came from her, felt the warmth of her body against his own. The close-fitting gown she wore seemed less than a veil.

" So you have never known until now that I am desirable? " her naked beauty seemed to be murmuring to him. " That I am a woman? A woman to be enjoyed by any man." She looked at him. " By you, too," her eyes said.

Pierre tossed restlessly on his bed that night. In earlier days he had heard from boon companions all sorts of rumours about Ellen Vassily. " There's something nasty in the joy she excites in me," he thought. " I wonder if it's true about her lovers. . . . They even say her own brother Anatole . . ."

In November, Prince Vassily had to go on a Government tour of inspection through four provinces. The eve of his departure was Ellen's birthday, and in celebration Prince Vassily gave a supper-party to a few select friends and relations.

After the guests had departed, Ellen and Pierre remained for a long time alone in the little drawing-room.

"Aline," said Prince Vassily, to his wife, as he paced irritably to and fro, "go and see what they are doing."

The princess returned a few moments later.

"Just the same!" she said.

Prince Vassily frowned, and one corner of his mouth twitched with an ugly, brutal effect. Suddenly he flung back his head and strode resolutely into the drawing-room. He walked quickly up to Pierre. The prince's face was so impressively solemn that Pierre got up in alarm on seeing him.

"Thank God!" said Prince Vassily. "My wife has told me all about it." He put one arm round Pierre, the other round his daughter. "My dear boy! Ellen! How glad I am!" His voice faltered. "I loved your father . . . and she will make you a good wife. . . . God's blessing on you both!" Tears were moist on his cheeks.

Six weeks later they were married.

*　　*　　*　　*　　*

"Soldiers! The Russian army is coming to meet you, to avenge the Austrian army, the army of Ulm. They are the forces you have defeated at Hollabrunn, and have been pursuing ever since. The position we occupy is a powerful one, and while they will march to outflank me on the right, they will expose their flank to me. Let every man be fully inspired by the idea that we must subdue these minions of England, who are seized with such hatred of our country. This victory will conclude our campaign.

NAPOLEON."

Such was the proclamation read to the French troops on the eve of the battle of Austerlitz. Fresh reinforcements from Russia had joined Kutuzov's army, also a large Austrian force under General Weierother. The Emperor Francis of Austria and the Tsar Alexander had met at Olmütz and summoned a council of war, where it was decided—against the advice of Kutuzov—to advance at once and fight a general engagement with Napoleon.

The allied armies advanced to a point west of Austerlitz, where the main Russian force took up their position on the Prätzen heights, facing the French army on the opposite hillside two miles away.

Napoleon himself rode among the bivouacs while the

proclamation was being read to his troops. The soldiers lighted wisps of straw and ran after him crying " *Vive l'empereur !* " The shouting and the flares went on for a long time before they died down. The allied armies, two miles away, thought the French must be putting out their camp-fires and beating a hasty and confused retreat. On such trifles hang the destinies of nations.

At ten o'clock in the evening the allied generals held a final council of war in Kutuzov's quarters. Kutuzov, his uniform unbuttoned, and his fat neck bulging over the collar, was sitting in a low chair, his pudgy old hands laid limply on the arms. His counsels for delay had been ignored and he had said all he had to say. He was almost asleep.

With the air of a man who has not a moment to lose, Weie-rother, the Austrian staff-commander, glanced impatiently at Kutuzov's drooping eyelids, and began explaining the plan of attack. The brunt of the action was to fall on the Russians, who were to be the first to descend from the Prätzen heights, so as to attack the French right flank and drive it back to the Bohemian mountains.

Kutuzov had begun to snore. He was exhausted by many nights without sleep. Weierother looked at him with contempt, then went on with his long and intricate account of the disposi-tion of forces for the morrow.

" If Napoleon could have attacked us, he would have done so to-day," he said. " Personally, I doubt if he has as many as forty thousand troops."

" In that case he is going to meet his ruin in awaiting our attack," observed a Russian general ironically.

" The enemy have extinguished their fires and a continual noise has been heard in their camp," retorted Weierother. " That means they are either retreating—the only thing we have to fear—or changing their position. But even if they were to take up their position at Turas, it would merely be saving us a good deal of our trouble, and all our arrangements would remain unaltered in the slightest."

" How can that be? " said Prince Andrey, who had long been awaiting the opportunity to express his doubts. But at that moment Kutuzov opened his eyes, cleared his throat huskily, and looked round at the generals.

" Gentlemen, the disposition for to-morrow—for to-day rather, as it's nearly one o'clock—can't be altered now," he said. " You have heard it, and we will all do our duty.

And before a battle nothing is so important . . . as a good night's rest."

* * * * *

Seated on a little grey Arab horse, a few paces in advance of his marshals, Napoleon was gazing intently and silently at the hills occupied by the enemy. He had slept well, and felt in excellent spirits. It was nine o'clock in the morning of December 2, 1805, the anniversary of his coronation.

Above a sea of mist he could discern the Russian troops moving across the hills in the distance, and hear the steady noise of firing in the valley. His face, still, thin, and handsome, did not stir a muscle, his glittering eyes were fixed on one spot. His forecast had proved correct. Part of the Russian forces were going down into the valley towards the ponds and lakes, while part were evacuating the heights of Prätzen, which he regarded as the key of the position. Soon the Russian left flank would become hopelessly exposed by its vain attack on the French right, and then he would launch the pick of Soult's and Bernadotte's forces in a smashing counter-stroke which would capture the Prätzen heights.

Half-an-hour later Kutuzov and Prince Andrey were following a column of carabineers down the heights. The fog was beginning to lift, and a mile and a half away the French troops could be vaguely perceived on the opposite hills. Below on the left the firing had become much louder.

Prince Andrey turned to an adjutant, and asked him for the loan of his field-glasses.

" Look! look! " cried the adjutant in horror, pointing not to the opposite hillls, but straight down the hill before them. " It's the French! "

Not two hundred yards away, advancing rapidly up the hill-side towards the Russian infantry on their right, was a dense column of French soldiers.

" We must warn the Apseron regiment," yelled Andrey to Kutuzov. But at that moment volleys rang out close by on all sides, everything was lost in a cloud of smoke, and suddenly a hoarse Russian voice shouted:

" It's all up, mates! "

Instantly, as if the cry were a command, a pell-mell rush of fleeing troops swept by Andrey. When they had gone past, he saw Kutuzov pressing a blood-soaked handkerchief to his cheek.

" You are wounded? " gasped Andrey.

" The wound's not here, but there," said Kutuzov, pointing
to the running soldiers. He lashed his horse and rode to the
right, followed by Andrey. A fresh onslaught by flying crowds
carried them back as on a wave. They struck out left and
right and forced their way through to a Russian battery still
firing on the hillside, though the French were racing towards it.

A little higher up stood Russian infantry, from which a
general on horseback detached himself and rode towards
Kutuzov. " Stop those wretches," gasped Kutuzov, pointing
to the flying soldiers. But at that instant came a volley from
the French, the general clutched his leg, several soldiers fell,
and the second lieutenant standing with the regimental flag
let it drop from his hands.

Prince Andrey jumped off his horse and ran to the flag.
" Lads, forward," he screamed, seizing the staff of the flag.
Balancing with difficulty the heavy staff, he stumbled forward.
Suddenly he felt a violent blow on the head and everything
went dark around him.

The French captured the Prätzen heights and their cavalry
swept on in pursuit of the Russian rearguard, now surging in
panic disorder along the banks of the ponds near the village of
Augest. On the narrow dam over the Satschan pond a throng
of men with faces wry with the terror of death struggled madly
with one another in the rush to get across, amid army wagons
and cannons, under horses' legs and between gun-carriage
wheels, crushing and suffocating one another, dying, stepping
over the dying, turning and killing each other, stumbling
onwards, while every few seconds a cannon-ball tore the air
and smashed down among them, or a grenade burst and flung
over a wide circle the blood and flesh of those it had killed.

" Get on the ice," screamed a soldier, knocking down two
others and floundering on to the slippery ice of the millpond.
A general at the far end of the dam lifted his hand in warning.
Just then a cannon-ball zoomed over the crowd, everyone
ducked; the general fell from his horse with a wet splash into
a puddle of blood.

" On the ice! Get on the ice! " yelled countless voices.
Hundreds of soldiers began running from the dam on to the
frozen pond. Others, finding their way to the ice blocked by
horses and cannon, lashed the horses on to the ice, dragging
the heavy gun-carriages behind them.

The ice, swarming now with soldiers, horses and artillery,
began to splinter and crack. Huge pieces broke away, and

men and horses found themselves struggling in the water. Meanwhile the cannon-balls fell in a thickening storm, shattering the pond and its mass of shrieking, drowning victims into a *mêlée* of ice and blood.

* * * * *

" To the health of beautiful women . . . and their lovers," said Dolohov, raising his glass of champagne to Pierre and gazing boldly into his eyes.

They were guests at a dinner of the English Club in Moscow, and sat facing each other across the long table. As usual, Pierre had drunk too much. Indeed, ever since his marriage he had been drinking more and more heavily. He spent most of his time sitting alone in his study with a bottle of wine at his side. People said the way he neglected his lovely wife was shameful. Fortunately, there was never any lack of admirers to escort Ellen to the balls and *soirées*, where her beauty still reigned without peer.

Dolohov, who had been restored to officer's rank for bravery in action, was on leave from the front. He and Ellen had been about a good deal together of late. Pierre knew no reason whatever to believe there was anything between them. But at the look in Dolohov's eyes as he raised his glass, Pierre lurched to his feet, leaned forward unsteadily over the table, and said in a low voice:

" You . . . you blackguard . . . I challenge you."

Pierre's second was his friend, Nesvitsky, and Dolohov's was young Nikolay Rostov. An officer called Denisov agreed to act as umpire. The five met at the Sokolniky copse near Moscow at eight o'clock the next morning.

Denisov gave Pierre and Dolohov their pistols, stepped back, and cried, " At the word ' three ' you may advance towards each other and fire! O-one . . . two . . . three! "

Dolohov walked slowly towards Pierre, his ice-blue eyes intent on the face of his antagonist, and his lips, as always, twisted into a smile. Pierre held his pistol in his right hand, with the arm fully outstretched. He was obviously afraid of killing himself with it. He had never held a pistol before.

Pierre shut his eyes and fired. When he opened them again he could see nothing for the smoke. He stood still awaiting Dolohov's shot. The smoke cleared. Dolohov was clutching his left side, and Nikolay Rostov was supporting him. " It can't be over . . . already," moaned Dolohov. " My mother . . ." He fell limp in Rostov's arms.

Three hours later Pierre was sitting in his study when Ellen rushed in. " I'm the laughing-stock of all Moscow," she cried furiously. " You, you of all people going in for deeds of valour. You were drunk, and didn't know what you were doing, and you've killed "—her voice rose to a scream—" a better man than you in all respects."

" Don't speak to me . . . I implore you," muttered Pierre huskily.

" Why shouldn't I speak? I tell you there aren't many women with husbands like you who wouldn't have taken a lover, only—only I haven't done it," she cried.

" We had better part," groaned Pierre. He was in physical agony, and felt as if he were choking.

" Part, by all means," said Ellen, " if you give me a fortune."

Pierre jumped up from the couch and staggered towards her. " I'll kill you ! " he shouted. He snatched up a marble slab from the table.

Ellen shrieked and darted away from him. A spasm of loathing distorted Pierre's face; he flung down the slab, shivering it into fragments. " Go! " he roared. " Go! " She ran out of the room.

A week later Pierre made over to his wife the revenue of all his estates in Great Russia, which made up the larger half of his property.

*   *   *   *   *

He began to spend more and more time at his club. The life he had been leading in Petersburg now filled him with loathing. He could no longer endure the tedious ceremonial of service at Court, and the brilliant and inane round of society revolted him. He took to drinking heavily again, sought out the gay companions of his bachelor days, and soon his orgies of dissipation became such a byword in the capital that every-one began to say he was besmirching not only his own name, but that of the lovely Countess Ellen. Pierre felt there was justice in this charge, and, to avoid compromising his wife, he left Petersburg for Moscow.

In easy-going Moscow, with its love of indolence and its dislike of formality, he felt comfortable, warm, at home, and snugly dirty, as in an old dressing-gown. Everyone, from the old ladies to the children, welcomed him back like a long-expected guest. He seemed to them a prince of good fellows, a delightful, kind-hearted, good-humoured, eccentric, a gener-ous and jovial Russian gentleman of the old school. Charities and benevolent societies, schools, subscription concerts, and churches never appealed in vain to him.

As soon as he was lolling in his place on the sofa at his club he was surrounded by a circle of his friends. After a few bottles of margot, everyone was laughing or talking excitedly around him. Whenever there were quarrels, his kindly smiles and casually uttered jokes were enough to reconcile the bitterest enemies. He was the most popular man in Moscow.

But, for all his carefree air, Pierre often reflected sombrely that he was merely the wealthy husband of a faithless wife, a retired *kammerherr*, fond of eating and drinking and talking, and little else—a man, in short, who was idling away his life instead of making the most of it.

Like many other men, especially Russians, he allowed his intelligence to cripple his desire to act. He saw too clearly the sham and falsity of life. Every sphere of human effort appeared to him tainted with evil and deception. Whatever he tried to be, whatever he took up, quickly seemed corrupt and futile to him. Meanwhile he had to live, had to occupy himself with something. It was an agony beyond endurance to be reminded of the insoluble problems of life, so he abandoned himself, simply in order to forget them, to any and every form of distraction, especially the most potent of all, drink and women.

* * * * *

At Bleak Hills there was still no news of Andrey when his wife's labour commenced. A relay of horses had been sent to the high-road for the German specialist, who was expected every minute, and men were despatched with lanterns to guide him over the holes in the ice.

Princess Marya could no longer read her book; she sat in silence, her luminous eyes watching the wrinkled face of her old nurse, who, looking up from the stocking she was knitting, kept saying, " God is merciful, doctors are never wanted."

Suddenly one of the windows blew open, and a draught fluttered the curtain and swept chilly through the room. The old nurse put down her stocking and walked over to the window.

" Princess, my dearie, there's someone driving up the avenue. With lanterns—it must be the doctor ! " she said.

" Ah, thank God ! " said Princess Marya. " I must go meet him ; he does not know Russian."

Princess Marya went out to the head of the stairs. A footman with a candle stood on the first landing, and down below the butler was opening the door.

She heard a voice that seemed familiar to her, the butler answered something, then steps in thick overshoes began mounting the lower, unseen, part of the staircase.

"It's Andrey!" thought Marya. "No, it can't be"—and just then, on the landing where the footman stood with a candle, there came into sight the face and figure of Prince Andrey. He was pale and thin, and his face had a strangely altered, softened, and agitated expression. He went up the stairs and embraced his sister.

"You did not get my letter then?" he asked. "The French were very good to me and looked after me till I was well." The doctor, whom he had met at the last station, followed him upstairs. Andrey flung off his fur coat and overshoes, and went with the doctor into the little princess's room.

Lise was lying on the pillows in her white nightcap, her black hair lay in curls about her swollen and perspiring cheeks, and she was smiling joyfully. The agony had only just left her. Her eyes were full of terror, and when they rested on Prince Andrey at the foot of the bed they showed no change in expression. He went round the bed and kissed her tenderly on the forehead.

"My precious," he murmured—a word he had never used to her before—"I love you so, and we are going to be very, very happy." She stared at him with a face of inquiry, almost of reproach.

The pains began again, and the old nurse asked Prince Andrey to leave the room. He went into the next room and sat down. A few minutes later a woman ran out and gave Andrey a panic-stricken glance. He buried his face in his hands. Helpless, animal groans were coming from the room. After an eternity, the door opened and the doctor came out. He had no coat on, his face was white, and his lower jaw quivered.

Prince Andrey went into the room. He saw the trembling hands of the old nurse holding something red and tiny, squealing and grunting. "Your son," she muttered. He went to the bedside. His wife was lying dead, and her short upper lip was turned up a little with the same childish appealing charm of old.

Two hours later Prince Andrey went softly into his father's

room. The old prince knew everything already. Without a
word, his rough old arms closed like a vice round his son's
neck and he burst into sobs.

*   *   *   *   *

" So this is all we fought for," reflected Ensign Nikolay
Rostov bitterly. " So this is how we've saved the freedom
of Europe ! "

It was a sunlit afternoon in June 1807. Nearly eighteen
months had passed since the battle of Austerlitz. The French
had gained victory after victory—Jena, Eylau, Friedland.
Finally the Tsar Alexander had become tired of the struggle
and arranged a truce. To-day he was to meet Napoleon at
Tilsit to sign the terms of peace.

In the public square two battalions, one Russian, the other
French, stood facing each other. The two Emperors rode to
meet each other between them. The handsome, youthful
Alexander wore the uniform of the Horse Guards, Napoleon a
tricorne hat and a blue uniform over a white vest.

Both Emperors dismounted and shook hands. Napoleon
had a repulsive smile on his flabby white face.

Nikolay had just come back from a visit to his friend Denisov,
lying with a wounded leg in field-hospital. Young Rostov
could not get the memory of the filth and disease and neglect
out of his mind, and the stench of rotting corpses was so strong
in his nostrils that he still kept looking round to see where it
came from.

Men had died hideously in battle, he said to himself as he
watched the two Emperors; they have been blown to pieces,
their limbs have been wrenched off, for what? Merely for
Alexander to embrace like a brother this smug, complacent
fiend, still the arch-tyrant of Europe. . . .

Two years later, in 1809, the friendship between the two
monarchs had become so close that when Napoleon declared
war on Austria, a Russian corps crossed the frontier to fight
side by side with the French against their old ally.

*   *   *   *   *

Prince Andrey spent most of his time nowadays on his estates
at Ryazan, leaving his infant son, Nikolushka, in the care of
the old prince at Bleak Hills.

In May 1809 certain duties in connection with the Ryazan
estate made it necessary for Prince Andrey to visit the marshal
of the district. This marshal was Count Ilya Rostov. He

welcomed his distinguished guest warmly, and begged him to stay the night.

During the course of the evening Prince Andrey glanced several times at Natasha, who appeared to him absurdly gay. "What on earth can she be so happy about?" he kept asking himself.

Alone in his room, he found sleep eluded him. He got up and flung open the window. The night was fresh and bright and silent. To the right was a great, leafy tree, and above it the moon, almost full, in a starless spring sky.

Suddenly he heard the chatter of girls' voices overhead. "Sonya, Sonya, do look, what a moon!" said a girl from the window above. She must have been leaning right out of the window, for he could hear the rustle of her dress and even her breathing. All was hushed and stonily quiet, like the moon and its lights and shadows.

"Come to bed, Natasha; it's after one o'clock," protested another voice.

"Oh, but do look. It's exquisite!" murmured the first voice. Prince Andrey waited while the girl remained there several minutes. He heard now and then a rustle or a sigh.

"O my God! what does it mean?" she cried suddenly. "Well, to bed, then!" And she closed the window with a slam.

Next day Prince Andrey went on to Bleak Hills. His father noticed he was strangely moody and restless. Prince Andrey told him he was going to Petersburg to attend a great ball in honour of the Tsar. "After all, I'm only thirty-one," he said, almost apologetically. "It's too early yet to bury myself for life in the country."

The Rostovs, too, were going to Petersburg for the ball, which was to be Natasha's début in society.

*　　*　　*　　*　　*

Natasha and Sonya both wore white dresses and red roses in their hair. They knew that many people at the ball, which was one of the most brilliant ever held in Russia, were glancing at them with admiration. But neither of the girls felt happy. The orchestra had been playing for nearly half-an-hour, and no one as yet had asked either of them to dance.

Pierre Bezuhov went up to Prince Andrey and took him by the arm. "You always dance," he said brusquely. "Here's the young Rostov girl; ask her."

Prince Andrey went forward in the direction indicated by

Pierre. He looked very attractive and gallant in his white uniform of a cavalry colonel, and many eyes followed him as he walked across and bowed before Natasha's tremulous, despairing face. He raised his hand to put it round her waist before he had finished uttering his invitation.

" I have been waiting such a long time for you," the young girl seemed to say in the smile that appeared through her starting tears.

Prince Andrey was one of the best dancers of his day. Natasha danced exquisitely. Her face beamed with a rapture of happiness. And Prince Andrey, as they whirled round and round, as his arm drew that slender, supple waist nearer to him, as he felt her stirring close and smiling gaily up at him— Prince Andrey knew the intoxication of her beauty had gone to his head.

Next day Andrey called at the Rostovs, and in the weeks that followed became a constant visitor to their lodging. Everyone in the house knew why he came, of course, but no one dare breathe a word about it to the scared and flushed young girl, until one morning her mother said to her gravely:

" What has he said to you, Natasha? "

" Mamma, does it matter his being a widower? " she asked instead of answering.

" Hush, Natasha. Pray to God. Marriages are made in heaven."

" Mamma, darling, how I love you! How happy I am! " cried Natasha, hugging her mother.

Prince Andrey had to obtain his father's consent before he could marry. He set off for Bleak Hills.

The old prince listened to his son's request without showing a trace of the wrath it aroused in him. Then in a calm tone he answered, " Firstly, the marriage is not a brilliant one from the point of view of birth or fortune. Secondly, you are still in very delicate health and the girl is very young. Thirdly, the girl is too young and inexperienced to be entrusted with the care of your son.

" Fourthly," he added, " I beg you to postpone the marriage for a year; go abroad and get really well, and then, if your love—your passion—your obstinacy—are so strong, then get married. And that's my last word about it."

Prince Andrey knew his father would never alter his mind. He agreed to the condition of a year's delay, and returned to Petersburg.

He approached Natasha with downcast eyes. " I have loved you from the first minute I saw you," he said. " Can I hope? "

She came nearer to him and stopped. He took her hand and kissed it.

" Do you love me? " he asked.

" Yes, yes," she said, almost angrily. She burst into sobs.

" What is the matter? " he asked, with anxious eyes.

" Oh, I am so happy! " she said, smiling through her tears.

She looked at him in dismay when he told her his father's terms. " It can't be helped, Natasha," he pleaded. " And a year soon passes." His face was set and unhappy.

" It's awful! Oh, it's awful, awful! " Natasha cried suddenly. " I shall die if I have to wait a year; it's impossible." She glanced at her lover's face and saw the pain and perplexity that tortured it.

" No, no, I'll do anything," she said, wiping away her tears. " I'm so ha-a-appy! "

Later, the count and countess entered the room and gave the betrothed couple their blessing. From then onwards Prince Andrey began to visit the Rostovs as Natasha's plighted lover.

When the moment of farewell came, she watched him leave the room, then flung herself down on the floor in an ecstasy of grief. " God, don't let him go! " she moaned. " Make him come back! Something dreadful will happen! "

Six months later Princess Marya wrote to Andrey in Germany that Natasha had tried to elope with Anatole Kuragin, the handsome and profligate brother of Ellen Vassily. Anatole had made love to her assiduously and promised her marriage. Pierre Bezuhov heard of his plan, and, knowing Anatole had a wife in Poland, he had challenged the young scoundrel to a duel. Anatole had vanished from Petersburg. Natasha had written to Marya asking her to inform her brother that she released him from his engagement.

*   *   *   *   *

On a sultry evening in June 1812 the Tsar Alexander was dancing a mazurka in the palace at Vilna. Suddenly a general of his staff, Balashov, entered the hall, and walked straight across the floor, brushing aside the dancers in his path until he reached the Tsar. Their gasps of indignation changed to those of astonishment; Balashov, without any regard for etiquette, without a moment's hesitation, had gripped the

Tsar's arm and stepped between him and the lady. The Tsar looked at him in amazement, then, seeing the expression in Balashov's eyes, murmured a word of apology to his partner, and accompanied the general out of the hall.

A few hours later the Tsar told Balashov to deliver in person to Napoleon the following letter:

MONSIEUR MON FRÈRE,
I learnt yesterday that in spite of the loyalty with which I have kept my engagements to your Majesty, your troops have crossed the frontiers of Russia. If your Majesty consents to withdraw your troops from Russian territory, I will pass over the whole incident unnoticed, and agreement between us will be possible. In the opposite case, I shall be forced to repel an invasion which has been in no way provoked on my side. Your Majesty has it in your power to preserve humanity from the disasters of another war.

ALEXANDER."

Balashov made his way through the French lines and was admitted to an audience with Napoleon. The Emperor had just finished dressing, and smelt abominably of eau de cologne. One black lock of hair was plastered down across his broad forehead; his plump face and neck were unhealthily white; his short, stout body, with its narrow shoulders and rotund stomach, seemed to caricature his air of imposing dignity.

" I am no less desirous of peace than the Emperor Alexander," he snapped, when Balashov had given him the Tsar's message. " Haven't I been doing everything I can for the last eighteen months to obtain it? "

He began striding to and fro, his neck swelled, and it was obvious to Balashov he was working himself up to a state of uncontrollable fury.

" Such demands may be made to a prince of Baden, but not to me," he shouted. " You say I began the war? Who was the first to join his army? The Emperor Alexander. And you offer me negotiations when I have spent millions, when you are in alliance with England, and when your position is weak—you offer me negotiations."

Napoleon laughed maliciously, took a snuff-box from a pocket of his white waistcoat, and applied a pinch to his nostrils. " You haven't two hundred thousand troops," he added, with a smirk of contempt, " and I have three times as many. I give you my word of honour." He seemed unaware that there was no one left outside France who believed in his word of honour.

He walked sharply up to Balashov, gesticulating volubly and waving his white hands almost in his face. " I'll thrust you beyond the Dwina, beyond the Dnieper," he yelled, a dull purple flush in his white cheeks. " I'll restore the frontier that Europe was criminal and blind enough to let you overstep. Yes, that's what you'll gain by defying me." He strode up and down the room, his thick shoulders quivering. He put the snuff-box in his pocket, took it out again, applied several pinches to his nose, and stood still facing Balashov. He looked at Balashov sardonically and said, " And yet what a fine reign your master might have had ! "

As Balashov left the audience-chamber, he observed that Napoleon's fat left calf was twitching. Napoleon himself had noticed it immediately—it was the greatest of all omens of success to him.

The war had begun.

*　　*　　*　　*　　*

To Napoleon's surprise and fury, the enemy armies refused to be drawn into a major engagement, as the French Grand Army of four hundred thousand men advanced farther and farther into Russia. Instead, they retired steadily and in good order, Prince Bagration's forces withdrawing from Wolkowysk to Mohilev, and those under General Barclay de Tolly from Vilna to Vitebsk. Always the Russians were ready to fight minor skirmishes and gain small victories, but whenever Napoleon tried to hold them in a decisive conflict, they simply abandoned their positions and fell back again.

Bonaparte felt sure they would make a stand before the town of Smolensk. Accordingly, he arranged his forces for a " Napoleonic battle ". Murat's cavalry would charge, the general advanced guard would attack and hold the enemy, and finally the main body under Davout would swing in on his rear and annihilate him. But the Russians gave up the town without firing a shot, and retreated towards Moscow.

The Tsar himself now began to feel that these tactics were not in keeping with the glory of war, and he sent old Marshal Kutuzov to the front to assume the chief command, with orders to fight a pitched battle with the French before they could threaten Moscow.

Neither Napoleon nor the Tsar realized that the all-important factor in this war was not brilliance in strategy, not the move-

ments of great armies, not victory in battle, but the instinct
of the Russian people. That instinct was to lure on the
invader into a vast and hostile wilderness, to cut off his supplies,
to starve and harass him until, like a wounded, hungry, and
exhausted beast, he was glad to make any escape he could find.

And that instinct was deep-rooted in the peasant soul of
Kutuzov. To the annoyance of the Tsar, who wanted military triumphs that would resound throughout Europe, Kutuzov
merely continued the policy begun by Bagration and Barclay
de Tolly—the policy of eluding the French army, and drawing
it farther and farther into Russia. The Tsar and the Court
at Petersburg, imbued with French notions of fame and
glory, began to scorn Kutuzov as a weary old dotard at first,
and then as a coward and a shirker. His German generals,
too, became more and more exasperated by his apparent
failure to understand their ingenious plans for encircling and
destroying Napoleon's army.

The mild and simple old Marshal always seemed to be
doing his utmost to fulfil the Tsar's instructions. He listened
with respectful humility to each of his advisers. Yet somehow he still went on dodging and retreating before the French,
and to every objection he always had a plausible excuse.
Finally, the enraged Tsar sent him a peremptory order to
fight an engagement at Borodino: otherwise, he said, Moscow
would be lost. And Kutuzov, too, thought it would be no
bad thing to have at least one pitched battle with the French.
If the beast could be dealt a mortal blow. . . . On the other
hand, reflected Kutuzov, if he lost even a fourth of his army,
the French would be able to take Moscow.

Napoleon was overjoyed when he learnt the Russians would
fight at last. He went over in his mind the course of this
weird Russian campaign. During the past two months not a
victory had been gained, not a flag, nor a cannon, nor a
corps had been taken. His troops were losing heart—nearly a
third of them had been picked off by Russian sharpshooters
or had deserted—and the efficiency of his great war-machine
had slackened to such an extent that it was almost impossible
to preserve discipline.

The battle began with a cannonade of hundreds of guns on
both sides, and the main action was fought on a plain seven
thousand feet wide. Soon the plain was covered with smoke,
and the French and Russian armies were grappling in fierce
combat.

Napoleon had a cold. He strode to and fro impatiently, giving hurried commands to his marshals. The Russians were stubbornly resisting all the onslaughts of his finest troops. The slaughter went on for ten hours. The Russians still held their ground.

An uncanny feeling of perplexity and depression began to steal over Napoleon. His soldiers were the same, the generals the same, there had been the same preparations, the same disposition of forces. He himself was the same, or, if anything, more experienced and skilful than ever before. The enemy was the same as he had defeated at Austerlitz and Friedland.

All the former manœuvres that had been invariably successful in the past had been tried—the concentration of batteries on one point, the advance of reserves to smash the line, the cavalry attack of his " men of iron ". And, far from victory being assured, reports poured in of killed and wounded generals, of more reinforcements needed, of troops in complete disorder, and of the Russians being impossible to move.

The news that the Russians were attacking the left flank of the Grand Army aroused a nightmare horror in Napoleon. He mounted a horse and rode over to Semyonovskoye.

The smoke was slowly moving from the plain through which Napoleon rode, and everywhere around him, singly and in heaps, he saw men and horses lying in pools of blood. Such a shambles of killed and wounded had never been seen by Napoleon before, nor by any of his generals. The deafening boom of the cannon was like a horrible accompaniment to the scene.

Napoleon rode up to the height of Semyonovskoye, and through the smoke he saw a mass of soldiers in unfamiliar uniforms. They were Russians.

The Russians stood in serried ranks behind Semyonovskoye, and their guns kept up a ceaseless roar and smoke all along their lines. It was no longer a battle: it was a massacre. It made both victory and defeat a mockery. Napoleon gazed at it in stupor. For the first time in his life, war appeared to him meaningless and infernal.

One of the generals, riding up to Napoleon, suggested that the Old Guards should advance into action. This assault would almost certainly have won the day for him.

Napoleon sat mute with chin sunk on breast. The general repeated his suggestion.

" Eh? " said Napoleon wearily. He stared with dimming

eyes at the general. "No," he said in a low voice. "I'm not going to let my Guard be *butchered*!"

* * * * *

Behind Semyonovskoye, not yet in action, but under heavy artillery fire, was stationed Prince Andrey's regiment. For six hours a barrage of hundreds of enemy cannon had been concentrated upon the oat-field in which they stood patiently awaiting the order to advance. Without leaving the spot, without discharging a single round of ammunition, the regiment had already lost a third of its men.

Pale and haggard, Prince Andrey walked to and fro, his hands clasped behind his back and his eyes fixed on the ground. There was no need for him to give any orders, and nothing he could do. Everything was done of its own accord. The killed and wounded were dragged behind the line and the ranks closed up.

A whiz and a thud! Five feet away from him the dry earth was thrown up as a cannon ball sank into it. A chill ran down his back. He glanced at the ranks. Probably several men had been struck.

"*M. l'aide de camp*," he shouted, "tell the men not to crowd together!"

The adjutant, having obeyed this instruction, walked towards Prince Andrey.

"Look out!" came the frightened yell of a soldier, and like a bird, alighting with swift whirring wings on the earth, a grenade dropped a few feet from Andrey.

"Lie down!" shouted the adjutant, flinging himself to the ground. The shell was smoking and rotating like a top between Andrey and the recumbent adjutant.

Prince Andrey stood there hesitating. "For shame, *M. l'aide de camp*," he said slowly. "What sort of example . . ."

He did not finish. There was a rending, crashing sound, a burst of stifling smoke, and Prince Andrey was sent spinning over to the earth. Several officers ran up to him. He was unconscious, and a great stain of blood was spreading from the right side of his stomach.

Militia-men with a stretcher carried Prince Andrey to an ambulance station on the edge of a birch copse half-a-mile away. The ambulance station consisted of three tents. From one of these emerged a doctor wearing a bloodstained apron, and with small hands wet with blood, in one of which he carefully held a cigar between thumb and little finger, so that

L 2

it would not be stained. He glanced at Andrey's wound and yelled to an assistant inside the tent, " This one immediately! "

When Andrey recovered consciousness he was lying on a wooden table inside the tent. Someone was sprinkling water over his face and murmuring, " You'll be all right now. You'll be all right now."

On the next table was lying the naked body of a man with his face turned away from Andrey, who thought the hue and curliness of his hair seemed queerly familiar. One of the man's plump, white legs was twitching rapidly and spasmodically; two assistants were pressing upon his chest to hold him down, and a doctor, very pale and trembling, was severing the other red and lacerated leg. The stoutish young man writhed his head in agony. " Oo-ooooh," he sobbed.

" My God," thought Prince Andrey. " What is he doing here? The handsome adjutant, the darling of all the gay ladies in Moscow, Ellen Bezuhov's brother, Anatole Kuragin. The man who robbed me of Natasha," he remembered wildly, before he swooned into darkness again.

*   *   *   *   *

Kutuzov, with his grey old head hanging, and his corpulent body sagging into a heap, had remained seated throughout most of the battle on a bench outside his hut. He issued no orders, he merely gave his assent or gently demurred to whatever was proposed to him.

" Yes, yes, do so dear boy, by all means," he would say to his generals, or " Yes, go along, old man, and see for yourself," or " Well, perhaps we'd better wait a bit longer." He appeared to take little interest in what was said to him. The German generals—Winzgerode, Pfuhl, and the rest—complained bitterly to each other that he did not even seem to care whether the battle resulted in a victory or a defeat. They were right. Kutuzov's sole concern was to deal such a blow at the Grand Army that it would not recover.

The day closed with the withdrawal of both sides from an indecisive action. Over the plain that had been so bright and stirring a sight in the morning sunshine, with its glittering bayonets and fine uniforms, now hung a dark mist of smoke which reeked sourly of saltpetre and blood.

*   *   *   *   *

Pierre Bezuhov poured out with a shaking hand another glass of wine, swallowed it in one gulp, then peered again with bloodshot eyes at his open Bible.

" Here is wisdom," he read, " ' Let him that hath under-standing, count the number of the beast, for it is the number of a man, and his number is six hundred three score and six.' " ˈ

Pierre was dirty, unkempt, and unshaven. He had slept in his clothes ever since the French had entered Moscow, five days ago. He was hopelessly intoxicated, and alone in his great mansion. Everyone who wanted to flee from the invader, and could manage to do so, had already left Moscow. For days the roads out of the great city had been blocked by almost endless processions of carts bearing noble and *bourgeois* families and their innumerable belongings—furniture, pictures, jewellery, food—everything that could be saved from the hands of the spoilers.

Kutuzov had withdrawn his army a hundred and fifty versts east of Moscow. The Tsar fumed, the German generals pro-tested in vain. Kutuzov listened to countless pleas that he should attempt to recapture the second city in Russia, nodded courteously to every argument—and did nothing. The Tsar sent him irate letters declaring that there was nothing to prevent Napoleon from advancing on Petersburg itself, from conquering the whole of Russia.

Kutuzov knew better. The French morale had been shattered by Borodino. Their troops had entered Moscow weary, baffled, and exhausted. All discipline had vanished, and the soldiers drank and rioted and pillaged throughout the city. They were lighting fires everywhere in this town of wooden houses. . . . Soon there would be conflagrations and disorder, lack of food and supplies, and a starving, dis-heartened, and panic-stricken rabble of soldiery would have only one thought in its head—to get away from the vast, white, silent horror that was unconquerable Russia.

Pierre glanced at the verse in the Apocalypse again, then began hazily working out a code on a piece of paper. " Sup-pose I write down the French alphabet," he thought, " making the ' i ' and ' j ' one letter as they were originally, and then write underneath the Hebrew system of numbers, in which the first nine letters represent the units, and the next the tens."

a b c d e f g h i k l m n o p
1 2 3 4 5 6 7 8 9 10 20 30 40 50 60

q r s t u v w x y z
70 80 90 100 110 120 130 140 150 160

After trying various Napoleonic titles on this code, Pierre found that if he turned the words " le empereur Napoleon " into the corresponding figures for the letters, and then added these figures together, they came to 666. " So Napoleon is indeed the Beast of Revelation," he decided.

Feverishly, Pierre turned to his Bible again. In the same thirteenth chapter of the Apocalypse, verse five, he read, " And there was given unto him a mouth speaking great things and blasphemies, and power was given unto him to continue forty and two months." Working out the words " quarante deux " (forty-two), Pierre found that the sum of the numbers again came to 666. And Napoleon was in 1812 forty-two years old.

" Who will put an end to the power of the Beast? " Pierre then asked himself. He tried " l'empereur Alexandre " and " la nation russe ", but neither would do. He wrote down his own name " Comte Pierre Bezuhov ", but the sum was still wrong. He changed the spelling, put " s " for " z " and " f " for " v ", and still it was wrong. He tried " le russe Besuhof "; it added up to 671. This was only five too much, the extra five was due to an " e " too many. Pierre decided to drop the " e " from " le "; this was incorrect spelling, of course, but it would balance the incorrect spelling of " le empereur Napoleon " which should not have an " e " in the " le ", but only an apostrophe. He tried " l'russe Besuhof "; it added up to exactly 666!

This discovery greatly excited Pierre. He opened another bottle of champagne and drank it off as he lurched to and fro in his study. So he, the worthless idler whom nobody cared a straw about, had been appointed by destiny to destroy the blackest tyranny ever known in Europe!

He dragged open a drawer, took out a pistol, and thrust it under his coat. He would go out and kill Napoleon that very day.

He stumbled down the stairs and into the street. A livid glow flickered over the city. Moscow was already on fire in a hundred places.

No one in the hurrying throng on the pavement took the least notice of him as he walked unsteadily towards the Kremlin, which Napoleon had boasted would become the first palace in his new Oriental Empire.

Suddenly Pierre's attention was drawn to a group of Armenians seated among their household goods and chattels in the middle of the road. Among them was a very old man wearing a new sheepskin and a pair of fine long leather boots. Close to him sat a young girl of pronounced beauty, with her arched black eyebrows, soft skin, and perfectly oval face. Over her head she had a bright silk kerchief, a satin mantle covered her shoulders, and around her throat gleamed a diamond necklace.

Two French soldiers were standing in front of them. One soldier bent forward and whispered something to the old man, who began hurriedly pulling off his boots. The soldier put them under his arm. With a sudden, brutal movement, the other soldier grasped the necklace round the throat of the young girl.

"Let that woman alone," roared Pierre. He advanced menacingly. In an instant he was surrounded by a *mêlée* of passers-by, who shouted approvingly as he fought with the soldiers.

Round the corner of the street came galloping a patrol of French Uhlans. They dismounted, the officer gave a curt order, and Pierre was seized and overpowered.

"Do you speak French?" demanded the officer. Pierre made no reply. He stared wildly about him with his blood-flecked eyes. His clothes were stained and torn and his face smudged with dirt.

"He looks like an incendiary," said the officer, searching him with agile fingers. "Ah, he is armed. Put him under close guard," he added, turning to a lieutenant, "and take him to the Zubovsky barracks."

He was conducted to a shed rigged up out of charred beams and boards for the prisoners of war, which stood in the barracks-yard. He entered and found himself among a score of men lying on straw palliasses on the damp earth. Some were poor tradesmen, others looked like thieves or vagabonds, and a few were wounded soldiers who had been left behind during the great exodus from the city. All began excitedly asking him questions. Pierre said nothing, and sat down on some loose straw near the wall.

"Here you taste this," said a soldier in a ragged uniform, handing Pierre a cold roast potato. Pierre had eaten nothing all day. He thanked him and began munching.

"My name's Platon, surname Karataev," went on the soldier. He was a little wizened man, about fifty years old, with a humorous twinkle in his eyes.

"Eh, me dear, don't grieve," said Karataev, noticing that

there were tears in Pierre's eyes. "Don't grieve, darling," he added in the tender, caressing sing-song which Russian peasant women use with little children. "Trouble lasts an hour, but life lasts for ever. And we get on here finely, thank God; nothing to vex us."

After a short pause, Karataev got up. "Well, I dare say you're sleepy, sir?" he said, and began rapidly crossing himself, murmuring, "Lord Jesus Christ, holy Saint Nikola, Frola, and Lavra, have mercy and save us!" He sighed and sat down on his straw. "Let me lie down like a stone, O God, and rise up like new bread," he murmured, lying down and pulling his military coat over him.

"What prayer was that?" asked Pierre. "Frola and Lavra—I've never heard of them."

"Eh, to be sure," muttered Karataev sleepily; "they're the horses' saints. One must think of the poor beasts, too."

* * * * *

When the French had advanced towards Moscow, old Prince Nikolay Bolkonsky had been forced to leave his estate at Bleak Hills and fly to another at Bogutcharavo. The shock of this uprooting, followed soon after by the news that his son was again wounded, this time perhaps mortally, was too much for his years. He had collapsed with a stroke one afternoon while tending the garden, and died after three days' illness.

"I longed for his death, I wanted it, so that I could be free," moaned Princess Marya to herself, the morning after the funeral. Mademoiselle Bourienne approached her. "Please go away, go away," sobbed Marya.

"Your brother is at Mytishchty," she said. "The district marshal has just arrived with the news. They were sending him to a hospital away from the French, but he has fallen so ill that he cannot be moved. The Rostovs, too, are at Mytishchty, on their way from Moscow."

Princess Marya sent for little Nikolushka, ordered a carriage, and set off for Mytishchty. Andrey, she was told, was lying in a hut near the station.

Gently she opened the door of the hut. Andrey, a thin wasted spectre of his former self, was lying on a pallet in the corner. And at his side knelt Natasha Rostov.

Princess Marya did not enter. Instead, she softly closed the door again. "Come, Nikolushka," she said, taking the little boy by the hand. "Daddy is asleep, we must wait."

Inside the hut, Prince Andrey was smiling and holding out his hand to Natasha.

" You? " he said.   " What happiness! "

With a swift but infinitely tender movement, Natasha took his hand in her own and kissed it.

" Forgive me! " she said in a whisper, lifting her head and glancing at him.   " Forgive me! "

" I love you," said Prince Andrey.

" Forgive me," repeated Natasha in a hardly audible, broken whisper.

He lifted her face with his hand so that he could look into her eyes.   " I love you more than before," he said.

Her eyes, swimming with tears, looked at him with timid and hopeful joy.

The door opened and the doctor entered.   " I must beg you to retire, madam," he said respectfully.

An hour after Natasha had left the room Prince Andrey fell into that sleep which knows no awakening in this world.

    *   *   *   *   *

" Father, you must let me go into the army," said Petya with knitted brows.

" At sixteen years old!   A fine warrior you'd make! " said old Count Rostov, laughing.   " Don't talk nonsense; you've your studies to attend to."

Countess Rostov clasped her hands in anguish, and said angrily to her husband, " See what all your talk about the war has done."

" It's not nonsense, father.   Fedya Obolensky's younger than me, and he's going.   What's more, I can't study now when . . ."   Petya stopped, reddening, then went on, ". . . when the country's in danger."

" Hush, hush!   Nonsense . . ."

" But you said yourself you would sacrifice anything."

" Petya, be quiet! " cried the count, glancing at the countess, who was staring with white face and fixed eyes at her younger son.

The Rostovs were in Petersburg.   They had lost most of their fortune through the war, and now lived in straitened circumstances.

    *   *   *   *   *

Princess Marya, who was staying with an aunt in the capital, had been visiting the Rostovs a good deal of late, chiefly in order to console Natasha.   The Countess Rostov could not help reflecting upon the fact that Marya had inherited large estates from her brother and father, and that Nikolay was expected home on leave almost any time now. Sonya could scarcely sleep, and looked like a ghost, poor girl; but of course it was impossible for her to dream of marrying Nikolay.

The countess decided to speak to Sonya very firmly. She sent for the white-faced girl, and, in the tone of a governess admonishing an unruly child, upbraided her harshly for persisting in "this foolish infatuation". Sonya gazed at her stonily and did not reply. The countess began to weep, and her voice faltered. 'At last she threw aside all pretence at authority, and begged and implored Sonya to repay all the family had done for her by renouncing her love for Nikolay. "I shall have no peace of mind until you make me this promise," she said.

Sonya burst into sobs, and stammered in a choking voice that she would do anything, would sacrifice anything but that. All her life she had given up to others what she held dear. Her position in the Rostov household was such that only by the way of sacrifice could she reveal her virtues. She was used to sacrifice, and liked it. But in every renunciation hitherto she had been happy in the thought that by her very self-sacrifice she was heightening herself in the eyes of herself and those around her, and was becoming worthier of Nikolay, whom she loved beyond everything in life. And with these half-stifled words she turned and ran out of the room.

The following day the countess sat down at her escritoire and began writing to her son. "Sonya," she said gently, raising her head from the letter as her niece passed by her. "Sonya, won't you write to Nikolenka?" she went on in a soft and trembling voice. And in the weary eyes that looked at her over their spectacles, Sonya read all that the countess meant by those words. Those eyes betrayed entreaty and dread of a refusal and shame at having to beg.

Sonya went up to the countess, and, kneeling down, kissed her hand.

"I will write," she said.

Nikolay was at Voronezh, and had just been to a thanksgiving service for the Russian victory at Borodino, when he received the two letters. He knew one was from Sonya, and gazed at it reflectively for a few moments before opening it. For some weeks now he had experienced a growing feeling of regret and humiliation at the thought of marrying her. He had lately incurred heavy gambling debts, his family was ruined, and undoubtedly he ought to be looking round for a wealthy heiress. . . . "No, that isn't it," he said to himself vehemently. "No, I don't love Sonya in the right way. It's all a muddle, a fearful muddle! I don't love her at all! What do I want? Freedom, release from Sonya. Nothing but misery for us both can come of my marrying her. My God! take me out of this awful, hopeless position!" And all at once he clasped his hands and began praying fervently. "Yes, prayer will move mountains," he mused, as he unclasped his hands and picked up Sonya's letter. "You have only to believe," he said to himself, as he tore open the envelope.

"DEAREST NIKOLENKA,
    "It would be too painful to me to think that I could be a cause of sorrow and discord in the family that has overwhelmed me with kindness. The one aim of my life is the happiness of those I love. Therefore I beseech you, Nikolas, to consider yourself free, and to know that, in spite of everything, no one can love you more truly than your—
                                                        SONYA."

Two days later the Tsar attended a great military parade in Moscow. Petya tried to get through the crowds so that he could appeal to the Tsar in person to let him go fight for Russia. But so dense was the throng that he never even saw the Emperor Alexander. He returned home burning with disappointment, and told his father he would run away from home if he could not join the army. At length the old count weakened, and, unknown to his wife, obtained for the boy a commission in a regiment of hussars serving under Bagration a hundred versts north-west of Moscow, and therefore unlikely to engage with the French army.

A week after Petya left his terrified mother to join the regiment, Nikolay arrived home on leave. The countess lost no time in acquainting him with their desperate financial plight. She introduced him to Princess Marya, and Nikolay soon divined his mother's plan. Soon, whether he willed it or no, he found himself more and more in Marya's company.

One Sunday morning the footman came into Marya's drawing-room and announced that Count Nikolay Rostov had called. The young princess showed no sign of embarrassment, but a faint colour came into her cheeks, and her eyes shone with a new, radiant light.

When Nikolay entered the room, he started. " Either black
suits her wonderfully or she really has grown better-looking,"
he thought. For as she gazed at him, her face seemed transformed by a sudden ardour which gave it an unexpected and
impressive beauty.

" She loves me," he thought, and, for some reason he could
not explain, a warm glow of gratitude suffused his heart. He
tried to hide his embarrassment by caressing little Nikolushka.
Now and then he glanced at Marya. With gentle, shy,
luminous eyes she was watching the child she loved in the
arms of the man she loved. Nikolay caught her look, and,
divining its beauty, suddenly flushed with delight.

From that day onwards he sought her society of his own
accord. He felt many a twinge of self-reproach about Sonya
. . . but he also felt that some force he could not understand,
but which comprised his family's need, his own easy-going
nature, and Marya's goodness, in some strange confusion, was
driving him on.

Nikolay and Princess Marya were betrothed three weeks
later.

*   *   *   *   *

Kutuzov had guessed aright. Napoleon's army suffered a
mortal blow at Borodino. Like a wounded beast it had crept
to Moscow, only to find there that its life-blood was ebbing
faster than ever. Food had run out, and half the town was
in flames.

Napoleon was being vanquished by an enemy that would
not fight. And it was a defeat from which he was never to
recover.

He sent envoys to Kutuzov to arrange terms of peace.
Kutuzov answered gruffly, " Get out of Russia ! "

At length a madness seized upon the Grand Army, the
madness of a trapped and dying animal. And even when
Napoleon had ordered the retreat from Moscow, the madness
still went on. Instead of taking all the food they could find,
the soldiers loaded themselves with booty. Instead of keeping
in close order, they straggled from their units. There was only
one aim in every man's mind—to escape, and the devil take
the hindmost.

On the morning of the 17th October, 1812, the door of the
shed in which Pierre was held prisoner was flung open, and
a captain outside shouted harshly, " *Filez ! Filez !* "

The prisoners crowded outside, huddling together for

warmth. Pierre had on a dirty, tattered shirt, a pair of soldier's trousers, and a peasant's coat and cap. His feet were bare. The lower part of his face was overgrown with beard; his long, tangled hair, swarming with lice, fell in matted curls over his forehead. But his eyes had a look of firmness, calm, and intelligence such as his friends in society had never seen in them.

Near by stood an escort of French soldiers in marching order, with shakoes, muskets, and knapsacks. Troops and trains of baggage were moving down the street.

Pierre went up to the captain and asked him what was to be done with the sick prisoners.

" They've to damn well march the same as the rest," snapped the captain brutally.

" But some are in agony . . ."

" Get into line," roared the captain, pushing Pierre. Altogether, with the prisoners from other sheds, about three hundred starved and limping wretches formed up behind the French escort. In the rear came the baggage-wagons, on one of which sat a number of women with rouged faces, wearing brightly-coloured dresses, and singing and laughing coarsely.

They marched along the Kaluga road and reached open country at nightfall. Here the prisoners were given horseflesh and told they could light camp fires and sleep beside them.

They marched on next day over snow and slush, overtaking other troops of soldiers with their bands of prisoners. Platon Karataev walked by the side of Pierre and tried to comfort him.

Three weeks later the convoy of prisoners which included Pierre had shrank from three hundred to ninety. Half the transport with stores of food had been seized by soldiers in front, and the other half had been raided by marauding Cossacks.

The tattered soldiers, many of whom, like the prisoners, had no boots, but only bandages round their swollen feet, were continually changing, joining the column as it marched, and dropping behind it again. They nearly all belonged to different regiments. They quarrelled incessantly. Night and day there were false alarms of raiding Cossacks, and in their panic to escape to other parts of the line, the soldiers often shot one another or trampled one another underfoot. But their biggest grievance was that they had to stand sentinel at night over the groups of prisoners, cowering together for warmth on the snow.

All along the way of march lay rotting carcases of men and horses. . . .

Pierre had long since ceased to think about his former life as a man of wealth and society. He did not know that his wife, Ellen, was dying in Moscow of an illness that baffled the specialists, but even if he had known, it would have seemed to him as remote and meaningless as if it were happening on another planet.

During his three weeks' march he had learnt a new and consolatory truth. There was a limit to suffering, and that limit was very soon reached. A man troubled with insomnia and lying on a feather bed must suffer just as much as he did, dozing at intervals on the bare, damp earth. He could keep warm in the daytime on the march, and at night there was a place near the camp-fire, and the lice that devoured him helped to keep the cold away. Every morning, when he examined his naked feet, he thought he could not possibly walk another hundred yards on them, but he would set off limping, and after an hour or two he had forgotten them, though by evening they looked worse than ever.

Platon Karataev told him naïve peasant stories with a smile on his thin face and a peculiar joyful light in his eyes. They were absurd stories, usually with some far-fetched religious moral. But it was not the stories themselves, but an ecstatic gladness that beamed in Karataev's face as he told them, that vaguely filled and rejoiced Pierre's soul and gave life a new meaning to him.

Often Karataev would say something directly opposite to what he had said before, but both sayings were equally true. He liked talking, and talked well, adorning his speech with jests and proverbs which Pierre often suspected he had invented himself. But the great charm of his talk was that the simplest incidents—sometimes the same that Pierre himself had seen without noticing them—became in Karataev's account of them full of significance.

When Pierre, impressed by the force of his remarks, asked him to repeat what he had just said, Karataev was never able to recall the words. He did not understand, and could not grasp, the meaning of words taken apart from the sentence. Every word and every action of his was the expression of a power uncomprehended by him, and this power was his life. But his life, as he looked at it, had no meaning as a separate life. It had meaning only as a part of all the life around him, of which he was at every waking moment fully conscious. His words and actions flowed from him as smoothly, as inevitably, as spontaneously, as perfume exhales from a flower. He could not perceive any meaning in an act or word taken separately.

Acquaintances, relations, friendships, loves, in the sense that Pierre had always understood them, Karataev had none. But he lived on affectionate terms with every creature with whom he was thrown in contact, and especially so with man— not with any man in particular, but simply with every man who happened to be before his eyes. He loved his comrades, loved the French, loved Pierre, who was his neighbour. But Pierre felt that, in spite of Karataev's tenderness towards him, he would not suffer a moment's grief at parting with Pierre. He would merely go on loving everyone and everything around him as before. And Pierre began to have the same feeling towards Karataev. He felt that he, too, was becoming possessed of the poor soldier's childlike spirit of truth and simplicity; that he, too, was no longer a separate being, with his own selfish loves and fears and hates, but part of a great whole that would endure and love for ever.

Karataev began to sicken with fever, and the soldiers had been ordered to shoot all prisoners who lagged behind. Day after day he struggled on. But one morning Pierre missed him on the march. He looked back. Karataev was sitting under a birch-tree, and two French soldiers were bending over and talking to him. Pierre dared not look back again, even after he heard the sound of a shot.

*   *   *   *   *

The Tsar and his German generals were now urging Kutuzov to swoop down in force upon the Grand Army and annihilate it. But the wily old Marshal ignored all commands, requests, and pleas to this end. His object was not to keep Napoleon in Russia, but to drive him out of it. The wounded beast was now in flight through a desolate countryside, harassed and starving, and it would destroy itself. His forecast proved correct; the Grand Army had only a tenth of the men with which it entered Russia when it finally reached the frontier again.

Kutuzov contented himself by sending out roving bands of skirmishers to attack the straggling columns. One of these marauding bands was led by Denisov, the officer who had acted as umpire at Pierre's duel with Dolohov.

Denisov heard one morning late in October that a French company had lagged behind the march near a village a few miles from Smolensk. He was riding towards this place at the head of his Cossacks when he was met by a young officer on horseback. The newcomer was a boy with a broad, rosy face and keen, merry eyes. He gave Denisov a letter from the general of his regiment, explaining that the youngster had tired of inaction and wanted to join the irregulars in their raids.

" So you're Petya Rostov," said Denisov gravely. " I know your brother Nikolay. Well, I'll let you come with me, if you promise to keep in the rear. There's going to be some hot work in a few minutes."

He turned his horse's head, and set off towards the village. Petya followed well in the rear of the band, as he had agreed. But suddenly the Cossacks applied their spurs and set off at full gallop. Petya heard the noise of firing in front. He gave his horse the reins and soon was flying in a tumultuous rush amid the foremost Cossacks. Already he could see the French soldiers; their muskets were levelled at the Cossacks. Behind the Frenchmen stood a strange-looking group of ragged peasants.

A volley of shots swept through the charging Russians. Petya flung up both arms and fell from the saddle. The Cossacks flew on, shot down several of the Frenchmen, then galloped round and round them, firing, until the rest laid down their muskets. " The Cossacks! " the tattered group of men in the rear kept shouting.

Denisov and his men dismounted and embraced the Russian prisoners. Among them was Pierre. For a full minute he stood there stupefied, listening to his comrades' wails of joy. Then he laughed wildly and cried, " Mates! Our own folks! Brothers!"

Denisov walked back to where Petya was lying. He picked him up and with trembling hands turned over the blood-stained, mud-spattered boyish face that was already pale in death.

The Cossacks feared and respected Denisov because he never betrayed the least sign of emotion. Now they turned and gazed at their leader in astonishment. Denisov was howling like a dog.

* * * * *

The Cossacks took Pierre to Orel, where he fell ill and spent three months in hospital. The full strain of his hardships and privations as a prisoner only came upon him now; he lay in a delirium clouded with vague memories of dark grey weather and rain and sleet, of burning pains in his feet and side, of anguished faces all around him, of snarling commands and cries for mercy.

Only by degrees could he become used to the idea that there was no one to drive him on to-morrow, that no one would take his warm bed away from him, that he was sure of getting his dinner and tea and supper. But it was many weeks before he could shake off the feeling that he was a prisoner, and always in his dreams he was on the weary march over the snow and slush of the wastes again, hungry, cold, and exhausted.

Similarly, he had to be told again and again, before he could grasp the news, of the death of his wife from incurable illness, of the death of Prince Andrey, of the overthrow of the French.

But at length a joyful feeling of freedom began to steal over him. "Oh, how happy I am! how splendid life is!" he would repeat to himself. At first he thought this feeling was inspired by the material comforts around him—the snowy-white table with its dish of savoury broth, the soft, clean bed into which he climbed at night. But gradually he became aware that it was an inner freedom, quite independent of all external circumstances, that made him so happy.

The abiding worry of the old days, the question of the object of life, had suddenly vanished never to return. He did not need to seek any longer for such an object, because now he had *faith*. ⸰Not faith in principles or words or ideas, but faith in a living and universal God. His search for an object in life had only been a seeking after God. And then, suddenly, while he was a prisoner, he had come to know, not through words or arguments, but by his own feeling, that God is here and everywhere. He had come to see that the God of that poor simple fellow Karataev was grander, more real, and more true, than the Architect of the Universe recognized by the theologians.

Pierre felt like a man who finds at his feet what he has been straining his eyes to perceive in the distance. All his life hitherto he had been gazing through the telescope of intellect, far over the heads of all around him, unaware that he had no need to strain his eyes, but had only to look upon what was nearest to him.

Now, however, he had learnt to see the great, the eternal, and the infinite in everything, and the closer he looked at it the calmer and happier he was. He could throw away the telescope of intellect. The awful question which had racked his mind in the old days—the question: What for?—had no existence for him now. To that question, What for? he had now always ready in his soul the simple answer: Because there is a God—that God without whom not one hair of a man's head falls.

* * * * *

"Then a patrol came up and rescued us," said Pierre.

"I am sure you are not telling us all. I am sure you did something," said Natasha—"something good."

It was a year later. Pierre was sitting with Natasha in the home of Countess Marya Rostov and her husband, Count Nikolay, in Petersburg.

Pierre began to tell them about Karataev. He rose from his seat and began walking up and down, Natasha following him with her eyes.

"No," he said, stopping short in his story. "You cannot understand what I learned from that man, that happy and simple creature."

Countess Marya was not listening to him. She was thinking of something else that absorbed all her attention. She saw the possibility of love and happiness between Natasha and Pierre. And this idea, which occurred to her for the first time, filled her heart to overflowing with gladness.

With shining, eager eyes, Natasha still gazed intently and persistently at Pierre, as though she longed to know something more in his tale of adventures, something that he had left unsaid.

It was three o'clock in the morning. The footmen, with austere and reproachful faces, came in with fresh candles, but no one noticed them.

"They say sufferings are misfortunes," said Pierre. "But if I were asked, Would I remain what I was before I was taken prisoner or go through it all again? I should say, For God's sake let me be taken prisoner and eat horse-flesh once more."

" We think that as soon as we are torn out of our habitual life, all is over. But it is only the beginning of something new and good. As long as there is life, there is happiness." In shamefaced, glad confusion, Pierre turned towards Natasha. " That I say to you," he said.

" Yes, yes," she said, " and I would ask for nothing better than to go through it all again."

Pierre looked hard at her.

" Yes, and nothing more," Natasha declared.

" Not true, not true," cried Pierre. " I am not to blame for being alive and wanting to live. Neither are you."

All at once Natasha let her head fall into her hands and burst into tears.

" What is it, Natasha? " said Countess Marya.

" Nothing, nothing." She smiled through her tears at Pierre. " Good-night. It's bedtime." She ran out of the room.

Pierre got up to take his leave.

" Wait a moment," said Countess Marya.

Pierre looked into her eyes.

" I know that she loves . . . that she will love you," Countess Marya corrected herself.

" What makes you think so? You think I may hope? You think so? . . ."

" Yes, I think so," said Countess Marya, smiling.

" No, it cannot be! How happy I am! I have loved her from the first moment I saw her," said Pierre, kissing the Countess Marya's hands.

" Write to her parents," said Countess Marya. " And leave it to me. I will tell her when it is possible. I desire it to come to pass."

A light came into her eyes that was diviner than any knowledge.

" And I have a feeling in my heart that it will be so," she said.

EPILOGUE

Histories without number have been written about the Napoleonic Wars. Yet we have still to learn why millions of men should have given up their work and left their homes in order to move across Europe and murder and pillage and burn for more than twenty years.

For our historians present this great drama to us as if its

actors were not entire peoples, but a few generals and kings and priests and writers, and other notable figures who are supposed to represent the masses.

They are quite content to explain an event by saying it was due to the will of some famous person or other. And if there were only one historian writing about each event, such an account might appear quite plausible to the reader. But unfortunately the same event is described by several historians of different views and different nationalities. Thus, one historian ascribes a certain action to Napoleon, while another declares it was due to the Tsar Alexander. To make this confusion even worse, historians often quarrel about the nature of the power exercised by a famous person in causing such an event. Thus, Thiers—a Bonapartist—says that Napoleon's power was derived from his genius and his virtue, while Lanfrey —a Republican—asserts that it rested upon his cunning in duping his followers.

Now, if we examine this claim put forward by modern historians that the power which causes an event is vested in a leading figure by the combined will of the people he represents, we shall see that it is really void of meaning. Let us set it down as follows:

What is the cause of an historical event? Power.

What kind of power? The combined will of the masses vested in one person.

On what condition is the will of the masses vested in that person? On the condition of that person's expressing the will of the masses he represents. That is, power is power. That is, there is no meaning in this statement.

Our historians have therefore no grounds whatever for their countless assertions that such and such an event in the Napoleonic Wars was due to the will of such and such a figure. To show how little we do know about the causes of these events, let us consider Napoleon's invasion of Russia.

Did Napoleon simply order his army to march into Alexander's kingdom? No. He commanded one day certain papers to be written to Vienna, to Berlin, to Petersburg, etc., the following day he issued instructions and decrees to the army, the fleet, the commissariat, and so on—hundreds of separate commands.

Now, all through his reign Napoleon was giving command after command to invade England. He wasted more time and energy on this undertaking than on any other during his whole career. He was burningly eager to accomplish this aim, and it was very much to his interests to do so. On the other hand, he was loth to invade Russia, and frequently declared that his best advantage lay in an alliance with her.

Nevertheless, his soldiers marched into Russia, and did not cross to England. Why? Simply because the course of events allowed his commands to invade Russia to be obeyed, while rejecting those to invade England.

Events take their own path, whether generals, kings, and other illustrious folk like it or not. And where those events appear to spring from their own actions, this is not really so; the truth is that the events *comprise* those actions.

Of course every event is caused by some kind of power. But this power is still a mystery to us, and is likely to remain so. Ancient writers used to describe it as the intervention of the Deity in human affairs. We have abandoned this theory, but have not yet found an adequate substitute for it.

We might learn more about this mysterious power if our historians would view their subject not as a symposium of the activities of " great " men, but as the record of the life of an entire people. To fulfil such a task is impossible, but in the attempt much light would be thrown on the places that are still most obscure.

Instead of regarding the French Revolution and the Napoleonic Wars as a stage for Rousseau, Voltaire, Louis XIV, Napoleon, Alexander, Metternich, etc., let us study this gigantic happening from the standpoint of ordinary men and women.

In 1789 there is a ferment in Paris. It grows and spreads, and overflows into a great movement of peoples from west to east. In 1812 this eastward movement reaches its farthest limit, Moscow. Then just as suddenly, and inexplicably, a counter-movement sets in, surges westwards, dragging along with it, like the first movement, the peoples of Central Europe. This counter-movement reaches the starting-point of the first movement, then collapses.

During the period of twenty years occupied by these movements, a vast number of fields are left untilled, houses are burned, trade changes its direction, millions of men grow poor and lose their homes, and millions of Christians professing universal love murder and maim one another.

Then the turmoil among the peoples begins to subside. The waves lashed by the tempest slowly abate. Eddies form on the

quietening surface where the diplomats are at work, imagining
the calm is the result of their own efforts.

All at once the tranquil sea is convulsed again. ' The diplomats at the Congress of Vienna believe that their own squabbles
are the cause of this fresh commotion. They look for wars
between their own sovereigns. Another European tornado
seems inevitable. But the storm they feel approaching does
not come from the quarter where they look for it. It rises
again from the same starting-point—Paris.

Napoleon comes back to France alone. Everyone greets
with enthusiasm the man they have been cursing the day before
and will curse again within a month.

This man is needed for the last act of the drama. The act
is performed. The actor is told to undress and wash off his
powder and paint. He will be needed no more, though on the
solitude of his island he will go on playing a pitiful farce to
himself, lying and intriguing, justifying his conduct when a
justification is no longer required. Yes, all he will do henceforth will be to reveal to the world how petty was the thing
that men took for power—while an unseen hand guided it.

The Stage Manager, now that the drama is over, and the
puppet stripped, shows him to us. " See, what you believed in!
Here he is! Do you realize now that it was not he but I that
moved you! "

The day may come when our historians can tell us all about
the puppets—not only the leading figures, but also the humblest
—in this show we call life. But when shall we begin to discern
the purposes of the Stage Manager?

Historians are fond of saying that Napoleon should have done
this, or Alexander should have done that. Now, to my mind
it is impossible to define any action of Napoleon or Alexander
as beneficial or harmful to humanity in general. If anyone
dislikes the career of Napoleon or Alexander or any other historical personage, it is only because that career seems incom-
patible with his own limited idea of what is good for humanity.
I regard as good, for instance, the preservation of my father's
house in Moscow in 1812, and the glory of the Russian army,
and the restoration of the balance of power in Europe, and the
enlightenment of the masses, and so on. These ends were
accomplished, directly or indirectly, through the actions of
historical personages. Yet I am bound to admit that the
historical personages concerned also accomplished many other
ends which are quite beyond my knowledge.

Every atom in the universe is a thing complete in itself, and at the same time is only a part of a whole so vast as to be inconceivable by man. And in the same way every individual alive to-day bears within him his own ends, and yet bears them so as to serve the ends of a world development unknown to man.'

A bee settling on a flower has stung a child. The child says the object of the bee is to sting people. A poet admires the bee sipping honey from the cup of the flower, and declares that the bee lives solely in order to imbibe this nectar. A bee-keeper, observing that the bee gathers pollen and brings it to the hive, maintains that the bee's purpose is to gather honey. Another bee-keeper, who has studied the life of the swarm more closely, maintains that the bee collects this honey to feed the young ones and to rear a queen, and therefore devotes itself entirely to the perpetuation of its species. A botanist notices that the bee flying with the pollen fertilizes a pistil, and in this he sees the true function of the bee. Another declares that the bee lives in order to contribute to the hybridization of plants. And so on.

Who is to say that we shall not go on discovering other reasons for the bee's existence? But shall we ever know what is the final and ultimate aim of the bee? The higher the human intellect rises, the more obvious it becomes that the final aim of the bee is beyond its ken.

And the same is true of the final aims of historical figures and peoples and nations.

THE LAY OF THE NIBELUNGS

" Das Nibelungenlied ", The Lay of the Nibelungs, was written in the twelfth century A.D., probably at Worms (Germany), by a poet whose name is unknown. Its language is middle high German; its verse is a quatrain rhyming in couplets, each half-line of which carries three stresses, save the eighth, which has four. Its manner is that of the Minnesingers, poets of love, but modified for narrative. Its subject is the later exploits of Siegfried, his murder, and the disaster that overtakes his avengers and their enemies; his death divides the Lay into two parts, and the second part is called " Der Nibelungen Not ". The characters are taken from earlier tales of heroic half-gods, but the treatment of them is more familiar. It was not until the nineteenth century, when the Germans selected Siegfried for their national hero, that the poem became well known. The following is the first part of the " Nibelungenlied " translated and condensed.

I

(i) There grew in Burgundy a girl so fair that nowhere was one fairer. She was called Kriemhild. Three kings warded her: Gunther, Gernot and Geiselher; she was their sister. They dwelt at Worms on the Rhine, and there did many knights serve them till their days' end, when they died wretched, through two women's spite. Her mother was a rich queen called Ute; her father was called Dancrat.

Kriemhild dreamed she reared a wild hawk and two eagles clutched it. Greater grief there could not be in the real world. She told her dream to her mother, who said, The hawk is a husband. God guard him; for if He do not, he is lost to you. Kriemhild said, I will live without man's love. I will be as fair in death as I am now, for never having known the sorrow there is in man's love. If you will be glad at heart in the world, said Ute, it must be through man's love. May God join you to a good knight's body. Kriemhild said, Love is often paid in pain. I will shun them both, the love and the pain.

Kriemhild in her heart forebore all love.

(ii) There grew in the Netherland a king's child, whose father was called Sigmund and whose mother Siglind. They dwelt in a strong burg on the Rhine called Santen. The child was called Siegfried. In his youth many wonders were told of his and such honour he had, so shining was his body, many women loved him.

When Siegfried came of age and went to court his father held hightide. The women threaded gems in the gold of his dress and wove them into the woof and into the hem; and the wise men taught him how to win men and land. Many swordsmen went to the minster, at the summer sunstead, when Siegfried was made knight, sang mass to God's praise, and fought. The hightide lasted till the seventh day. Siglind the rich gave out red gold for love of her son. No wanderer went poor in the land. Horses and gear fell from her hand, as though man had not one day longer to live.

Now that he bore arms, Siegfried began to think of a woman to woo. He said, I will have Kriemhild, the fair maid of Burgundy, for her fairness. To Sigmund it was pain. Siegfried said, I should wish to live without woman's love, if I might not woo where my heart was. His mother wept. Siegfried said, Help me make ready for the journey to Burgundy. It was pain to the men, and the women wept.

On the seventh morning Siegfried rode with twelve knights into Worms. Gold were their garments, gold their reins, silk their breastbands and bright their shields; their swordpoints rode by the spurs. Picked horsemen bore spears. People gaped.

King Gunther bade Hagen say who the comelings were. He stepped to the window and, turning his eyes on them, said, Although I have never seen him, yet I know that is Siegfried. He slew the Nibelungs. He found the Nibelungs' hoard, holed out of a hollow hill and warded by two king's sons. He saw precious stones that one hundred wagons could not carry, and red gold still more. He slew the two kings' sons with his broadsword Balmung. He won the tarncape from the dwarf Albrich. He won the hoard. He bore it back to the hill and set Albrich wardsman over it. He slew a dragon. He bathed in the blood and his skin became horn; no weapon can cut him. Receive him well, he has done so many wonders.

Siegfried dwelt with King Gunther a year. At sports he was the best, whether at stonethrowing or at archery, and the ladies liked to watch him. They said, How well he is made. It is the hero from the Netherland. Often Siegfried thought, How may I see the maid whom I love in my heart and have loved long? He dwelt with King Gunther a year, and did not see Kriemhild.

King Gunther held hightide. Tell me, he said, how our hightide may be made most worthy of praise. Ortwein said, What is man's joy without fair women? Let your sister go before your guests.

One hundred knights went with drawn swords by Kriemhild and one hundred and more ladies went with her mother Ute and more ladies followed Kriemhild when she came like dawn out of dull clouds to take part in the hightide. Care voided the hearts of many who had lodged care long. To Siegfried it was joy and grief. He thought, How did I hope to love her?

When Kriemhild saw him stand before her, her tint became flame. She said, Welcome, Sir Siegfried. Her greeting raised his mood; love urged them to each other.

Never in summertime or on maydays had he borne joy in his heart so high as he had there, as she stood beside him. Many thought, If I had gone beside her, as I saw him go, or lain with her! Each day at daybreak for twelve days man saw the knight with the lady. Siegfried stayed at Worms for love of Kriemhild. When he was urged by love he had great distress. Therefor later he lay wretched, dead.

(iii) There sate a king's daughter over the sea, fair and strong. She shot the shaft with knights for her love, cast the stone and sprang after it. Who craved her love must win these three games: who lost one, lost his head.

Gunther said, I will go oversea to Brunhild and stake my life for her love. Siegfried answered, Give me your sister Kriemhild and I will help you. They swore an oath.

. . . I have heard there be wild dwarfs that dwell in hollow hills and that wear cloaks called tarncapes and who wears a tarncape cannot be cut or hurt, nor can he be seen, although he can see, and he becomes as strong as twelve men; and this is true. Siegfried took his tarncape and with many wiles won Brunhild. . . .

Gunther said to his sister, We will go wooing in a far land, I and Siegfried and two of my men, Dankwart and Hagen, and we need fine clothes for the journey; and Kriemhild called thirty ladies from the chamber, skilful in needlework. They laid gems in silk as white as snow and as green as clover and in ermine with flecks as black as coal. Then they trimmed them

with rare fishskin and covered them with goldthreaded silk
from Morocco and from Libya. In seven weeks the clothes
were ready.

A strong ship was builded on the Rhine. The goldred
shields were borne down to the strand and the weapons were
loaded on the ship. I will be master, said Siegfried, I know
the water-roads. He took an oar and thrust the ship off from
the bank. The stout sailrope stretched tight. Wind bore the
ship under her sail.

Twenty miles they fared before night fell and on the twelfth
morning they came to Brunhild's land. Siegfried said, Let
Gunther be my lord and let me be his man. He led a horse
on to the strand and held it by the bridle till Gunther sat in the
saddle. Snowbright were his horse and his dress, new whetted
the spears, well wrought the swords and the shield rim shone.
Thus they came to Brunhild.

Six-and-eighty towers they saw, three broad palaces and a
fair hall of marble green as grass. There sate the king's
daughter with her menie. She said, Let me hear who the
knights are from over the sea. One said, I have seen none
before, but one who is like Siegfried. Another seems to be a
king. A third has a grim, quick look. The youngest is of
friendly bearing and good breeding.

When Siegfried saw the king's daughter, he said, This
knight, Lady Brunhild, is my lord. He is a king on the Rhine
and is called Gunther and if he has your love he asks no more.

She said, If he masters me in my games I will be his wife. If
I win, you shall all die. He shall fling the stone and spring
after it. He shall cast the spear.

Gunther said, For your fairness I will dare all.

Brunhild bade them bring her armour, a golden breastplate
and a shield with gems. She donned a white weaponshift,
that no weapon might hurt her. Meanwhile Siegfried went to
the ship where he had hid the tarncape; quickly he slipped into
it; no-one could see him.

Three men bore to the games ring a large sharp heavy spear
and twelve knights carried a large round broad heavy stone.

Then Brunhild wound her sleeve round her white arm, took
the shield and swung the spear on high. Siegfried went to
Gunther and said, Have no fear of the queen. Let me hold
the shield. Make as though you threw, but I will do the
throwing.

Brunhild shot the shaft at Gunther's shield, held in Siegfried's hand.   Fire sprang from the steel: blood burst from Siegfried's mouth.   He took the spear and thought, I will not kill the queen. He turned the spear bout, point towards him, and cast it back. The butt struck her breastplate, that it rang.   Fire flew from the iron: Brunhild could not withstand the blow.   Thanks, Gunther! she said, and sprang to her feet.

Then she went to the stone and flung it far and sprang after it, that her armour clanged.   The stone fell thirty feet away, yet she reached it.   Siegfried was tall and strong; he flung the stone farther and sprang farther and he carried Gunther as he sprang.

Brunhild said to the men in her menie, Now you shall all be underlings of King Gunther.   The knights laid their weapons before Gunther's feet.   They thought he had won the queen with his own strength.

Siegfried went to the hall where the ladies were and said, Why do we not begin the games ?   Brunhild said, How is it you did not see the games, which Gunther won?   And Hagen answered, He was by the ship.   Well for me, said Siegfried, my journey is done.   Now, fair lady, you shall follow us to the Rhine.

(iv) Tidings came to Burgundy that Brunhild's menie had been seen.   Kriemhild said, My maids, seek out your best dresses from the press.   Gunther landed from the ship holding Brunhild by the hand, and Kriemhild went to greet her. Kriemhild said, Welcome in this land, to me and to my mother, and to all men true to us.

Hagen held war games.   At dusk, when the sun's light sank and it began to cool, the knights and ladies went to the burg. Seats were set and the king sat at table with his guests; by him sat Brunhild.   The tables were laden with food.   The cup-bearers poured water into the goldred beakers.   Better had suited a king's wedding, or so some said.

Siegfried went to Gunther and said, You swore with your hand you would give me your sister, if we brought Brunhild home.   Gunther said, I will join you to her.   He bade her come before him.   With even step she came to where the king stood and Gunther said, Sister, release me of my oath.   I swore a knight should have you.   Kriemhild said, Dear brother, I shall always do as you bid me.

For love and gladness Siegfried grew red.   Both stood together and Gunther asked Kriemhild, Would she take the

knight? She betrothed himself to him and he himself to her.
Then he took her gently in his arms and kissed her. Joy and
loud shouting rang in Gunther's hall.

Siegfried sat by Kriemhild and Gunther by Brunhild.
Brunhild wept; hot tears ran over her bright cheeks. My
land and my burg and my men are under you, said Gunther,
you should be glad. I weep for your sister, said Brunhild,
seeing her sit by Siegfried, your liegeman. Gunther said, I
will tell you another time, why I gave Siegfried my sister.
Brunhild said, Did I know where to go, I would flee and never
lie with you, till I knew why Kriemhild is Siegfried's bride.

The knights left table and the burg round rang with their
game cries.

Gunther thought, I will lie with the lady. Men called the
knights from their games. Lightbearers brought light.

When Siegfried lay with Kriemhild and played love with her,
her body became his. When Gunther lay with Brunhild he
had better have lain with another. The lightboys left, the door
was shut; in white linen Brunhild went to bed. The king
quenched the light with his hand and went to where he found
the lady and lay near her; he clasped her in his arms. She
said, Sir Gunther, put that by. What you have in your mind
may not be. I will remain a maid, till I hear why you gave
Kriemhild to Siegfried.

He fought for her love and rent her shift. She grasped a
girdle she wore about her middle, bound his hands and feet,
bore him to a nail and hung him on the wall. He nearly had
his death of it.

He began to plead, Loose these bonds and I will never lie
with you. In peace she lay, and the night long he hung, till
the bright day shone through the window. Scant strength
he had then in his body. Now tell me, Lord Gunther, said
Brunhild, if your men found you bound? He said, Even if it
be small honour to me, for your maidenhood's sake, take me
by you and I will not touch your shift with my hand.

She loosed his bonds and he went to bed again, laying himself
so far that he did not touch her white shift.

At mass next morning Gunther said to Siegfried, I have
brought the devil home. I meant to love her and she bound
me fast. She bore me to a nail and hung me on the wall.
Siegfried said, I will make her lie so near you tonight that she
may not withhold her love. Gunther said, See how my hands
are swollen. She held me as though I were a child. Blood

burst from under my nails. Siegfried said, I will come to
your chamber to-night, hid in my tarncape. As the linkboys
go out I will quench the lights they carry; by that you will
know I am there. May I lose my life, if I do not bring her
near you. Gladly, said Gunther, if you do not touch her.
On that, said Siegfried, I will plight my troth. Gunther
believed him.

To Gunther the day seemed thirty days long. When table
was done, men called Brunhild and Kriemhild to their chambers.

Siegfried lay with his wife and she played with his hand, till
he vanished. She called, Where is he gone? Who took his
hand from mine?

Siegfried quenched the lights in the linkboys' hands. Gunther shut the chamberdoor and shot across it two strong bolts.
Then began a game between Siegfried the strong and Brunhild
the fair that Gunther was lief and loth to see.

Siegfried laid himself by the queen. She said, Leave what
you have in your mind, how dear soever it may be to you,
that you may not grieve tonight as you grieved yesternight.
He held his voice and bore himself as though he were Gunther
the rich. He clasped the maid in his arms. She threw him
from the bed to a bench, that his head rang. Siegfried sprang
up. As he fought with her, unwillingness overcame him: I
do not use such strength on women! Brunhild cried; she
gripped him in her arms to bind him in bonds as she had
bound the king. She showed him her body's mastery. She
bore him in her arms and put him between the chest and the
wall.

Shall I, he thought, lose my life by a maid? Then in time
to come all women will be wanton with men, who otherwise
would never be.

With great strength Siegfried withstood Brunhild. He righted
himself and they gave each other blows about the room.
Gunther feared for either's life, but more for Siegfried's.
Had he dared, he would have helped him. Long they fought
before he brought the maid back to her bed. She gripped his
hands, that blood burst from under the nails. He held her
down on the bed, that she cried aloud. She grasped the
girdle that was about her middle to bind him. His hand
withheld hers, that her whole body cracked. She said, King
Gunther, leave me my life. I will strive with your love no
more. I see now you may be woman's master.

Siegfried stood up, as the maid lay, as though to cast off his clothes. He drew a gold ring from her finger and took her girdle.

Then the king and the fair maid lay with each other, and he played love with her. All shame and anger melted from her. Her bright tint grew pale. How her strength yielded to love! Now she was no stronger than another woman. Lovingly he stroked her limbs. How lovingly he lay with her, in love, till the light day!

II

(i) Siegfried rode back to the Netherland with Kriemhild. Sigmund said, Now my son Siegfried shall be king.

Siegfried lived and ruled and gave judgment in the Netherland for twelve years. Kriemhild bore a son, who was called Gunther, after his uncle. In the same time Siglind died.

Brunhild also bore a son, to Gunther, in the Rhineland. He was called Siegfried, after the hero.

Siegfried had under him the Nibelungs' land; he held the largest hoard hero had ever won. He was the best knight who ever sat a horse. Man dreaded his strength.

Every day Brunhild thought, How high Kriemhild holds her head! Yet her husband is our liegeman. She asked Gunther if she might not see Kriemhild in his land again. He answered, They dwell too far! However mighty a man may be, said Brunhild, he must do as his lord bid. Gunther smiled. She said, Dear lord, for love of me, let me see Siegfried and your sister in this land again.

Gunther sent messengers to Siegfried, begging him to come to Worms.

Siegfried said, How shall I carry Kriemhild through forty lords' lands? His knights answered, Ride to the Rhine with a thousand men.

The messengers told Gunther, Siegfried would come, and showed him the gold he had given them. Hagen said, He may well give fullhanded. He owns the Nibelungs' hoard. He could not spend it if he lived for ever. And he shall come to Burgundy!

When Siegfried came with his knights, men could not see him for the dust and press. Saddles were emptied, knights' hands lifted ladies on to the grass. Twelve hundred knights sat down to table with Siegfried. Brunhild thought, No liegeman could be so rich. Night fell.

(ii) Day broke. Horns blared, flutes blew, drums beat to early mass. Clang of bells called all to the broad minster.

It was before matins that the two queens sat together. Kriemhild said, I have a husband in whose hands all this realm should lie. Brunhild said, How may that be while Gunther lives? Kriemhild said, See how he goes before the knights, as the bright moon goes before the stars! Brunhild said, Brave and true he may be, but your brother Gunther goes before him. When the king played my games, Siegfried himself said he was Gunther's man. Kriemhild said, How should my brother have given me to a liegeman? He has more worth than my brother Gunther. Brunhild said, You hold yourself too high. We will see if you are held in honour so high as I. Kriemhild said, Today man shall see me, your liegeman's wife, go before the queen of Burgundy. Dress, my maids, she said, and they sought rich clothes. Kriemhild with her thirty maids went to the minster. Thirty queens might have worn the riches on her.

People wondered that the two queens did not go together. Brunhild called to Kriemhild to stand still: The man's wife shall not go before the king's! Kriemhild answered in anger, Better you had kept quiet. You have shamed your fair body. Might a man's mistress ever be a king's wife? Who is the mistress? asked Brunhild. Kriemhild said, Siegfried, not Gunther, had your maidenhead. Brunhild said, I will tell Gunther of it; she began to weep. Kriemhild went into the minster with her menie.

Brunhild waited for Kriemhild as she came out of the minster and said to her, You called me a man's mistress. Where is your proof? Kriemhild said, I prove it by the gold ring on my finger. Siegfried brought it to me after he had lain with you. Never did Brunhild see a more sorrowful day. I know the gold, she said, it was stolen from me. Kriemhild said, I am no thief. I prove it by the girdle I have on. I have not lied: Siegfried knew you. She wore a girdle of Nineveh silk sewn with gems. When Brunhild saw it she began to weep.

The king came and Brunhild said to him, Your sister says I am Siegfried's mistress. She has my girdle I lost and my ring of red gold. Rid me of this shame. O, that I was ever born! Gunther said, Call him, and Siegfried came.

Gunther said, My wife Brunhild tells me you knew her first, or so Kriemhild says. Did you?

No, said Siegfried, and if she has said so I will not rest till she grieve for it. I will swear it before your host. The men of Burgundy stood in a ring and Siegfried gave Gunther his hand on oath. Gunther said, Now I see you are guiltless. Siegfried said, We should rear women that they hold no rash speech. Do you forbid it your wife, and I will forbid it mine.

Brunhild was in such woe that all Gunther's men were sad-hearted. Hagen went to the queen and said, Siegfried shall grieve for this. Either he shall die, or I shall. Gunther said, He has done us nothing but true service. Let him live. Why should I bear him hate?

Every day after Hagen told Gunther, if Siegfried no longer lived, many kings' lands would become his. Gunther said, His strength is so great, none dare come near him. Not so, said Hagen, we will do it quietly. Gunther said, How may that be? Hagen said, Let me but hear one thing from Kriemhild, and he shall lose his life.

Hagen went to where he found Kriemhild. She said, I grieve that I said ill of Brunhild. My body is blue for it. Hagen said, Tell me how I may best serve you. Kriemhild said, I would be free of all care if Siegfried were well guarded. Hagen said, I will ride by him. Kriemhild said, Siegfried is strong and brave. When he slew the dragon by the hill he bathed in the blood and no weapon may hurt him; yet I will tell you where man may wound him. When the hot blood flowed from the dragon, and he bathed in it, a broad limetree leaf fell on his shoulder. There man might wound him. O, what grief that gives me! Hagen said, Sew on his garment a small sign to show me where I must guard him. She said, I will sew on his garment a small cross of fine silk. Then you may guard him.

Thus Siegfried was betrayed.

(iii) Gunther said, Let us hunt. Willingly, said Siegfried. Lend me a huntsman and some brachs and I will ride with you into the wood.

Siegfried went to where he found Kriemhild. He said, God grant I come home whole: I am going hunting. Kriemhild thought of what she had told Hagen and said, Leave your hunting. Last night I dreamed I saw two boars hunted on the heath: the blooms became red. He said, I shall come back. No-one here harbours hate or envy of me. Kriemhild said, I dreamed I saw two hills fall on you in the dale, so that I saw you no more. He clasped her in his arms and took his leave.

Sumpterhorses bore bread and wine, flesh and fish, to the skirt of a dense wood. An old huntsman took a hound and brought the knights to the coverts. All the brach started Siegfried slew: nothing outran him. The first beast he slew was a boar and after he found a grim lion. He shot with his bow a sharp arrow; the lion leaped three leaps, no more.

A blast was blown on a horn and men brought fells to the fire. Siegfried said, I heard a hornblast, we must go to the restingplace. He rode to the restingplace. His spear was long and strong and broad and it swung to his spur. He bore a horn of red gold. What prickwork he bore on his quiver! A panther-fleece decked it. He carried a bow another man had needed an engine to bend. He bore too Balmung his broadsword. His garment was of black otterskin, whereon shone gold flitter; his hat was of sable. His quiver held good arrows, with shafts of gold and heads as broad as a hand.

When the huntsmen called him to table, Siegfried said, I wonder that the scullions bring so much food, yet the cupbearers bring no wine. There should be seven sumpters with mead and clear drink. Gunther, with falsehood in his mind, said, The fault is Hagen's. Hagen said, I thought the hunt was at Spechtshart, I sent the wine there; but I know a clear spring close by, near a hill under a limetree. Thirst urged Siegfried, he said he would go to the spring. Hagen said, I have heard none can outrun you. Will you race with me to the spring? Good, said Siegfried, and like two panthers they ran through the clover, Siegfried came to the spring first.

The spring was clear and cool. When Gunther knelt to drink, Hagen drew away Siegfried's bow and sword and sought the sign on his shoulder. When Siegfried drank, Hagen shot him through the cross, that his heart's blood welled out through the wound. The spear stuck deep in his heart. Yet Hagen fled as none on earth had fled a man before.

Siegfried sprang up from the spring. The spearshaft stuck from his shoulder. He took his shield and struck Hagen so hard that gems burst from the shield rim and the ring of the blow rang in the woods. Hagen fell to the dale floor.

Siegfried's tint was wan from the death wound; he fell. Blood ran from his wound. He cursed the untrue men who had killed him: May their shame sunder them from all knights! Nothing on earth is left of me but my wife Kriemhild. God have mercy on me, that I bore a son whose father died by his friend's hand! Never did man do murder so foul.

Before the wood of Oden there lies a hamlet, Odenheim;
there still flows the spring, where Siegfried was slain.

(iv) Bells rang to the minster. Kriemhild awoke, woke her
maids and a linkboy bore light into the chamber. He said,
Be still. There is a knight lying dead before the door. Kriemhild sank to the ground, her grief was great. Her ladies said,
It may be a stranger. She said, No, it is Siegfried. Brunhild
thought it and Hagen did it.

She let herself be led to where she found him and raised his
head in her white hand. She cried, Woe to this land! His
shield is not hewn by spears. He died by murder. Her ladies
cried and moaned.

They drew his body from the clothes and washed his wound
and laid him on a bier. Smiths made a coffin of silver and
gold and lined it with good steel and men raised the dead body
from the bier, swathed it in a costly shroud and brought it to
the minster. How the bells tolled! The priests sang.

Kriemhild said, All my gladness is laid in his body. I will
watch three days and three nights.

On the third morning men bore him from the minster to the
grave. The folk wept. Kriemhild lay in swoon that day, that
evening and the second day. Siegfried was buried.

LA DIVINA COMMEDIA

By DANTE ALIGHIERI

" When first the glorious Lady of my mind was made manifest
to mine eyes, even she who was called Beatrice . . . she
appeared to me at the beginning of her ninth year almost, and
I saw her almost at the end of my ninth year. . . . At that
moment, I say most truly that the spirit of life, which hath its
dwelling in the secretest chamber of the heart, began to tremble
so violently that the least pulses of my body shook therewith;
and in trembling it said these words : ' Here is a deity
stronger than I ; who, coming, shall rule over me'. . . .

" After the lapse of so many days that nine years exactly
were compelled since the above-written appearance of this most
gracious being, on the last of those days it happened that the
same wonderful lady appeared to me dressed all in pure white,
between two gentle ladies elder than she. And passing
through a street, she turned her eyes thither where I stood
sorely abashed : and by her unspeakable courtesy, which is
now guerdoned in the Great Cycle, she saluted me with so
virtuous a bearing that I seemed then and there to behold the
very limits of blessedness."

So wrote Dante in the autobiographical prose and sonnet
account of his love for Beatrice Portinari, called " La Vita
Nuova". It was a love that was to last him through life;
after Beatrice's early death at the age of twenty-five, this pure
passion for her earthly semblance became etherealized still
further through exile and suffering : Beatrice became for
Dante in his sojourn in strange cities the symbol of heavenly
wisdom and the inspiration of his great poetic vision, " The
Divine Comedy". From her seat in the ultimate circle of
heavenly bliss, she reached her hand to soothe his troubled spirit
and draw him with smiling compassion through the centre of
all suffering and evil (the Hell of his Vision) up the mount
from whose garden summit Adam fell, to bring him at last
into the presence of God himself and all his saints and angels.

The Inferno

In the midway of this our mortal life,
I found me in a gloomy wood, astray
Gone from the path direct: and e'en to tell,
It were no easy task, how savage wild
That forest, how robust and rough its growth,
Which to remember only, my dismay
Renews, in bitterness not far from death.
Yet, to discourse of what there good befel,
All else will I relate discovered there.

Lost in these dark ways, and striving to reach and ascend the mount that would lead him upwards into a purer and a clearer air, Dante sees luring him in his track the gay-coated leopard of sensual pleasures. And then, barring his path onwards, scaring him from it, the lion Ambition and a lean-flanked wolf of Avarice appear. He despairs of any progress, beset by such persistent adversaries, when he meets a sombre figure, whose voice when he hails the earthly traveller seems to be as of one whose tongue hesitates through long disuse of speech. This is the great Latin poet, Virgil, long Dante's model and his guide to the summit of Parnassus.

To him Dante tells of his journey, of the mount he seeks and the beasts that bar his way thither. Virgil tells him that he cannot proceed on that path, but there is another, along which, if he has courage to adventure, he will himself conduct him. It leads through dark places, yes, through Hell itself, but it will emerge, with faith to guide, upon the secure path of the sacred mountain.

Dante hesitates, appalled at the prospect of the dark, downward path through the eternal retribution upon sin; but when Virgil tells him that he shall have for safeguard the grace of that divine lady in Heaven who was wont to be his beacon star, the lady Beatrice, even she who has sent Virgil upon this mission of relief for the wayworn wanderer, Dante gratefully agrees.

So the two, faring onwards, come to a gate, upon which Dante reads the inscription:

Through me you pass into the city of woe:
Through me you pass into eternal pain:
Through me among the people lost for aye . . .
All hope abandon, ye who enter here.

It is the gate of Hell, upon the far side of which lies the first of those regions where those eternally shut out from the divine love must everlastingly suffer for their sins. The first region, which lies this side the infernal river Acheron, is the abode of those, both fallen angels and humans, who passed their days in apathy, neither denying nor affirming God, the Indifferents, colourless beings without sin or virtue; and they:

> With hands together smote that swell'd the sounds,
> Made up a tumult, that for ever whirls
> Round through the air with solid darkness stain'd,
> Like to the sand that in the whirlwind flies . . .

Passing through the helpless scurry of these souls, in whose punishment as, ever in Hell, Dante sees the condign correspondence with their sin—they lived indifferent, and indifferent hurricane chastises them—passing through these, they come to the first of Hell's five streams, Acheron. Here Charon waits, the ferryman, with his blazing eyes compelling the inrush of damned souls into the boat that conveys them to their appropriate portions in Hell.

When Virgil has explained his divine authority for guiding a mortal over the river, Charon sullenly accepts Dante's transport beyond death, and in the first circle of Hell proper, the outermost and least painful one, where Virgil himself belongs, they come amongst the lamenting shades of those who knew not Christ, living before his advent; now they know of the divine love and know also that they are eternally severed from it. In this their punishment consists.

The two pass next into the horrid tracts of Hell where the conscious sins are punished, regions that narrow in ordered sequences and intensify progressively in their torments towards the centre where Satan stands in frozen anguish thigh deep in the lake Cocytus. When they have passed the dread judge, Minos, they see the carnal sinners, and first among them those who have committed adultery. As dark passion has driven them, so are they now borne ceaselessly about upon murky currents of air, two by two, lover and loved, racked with repentance that can never redeem them.

Two float towards the travellers whom Dante questions. They are Paolo and Francesca, whose dolorous passion still trembles down the ages, immortalised in Dante's vision.

Francesca was married at her father's will to a lord of Ravenna, Guido da Polenta, who, though of courageous heart, lacked the physical graces of his brother, Paolo. So it came about that Paolo and the young bride found similar

interests, reading together the old romances of Arthur and
of Guenever, and the guilty passion of the knight Lancelot
for his sovereign's queen. This book it was and one passage
in it that brought about their death by the hand of the wronged
husband and plunged them into the second circle of Hell.

Dante's compassion was such that he fell fainting to the
ground.

Then they pass on through the two circles of the other
fleshy sinners and see the gluttons wallowing in mire, rained
on by dirty water, hail and snow, for the wine they immoderately
drank on earth; the hellhound, Cerberus, ravens them with
clashing jaws, even as they clashed their teeth against the bones
of succulent meats. In the fourth circle, where Pluto, god of
riches, holds dismal sway, they behold two semicircles of shades,
equally guilty, though oppositely inclined, the avaricious and
the prodigal. They are engaged in a gruesome parody of
play, each side rolling huge weights until they come hurtling
together, everlastingly repeating the collison, wailing and shrieking and upbraiding each other, the ones who recklessly spent
and those who criminally gathered.

Scarcely has the tumult of these damned souls faded behind
them, when Dante and his guide come to a loathsome bog.
It is Styx, and while a waterman shade ferries them across,
Dante questions his guide about the naked creatures he sees
rising from the marsh, all clotted with filth, tearing at each
other. They are the wrathful, Virgil tells him, and underneath them, making the thick surface bubble with their sighs,
are the souls of the " gloomy-sluggish ", who, given over to
the deadly sin of dumpish sloth, failed to look outside themselves
and praise the gladness and joy of God's creation.

Over the waters seething with turbulent and sluggish
souls Dante begins to discern the fiery pinnacles of Hell's
capital, the city of Lucifer. Hitherto, they had traversed, as it
were, the mere countryside or provinces of Sin's realm, those
outlying parts where the excesses of incontinence are punished.
But through the gates of that lurid city are racked in anguish
unspeakably more awful the souls of those who have sinned
brutishly against nature and of those who have been guilty
of deceit or guile.

Three furies bearing the Medusa's head, whose aspect turns
all who look upon it to stone, rush out upon the pilgrim and
his guide. And had it not been for the arrival of an angel
there, the gates enclosing the terrible mysteries of God's justice

must have remained for ever closed against one who still bore the fleshy covering of the earth-dwellers.

Encamped in agony within the walls, cased in burning sepulchres, not to be sealed until the day of judgment, are the souls of heretics, all those, who through pride have misrepresented God's revealed will. This is the sixth circle, lying outside the great river of boiling blood, Phlegethon, the stream that Dante must cross if he is to penetrate through agony on to the longed-for mountain path, winding upwards towards the stars.

But how to get across? There is no ferryman here, only centaurs, horses below and men above, wild symbols of violence, galloping along the river banks, chivvying the tormented souls in the bloodstream as they try to scramble ashore, transfixing them with arrows.

But Virgil, with the power that his divine mission bestows, persuades a centaur to carry them over to the plain that lies beyond. As they course upon the broad horse-back, cleaving the crimson flood, Virgil explains that in this threefold seventh circle are punished those who have been guilty of violence against their neighbour, against themselves, or against God. The first class, murderers, swirl to everlasting in the river of blood.

"And there," Virgil adds, pointing to the farther shore, "upon the blistering sands and under flakes of fire, accomplish their burning destiny those who have sinned against God, or against God's creation, Nature."

Virgil explains that the third class, that of the sinners against nature, includes usurers; they have their place among the blasphemers, sodomists, murderers, tyrants and suicides, because God's pronouncement through the scriptures was that man should farm and manufacture, be agriculturist and artisan; and the usurer, who neither "replenishes" the earth and "subdues" it nor "eats his bread in the sweat of his face," therefore sins against the law of nature.

The centaur lands them on the inner shore of the river, and they enter the mystic wood. This is peopled—or, rather, occupied—by those who have done violence to their own persons, the suicides:

> We entered on a forest, where no track
> Of steps had worn a way. Not verdant there
> The foliage, but of dusky hue; not light
> The boughs and tapering, but with knares deformed
> And matted thick: fruits there were none, but thorns
> Instead, with venom filled.

Here the brute harpies make their nest. . . .
Broad are their pennons, of the human form
Their neck and countenance, arm'd with talons keen
The feet, and the huge belly fledged with wings.
These sit and wail on the drear mystic wood.

Dante breaks a twig from one of the trees; to his horror, blood spurts out, and a voice from the tree moans, " Why wound you me? " The suicides are the trees in that wood. And one of them explains that at the last judgment, when every other soul shall be reinvested with its body, theirs only will not clothe them; because they wilfully dispossessed themselves of their bodies, after the judgment their fleshy semblances shall hang upon the boughs beside them, sad trophies of their sin.

Issuing from the ghostly grove, Dante and Virgil proceed along a causeway beside a tributary stream of Phlegethon that winds its gory way over the burning sands towards the centre of Hell. They see blasphemers roasting at full length, unable to rise, usurers squatting dismally with their chins on their knees, and sodomists racing without halt or rest, like light-footed athletes, the soles of their feet spurred onward by the burning contact. A troop of these rushes up below them and, as they come abreast, they join hands and circle round in an awful semblance of hilarity. It is the only way, since move they must, that they can keep pace with the slowly-treading travellers and speak with them.

Dante and Virgil have now come to the verge of the eighth pit, the Maleboge, guarded by the loathsome amphibian monster, Geryon, whom Virgil, borrowing Dante's girdle-cord, attracts from the depths. On his scaly back they descend. Below, Dante sees the ten furrows or trenches that circle round the midmost pit of Hell where the mountainous Satan sticks axle-wise, waist-deep in the frozen Cocytus.

From above, this eighth region appears like a vast wheel composed of ten concentric circles, spoked by the cliffs that bridge and span the trenches and banks between, converging to the centre. The circumference is sheer stone. The murky air stinks of excrement and pitch, of putrescent flesh and of the lazaretto.

Dante, his face blackened with the fumes, reeling under the stench, follows his guide over the transverse cliffs, peering into the furrows where deceit and malice in ten kinds suffer their appropriate retribution. There he sees scourged pimps and

procurers; flatterers submerged in excrement; those who
trafficked in holy offices poked head downwards in holes; here
loom through the thick air naked forms walking backwards,
tears trickling down their buttocks from faces that hang between their shoulder blades—diviners, formerly, of the future,
who must now to all eternity look back and walk with their
heels foremost. Shoals of barterers in state offices drift beneath his feet on floods of burning pitch, gaping their mouths
and nostrils out like frogs; foul demons disport themselves,
harpooning and lugging them ashore. A troop of hypocrites
pass, brilliantly apparelled in cloaks of gilded lead; as they
tread their heavy way they crush underfoot the eternally
prostrate form of the arch-hypocrite of them all, Caiaphas,
who betrayed Christ. In the seventh trench of Maleboge,
thieves live on for ever intimately interwoven with nests and
tangled complexes of serpents in a constant process of trans-
formation—thief into serpent, serpent into thief.

In the eighth trench, the damned souls are unrecognizable;
they are enwrapped with the flames of their own guilty con-
sciences. These are the shades of the evil counsellors, of those
who, endowed with wisdom, abused the divine gift to mislead
others.

Next, through the darkening air and the intensifying miasma,
they come to the last trench before the frozen central pit of
Hell. With all manner of filthy diseases staining and scaling
and puncturing and peeling their spirit bodies, appear the
falsifiers: forgers and alchemists who have falsified *things*;
falsifiers of deeds, who have impersonated others for evil ends;
falsifiers of words, like Potiphar's wife. As they claw at their
itching scabs, even here in their torment they rant at each
other and exchange scurrilities. Fascinated, Dante lingers to
listen, but feels ashamed when Virgil sternly rebukes him for
attending to their filthy chat.

The brink of Hell's centre, the frozen lake, Cocytus, whence
all the infernal rivers have their source and evermore return,
is brooded over by vast figures, looming dimly through the fog.
They take their type from Nimrod, stupid in wit as he is huge
in bulk, for they are those biblical giants who attempted in
ancient times to persuade man to surpass nature and the
author of nature.

In four concentric rings, ranged upon the frozen pit, under
the mill wings of Satan in its centre, Satan for ever trying to
rise, for ever settling himself firmer with his ice-creating wings,

under the shadow of the "everlasting no", are racked the doubly fraudulent, those who have treacherously deceived: who have slain their kindred, betrayed their country, exterminated their relatives, or betrayed their masters and benefactors. Each circle takes its name after the archtype of the sin. And so the last circle directly beneath the archtype of all evil, is called Judecca, from Judas who betrayed Christ.

And now Dante, if he is to emerge in the bright hemisphere of hope, and rise with the morning sun under the fair mount of his desire, must make the last, terrible assay. Virgil, with the compassion and the understanding that have upheld his fellow poet through all the terrible journey, bears Dante up and starts upon that final descent whose object is high Heaven and all the stars.

Virgil and his friend climb down the towering flank of the fiend, descend through the shaggy hair, until, with wonder, Dante finds they are climbing upwards, into the light of the kindly sun.

PURGATORY

Dante, released from the gloomy regions of sin, looks joyfully abroad, bathing his soul with the pure lights and colours of the dawn; he sees the orient sapphire deepening on the clear brow of the sky and the four day stars composing the lustrous constellation of the moral virtues, Prudence, Justice, Fortitude and Temperance.

They have arrived on the shores beneath Mount Purgatory, glad, yet bewildered, for they know not which way to proceed towards the crown of the mountain. Soon they are joined by an ancient man, sombrely clad; it is that virtuous Roman, Cato, who gave his life for liberty. To him Virgil addresses himself, explaining that his companion is seeking that same liberty that was so dear to the Roman. ¿Cato then instructs Virgil to take Dante down to the seashore where there grows the reed of humility. With this rush must all gird themselves who seek ascent of the sacred mountain. Afterwards they may follow the rising sun up the steeps towards Eden. By the verge of the sea, rippling under the cool morning breeze, Virgil presses his palms in the glittering dew and gently wipes away from Dante's face the sulphurous vestiges of Hell; then girds him with the lowly rush.

As they gaze seawards, they see bearing swiftly towards

them a bark with a heavenly steersman guiding towards those longed-for shores the souls of them who have won salvation.

At the foot of the mountain, while they hesitate which path to take, they meet a number of the souls of those who must linger at the base of Purgatory for a period thirty times as long as that in which on earth they lived in contumacy against the church. They are directed by these to a narrow mounting cleft, through which they pursue their way, passing as they go those other shades who must spend a period of expiation on the threshold of Purgatory, the souls of the late repentant. The denizens here, as well as those beneath, who had rebelled against church discipline, beg anxiously for Dante's prayers when he returns to earth. The power of prayer alone can expedite their purgation. Yet they cannot pray for each other in Purgatory; only those left on earth can help them.

When Dante and his guide have reached a place that is the cleansing abode of all those rulers on earth who, like Henry of Navarre, Ottocar of Bohemia, and Henry III of England, neglected their proper duties for ease or selfish war, evening is falling.

The resting place of the delinquent rulers is a fair grove, counterpart of the Garden of Eden. Their penance is that its very beauties, reminding them of their longed-for objective, makes their abode a torture to them. Into this imitation Eden, also, the serpent comes at night, and, as if to remind them that their wills are not yet pure in themselves, two flaming angels alight in their garden, with broken swords, an evening guard to chase away the evil presence. The four stars of the moral virtues set, and in their place shine forth over the mount the three beacon lights of the spirit, Faith, Hope, Charity. Neither the shades nor Dante and Virgil may ascend by night. Their journey is a moral one to Eden, and it must be made under the four daystars.

Dante sleeps in the grove and awakes to find himself outside the gate of Purgatory proper. Just before dawn, as on every night afterwards preceding his successive ascents of the shelves of the mountain, Dante dreams a prophetic dream, a dream linking him, as it were, with a higher stage of his pilgrimage. He dreams that a golden eagle is bearing him up into the empyrean, a vision that symbolizes regeneration through baptism.

Three steps, of Contrition, Sincerity, and Love, lead to the gates, where sits an angel, who brushes Dante with his wing, imprinting on his forehead seven P's, standing for *peccata*, the deadly sins. Through the purgation of each successive terrace circling the mount, the symbolic letters must one by one be cleansed away.

On the first terrace Dante's attention is at once caught by frescoes imprinted on the rockside. They represent various examples of humility. There he sees pictured the angelic annunciation to the Virgin Mary; David dancing before the Ark of the Lord, and other examples from sacred and profane history. This is the terrace where the proud on earth repent. Dante has not long to wait before he sees the awful manner of their penance. A cluster of indistinct shapes move along the ledge towards him, and, as they draw closer, he is appalled to see that each one of them is labouring under a huge slab of stone, so that it is bent almost to the earth under the weight of its burden. Yet, because they have repented of their pride, their only care is that the load is not heavier still, so that the term of their absence from God might be shortened.

One of these labouring shapes Dante recognizes as a former friend of his, the painter of miniatures, Oderisi, who had once brooked no rival to himself. Now he willingly admits the superiority of others. He has attained through suffering to an understanding of the transitory and trivial nature of fame. He sees how one school of painting or poetry succeeds another, borne up and then under on the wheel of human preference. In painting, once Cimabue, now Giotto; soon another. In poetry, Dante himself and his school—those who believed not in saying things beautifully, but in describing beautiful things truly—these too must give way to a new name, and that to another—motes puffed through the ray of eternity.

As they pass on, Virgil directs Dante's attention to the stone underfoot. Depicted there are examples of pride recorded in history and fable: Nimrod, whose shade he has left in Hell, he who incited men to build, instead of temples, a tower to climb into the very halls of God; Niobe who boasted of her fourteen children; Cyrus, the proud Persian, and many others.

As they mount the stairway to the second terrace, from mouths invisible they hear chanted the beatitude of the poor in spirit. And the gentle angel of the circle of the proud, brushing his wing across Dante's brow, erases one of the P's impressed there. He is purged from the sin of Pride, and so the ascent seems easier to him than did the first.

So the poets continue on their way, meeting upon each terrace with the examples of the seven sins, always seeing in the divine ordinance part corresponding with part, punishment with sin; and like the rhymes in a lofty poem ring on their ears upon the terrace of every sin washed clean the beatitudes of the Christian faith; pictured on every ledge they see the dance of the sin there punished, the counter-dance of its opposite virtue.

The second terrace contains the once envious, those whose eyes had turned with loathing and rage from the good things enjoyed by others. So now their eyelids are wired up as they grope blindly along the mountain side. With these, as with the proud, Dante knows that when his own preparation comes for Paradise he must abide some little while in atonement for his own sins, though the terrace of pride shall hold him longer than that of envy.

The words of one of the once envious, Guido del Duca, puzzle Dante. The shade has reproached mankind for fixing their hearts on those things that exclude partnership. Virgil explains the difference between goods of the world, material goods, and the gifts of the spirit; and how the more of the former a man has, the less must there be for others, whereas peace, love, and knowledge, the more a man possess these, the more are they shared among others. The lust for material goods is the source of all envy.

Discoursing thus, they mount on to the third terrace, that of the once wrathful, where a vision comes to Dante of the Virgin Mary and Saint Stephen, who was stoned to death, examples of meekness and patience. Then, passing on through a thick and acrid fog, there is wafted on their ears the tender anthem of the " Lamb of God " issuing in penitential chant from the wraiths of those who were borne along on earth upon the passionate fumes of anger. Here is Marco Lombardo, once a learned courtier, now one who bewails in Purgatory the turmoil and degeneracy prevailing in his native Italy.

Through visions of fabled examples of wrath, the poets turn up the ascent leading to the next terrace, and Virgil takes the opportunity to point out to his pupil the system of Purgatory. All creatures, he says, turn naturally to good; love for the extreme good, which is God, is as inherent in human nature as is the plant's instinct for its habitat, fire's motion towards its circumference, or heavenly bodies' inclination for their centre. Natural love, therefore, cannot err.

But there is also rational love, and this is fallible; it may be perverted or disproportionate. Since creatures cannot love or delight in evil either to themselves or the Author of their being, unless, indeed, they be monsters, it follows that perverse love rejoices in the evil done to our neighbours. Pride, Envy and Wrath are examples of perverse rational love. The four other sins that Dante is about to behold purged, Sloth, Avarice, Gluttony, and Carnality, are examples of disproportionate and laggard love; for Sloth withholds love, and the other three sins expend disproportionate love on objects that do not compose the Supreme Good.

Even as Virgil speaks, they arrive on the ledge of the slothful, and at once they are swept against the mountain side by a troop of shades whirling past, propelled on the consciousness of Lost Opportunity, rushing round and round the terrace in an effort to make up with the love they neglected.

The daystars set. It is night and, according to the law of the Mount, the pilgrims may go no farther before daybreak.

The next day they explore the three last circles under Eden. Among the souls of the avaricious, who are all cleaving as closely to the pavement as they did formerly to their worldly riches, ashamed to look upwards towards heaven, they remark the shade of Pope Adrian the Fifth, who repented him too late of his avarice, realizing the vanity of worldly riches only when he had reached the summit of earthly ambition. Here, too, they meet the poet Statius, one of the Christian poets of the Roman Empire. The travellers are surprised to see him among the avaricious, but he explains he was, in fact, a prodigal; here, as in Hell, the two shortcomings are punished together, being but the two facets of one sin—inordinate preoccupation with worldly goods, whether through grasping or squandering.

Then Statius delights Dante and his guide by telling them how his conversion to Christianity was occasioned by a prophetic passage in one of the pagan Virgil's own works, the famous Eclogue where Virgil seems to anticipate the coming of a new order consequent on the advent of the Messiah.

The gluttons on the next terrace gladly work out their salvation in extreme hunger and thirst, presenting among trees of luscious fruit and sparkling streams, emaciated and haggard appearances as they crucify in themselves the old Adam. The beatitude there sung is " Blessed are they that do hunger and thirst after righteousness."

They pass on to the last, narrowest ledge that circles the

mountain just beneath Eden. Here the souls of the unchaste are purged with flame, two classes of carnal sinners circling in opposite directions—those who have sinned against nature, and those who have exceeded the limits of indulgence sanctioned by human law. "Blessed are the pure in heart; for they shall see God" floats through the burning air.

To reach Eden, Dante himself has to pass through flame. Hitherto, he has not physically suffered in Purgatory, except through the labour of ascent from terrace to terrace, labours that have grown progressively lighter as the P's of the seven sins have been brushed from his brow by angels' wings. But in Eden he is to meet Beatrice, the ideal love of his youth. The flames, that are the conscience of the carnal sinners, scorch him, too.

Dante's last dream on the night preceding his entrance into the Garden of Eden is of the biblical characters, Leah and Rachel, signifying respectively types of the active and contemplative life in its apotheosis of goodness.

And now, on his awakening, Dante finds himself purged clean of the effects of our first parents' fall. He has reached the point where he no longer needs direction from State—or Church—henceforth, he is emperor over himself and his own bishop. For his further guidance, he is dependent on Divine Wisdom alone. Nor can human wisdom (Virgil) explain things any further to him. He is ready to meet Beatrice and the gracious saints in Heaven.

The poets enter Eden and find it full of the song of birds accompanied by the murmur of leaves whispering in a scented breeze. They come to a stream, crystal clear, that runs through trees so thickly growing that no beam of sun or moon can penetrate there, and on the far bank, picking flowers along the grassy verge they see a beautiful lady.

This is Matilda, type of the active life, prefigured in Dante's third dream. She is to be his guide through Eden. Dante learns from her that the stream is one of two in Eden, from both of which he must drink before partaking of the joy of the celestial spheres. This is Lethe that purges away all evil thoughts and experiences; the other, Eunoë, will restore to his memory all the good in his life, including all that incidental good that has sprung out of evil and has thus been washed from memory in the first draught.

As Dante and Virgil walk along one side of the stream, accompanying the gracious lady on the other bank, they see a

pageant approaching them. It represents the triumphal
chariot of the Church, drawn by a griffin, half bird, half
animal, who symbolizes the twofold nature of Christ. The
three theological and four cardinal virtues accompany it in
dance. Twenty-four elders, who are the books of the Old
Testament and seven more to make up the books of the New,
form the reverent following of the car.

Suddenly, in a blaze of glory, spirits of the blessed rise up all
round the car, and in the midst of them, apprehended, though
not recognized Beatrice:

> A virgin in my view appeared, beneath
> Green mantle, robed in hue of living flame:
> And o'er my spirit, that so long a time
> Had from her presence felt no shuddering dread,
> Albeit mine eyes discerned her not, there moved
> A hidden virtue from her, at whose touch
> The power of ancient love was strong within me.
> No sooner on my vision streaming, smote
> The heavenly influence, which, years past, and e'en
> In childhood, thrill'd me, than towards Virgil I
> Turn'd me to leftward. . . .

But Virgil cannot help Dante now. More than human
wisdom is needed to understand the further journey of the soul.

Now Dante must listen to the reproaches of Beatrice for
having abandoned the high ideals of his youth, embodied in
her, for having turned towards visions of false good when she
had left the body. So great is his shame and repentance that
he falls swooning to the ground. When he recovers consciousness and is bidden to drink of Lethe and look up at Beatrice,
he sees reflected, beaming alternately in her eyes, the mystery
of the incarnation itself, the mystic union of the divine and
human nature. Beatrice has transcended her human semblance
and becomes henceforward the impersonation of Divine Wisdom.

He walks with the procession until it comes to the Tree of
the Knowledge of Good and Evil. The tree represents the
principle of obedience, and therefore of Empire. With
allegorical significance, the car of the Church is fastened to the
tree, thus denoting the ideal relations of Church and State.

Yet only for a short time, for soon the attendant pageant
disappears and the garden is left empty save for Beatrice,
Matilda and the poets—that fair garden which, had it not been
for the defection of man, might now have been filled with
happy souls.

Then, in this deserted paradise, Dante sees an allegorical

representation both of the Church's own sins and the persecutions wrought upon her by Roman emperors, heretics and schismatics.

Afterwards, Beatrice, telling Dante to cast off all ceremony and walk by her side, leads him to the river Eunoë. He drinks of the sparkling waters, refreshing his soul with the memory of every good act he has ever done, and

> Return'd
> From the most holy wave, regenerate,
> E'en as new plants renew'd with foliage new,
> Pure and made apt for mounting to the stars.

PARADISE

Now that Dante has risen again to Eden and regained, symbolically, the state of Man's primal innocence, he is ready, through the Grace of God, for that further divine revelation that Adam forfeited through the fall. Dante sets forth with Beatrice through the revolving spheres of the Heavenly Will, manifesting itself in the planetary circles from the Centre beyond space and time.

As Dante proceeds through the circles, the sun being conceived as revolving round the earth, Beatrice, his new guide, explains to him how each class of heavenly spirits, though they *abide* eternally with God in the empyrean, yet *manifest* themselves in the sun, moon, and planets according to their heavenly natures; for the souls in Heaven are infinitely various, and some, through some blemish on earth, though taintless now, are yet less perfect in degree than others. So it is that in the innermost and smallest circle, that of the moon, there manifest themselves the souls who have attained the least degree of excellence. The moon is the symbol of inconstancy, and those who appear in it to Dante and his guide have wavered overmuch on earth in their love towards God.

Before Dante meets representatives of the heavenly choir, some earthly misconceptions must be cleared away from his mind. He cannot understand, since all matter *falls* to its place, why he should effortlessly, and, as it were, naturally, be *rising*, thus violating the laws of motion. Beatrice explains to him that what is indeed natural, since all things seek their true place, is for the spirit to *ascend* towards God, in whom it lives.

Still troubled by the scientific, material experiments of

his time, Dante asks Beatrice about the dark places on the moon's surface. He has heard it said on earth that the shadowy places are those parts of the lunar matter that are less dense. Beatrice proves to him that even as a material explanation this must be false. She tells him that the brightness of all the heavenly bodies varies according to the quality of the divine effluence that shines through them. As joy shines through the eye, so God through all the stars.

Now, as they penetrate into the moon, merging into it with their spirit bodies, as the Holy Ghost must have mingled with Mary, Dante sees faintly on the surrounding radiance resemblances to human features so finely traced that he looks behind him, thinking they must be reflections. Beatrice smiles as she tells him he has mistaken for illusion the greatest reality he has ever seen; for these are heavenly souls, not indeed as they appear in God, but as they manifest themselves to Dante, by divine provision, in the material heavens.

Here, in the lowliest circle of the blessed, Dante talks with Piccarda, the sister of his old friend, Forese; and from her he learns of the contentment in its assigned place of every soul in Heaven. The quality of love placates the will, so that each one yearns only for what it has. How could it be otherwise, for did they yearn to be closer still to God, their wills would be at variance with the Divine Will; and in Heaven is no discord.

" God's Will," she tells him, " is our peace; it is the sea to which all moves that it has created or nature has made."

In the next circle, that of the planet Mercury, Dante meets the souls of the over-ambitious. He speaks with the spirit of the Roman emperor, Justinian, the codifier of Roman law, and the type, therefore, of Imperial peace. He explains to Dante how he left the conduct of the campaign against the Ostragoths to his general Belisarius, while he occupied himself with the problems of civil and imperial administration. Then he proceeds to give an account of the relations of peace and empire to God's purpose in the redemption of mankind. It was needful, he explains, that peace should be established in the Empire to establish circumstances favourable for the Incarnation. This peace was achieved under Julius Casear and Augustus.

Then, reading Dante's unexpressed question about the nature of the Redemption—why it was necessary for God to become man, Justinian explains that in no other way, short of a free pardon, could man have been re-established. Only united with God's own person could he become sufficiently humbled to restore himself.

In such ways, learning of God's mysteries as he makes his Heavenward journey, Dante reaches the circle of the planet Venus, which represents earthly love. In their eternal cosmic dance, appear the souls who have forfeited some of their brilliance because of overstrong human affections. Among these, he meets with another friend of his, Carlo Martello, King of Hungary.

Dante is shown by another once amorous soul, Folco, the troubadour, how the conical shadow of the earth reaches to the planet Venus, but extends no farther. By this the trouba-dour indicates that the effects of earthly sin modify the bright-ness of heavenly souls in the first three circles only. He adds that there is no repentance for sin in Heaven and that sins are only remembered by those who have committed them as the occasions of the divine mercy that led them into the starry spheres.

The four planetary heavens beyond the earth's shadow, the Sun, Mars, Jupiter and Saturn, stand respectively for the four cardinal virtues, Prudence, Fortitude, Justice and Temperance.

The spirits manifesting Prudence are so dazzling in their splendour that their brightness makes them stand out even against the sun's disc. They are rejoicing in the vision of the Holy Trinity. Then, to welcome the travellers, twelve of the radiant souls form a crown of living light and circle slowly round the heads of Dante and Beatrice, chanting a song of unearthly beauty. Detaching himself from the rest to further instruct the questing spirit of the poet, there descends the " saintly doctor ", Thomas Aquinas, from whose mighty system of theology Dante had learnt so much.

Thomas Aquinas belonged to the Dominican order of mendicant friars. He therefore, in courtesy and humility, speaks the praises of the saintly founder of the brother order, Francis of Assisi; at the same time he censures his own order for having fallen so far from the high standards of its founder. Now Dante perceives another circle of glorious lights enclosing the first, circling with it as if composing a double rainbow and uttering sounds ineffably sweet. In this is represented the Franciscan order, and just as the Dominican, Thomas Aquinas, had extolled the brother order, now Bonaventura, the Francis-can, tells of the high endeavours of St. Dominic to convert heretics to the true faith.

Another denizen of this sphere next comes forward. It is the spirit of the wisest mortal God raised to rule, Solomon. Him Dante questions about the resurections of the body, wondering if the sense organs will not then impose limitations upon the delight of spirits. He is thinking of pain and weariness of body. But Solomon assures him that since body and soul are one, when the spirits are re-invested with the lacking part they will be more pleasing to God, and must therefore themselves joy more. Their senses then will be subject only to delight.

Dante and Beatrice have left the sun, and just as they reach Mars, upon the planet's ruddy glow there appears a white cross on which in an ineffable splendour flashes the figure of Christ. Over and about the limbs of the cross float radiant spirits chanting hymns of victory.

It is here in the sphere of Mars that the souls are manifested who fought and died in Christ's battles, for the cause in which alone men may guiltlessly fight each other.

Passing into the next sphere of heavenly influence, that of Jupiter, they behold upon the white radiance of the planet spirits painting forth in letters of flame the word *Wisdom*; then others, twining round the characters thus formed, shape them into the Roman eagle, symbol of law and justice. In token of how justice is one and undivided, the voices of the rulers who compose the eagle issue as one voice.

From the last planetary sphere, Saturn, from whose seal Temperance is impressed upon the plastic soul, Dante sees reared a ladder of flame leading up beyond the range of his mortal sight—Jacob's ladder. It passes up through into stellar heavens and through the last circle within space and time where is the constellation Gemini, the Twins, the star group presiding over Dante's own birth. Here, after a brief vision splendid, wherein the poet sees Christ and the Virgin Mary, he undergoes a celestial examination in the three underlying and uplifting constituents of salvation: Faith, Hope, Charity. His questioners are, St. Peter, St. James and St. John, and Dante's answers satisfy them well.

He may now ascend farther, and enters the *primum mobile*, from which wide circle beyond the stars space and time take their measure. And here, reflected in the beaming eyes of Beatrice, he sees, revolving round a point of intense light, so fine that the smallest star would seem in comparison to it as large as the moon, the nine concentric circles of the heavenly powers.

Now Beatrice, gazing upon the point of light within the

circling hierarchies of heaven, reads reflected there problems that Dante longs to resolve about the creation.

These questions answered, the point of fire and the circles gradually disappear. Dante and Beatrice enter the empyrean, out of space and out of time. Here it is that Dante beholds the heavenly hosts of saints and angels.

After gazing in mute rapture upon this scene, Dante turns to Beatrice, but finds her gone to assume her seat in the eternal glory of God. Instead he sees by his side to instruct him, Saint Bernard, type of intuition and spiritual insight, he who, while yet on earth, is said to have beheld the Virgin Mary. Fittingly then, it is Saint Bernard who bids Dante look up and gaze upon his adored Lady. Radiant as the rising sun on the pale skies of morning Dante sees her enthroned.

When Bernard has explained to him the divisions in the angelic rose, how half is composed of those who looked *forward* to Christ's coming, the other half of those who looked *back* upon it, now it behoves Dante to supplicate the Virgin Mary that she may obtain for him his ultimate desire, a glimpse of the Trinity, and the Union of Man with God. The prayer is granted, and Dante contemplates the awful mystery of the Godhead:

> My tongue shall utter now, no more
> E'en what remembrance keeps, than could the babe's
> That yet is moisten'd at his mother's breast. . . .
> In that abyss
> Of radiance, clear and lofty, seem'd, methought,
> Three orbs of triple hue, clipt in one bound:
> And, from another, one reflected seem'd,
> As rainbow is from rainbow: and the third
> Seem'd fire, breathed equally from both. O speech!
> How feeble and how faint are thou, to give
> Conception birth. . . .
> For I therein, methought, in its own hue
> Beheld our image painted . . . As one,
> Who versed in geometric lore, would fain
> Measure the circle; and, though pondering long
> And deeply, that beginning, which he needs,
> Finds not: e'en such was I, intent to scan
> The novel wonder, and trace out the form,
> How to the circle fitted, and therein
> How placed: but the flight was not for my wing;
> Had not a flash darted athwart my mind,
> And, in the spleen, unfolded what it sought.
> Here vigour failed the towering fantasy:
> But yet the will roll'd onward, like a wheel
> In even motion, by the love impell'd,
> That moves the sun in heaven and all the stars.

FAUST

By JOHANN WOLFGANG VON GOETHE

This remarkable poem is based on a medieval legend that has attracted many writers before and since. Goethe has transmuted the simple story into a colossal poetic drama, fraught with philosophical symbolism. It consists of two parts, the first of which was published in 1808. This is the subject of the present digest. The second part is very obscure, and relates Faust's further adventures, first as the lover of Helen of Troy and then as a worker for the good of mankind constantly assailed by temptation. In spite of Mephistopheles he eventually attains salvation.

IT is late on Easter Eve. A high, vaulted chamber; the moon behind dusty stained-glass windows dimly illumines the ancient vellum tomes stacked in crooked piles along the smoke-stained walls; here and there its rays pick out instruments of the chemist's art: crucibles, beakers, jars of pickled embryos, heaps of mathematical apparatuses for measuring the heavens and probing into the secrets of matter and motion flicker uncertainly in the pale rays.

Encircled in the orange beam of a reading lamp, a man is sitting at a lectern. His sombre scholar's gown tones with the gloomy surroundings. He is middle-aged and stooped with much study. Only his eyes gazing at the gothic characters of the folio before him glow with the fire of the searcher after truth, the insatiable, devouring fire of the spirit that will not be deceived, that will not retreat and cannot stay, that must still go questing through all appearances towards the core, the secret principle of all things living.

It is Faust, the German master-scholar, reverenced far and wide for his learning and his goodness.

But on this Easter Eve his heart is bitter. A quarter of a century of incessant toil has shown him the vanity of human knowledge. His eyes leave the printed page and rove over his chamber, that musty storehouse of the human brain's researches. He muses:

> Alas! I have explored
> Philosophy, and Law, and Medicine;
> And over deep Divinity have pored,
> Studying with ardent and laborious zeal:
> And here I am at last, a very fool,
> . . . to feel that nothing can be known!
> This is a thought that burns into my heart.

It seems to Faust that all these years of toil have been vainly spent; for, wrapped in his fruitless studies, immured amongst his books, he has never yet *lived*. Yet by " living " he does not mean joining in the so-called pleasures of the world, loving, laughing, dancing; in any case, he is too old, his chance has passed. No, he would not go back. But there is a way to life, to the innermost participation with the forces of nature themselves, to communion without words, to super-human life. And that way lies through the very book before him there—the magical system of Nostradamus, the alchemist. Why, he asks himself, to have puzzled over the cabalistic signs, the mystic spells, and yet to put them to no use?

He turns the leaves and chances on a mystic diagram. In a bright flash of intuitive illumination it seems to him that the secret of the universe is revealed to his inner eye; it seems that he sees the whole stupendous rhythmic unity of part answering to part, the everlasting reciprocity of things, the endless creation. And yet the spiritual revelation brings its aftermath of despair. He feels overwhelmed by his vision of the universe and the spectacle of illimitable nature, forth-welling fountain of life. No, though his parched heart pant for it, he cannot attain unity with the source of all things.

Then, turning over the pages, he comes across another sign, a figure that fills him with a wild hope—the sign of the Spirit of Earth. With this spirit he feels surging in his breast a tempestuous affinity, sweeping him to oneness with the power that threads through human hearts, winding the close texture of joy and suffering, weaving the design of Deity through earth and all her creatures.

Summoning all the resources of his long-sought knowledge, Faust utters the spell and summons the spirit into his presence. He is terrified by its awful splendour, inconceivable to human mind. But, overcoming his fear, he proudly challenges the spirit, claiming himself as its equal:

> Spirit, whose presence circles the wide earth,
> How near akin to thine I feel my nature!
> *Spirit* Man, thou art like those beings which thy mind
> Can image, not like me!

The Spirit of Earth vanishes, and his words, echoing in Faust's brain, sound the death-knoll of his last hopes from life. He may by a supreme effort of mystic contemplation stand upon the brink of ultimate knowledge; he cannot pass beyond the goal of ordinance. There is only one other way, onwards:

> Am I not like the gods?—Alas! I tremble,
> Feeling imprest upon my soul the thought
> Of the mean worm, whose nature I resemble.
> 'Tis dust, and lives in dust, and the chance tread
> Crushes the wretched reptile into nought.
> *(He looks round the book-strewn room.)*
> . . . Shall I find here the cure I ask,
> Resume the edifying task
> Of reading, in a thousand pages,
> That care-worn man has, in all ages,
> Sowed Vanity to reap Despair?
> That one, mayhap, has here and there
> Been less unhappy?

So Faust muses. As his mind seizes and dismisses as worthless every approach to Nature's secret, his eye rests on an antique goblet standing at his elbow. He addresses it, saluting the unknown shores whither its deadly contents will take him.

> I grasp thee—faithful friend art thou:
> Already do I feel the strife
> That preyed upon my powers of life
> Calmed into peace; and now—and now
> The swell that troubled the clear spring
> Of my vexed spirit, ebbs away;
> Outspread, like ocean, Life and Day
> Shine with a glow of welcoming;
> Calm at my feet the glorious mirror lies,
> And tempts to far-off shores, with smiles from other skies!

He is about to drain the poison when, silvery clear through the still air, ring out the joyful Easter bells and a chorus of pure young voices chanting a paschal hymn. There well up in him long-forgotten feelings from childhood's days. He is a boy again, and his heart is buoyed with the same exultation that once sent him roving through the spring fields, shedding tears of gladness. Tears stand in his eyes again as he pushes the goblet from him and stands listening to the glad tidings chiming over the housetops of the old town.

On Easter day, Faust and his favourite pupil, Wagner, an eager, intelligent boy in whom Faust sees his own lost youth, wander abroad among the festive crowd. They pass as it were through a cross-section of everyday life, the interests and types that compose it: students hurrying towards inns for heavy beers and light kisses; pretty wantons, staid bourgeois misses longing to lose their respectability, if only they should not lose prospective husbands by it; middle-aged bourgeois men encouraging wars abroad so long as there is peace at home; soldiers singing rollicking ballads of love and glory on the battlefield; beggars to whom holidays are harvest days; peasants dancing a round.

Gazing at the gay throng crowding through the meadows and gliding in boat-loads down the river, Faust, in his gush of holiday life, feels that he, too, is a man. Through all the years of his seclusion that first and simplest pleasure had escaped him.

But the feeling of human companionship does not last. It is the young Wagner who breaks the spell as he prattles rapturously about the transporting delights of learning, of the noble quest of knowledge for its own sake. Such talk reminds Faust of the agonizing *impasse* to which his own labours have brought him; of the irreconcilable opposites in his own nature.

Then Faust invokes the spirits of the middle air, hovering between earth and Heaven, calls upon them to bear him away— it matters not where, so it be to a more varied, a richer life. Wagner tries to dissuade his master, warning him that such spirits are evil. But Faust is not listening; he has noticed something:

> *Faustus* Do you see that black dog, where through the green blades
> Of the soft springing corn, and the old stubble,
> He runs, just glancing by them for a moment?
> *Wagner*   Why, nothing
> But a rough poodle-dog, who, in the way
> Of dogs, is searching for his master's footsteps.
> *Faustus* Do you observe how in wide serpent circles
> He courses round us? nearer and yet nearer
> Each turn, and if my eyes do not deceive me
> Sparkles of fire whirl where his foot hath touched.

Wagner sees nothing extraordinary and convinces Faust, who determines to take the creature home and keep him as a pet.

Back in his chamber, Faust composes himself to a suitable study; he begins to translate a passage from the New Testament—" In the beginning was the Word ". As he struggles to get at the meaning, rejecting one term after another as he endeavours to interpret the Creation, the dog keeps on growling. At last Faust realizes it is no ordinary dog, but an evil spirit. He tries to exorcise it with his magic art and at last, when he threatens to apply the most potent spell of all, the dog trans-

Hagen, The Traitor

A scene from the " Nibelungenlied "

Mephistopheles appears to Faust

Faust and Marguerite

Scenes from " Faust "

forms itself and Mephistopheles comes forward in the dress of a
travelling scholar. He asks Faust if he can serve him in any
way and introduces himself.

Mephistopheles then tempts Faust, representing himself as
the purveyor of all the world's pleasures:

> *Faustus* I am too old to yield myself to pleasure
> Too young to have the appetite departed.
> What can earth give me now? " Refrain, refrain ! "
> This is the everlasting song—the chime
> Perpetually jingling in the ears,
> And with hoarse accents every hour repeats it. . . .
> The in-dwelling spirit,
> Whose temple is my heart, who rules its powers,
> Can stir the bosom to its lowest depths,
> But has no power to move external nature;
> And therefore is existence burdensome,
> And death desirable, and life detested.

And now, though no promise of Mephistopheles deceives Faust,
he decides, since he seems to be a slave in any case, to accept
the offer made him : Mephistopheles to serve him in this world ;
he to serve Mephistopheles *afterwards*.

As Faust goes into his antechamber to prepare for their
journey through the world's pleasures, Mephistopheles muses
on the nature of his victim, on " the eager, restless mind " whose
imagination, ever pressing on, anticipates all earthly pleasures
and renders them insipid even before they are tasted. " And
though," he concludes, " he had not sold it to the devil, a soul
like his could not escape from evil."

They go forth, and in the witches' kitchen, where the grey
apes sit ceaselessly beside a huge cauldron, stirring the Hell's
Broth, Faust at one burning draught regains his lost youth.
Mephistopheles smiles, " With this draught in him," he
murmurs, " he will meet a Helena in every street."

A Street

> *Faustus (to Margaret passing on)* Fair lady may I offer you my arm;
> And will you suffer me to see you home?
> *Margaret* I am no lady—and I am not fair.
> I want no guide to show me the way home.
> (*Disengages herself and exit. Enter Mephistopheles.*)
> *Faust* Hearken here, sir, get me the girl; and fast.
> *Mephistopheles* What—she? She was but now at church
> At her confession—I was there.
> And, hid by the confession chair,
> Was listening to her from my lurch.
> Poor thing—she is all innocence—

Had nothing in the world to tell!
With such to meddle is not well.
Her purity is a defence
That leaves the tempter no pretence.
Upon this child I have no power.

Faust   She's past fourteen, if she's an hour!

Mephistopheles   My friend, give up this hopeless game.

Faust   She must, this very night be mine:
You and I part if you decline

Mephistopheles   Now, not to take or give offence,
Believe me, here all violence
Is useless—in a little while
The damsel may be won by guile.

Faust   Make me out some present.

Mephistopheles   Presents so soon! this promises
Speedy success—they all love dress!
Oh, I know many a place of pleasure
Where such things are, and many a treasure
Buried of old, and soon will find
Some lure to win the young thing's mind.

> *Evening (a neat little room).*

Margaret   I would give something now to know
The gentleman who met me, though;
He had a proud and princely air,
    Is one of the nobility;
Look on his brow, you read it there,
·And if he were not, he would stare
With somewhat more civility.   (*Exit.*)

> (*Enter Mephistopheles and Faust.*)

Faust (looking round)   The spirit of contentment, maiden dear,
Is breathing in thy very atmosphere;
I feel it sway me while I linger here.
The sense of neatness, felt in everything,
Speaks with a mother's voice, and bids thee spread
The little table with its covering,
The floor with clean sand crackling to the tread.
Everywhere round the hand beloved I trace.
That makes a paradise of any place. . . .

> But thou, accursed, what art thou?
> What brings thee to her chamber now?
> . . . should she now return and meet
> Thee here, how would the boaster shrink
> Into the coward! at her feet
> In what confusion sink!

While Faust is meditating, sitting at his beloved's bed, Mephistopheles comes in with a casket of jewels and lays it in the wardrobe. They leave the room and shortly afterwards Margaret comes in and starts to undress, singing an old song. When she goes to put her clothes away she finds the casket and tries on the jewels before the mirror.

At last, by winning the goodwill of Margaret's friend and neighbour, Martha, Mephistopheles arranges a meeting in Martha's garden, and while he keeps the neighbour engaged pretending to be a possible suitor, Faust learns from Margaret of her simple daily round, her joys and sorrows. He asks her to forgive the liberty he took in addressing her in the street. She owns that she was vexed to feel she could not be so angry with him as decency required.

Faust has fallen in love, deeply, sincerely, with this innocent young girl. His love purifies him and engenders new depths of feeling for nature in all its multifarious aspects. What the skill of scientist and magician could not penetrate into, what no proud intellectual demands could obtain, is yielded simply to him now. And in a forest cavern where he has retired to abandon himself to the sublimity of nature, he offers a prayer of thanksgiving for his release from the bondage of thought. Yet there is another bondage that subjects Faust, and, go where he will, the reminder of it is ever present.

> Alas! even now I feel MAN's joys must be
> Imperfect ever. The ecstatic bliss,
> Which lifts me near and nearer to the gods;
> This is thy gift; but with it thou hast given,
> Inseparably linked, this vile associate,
> Whom I abominate, but cannot part:
> Cold, insolent, malicious, he contrives
> To make me to myself contemptible;
> And with a breath will scatter into nothing
> All these high gifts; with what officious zeal
> He fans my breast into a raging flame
> Of passion, to possess that perfect form
> Of loveliness! Thus, from desire I pass
> On to enjoyment, and, uneasy still,
> Even in enjoyment languish for desire!

As Faust muses thus, Mephistopheles appears and begins with subtle art to lure him away from his solitary sojourn, conjuring up to his mind a picture of Margaret, sitting alone, pining for her lover.

So Faust returns and meeting Margaret in Martha's garden he arranges to enter her chamber that night. He gives her a drug to make her mother sleep soundly. She cannot refuse him. :

But the very night their love is consummated, the first act is played of the tragedy of reprisal. The drug that was to have made Margaret's mother sleep more soundly—a potion supplied by Mephistopheles—is in fact poison. Margaret's mother dies.

The second act follows swiftly.   As Faust and his companion
walk at midnight under Margaret's window, Faust with another
casket of jewels for his love, Mephistopheles with a guitar
singing a coarse serenade, Margaret's soldier brother, Valentine, home from the wars, accosts them.   The rumour of his
sister's shame is on everyone's lips.   He dashes the guitar from
the serenader's hands and provokes a duel.   With Mephistopheles' aid Faust wounds Valentine mortally.   Margaret
and several neighbours rush out.   The dying soldier, pointing
at Margaret, breathes out his life in a terrible recrimination:

> Already do I see the day,
> When all, with loathing, turn away
> From thee, as from a plague-struck corse,
> I see the gnawings of remorse:
> . . . Abandoned outcast of the street,
> How wilt thou bear their eyes to meet?
> Never, as once, the golden chain
> To wear in pride—never again!
> Never again, that fairest face,
> To shine at church, in the high place,
> And never more the dance to grace;
> No more in modest pride to deck
> With frills of snowy lace thy neck;
> But in some filthy nook to lie,
> 'Mong strumpets live—'mong beggars die;
> And find, for thee, heart-broken one,
> Though God has mercy, Man has none.

In an anguish of sorrow and repentance, Margaret attends
service at the cathedral.   But the Evil Spirit stands behind her
as the Choir chants the *Dies Irae*:

> *Evil Spirit*   How changed is everything
> With thee, poor Margaret,
> Since when, still full of innocence,
> Thou to this very altar
> Dids't come, and from the little old thumbed prayer-book
> Didst lisp the murmured prayers;
> Half with the children out at play,
> In a child's happy fancies, thy young heart,
> And half with God in heaven.

That night, the 1st of May, has been eagerly awaited by
Mephistopheles; it is Walpurgis Night, where, on the craggy,
wooded heights of the Brocken, all the powers and the instruments of evil assemble for their sabbat dance.   There and there
only, Mephistopheles says, does life prove to be of something
worth.   He takes Faust with him.   Here they see and assist
in a nightmare phantasmagoria of all the evil in the world—

thoughts, theories, persons, things, impulses, acts, all are indiscriminately mingled in the hellish dance. Though the sabbat lasts only a few hours, it represents a change in Faust that could only have occurred over a longer period.

After the orgy he learns what Mephistopheles has hidden from him. Margaret has given birth to a child—the last victim but one of the fourfold tragedy Faust's sin had engendered. Margaret, in a delirium, kills the child to conceal her shame. They find it and she is sentenced to death. In her native town where she languishes in the condemned cell, a warrant is out for Faust's arrest. Notwithstanding this, as soon as he hears of Margaret's plight, remorse and pity kindling out of the ashes of his passion, Faust commands Mephistopheles to help him rescue Margaret from the prison.

> (*Margaret's voice heard singing a mad song.*)
> *Faustus* (*opening the cell door*)   She feels not that her love is listening
> Hears but the chains that clank, and the straw rustling.
> *Margaret* (*hiding her face in the straw of her bed*)
> Woe! woe! they come!—Death, bitter death!
> *Faustus* (*in a low voice*)   Hush! hush! 'tis I who come to rescue thee!
> *Margaret* (*rolling herself at his feet*)   Art thou a man?   Have pity upon me!
> *Faustus*   Hush! hush! these screams and shrieks will wake the keepers.
> (*He takes hold of the chains to unlock them.*)
> *Margaret* (*throwing herself on her knees to him*)
> Savage, who gave this cruel power to thee?
> It is not more than midnight now—have mercy!
> Is it too long a time to wait till morn?
> And I am still so young—so very young!
> And must I die so soon?—and I was fair—
> And I was fair, and that was my undoing.
> Oh, if my love were here—but he is gone—
> Torn is my garland—scattered all its flowers—
> Oh, do not grasp me with such violence—
> Ah, spare me! sure I have not injured thee:
> Let me not weep and pray to thee in vain!
> Spare me—I never saw thy face before.
> *Faustus*   Thy lover, Margaret, kneels at thy feet;
> He comes to open these sad prison gates.
> *Margaret*   Let us kneel down, and call upon the saints.
> See! see! beneath us hell boils up—the devil
> Is raving there below in hideous rage!
> *Faustus* (*in a low voice*)   Margaret!—Margaret!
> *Margaret* (*with eager attention*)
> Where is he? Where? I heard my own love's voice.
> (*Springs up—her irons fall off.*)
> Now am I free, none, none shall keep me from him.
> I'll clasp his neck, will lean upon his bosom;
> I heard him call; he's standing on the threshold;

I heard him call the name of Margaret;
Amid the noises and the howls of hell,
And threats and taunts, and laughs of devilish scorn,
I heard my own love's voice—his loving voice!

Faustus   'Tis I.

Margaret   'Tis thou—oh, tell me so once more!
                          (*Presses him to her bosom.*)
'Tis he, 'tis he—my pangs, where are they now?
Dungeon, and chains, and scaffold, where are they?
'Tis thou, and thou hast come to rescue me.
I am already free: look—there's the street
Where we first met—where first I saw my love—
And yonder is the cheerful garden, smiling,
Where I and Martha used to wait for thee.

Faustus   Come, come with me.

Margaret   Oh, stay a little while—
Some moments more—I love to stay with thee!

Faustus   Haste, haste! ah, linger not,
One moment more—a moment's lingering now
Will cost—we cannot tell how much.

Margaret   How! what!
And hast thou then forgot that kiss of thine,
My love? So short a time away, and yet
To have forgotten all those sighs of love!
Why do I feel so sad upon thy neck?
Oh, there was once a time when all thy words,
And every glance of thine, seemed heaven to me.
And warmly didst thou press me to thy heart!
Oh, let me feel once more that loved embrace!
Alas! thy lips are cold and dumb—ah, where,
Where is thy love? Who robbed me of thy love?

Faustus   Come, come—take courage, follow me, my love.
I love thee with unutterable love;
But follow me—this one—this one request.

Margaret   . . . Knowest thou whom thou art delivering? . . .
My mother, I have murdered her—my child,
I drowned my child—and was it not thy child,
Thy child and mine? Yes, thine! And thou art here,
I scarcely can believe it is thyself.
Give me thy hand—it is not then a dream;
Thine own dear hand. Oh, God! his hand is moist—
Wipe, wipe it off! methought it felt like blood!
What hast thou done? Ah, sheath thy bloody sword;
Ah, hide it from me.

Faustus   Think not of the past;
That which is done, is done. Come, this delay
Is death to me!

Margaret   No; thou must yet remain,
Till I describe to thee the graves, which thou
To-morrow must see made: the best place give
To my poor mother; near her lay my brother;
And by their side, a little space away,
Place me; and on my right breast lay my child;

No other will lie with me in that bed!
To nestle down in quiet side by side
To thee—oh what a happy thing it was—
A happy thing that never more can be.
I feel as if I forced myself on thee,
And that thou wert repelling my embrace;
And yet thou art the same—and yet thy looks
Are good and kind, as they have ever been.

Faustus   Oh, if thou feelest that 'tis I, come, come.
Margaret   And then, whate'er I do, at last they'll seize me.
Faustus   Thy life's at stake.
One step, and thou art free.
Margaret   Oh, that we had left yon hill behind!
See there, my mother sitting on a stone—
Icy-cold comes a dead hand on my temples.
My mother there is sitting on a stone,
And her grey head is trembling, and her eyes
Close, and she now has ceased to nod; her head
Looks heavy, and she sleeps too long—too long—
Oh, when she sank to sleep how blest we were!
It was a happy time!
      (*Faust tries to force her away.*)
Touch me not; no, I will not suffer violence:
Seize me not with that murderer's grasp; whate'er
I did was done for thee, my love.   I did
Everything my love asked me, willingly.

Faustus   Day dawns—oh, hasten hence, my love! my love!
Margaret   Day! yes, 'tis day, the last, the judgment-day;
My bridal day it should have been; tell none
That thou hast been with poor weak Margaret.
Alas! my garland is already withered;
We'll meet again, but not at dances, love . . .

Faustus   Oh, that I had never been born!
Mephistopheles (*appearing at the door*)   Away, or you are lost;
My horses shiver in the chilling breeze
Of the grey morning.
Margaret   What shape is that which rises from the earth?
'Tis he, 'tis he, oh, send him from this place;
What wants he here?   Oh, what can bring him here?
Why does he tread on consecrated ground?
He comes for me.

Faustus   Oh, thou shalt live, my love.
Margaret   Upon the judgment-throne of God, I call;
On God I call in humble supplication.
Mephistopheles (*to Faustus*)   Come, or I leave thee here to share her fate.
Margaret   Father of heaven, have mercy on thy child.
Ye angels, holy hosts, keep watch around me.
Henry—I am afraid to look at thee.
Mephistopheles   Come—she is judged!
Voice (*from above*)   Is saved.
Mephistopheles (*to Faustus*)   Hither to me!
            (*Disappears with Faustus.*)
Voice (*from within dying away*)   Henry! Henry!

THE ODYSSEY

By HOMER

*So little is known about the life of Homer that some doubt is
cast by certain scholars upon his very existence. He is,
however, generally accepted to be the traditional author of
the " Iliad " (which describes the Trojan war) and the
" Odyssey". Even in translation the lofty poetic conceptions
shine through and reveal why this should be regarded as part
of the great literature of the world.*

Now after the fall of Troy the Greeks returned, each to his
own home, all save crafty Odysseus. For he had incurred the vengeance of Poseidon, and the sea-god swore
never to let him see again his home in distant Ithaca, or
embrace again his wife, the chaste Penelope. So for ten years
she and her son Telemachus waited in vain for Odysseus'
homecoming.

In Ithaca all thought Odysseus dead, and the princes and
nobles from all the islands round came and dwelt at his house
and sought the hand of Penelope. She would have none of
them, but they stayed by her, feasting and making merry,
until she should at last be driven to make a choice. Telemachus and the faithful servants of Odysseus they hated, and
determined to destroy.

Now all this time Odysseus was a prisoner on the island of
the Nymph Calypso. She loved him and offered him immortality if he stayed with her, but he cared nothing for her gift,
and sat all day on the sea-shore, gazing on the waves and
straining his soul with tears for Penelope and Ithaca. And so
he pined on Calypso's isle for the space of eight years.

Poseidon remained relentlessly his foe but the other gods,
especially the grey-eyed Athene, took pity on the wanderer,
and while the sea-god was away in Ethiopia ordered the Nymph
to release her prisoner and set him on a raft that might bear
him to Ithaca. At first Odysseus was much afeared, but then
he made himself sails, took store of provisions and set out across
the sea.

For four days all was well; on the fifth Poseidon, returning from the Ethiopians, saw him on the raft and was filled with anger. In rage he gathered the clouds and troubled the waters of the deep, stirring them with his trident; and he roused all the winds and set them fighting in the sky, and he raised gigantic waves. Then were Odysseus' knees loosened with fear, and he cried out: "Oh wretched man that I am! Would to god that I had died beneath the spears of the Trojans, rather than be overtaken, forgotten and alone, by a pitiful death!" Even as he spoke, a great wave smote down on him, and brake the mast in the midst and cast him into the waters. But he forgot not the raft for all his wretched plight, but seized and held to it in the tumult of the sea.

But then Ino, the sea nymph, saw and took pity on him, and gave him part of her veil which, if he wrapped it round him, would bear him safe to the coast of the Phaeacians. And as a vast wave, more terrible than any before, struck the raft and scattered it into fragments like a heap of parched rusks, he wrapped the veil round him and was swept forth into the deep. As he was whirled through the waters he clutched at a rock, but the backwash leapt on him and dragged him back again into the sea. And as when the cuttlefish is dragged forth from his chamber, the many pebbles clinging to his suckers, even so was the skin stripped from his strong hand against the rock, and the great wave closed over him. But at length, by the help of the gods, he was cast up on shore, and a great stream of sea-water gushed out through his mouth and nostrils, and he lay swooning without breath or speech. So he lay until his strength returned to him. Then, climbing up the slope from the shore, he lay down between two bushes and covered himself in a pile of fallen leaves.

The chief of the Phaeacians had a daughter called Nausicaa, and to her Athene appeared in a dream, and bade her rise the next morning and take the garments of her father and brothers and go down to the sea-shore to wash them there. So the next day mules were yoked to a high cart and she and her maidens filled it with the garments to be washed, and her mother gave her a basket containing all manner of food, and a bottle filled with wine. And her mother gave her soft olive oil also, that she and her maidens might anoint themselves when they had bathed.

Now when they had washed the garments, and bathed, and eaten their meal, Nausicaa and her maidens threw aside their clothes and fell to playing at ball. And at length, just as they were about to cease their game, Athene guided the arm of the princess so that she missed the girl to whom she threw and cast the ball into the water, at which they all raised a piercing cry. Then Odysseus awoke, heard the girls' voices and sallied out from under the bush, holding a leafy bough before him to hide his nakedness.   At the sight of him, naked and all crusted with salt sea foam, the maidens fled screaming.   But Nausicaa fled not but stood firm facing him.

Odysseus considered whether he should clasp the knees of the lovely maiden and so make his prayer, or should stand as he was and beseech her with smooth words from a distance, begging her to lead him to the town and give him raiment.   And it seemed better to him to stand apart, lest the maiden should be angry if he touched her knees.   So he stood and with sweet and cunning words explained his plight.

When Nausicaa heard his story, she pitied him, and gave him garments, and led him to the town and to the palace of her father Alcinous.   And Alcinous received him kindly, and feasted him and bade him tell his story.   And Odysseus told all that had befallen him since the taking of Troy:

" I am Odysseus, son of Laertes, who am in all men's minds for all manner of wiles, and my fame reaches to heaven.   These, then, were the troubles of my journeyings which Zeus laid on me as I came from Troy.

" The wind that bore me from Troy brought me to the land of the Cicones, and I sacked their city and slew the people, and divided their wives and goods amongst my men.   Had we directly sailed on all would have been well, but the others would not hearken to me, but killed many sheep by the beach and stayed on land to feast.   Meanwhile Cicones gathered from all the country round and fell on us, and we did not escape to sea without much loss.

" Then for nine days I was borne by dangerous winds over the teeming deep, and on the tenth day we set foot on the land of the lotus-eaters.   I chose out three of my men and sent them as ambassadors to the people of the land, and the lotus-eaters received them kindly and gave them the lotus to eat.   Now whoever eats the honey-sweet fruit of the lotus has no more wish to come back, but there he choses to abide, ever feeding on the lotus and forgetful of his homeward way.   Therefore I had to drag my three men back to the ships, weeping and sore against their will, and bind them beneath the benches.   And I commanded the rest of the company to get with speed on the ships and row away, lest they too should eat of the lotus and be unmindful of returning.

" Then we sailed onwards and came to the land of the Cyclopes, fierce giants with but a single eye in the centre of their forehead." And we anchored off the island and I went on shore with twelve men only. Not far from the sea we found a monstrous cave, wherein were many rich cheeses and much milk in vessels. And we sat down and feasted, and waited for the master of the place that he might give us the strangers' gift.

" In the evening he returned, a man gigantic of stature and terrible to behold. And he drove his fat flocks into the great cavern for safety in the night, and sealed up the door with a stone so great and weighty that a score of carts could not have raised it from the ground. At length he espied us, and in a voice so deep and huge that it filled us with terror, said:

" ' Strangers, who are ye? Whence sail ye over the seas? '

" And I answered,

" ' Sir, we are Achaeans wandering from Troy, and we come to beg you to give us hospitality, and give us the welcome that is due to strangers, in the name of Zeus, the protector of strangers.' So I spake, but he answered out of his pitiless heart,

" ' Thou art witless, my stranger, to think that we pay heed to Zeus or the gods, for we are children of Poseidon and better men than they.'

" Then without more words he sprang up and laid hands upon two of my fellows, and dashed them furiously to the earth so that their brains spilled forth on to the ground. Then he cut their bodies into pieces and made ready his supper. So he ate even as a mountain lion, devouring entrails and flesh and bones with their marrow. And we wept and called on Zeus when we saw his foul deeds, but could do nothing. And when the Cyclops had filled his huge maw with human flesh, he lay down and slept, stretched out amongst his sheep.

" At first I thought to draw my sharp sword and stab him in the breast where the midriff holds the liver, feeling for the place with my hand. But second thoughts withheld me, for so should we all surely have perished. For we should not have been able to roll away with our hands the great stone that blocked the door. So we wept together and awaited the dawn.

" Now when the early dawn shone forth, the Cyclops kindled his fire and milked his flocks, and seized two more of our men and made another meal. Then he moved away the great stone and drove out his flocks, and replaced the stone as before. Then, with a loud whoop, the Cyclops went towards the hills; but I was left plotting vengeance in the depth of my heart.

"And this was the plan that seemed best to me. There lay in the cave a great club of the Cyclops, a club of green olive wood, the size of the mast of a twenty-oared ship. I cut off from it about a fathom's length, and bade the others sharpen it down to a point and harden it in the fire. Then I hid it away beneath the dung which was lying in great heaps about the cave. Then I bid my men cast lots amongst them, which of them should join me in the enterprise, and plunge the stake into his eye when sleep overcame him. And the lot fell upon the four whom I would myself have chosen, and I appointed myself the fifth.

"In the evening Cyclops returned with his sheep, and as before he set the great stone in the door, and as before he seized two more of us for his supper. Then I went up to him and proffered him a bowl of the strong wine we had with us, saying,

"'Take and drink, sir, after thy feast of man's meat, and haply thou mayst take pity on me.'

"Then he took the cup and drained it off, and answered,

"'This is very nectar and ambrosia that you give me. Tell me now your name that I may remember you with a stranger's gift.'

"Then I handed him again the dark wine and said, 'Cyclops, my name is No-one, and No-one all men call me. Now forget not the stranger's gift that is due to me.'

"Then straightway he answered me out of his pitiless heart, 'No-one, I shall eat you last out of all your fellows; that is my stranger's gift to you.' Then, overcome by the wine, he sank backwards and lay with his face upturned. And, heavy with wine, he vomited forth fragments of human flesh.

"Then I thrust the stake into the ashes of the fire, and it began to glow terribly. And we drew it out and thrust it into his eye, and turned it about as when a man bores a ship's beam with a drill. And the breath of the flame singed his eyelids and brows all about, and the ball of the eye burnt away and crackled in the flame. And as when a smith dips iron in cold water, so did his eye hiss round the stake of olive.

"The Cyclops raised a great and terrible cry so that the rocks rang, and we fled from him to the farthest corners of the cave as he plucked out the stake and cast it from him, and called with a loud voice on the Cyclopes who dwelt in the neighbouring caves. And when they heard his cry they flocked round from every side, and, gathering outside the entrance of the cavern, asked him what ailed him and who was attacking him. And he answered,

" 'My friends, No-one is injuring me, No-one has done me harm!' And they answered, 'If no one is hurting thee it is a sickness sent by Poseidon, and we cannot aid thee.' And they went away and left him.

" But the Cyclops, groaning with pain, groped his way to the door of the cave and moved away the great stone, and sat across the entrance with arms outstretched to see if any tried to escape. So we quietly went to the sheep that were in the cave and clung beneath their bellies grasping the strong fleece. And so we passed the Cyclops, he feeling the backs of his sheep while we hung beneath in safety.

" As soon as we were free of the cave we drove the sheep to the ships and swiftly embarked. And when we had gone some distance from the shore I called out to Cyclops and taunted him. But he was mightily angered and broke off a great piece of the hill and flung it where he heard my voice, and the ship was near sunk by the mighty rock. But I, foolhardy, called out again taunting him, and declaring that it was Odysseus, son of Laertes, who had done this thing to him. Then he called upon Poseidon to avenge him, and the god heard him. And we sailed onward stricken in our hearts.

" Then we came to the island of Æolus, Keeper of the Winds. And he gave me an ox-hide bag wherein he bound all the contrary winds, and he made it fast with a silver thong that not the faintest breath might escape. Then he sent forth the west wind to blow for me and bear us safely home. For nine days we sailed, and on the tenth my native land came in sight, and we already beheld men tending the beacon fires. And from joy and weariness I fell asleep.

" Meanwhile my crew held converse together, and said that I was bringing home gold and silver in the bag given me by Æolus. And they resolved to see what was in the bag, and loosed the thong, and blasts poured out and swept us back to the high seas. And I was heavy of heart.

" And after many days we came to Circe's Isle. And I divided my men into two parties, leading one myself and giving the other to the valiant Eurylochus, who led his band towards

Circe's palace. All around the place roamed wolves and lions, yet they offered no harm to the men, but frisked and fawned around them, wagging their long tails like friendly dogs. And Circe came forth and opened the shining doors and bid them enter, and all heedlessly followed her, save Eurylochus who suspected treason. So Circe led them in, and set them on high chairs and served them with wine mixed with strange drugs to make them forget their homes and countries. And when they had drunk the wine she smote them with a wand and they became swine while retaining the minds of men. And she penned them weeping in sties and flung them acorns and mast, whereon wallowing swine do always batten.

" And when the men did not return from the house, Eurylochus ran back to the rest of us and told us how they had vanished. Then I took my sharp sword and made for the palace. But on the way Hermes of the golden sandals stopped me and told me what had befallen my men and gave me a herb to make me immune from Circe's spells. And he told me that when she raised her wand to strike me, I should draw my sword on her, and then she would ask for mercy and become my friend. And so it befell, and she lifted her spell from the men and they were taller and goodlier than before. And we dwelt for a year with the goddess on her island.

" And when the year had passed I besought Circe to let us go, and she consented on condition that I go to the borders of Hades and learn my way from the spirit of Tiresias, the blind soothsayer. And my heart was heavy within me at the thought, but I gave my promise and we set out. Even then we did not all go safe away. There was one Elpenor, the youngest of us all, not very valiant in war nor steadfast in mind. He was lying apart from my men on the roof of Circe's dwelling, heavy with wine. Now when he heard the voices of his fellows he was minded to descend by the ladder, but missed his footing and broke his neck at the bottom of the house, and his spirit went down to Hades. And we set out as Circe had bade us.

" Now we came to the limits of the world, to the place Circe had ordained for us, where all was ever shrouded in mist and cloud. And I dug a trench and poured in blood of sacrificial sheep, and the spirits of the dead smelt the blood and flocked to draw near it. Brides, and youths unwed there were, and old men of many and evil days, and girls yet fresh at heart; and many there were wounded with bronze-tipped spears, men slain in fight with their bloody mail about them. And I held my sharp sword above the trench and suffered not the strengthless dead to approach it until I had word with Tiresias.

And first came the soul of Elpenor, our companion, whom we had left unburied in the hall of Circe, and I promised to return and burn his body and build him a mound on the sea-shore. Then came the soul of my dear mother who I had left alive when I departed for Troy and I wept to see her, yet even so I suffered her not to approach the blood before the soul of Tiresias. At last came the spirit of Tiresias, with a golden sceptre in its hand; and I put up my sword and he drank the dark blood in the trench, and prophesied.

" ' I see before you many woes, yet even so you and your company shall return home safely if, when you come to the Isle of Thrinacia, where graze the golden herds of Helios, you restrain your spirits and do the herds no hurt. But if you hurt them, I foresee ruin for your ship and your men, and though you yourself may return home unharmed, it shall be in evil case and sorrows shall greet you in your house, and violence. And from the sea shall your own death come, even in your old age, and people shall dwell happily around you.'

" And I saw all the sorrows of hell. I saw Tantalus straining to drink the water that fled from him, and Sisyphus vainly toiling to roll a great stone to the top of a hill, and Agamemnon bewailing his cruel murder. And at length I fled from the place back to the ship, and we set sail to a fair breeze.

" Now Circe had warned us of the Sirens' voice and their field of flowers, and as soon as we drew near to their island I heated wax and with it stopped the ears of all my men. And I bade them tie me to the mast and for no reason release me until the isle was passed. And as soon as we drew near the Sirens called me with a sweet voice and begged me stay with them a while. And my heart was moved at their voice, and I signalled to my men to untie me. But when Eurylochus saw it, he came with more cords and bound me still faster, nor did he untie me until we had passed out of hearing.

" Not far on I saw smoke and a great wave and heard the sea roaring, and on the one side lay Scylla and on the other Charybdis. And Charybdis sucked down the salt sea-water and belched it forth terribly, like a boiling cauldron, and the rocks around roared horribly, and my men were seized with fear. And on the other side Scylla leant out and caught six of my men, and bore them writhing to the top of the cliff, and there she devoured them as they shrieked and stretched out their hands to me in their death-struggle. It was the most dreadful thing my eyes have seen in all my travail in the paths of the sea.

"When we had escaped the terrors of the Straits we came to the island of Thrinacia where grazed the herds of Helios, and I warned my men of Tiresias' prophecy, and they promised to leave the kine unharmed. But while I was away from them hunger and the evil counsel of Eurylochus incited them, and they killed some of the kine and ate them. Then great Helios was extremely wroth and besought Zeus to punish these insolent men who had killed his cattle, and Zeus promised to avenge him. And when we set sail, a fearful storm smote the ship and the waters followed it up, and all save I were drowned. But I was cast ashore on the isle of Calypso and dwelt with the goddess these eight years. But this you know, so why should I further rehearse it?" He ceased; and silence fell on Alcinous and all the noble Phaeacians.

Now when the noble Alcinous heard the tale, he pitied great Odysseus and set him on a swift ship and bore him to Ithaca. And as he lay sleeping on the shore, grey-eyed Athene came to him and told him of the woe that the wooers did in his house, and bade him disguise himself as an old beggar. And so it was done.

Then Odysseus fared forth from the haven by a rough track and came to the house of Eumaeus the swineherd who loved him but who knew him not in his beggar's guise, and Eumaeus entertained him kindly. And it happened that Telemachus, son of Odysseus, came to the hut and Odysseus revealed himself to him and Telemachus was much rejoiced. But he kept his beggar's guise, for he plotted much cunning to overthrow the suitors and regain his own.

That night the wooers feasted in Odysseus' house, and Odysseus came and sat by the door and begged for meat. And as he entered he passed Argos, his old dog, lying sick and full of vermin. And when Argos saw his master, he knew him and wagged his tail. But the others in the hall saw nought but an old man who begged bread from them. And all the suitors gave to Odysseus save only Antinous, the greatest of them all, and he reviled Odysseus and smote him with a stool. But he said nothing, brooding vengeance in his heart.

Now Athene put it into the heart of Penelope to make an end of her long waiting, and she bade the great bow of Odysseus to be brought down into the hall, and said to the wooers that

whoever could draw and shoot the bow, him would she wed and
go straightway to his house. And she laid out the bow before
the wooers and a quiver of goodly arrows.

So she promised, and the suitors were glad at her words.
But when they tried it, none could bend the polished wood, and
their hands grew weary with the trying. Then Odysseus came
and took up the bow, and the wooers laughed to see this evil-
seeming beggar take it up. But great-hearted Odysseus took
the polished wood, and even as one skilled on the lute easily
stretches a cord about a new peg, so he bent the bow between
his two hands, and strung it without effort. And the wooers
were amazed. Then great Odysseus flung off his rags and
seized a bright arrow, and leapt on to the threshold, terrible to
behold. And Telemachus stood at his side, clothed in gleaming bronze. And he drew the bow and let fly, and smote
Antinous through the throat as he drained his wine, and the cup
dropped from his hand as he was smitten, and he fell head-long,
and at once the red blood ran from his nostrils, and he spurned
the floor with his foot and the table was overthrown as he died
there. And the wooers leapt to their feet, and there was tumult.

Then the suitors looked for the spears and the shields of
bronze that were wont to hang in the halls, but there were
none, for brave Telemachus had cunningly removed them. So
they drew their two-edged swords and snatched up the tables
as shields and ran at mighty Odysseus. But Odysseus plied
with his bow, and noble Telemachus smote with the long spear,
and the chiefest of the suitors were smitten to the ground and
their blood defiled the choice food. Then some of them thought
to run to a nearby room where lay spears and brazen armour,
and when he saw them so armed brave Odysseus was much
afeared, and called upon Athene to aid him. And the goddess
watched over him, and guided the spears so that his smote down
the wooers, but theirs went wide of the mark and struck the wall
behind or hung in the gilded doorposts. Then she raised her
destroying aegis, and the suitors were filled with terror, and
Odysseus and Telemachus and the servants that were loyal
to them ran upon the lordly wooers and slew all that remained,
until none were left alive.

Then noble Odysseus made himself known to his wife, the
chaste Penelope, and so at last they found their happiness
together.

And this was the end of the wanderings of the great and
cunning Odysseus, noble son of Laertes.

THE AENEID

By VERGIL

*One of the most famous of the Latin classics, the Aeneid
tells in twelve books the story of the Fall of Troy, and the
adventures of the Trojan survivors under their Prince, Aeneas,
who was destined to found the Roman Empire. Homer, the
Greek Poet, wrote the story also in " The Iliad " but his
main character was Ulysses, the Greek hero. Though " The
Aeneid" is not supposed to be the finest of Vergil's poetry, it
is probably his best known work—certainly it is his most
entertaining. The first five books which tell of the sack of
Troy and of Dido's love for Aeneas and subsequent suicide,
must rank as one of the finest dramas ever written.*

AND now having been tossed on the seas for many long
years, the Trojan fleet bade farewell to the friendly
shores of Sicily and set their course once more for Italy.
For it was decreed that on Italian shores should Aeneas their
leader lay the foundations of that great empire that was to be
Rome.

But haughty Juno's unrelenting hate pursued them still,
nor was the cause of her anger hard to discover. Carthage,
founded by the Tyrian settlers, was beloved by her above all
lands, but already it was known among the immortals that in
times to come Rome would utterly destroy the proud city.
Because of that, though Troy had fallen, she still waged war
against the survivors and nursed in her heart the bitterness of
her slight at the hands of Paris who had preferred Venus to her.

Thus she sought Æolus, the ruler and gaoler of the winds and
tempests. To him Juno declared her wish. " Oh thou, to
whom Jove himself has given power over wind and storm, see
where that hated race of wandering slaves sails on their
prosperous voyage to Italy. Raise all thy winds, Æolus!
Sink and scatter my enemies and Deiopeia, fairest of the seven
daughters of the sea, shall be thy bride."

" The power I hold is thy gift," Æolus replied. " As thy
guest I feast with the immortals. Behold! I obey thy will! "
With his spear he pierced the wall of the cavern of the winds.
Darkness as of night itself hid the heavens. Lightning flashed

and awful thunder pealed. Aeneas himself was cold with the fear of death. "Alas!" he cried, "happy were those slain beneath the walls of Troy! Would I had shared the noble Hector's fate and could take my place among warriors killed honourably in battle."

While the pious prince bewailed his fate, the fleet was scattered, and before his eyes a ship turned over, overwhelmed, and the trembling pilot was flung headlong into the raging seas. But now Neptune himself, angered at this defiance of his powers over the seas, and well knowing his sister Juno's mind, raised his head above the waves and saw the distressed Trojan fleet. He summoned Æolus, angrily bidding him confine his powers to that sphere where they rightly lay, and even as he spoke, he smoothed the tempestuous waves and restored daylight again, so that the weary Trojans took heart, and plying their shattered oars, guided by him they sought the nearest land.

On the Libyan shores there lay a harbour so deep and so peaceful that ships finding refuge there had no need even to anchor. Here seven ships of the Trojan fleet found a welcome haven. Aeneas went forth to find them food. Spying a herd of deer he shot sufficient for their needs, and as they ate, he bade them be of good cheer. "Jove will soon reward us for the miseries we have suffered. Endure—and live for future joys."

Meanwhile in heaven, Venus reproached Jove for the sad plight of her son.

"Put away thy fears, my daughter," Jove answered her gently. "Thy people's destiny remains unaltered. Aeneas must fight a great war 'ere he rules in Italy. His son Ascanius, whose surname is Iulus, shall establish his father's kingdom in glory. For three hundred years shall the kingdom endure until a royal priestess, Ilia, shall give birth to twins sired by Mars. Of these shall Romulus, in the tawny hide of the wolf that suckled him, take up the line, and call them Romans after his own name. From the fair line of Troy a Caesar shall arise whose empire will be boundless—Julius, inheritor of great Iulus' name."

But Aeneas passed the night in restless misgivings, and as soon as morning broke, he set out to explore the strange land accompanied only by the faithful Achates. To them appeared Venus, disguised as a huntress and of her Aeneas implored knowledge of his whereabouts.

"Punic is the land, Tyrian the people, and fair Dido their

ruler," she replied. "She fled from Tyre with her followers to escape from her brother, Pygmalion. This dark and intricate story of crime is briefly this: Dido was wedded to Sychaeus, wealthiest of the Phoenicians, but Pygmalion, mad with lust and hate, slew him secretly, and for long months concealed the crime. To Dido at last appeared the ghost of her husband telling her of the crime, disclosing where lay hidden vast stores of gold and silver and bidding her fly. She obeyed, and came at last here, where having bought land, even now she raises the citadel of New Carthage—but who, I pray, are you?"

As Aeneas told her of long years of wandering, she broke in on him, unable to bear the heaviness of his sorrow.

"Whoso thou art, beloved of the immortals, I say to thee, go on to the courts of the queen. For thy comrades are restored to thee, thy fleet is safe. Only go on—turn thy steps where the path leads thee."

As she turned to go, the glory of the gods encompassed her and Aeneas knew that he had spoken with his mother. Now he pressed on until he stood above the courts of the temple that Dido was building. But his mother had caused Achates and himself to be hidden in a cloud so that they remained unseen. Aeneas saw fair Dido enter the precincts and take her place at the Judgment seat. To her entered the leaders of the Trojan ships he had thought lost, and begged mercy of her.

Dido spoke cheering words to them, promising them help and friendship, and as she finished, the cloud melted away, and looking up she saw Aeneas bathed in a radiance that was more than mortal. As he came forward speaking words of thanks and rejoicing, welcoming his companions with both hands, she stood watching him with awe and astonishment. Then again she spoke. "I too have known what it is to be an exile and a wanderer. Not ignorant of ill, I have learned to succour the distressed."

So saying she led Aeneas into her house, and ordered that the feast might be prepared. Aeneas sent Achates to the ships and ordered that his son, Ascanius, should be sent bearing gifts for Dido. Venus, still fearing that Dido, the beloved of Juno, should prove a false friend, bade Cupid change himself into the likeness of Ascanius, and take the boy's place. Then he should pierce Dido with his darts so that the queen's love should be fixed on Aeneas. It was done, and even as the queen caressed the lovely boy, the madness entered into her veins.

Then as the feast drew to a close, Dido turned to Aeneas and begged that he should tell them the story of the fall of Troy and of the wanderings of the Trojan fleet.

" Dreadful, O Queen, is the woe thou bidst me recall! How the Grecians pitiably overthrew the wealth and might of Troy. I myself saw these things in all their horror, and I bore great part in them.

" Broken in battle and weary of the siege, the Grecians, by Pallas' divine craft, built a wooden horse of tremendous proportions. In it they stealthily imprisoned a chosen band of men. Then allowing the story to circulate that they had temporarily abandoned the siege they set sail for Tenedos, which lies within sight of Trojan shores, and hid their fleet. But we believed they had run down the wind to Mycenae. We put away our grief, flung open our gates and rejoicing went forth to view the abandoned camps and the strange wooden horse.

" As the crowd argued among themselves what should be done with it, Laocoon ran down from the citadel, crying from afar : ' Wretched Trojans, what height of madness is this ? Trust not the horse, O Trojans.   I fear the Greeks even bearing gifts ! '

" But meanwhile, shepherds had dragged before Priam the king that wretch, who, to lay Troy open to his countrymen, had placed himself a willing prisoner in their hands, and had entered our citadel to betray it or to meet certain death at our hands. We would have slain him then, but that he cried out that he had been cast forth by the Greeks, so that we stayed our hand, and permitted him to tell his false tale. His name, he said, was Sinon.   He said that the Greeks, wearied of the war, longed to retire, but wind and tempest ever denied them safe passage— especially when at last the wooden horse was completed.   They sent priests to consult the oracles, and they brought back this dread message : ' With the blood of a slain maiden, O Grecians, you appeased the winds when first you came to the Ilian coasts ; with blood must you seek your return.'   The Grecians shrank back appalled, and Calchas the soothsayer retired to implore the Gods to appoint the victim.

" When asked about the wooden horse, the false Sinon raised his hands to Heaven and swore by all that he held sacred that he told us the truth.   Ulysses and Tydeus, he said, had violated the altar of Pallas without whose aid the Greeks were helpless. The outraged goddess had withdrawn herself, and by orders of Calchas, the soothsayer, was this horse reared to propitiate her what time the Greeks sailed to Mycenae to get fresh arms and men to renew the war.

" ' Calchas bade them raise it to this vast height,' went on Sinon, ' that it might not enter your city gates. If you destroy this offering to Minerva, then indeed are you lost; but if it enters into your city with due rites, then must woe attend the Greeks.'

" Thus were we ensnared, and another portent terrible and awful to view added weight to his words. As Laocoon, Neptune's priest, slew the sacrificial bull at the altar, lo, from Tenedos, two huge serpents came breasting through the waves. They gained the land, their eyes blazing fire, their tongues lapped and flickered in their hissing mouths. Unfaltering they made towards Laocoon and first his two little children they seized in their terrible embrace; then as the anguished father ran to their aid, him too they seized and though he struggled, his great strength was nothing in their terrible grasp. They left him dead, and glided away to seek sanctuary beneath the altars of Pallas.

" Now, indeed, terror seized us. All cried that the wooden beast must be drawn within our walls, and supplication made to its deity.

" And so we breached the walls, and laid open the city. We dragged it in, garlanded with flowers, while youths and maidens chanted joyfully and laid their hands on the ropes. Oh, Native land! O Troy! Four times in the very gateways did it come to a stand, four times did we hear the clash of arms in its hollow womb—yet we urged it on! Even then Cassandra opened her lips to warn us of coming doom, but by a god's curse, her words were unheeded.

" After feasting and rejoicing, while the exhausted city slept, the Grecian fleet returned from Tenedos and signalled by a torch to Sinon, who stealthily let loose the imprisoned Greeks from the horse.' Joyfully they greeted their comrades at the open gates, and swooped upon the city buried in drunken sleep.

" To me, lying peacefully in my father's house, appeared a vision of Hector, awful as he was in death. I cried out to him, but he heeded me not saying only: ' Goddess born, fly! The foe holds the city. Troy is fallen! To thee is given her holy things and household gods; seek for them a city! ' So spoke he and I awoke with the clash of arms and the sounding of trumpets in my ears. Madly I seized my weapons and rushed headlong into the fight, seeking my comrades.

"Who may unfold in speech that night's horror and death agony, or measure its woes in tears? The ancient city fell with her long years of sovereignty; corpses lay stretched about the streets and houses. Nor did the Trojans alone pay forfeit of their blood; valour remained even in conquered hearts and the Grecians fell. Everywhere was cruel agony, terror and the sight of blood.

"We fired by Coroebus, donned the armour of the Greeks we slew and thus disguised mingled with our enemies slaying many. But then our own people attacked us, misled by our Grecian crests, and as we retreated from them, the Grecians marking our alien tongue attacked us from the other side. Overwhelmed we fled, but few escaped slaughter.

"By cries and clamour we were led to the very palace of Priam, where the fighting was hottest. We renewed our courage to defend the royal dwelling, but the Greeks led by Pyrrhus, burst through the gateway and poured into the courtyards. Priam, the king, took the arms his aged hands could scarce carry, and prepared to defend his queen Hecuba and the hundred daughters of her house. She drew the old man within the sanctuary of the household altars, and pleaded with him to lay down his useless sword. Then burst into their sight Polites, one of Priam's children, hotly pursued by Pyrrhus, and as the boy ran towards his father, Pyrrhus flung his spear and Polites fell dead. At this, Priam, although wounded to death already, burst forth from his wife's restraining grasp, and flung his unavailing spear at his son's murderer. Then cried Pyrrhus: 'Go with this message to my sire, the son of Peleus; remember to tell him of my baleful deeds. Now die!' So saying he drew him to the very altar, slipping through the pool of his son's blood, and there slew him.

"Awful terror seized me. I saw that all around me had given up the fight. As in despair I stood, my mother Venus appeared, and bade me remember my aged father, Anchises, my wife, Creusa, and my little son, Ascanius, who were in deadly peril. 'Troy must fall,' she cried. 'Haste away, O son. I will never desert thee; I will set thee safe in thy father's court.'

"My aged father, who bore our household gods in his hands, I lifted on to my back. My little son I took by the hand. My wife followed us. Fearfully now, burdened with my loved ones, I took my way through the terrible city, and as I drew near the gates, my father cried the alarm. Panic seized me and I flew headlong. Creusa alas! what malign fate willed it! was torn from me. Either she could not follow me, or a Grecian band plucked her from my side. I did not dare return until I had placed Anchises and Ascanius in safety in the sacred grove. Then indeed I hastened back to the desolate city to seek her. As I stormed and searched endlessly, her ghost appeared and bade me search no more. Fain would I have clasped her to me, but she disappeared. ⸺

" So at last I returned, and found our company grown greatly, for all who escaped from Troy were gathered here. When morning broke and we saw the ruined city and the camps of the victorious Greeks, we sought the mountains. Here we abode and started to build our fleet from the timbers of the sacred grove.

" When early summer came, and the soft winds blew from the south, Anchises bade us prepare to sail, and we left our native shores for ever. So we came to Thrace which had always been friendly to Troy. Here I laid the foundations of a new city, calling it Aeneadae. But as I sacrificed to my mother, I disclosed a hidden, shameful tomb, and from within a spirit spoke, warning us to fly from these cruel and greedy shores. The spirit was that of Polydorus, who had been sent by Priam with much gold to be kept safe in the Thracian kingdom. When they had heard of Troy's downfall, they had murdered Polydorus and seized the gold. When his spirit had disclosed this shameful tale, we buried our murdered brother anew and with due rites. Then with a favouring wind sailed for that island sacred to Phoebus (Apollo). Anius its king and priest of Phoebus, welcomed us kindly, and we sought in the temples of Apollo a sign to direct us. The god bade us seek again the land where first our race saw light, and old Anchises, after consulting our records, declared it to be Crete.

" And so we sailed again for Crete, and here again I eagerly began to build the city anew. The ground was tilled and the people built houses. I had devised laws and the community was settled when we were visited by plague. Men, animals and crops alike were affected. Anchises wished us to return to Anius that we might consult Apollo again, when that night Apollo spoke to me as I lay asleep. ' Thou must change thy dwelling. Not to these shores did the gods counsel thee. There is a region Greeks call Hesperia, a younger race have called it Italy. This is our true dwelling place. Up, seek Corythus and the lands of Ausonia. Jove denies you Cretan fields! '

" We prepared to sail again.   This time a great storm came up and threw us out of our course.   When on the fourth day we sighted land we found it was the Strophades, abode of the Harpies.   We landed, and slew oxen for food, but as we feasted, the Harpies came down on us, and we were forced to battle.   We drove them back, but then Caleno, prophetess and chief of them all, came forth alone and cursed us.   Whereupon our men took fear, so we offered sacrifices in propitiation, and left those gloomy shores.

" After a prosperous voyage we came past Epirus and brought our ships to anchor near Buthrotun.   Here Helenus, son of Priam, ruled with Andromache, once Hector's wife.   Here we were kindly received, and we wept with joy to see a city ruled in Trojan fashion.   Before we sailed, Helenus again invoked Apollo's aid on our behalf and through his lips divine Phoebus spoke.   He told us that though Italy was near at hand our wanderings were not over.   We should know the appointed land when beside a river a sow should be found lying beneath oak trees.   Around her would lie her new-born brood—a litter of thirty.   Nor were we to shrink at hunger—the fates would protect us, and Apollo hear our prayers.   Through Helenus' lips still, the god warned us of dangers we would meet on the seas—the Greek cities to avoid, of Scylla and Charybdis, who guard the narrow strait of Pelorus; above all, he bade us sacrifice and pray to Juno, that her wrath might be appeased. In the woods of Avernus we were to meet a prophetess.   I was bade approach her with prayers that she might utter her oracles to guide and help me in the war I must fight in Italy.

" So ended the prophecy.   Now again we prepared to depart, loaded with gifts and sped by the kindness of Helenus and Andromache.   A prosperous wind sped us on our way, and the next morning in the clear light of dawn, Achates raised the cry: ' Italy! ' and we saw from afar dim hills and the low coastline.   But after performing due rites, we did not linger, for on these shores lay Grecian cities.   We avoided as we had been bidden the cliffs of Charybdis, but so great was the effort of our rowers that weary and ignorant of our course we drifted on to the coast of the Cyclopes, and here we anchored for the night, while mighty Aetna menaced and muttered above us.

" In the morning a wretched man came out of the forest, and flung himself upon our mercy.   His name was Achemenides and he had set out for Troy in Ulysses' company, but his

companions had abandoned him on these horrid shores. He
warned us to fly while there was yet time, for when Polyphemus,
who, though blind, was the greatest of the one-eyed giants, came
forth to tend his flock we would be lost.

" We hastened to cut our cables and put out to sea, taking
Achemenides with us, and as we drew away from the shore,
Polyphemus appeared, and hearing the sound of our oars,
roused with his cries the whole tribe of the Cyclopes. But we
escaped, and turning back again from the dread strait guarded by
Scylla and Charybdis, a fair north wind reached us.

" And so at last we came to Sicily, and here encountered
grief that no prophet had foretold, for on these shores Anchises
died. This was the last agony, this the goal of the long ways;
thence it was I had departed when God landed me on your
coasts."

Thus the Lord Aeneas told the history of his wanderings.
At last he was hushed, and here in silence made an end.

Now Dido was sore distressed because of her love for Aeneas,
and confessed to her sister Anna that for his sake she yearned to
break her vows of eternal fidelity to the memory of her husband.
And Anna encouraged her in her madness and bade her
enslave Aeneas, painting the glories of a union between Troy
and Carthage.

Then Juno seeing her loved Dido so deep in love, and careless
of all else, suggested to Venus that they should work together
to achieve the marriage—thinking thus to avert the ultimate
destruction of Carthage at the hands of the Romans. Venus,
well knowing her design, and that the fates willed otherwise,
pretended to agree.

Next day, Dido held a great hunting party in honour of
Aeneas. During the day, Juno caused a great storm to arise,
and Dido and Aeneas, separated from the rest of the party,
took shelter in a cave. Here Dido, flinging aside all sense of
shame, confessed her love to Aeneas, and he succumbed to her
passion.

Now the two rulers turned from their high purposes. The
building of Carthage ceased, and the Trojan fleet lay at anchor
in the harbour. The months passed in amorous dalliance,
but Jove looking down from heaven was ill-pleased, and sent
Mercury to Aeneas to bid him remember his quest, and to sail
immediately from Carthage. Aeneas listened, and struck with
shame, immediately yearned to be again on the seas. Alas!
he knew not how to tell Dido of his departure. In secrecy he

bade his captains prepare the fleet. Gladly they did so, all anxious to see the end of their journeyings.

But Dido was not deceived. Helpless, she found resort only in burning anger.

"And didst thou hope, traitor," she cried, "to mask the crime, and slip away in silence from my land? Under wintry skies thou preparest thy fleet, and hastenest to launch into savage gales. Fliest thou from me? For thy sake have I neglected my allies and the building of my city. For thy sake is mine honour smirched. I have not even a child of thine to comfort me!"

Aeneas, by Jove's command, remained unmoved. "My first duty lies to the Trojans," he replied. "If their destiny were here, gladly would I stay—but it lies in Italy, and I wrong them and cheat my son of his inheritance if I remain here."

Dido, in despair, went again to Anna and begged her to plead with Aeneas to stay. Anna's words had no effect on the Trojan leader, and hopeless and dismayed by doom, Dido resolved on death. In her dreams came warning and portents; the wine she sacrificed on the altars turned to blood—tortured by fears and forebodings reason deserted her, and the way out of life obsessed her thoughts. She went again to her sister, and bade her raise a great pyre in the inner court and place on it the bridal bed and the arms and dress of Aeneas. She told Anna that by means of magic rites she was resolved to drive forth the impious love that enslaved her. Anna believed her and did as Dido wished.

To Aeneas, sleeping on his ship, came Mercury: "Goddess-born, canst thou sleep on in such danger? She, fixed on death, is revolving craft and crime grimly in her bosom. Fliest thou not hence headlong, while headlong flight is yet possible? Even now wilt thou see ocean weltering with broken timbers, see the fierce glow of torches, and the beach in a riot of flame if dawn break on thee yet dallying in this land. Up ho! Linger no more! Woman is ever a fickle and changing thing!" So spoke he and melted in the black night.

Aeneas leapt up, and bestirred his crew. "Haste and awake!' A god sent from high heaven spurs us to speed our flight." He cut the hawser with his sword, and like zeal seized all the fleet. Their oars churned the water into white foam, and the channel widened between them and Tyrian shores.

As dawn broke, Dido saw the fleet standing out to sea. She

beat her breast, and tore her golden hair. " God," she cried,
" shall he go? Shall an alien make mock of our realm?
Go, pursue and destroy him! Oh, what madness do I talk?
Alas, Dido! Behold the faith of him who carried with him ever
his ancestral gods and bore his aged father in his arms. Could I
not have killed him—could I not have struck at him—by the
death of his son? Battle might have been dubious, but what
have I to fear—I whom death claims now! "

Then she cursed Aeneas and his race—and called upon her
people that there could be no peace between Carthage and the
cursed race through time immemorial.

So speaking she thought how soonest to end her life, and sent
for her sister and ordered that ceremonies round the great pyre
should begin. In madness she climbed on to the pyre, and
spoke her last words.

" I have lived and fulfilled Fortune's allotted course; and
now I shall go, a queenly phantom under the earth. I have
built a great city; I have avenged my husband's death.
Happy had I been had Trojan ships never touched our shores.
Death it will be—Death unavenged—but Death! " Her hands
touched the garments of the Lord Aeneas, then she picked up his
great sword. Her horrified people saw her stand upright and
salute the gods with it, then fall upon its point, while the blood
gushed forth.

From the seas, Aeneas and his men saw the flames of the
funeral pyre leap high in the sky. They knew not what it was,
though the knowledge of Dido's madness led them to gloomy
guesses, but they pursued their course.

Storms led them to seek again the shores of Sicily. Aeneas
rejoiced, for here were friends. Here too, was the tomb of
Anchises, his father. So having landed and greeted Acestes
the king, he ordered ceremonial games and contests in honour
of his father's memory.

While the games were in progress, the women down by the
shore mourned Anchises as custom demanded. Juno looking
down on them, found fresh opportunity to cause dissension
among the Trojan wanderers. For as they gazed on the ships
that so soon were to bear them again on their endless wanderings, a great longing seized them to remain where they were,
and to carry their search no farther. Then Juno caused discontent to rise among them, and her minions, entering into
them, caused one to suggest that they should burn the ships.
Madness spread among them. They snatched fire from

the hearths, set fire to the ships, and flung fuel upon the flames.

The news was carried to Aeneas as he presided over the games, and all the Trojans hastened to the shore. The women, their madness quite gone, looked with horror on their deed, and fled in panic before the wrath of their prince and their men. Then Aeneas called on Jove, who in pity sent a great rainstorm to quench the fire, and the ships were saved.

The Lord Aeneas, distressed in heart, pondered if he should not indeed remain on the shores of Sicily and grant peace at last to his weary people. But one of his old counsellors, Nautes, bade him found a city on the shores of Sicily, indeed, and leave there the sea-weary women, old men, and those whose hearts failed them. The rest should obey the gods, and go on to Italy. That night, in dreams, old Anchises appeared to Aeneas, and told him that Nautes counselled him wisely.

So it was done. After nine days' feasting, the new city was dedicated and Aeneas and his faithful band set sail once more. Again, in Heaven, Venus appalled by this new tragedy, pleaded with Jove to put an end to their wanderings and sufferings. Again Jove assured his daughter that her son's safety and ultimate reward was assured. But for the burning of the ship, one sacrifice only was demanded. During that night, Palinurus, Aeneas' chief pilot, was overcome with sleep as he stood at his post—the waves bore him overboard. Thus the sacrifice was paid, and Aeneas, unknowing that a price had been demanded for his safety, wept long for his faithful Palinurus.

Now at last they came to Hesperian shores. While the Trojan band lit fires and prepared the food, Aeneas sought the cavern of the Sibyl as he had been bidden by Helenus. After sacrifice and due rites, the priestess of Apollo gave tongue.

" Past at last is the peril of the seas. Heavier yet is the peril that awaits thee on Latin shores. Wars, grim wars, I see, and Tiber afoam with blood. Another Achilles shall fight against thee, and Juno's anger shall not be quenched awhile. An alien bride is again the source of Trojan wars. Thou shalt seek aid in all quarters, and it shall come from where thou hast least cause to hope—from the Greeks."

Thus ended the Sibyl. One boon more Aeneas craved— that he might be permitted to visit the nether regions and speak with the spirit of his father Anchises. Thus answered the soothsayer.

" Easy is the descent into Hell; all night and day the gate of dark Dis stands open; but to recall thy steps and issue to the upper air, this is the task and burden. Yet if thy pleasure is to plunge into the mad task, learn what first must be accomplished. Hidden in a shady tree is a bough with leafage and pliant shoot all of gold, consecrate to nether Juno, wrapped in the depth of woodland and shut in by dusky vales. But to him only who first hath plucked the golden tressed fruitage from the tree is given to enter the hidden places of the earth. But yet again a friend of thine lies a lifeless corpse, alas, thou knowest it not, and defiles all the fleet with death. First lay him in his resting-place and hide him in the tomb. So at last thou shalt behold the Stygian groves and the realms untrodden by the living."

Aeneas went forth wondering and returned to the camp. He was met by the news that the body of Misenus, once attendant on Hector, had been cast up on the shores. Him they buried with the rites ordained by the Sibyl. Then Venus sent twin doves to guide Aeneas to the golden bough.

Both conditions fulfilled, Aeneas returned to the Cavern, and the Sibyl called up Hecate, mistress of Heaven and Hell, who bade Aeneas follow her. So he went down into Hell, and saw many strange sights—the dreary pool of Acheron, and Charon, the ferryman who carried over the watery wastes the soul of the dead. He saw the unburied dead who could obtain no passage, and Cerebus, the three-headed dog, who guarded the portal of Hell. He saw Dido, standing among those who had taken their own lives, but she turned from him in anger. He saw all the horrors of Hell and Purgatory. But at length he came to the Elysian fields, and there at length he embraced his father Anchises. With him he talked long, and was given much wise counsel about the war he was to fight in Italy, and was assured again of the glories of the Roman line he was to found. Then Anchises accompanied his son to the twin portals of Death and Sleep and here bade him farewell. So Aeneas returned to the world.

On Ausonian shores, by the banks of the river Tiber, reigned old Latinus. He had no son to succeed. His daughter Lavinia was the heiress of his fortune and his kingdom. She was courted by all the neighbouring princes, but the one whose suit was favoured above all, and especially by the queen, Amata, was Turnus. Latinus would not have withheld his consent to the marriage but that when the oracles were consulted, the portents were against the match, and the soothsayers told the king that a foreign prince should wed his daughter, and that their seed should found a mighty empire.

This was the state of the kingdom when Aeneas and the Trojan fleet at last anchored on their shores, near where the Tiber rolls into the sea.'

Latinus received them kindly, and asked what they desired of him. Aeneas told him of the many portents and prophecies that had directed the Trojans to this land, and begged for permission to settle in peace and build a city.

Long pondered Latinus. There was no doubt in his mind. There stood before him that foreign prince of whom the soothsayers had spoken—his daughter's husband, the future ruler of his realm. At length he spoke, offering a fair treaty to Aeneas, and the hand of his daughter. "I firmly judge," he ended, "and, what I judge, desire."

So the compact was sealed, but in high Heaven, Juno's anger again burst forth, and she brooded how she could best delay the time when the Trojans must rule in Italy.

From the nethermost pits of Hell, she roused one of the Furies, and bade her attack the Queen Amata. It was done, and Amata, who ever favoured the suit of Turnus, was incited to stir up rage in the hearts of the Latin people against Aeneas, and to hide her daughter. Next the Fury visited Turnus, and roused in him a warlike passion. Lastly to the Trojan camp she flew, and by a trick caused a quarrel between a band of Trojan huntsmen and the keeper of the royal forests, which ended in bloodshed. Now were both sides roused to warlike ardour, and nothing but war would content them. The Fury's work was done, and Juno banished her again to Hell.

Latinus himself, for a long while withstood the war, but when he saw that all he could do was nothing, he cried: "With your blood will you pay the price of this, O wretched man. Thee, O Turnus, thy crime; thee thine awful punishment shall await. My rest was won, my haven at hand; I am robbed only of a happy death." Saying thus, he retired within his palace and dropped the reins of state.

Now all the princes of Hesperia hurried to prepare themselves for war. Turnus had assembled all his powers and all the Latin youths had thronged to his banners. Yet he craved more allies, and sent Venelus to Diomedes to beg his aid to crush this Trojan adventurer.

Aeneas himself, meanwhile, sunk in cares, slept one night on the banks of the Tiber. To him appeared the God of the river,

Father Tiber himself, and spoke thus: "Goddess born, here is thine assured home. Draw not back, nor fear the threat of war. The gods are with thee. This is their sign—when thou awakest, thou shalt see the white sow with her litter of thirty white young lying beneath the oak trees—even as it was told you by Helenus. And by this token shall Ascanius, thirty years from now, found a city, Alba of great renown. Now hearken, and I will help thee in thy present distress. A Grecian colony, under Evander, have founded a city here called Pallenteum, after Pallas, their forefather. These wage war ever with the Latin people. Offer them alliance. I will lead you to their city on the breast of my stream. Arise, goddess born, nor forget to address thy prayers and sacrifices to Juno and vanquish her wrath."

Then Aeneas awoke, and marvellous to relate, the milk white sow and her white litter were espied beneath the trees. These he sacrificed to Juno, then departed on his mission to Evander.

The Trojan ships arrived as Evander and his son, Pallas, observed a holy feast. When they knew the Trojans came in peace, Evander gave them a royal welcome, and assented to their desire for an alliance. He even promised to send in charge of his army his own beloved son, Pallas. But as the resources of his colony were not great, he suggested to Aeneas that they should also evoke the aid of the Tuscans, the colony of those who had broken away from the tyranny of Mezentius. They were a great and powerful people. The alliance was suggested, and was accepted.

While Trojans, Greeks and Tuscans feasted to commemorate the pact, Venus sought Vulcan, her husband, and persuaded him to make for Aeneas arms and armour that should render him impregnable in battle. When the gift was completed, she appeared before her son, radiant in her immortality, and laid the glittering arms before him.

Meanwhile Turnus, knowing that Aeneas was away, was inspired by Juno to attack the Trojan camp. They, perceiving the host of Turnus approaching, retired behind their ramparts as Aeneas commanded, and would not be lured out to fight, nor could Turnus assail the walls. Angered, he turned to where the fleet lay close under the walls. Exultingly he called for fire, and hurled burning brands into the ships. But the ships were built of holy pines from the Groves of Ida, the Mother of the gods, and by Jove's sanction, it was decreed that they could not be destroyed. Lo then! a wondrous sight. First a strange

Christian's fight with Apollyon

A scene from the " Pilgrim's Progress "

Gulliver and the Lilliputians

A scene from "Gulliver's Travels"

light, then a great glory, and the voices of the choir of Ida. Then came an awful voice: " Disquiet not yourselves, O Trojans, to guard ships of mine. Sooner shall Turnus burn the seas than these holy pines. You go free; go, goddesses of the sea; the mother bids it." And immediately each ship plunged like dolphins into the sea, and from it rose, wonderful to relate, each with a maiden's face.

Then were the hosts of Turnus afraid, but he called out that it was an evil portent for the Trojans, and ordered his troops to surround and besiege the camp.

Now Jove, the father of Heaven, called a council of the immortals.

" Lords of Heaven, why are your minds thus jealously at strife? I forbade Italy to join in battle with the Trojans. Why this quarrel in the face of my decree? War will come when Carthage shall attack Rome from the Alps—now let Italy be at peace." But Venus and Juno both spoke urging claims and the immortals were divided among themselves. Then spoke Jove again.

" Since it may not be that Latins and Trojans join alliance, what fortune each wins, what hope each follows, be he Trojan or Rutulian I will hold in even praise. Each as he hath begun shall work out his destiny. Jupiter is one, and king over all."

Meanwhile the Trojans in the camp sore beset by Turnus were in despair, until they saw the sails of his ships and courage revived.

But as Aeneas and his allies disembarked, the forces of Turnus ran to the attack and joined in bloody battle. Turnus himself faced Evander's son. " I alone must assail Pallas," he cried. " To me and none other Pallas is due." All drew back.

" For me, my praise shall ever now be in the lordly spoils I win, or in illustrious death. My father will bear calmly with either lot." So crying Pallas advanced, and calling upon the gods, hurled his spear. Alas, the gods heard his prayer and wept, for now was his appointed time. He fell with Turnus' spear in his breast, and the victor, exulting, despoiled him of the heavy sword-belt wrought in gold.

Then Juno, watching from above, saw the Trojans rally once again and begged Jupiter that she might save Turnus' life, at least for the time being. Permission being granted, she tricked Turnus into one of the ships and snapped its hawser, whereupon it ran out to sea on the ebbing tide, and by Juno's contrivances, Turnus was conveyed home to his father's city.

Mezentius took his place as leader of the Rutulian troops. Pressed hotly by Aeneas, his son Lausus rushed in to aid his father, and both were slain by the Trojan prince. Then the Rutulian troops retired, and left Aeneas victor.

Then a truce was declared while both sides buried their dead. Weeping and mourning, Aeneas paid the last solemn honours to Pallas, and sent the body in splendid, solemn state back to the father, Evander.

In the city of Latinus the old king held council. Diomedes, for whose help they had hoped, had refused an alliance.

While they yet argued, news was brought that Aeneas had moved to the attack. All was confusion, and Turnus buckled on his armour as he ran to command his troops. At the city's gates he met Camilla, who with her Amazon cavalry begged to be allowed to engage Aeneas in battle.

So it was arranged. Camilla at the head of the cavalry, moved off to engage Aeneas, and a sharp battle ensued, but at length Camilla herself was shot down, and again the Latin troops retired in confusion. As night fell Aeneas camped before the very walls of the city.

Then Turnus begged Latinus to allow him to meet Aeneas in single combat. The terms of the peace were drawn up between the Trojans and the Latins, and after solemn pledges and rites, the two heroes faced each other in an open square flanked by the packed ranks of both sides.

Juno watching from Heaven was in despair. She dared not intervene herself, for Jove had forbidden it. But she called Jaturna, the water nymph, sister of Turnus, and bade her save her brother. Forth went Jaturna and murmuring among the Rutulians caused them to break the solemn pledge and once more attack the Trojans. In the resulting confusion Aeneas himself was wounded by an arrow. The Trojans wavered seeing their leader cut down, but Venus herself miraculously cured the wound. Then Aeneas, scorning all else, sought Turnus. Jaturna, panic stricken, took the place of Turnus' charioteer, and for a time evaded the pursuit of Aeneas. The Trojan prince, meanwhile, saw the city undefended, and calling to his men scaled the walls and flung burning brands on to the roofs and into the streets so that the city was likely to perish in flames.

Despair seized the Latins. Amata, calling aloud that guilt alone was hers for this fate, hanged herself. Latinus poured dust on his head and ran through the city lamenting. Turnus, hearing the cries and lamentations, checked his chariot.

Jatturna tried to urge him on and trick him into safety. Then Turnus recognized her at last. " No, my sister," he said. " Now fate prevails, cease to hinder." He leapt from his chariot and rushed across the field of battle crying: " Forbear now, O Rutulians, and you, Latins, stay your weapons. Whatsoever fortune is left is mine; I singly must expiate the treaty for you all and make decision with the sword."

Aeneas, hearing the voice of Turnus, turned to meet him.

In Heaven Jove spoke once more: " Juno, it is finished. Thou hast had power to harry the Trojans over land and sea, to kindle war, to put a house in mourning, to plunge a bride in grief. Thou canst not keep Aeneas from his destiny."

Juno replied: " I know thy will, Jupiter, else would I have been on the battlefield with Turnus. I confess I counselled Jaturna to aid her brother—but now I retire. One thing I beg—that the Latins change not their name, their speech or their customs. Troy is fallen; let her and her name lie where they fell."

Jove smiled. " Still thou ragest! Yet I grant thee thy last desire. Italy shall keep her native speech and names. The Trojans shall mingle into her blood. Nor shalt thou be more honoured by any nation than by Rome."

So Juno was appeased, and withdrew.

Then Turnus fell back before Aeneas. One last effort he made, but strength deserted him, and deadly terror seized his limbs. As he wavered, Aeneas poised his spear and sent it hurtling at his enemy. Under the blow, Turnus fell, his leg doubled beneath him, and from the ranks of the Rutulians came a mighty groan. Then cried Turnus: " I have deserved it; nor do I ask for mercy; use thy fortune. Thou art conqueror, and Ausonia hath seen me stretch conquered hands. Lavinia is thine in marriage; press not thy hatred farther."

Aeneas stood wrathful in arms and lowered his hand; pity seized him and he could not bring himself to strike the death blow to his enemy. Then high on Turnus' shoulder he perceived the sword-belt that he knew—the luckless belt of the boy Pallas, whom Turnus had struck down with mastering wound. Aeneas, kindled to fury, cried in terrible anger: " Mayst thou, thou clad in the spoils of my dearest, escape mine hands? Pallas it is, Pallas who now strikes the sacrifice and exacts vengeance in thy guilty blood." So saying he fiercely plunged the steel full in the breast of Turnus. His limbs grew slack and chill, and life with a moan fled into the dark.

THE PILGRIM'S PROGRESS
FROM THIS WORLD TO THAT WHICH IS TO COME

By JOHN BUNYAN

Written in prison between 1660 and 1672, the work is a religious allegory told in the simplest and purest prose, whose effect is enhanced by the use of scenes of English provincial life and faithfully observed human types. Its enormous popularity is shown by the fact that it has been translated into more than a hundred languages.

ONE day, as I slept, I dreamed a dream. And in it I saw a man called Christian who was dressed in rags and bent down by a heavy burden on his back. In his hand was a book, and, as he read, his hand shook and he burst out sobbing. Then suddenly he turned, and hurried back to his home in the City of Destruction.

Here, his wife and children perceived his plight but would not listen when he besought them to follow him and leave the city. But Christian remained adamant. He knew he had to escape before destruction came. So he ignored their tears and the jeers of his neighbours and left by himself.

As yet, however, he knew only he was escaping. Where he was going he did not know, until one known as Evangelist, noticing his hesitation, asked him his trouble. To which Christian replied that he had read in the book he held that he, as all the others in the city, were condemned to die and come up for judgment, and that he was ready for neither. Whereupon Evangelist demanded why he stood still, and, on hearing that Christian did not know which way to turn, pointed out to him the way.

This led over a wide field and through a wicket gate in the distance. So Christian set out in this direction, but he had not gone far before two neighbours overtook him. These were Pliable and Obstinate who had come to force him to return to the city. But Christian was determined. Talking to his neighbours he assured them that he was setting out for better things than they could ever expect to find where they were. Although Obstinate told him he was a fool, Pliable listened, arguing that perhaps there were better things ahead. And still Christian remained unmoved. So much so, in fact, that Obstinate realized his task was impossible and turned to go home. Here, he received a further check, for Pliable had been partly persuaded and joined Christian. So it was that these two set out on their pilgrimage alone.

At first, the going was easy, except for the weight of Christian's burden, which slowed him up. But then, in my dream, I saw them come to a very miry slough in the midst of a plain. Unaware of the presence of this place, which was called the Slough of Despond, the travellers fell into its filth. And Pliable, angry with his friend for leading him into such a place, pulled himself to the bank and went back home, leaving Christian to fight his own way out.

This, however, was not so easy, for Christian's burden had weighed him down and he had sunk deep in the mire. Perhaps he would have suffocated in it, had not one called Help come along and asked him what he was doing in the slough, and, on hearing he was making for the wicket gate, pulled him out. As he did so, he explained that there were steps through the bog but that most men, either through the hurry or fear of dizziness, fell into the slimy filth.

Once more on firm ground, Christian proceeded doggedly on his way, though his burden grew very heavy. And, as he went, a stranger, Mr. Worldly Wiseman, from the town of Carnal Policy, came across the field and got into conversation. Noticing Christian's burden, he mentioned a village called Morality where there was a man called Legality who was renowned for lifting burdens. If he was out, he told Christian to ask for his son, Civility, who was almost as good. He also pointed out that if Christian was afraid of his own city, Morality was cheap and comfortable. So Christian thanked his new acquaintance and made for Legality's house.

This lay by a hill, Mount Sinai in fact, and it was when he was close under this that Christian realized his mistake. For, as he stood there, the sheer side of the hill looked as though it were about to crash down on top of him and crush him to death. Fire and rumblings also added to his terror as they rent the air from the side of the hill. Terrified that his end had come, Christian stayed, rooted to the ground, trembling with fear and in a cold sweat.

And, as he stood, Evangelist came to him the second time and disclosed Mr. Worldly Wiseman as an alien, Legality as a cheat, and Civility as a hypocrite, and called on rumbling thunder from the heavens to back up his words. Then, comforting Christian, he directed his steps back again to the way that led to the wicket gate.

Here, Christian found Good-will, who pulled him quickly through the gate as it was within range of the Devil's castle and his arrows. Once through, however, he was safe and Good-will directed him on to the straight and narrow way which he had to follow. But still was Christian weighed down by his burden, for Good-will had no authority to release him of it.

Thus Christian progressed until he came to the house of the Interpreter. Here he was welcomed in and shown many things, including a picture of a grave person with eyes uplifted, a Bible in his hand, the law of truth written on his lips and the world behind his back. This man, he was told, would be his only guide during his pilgrimage, so that if he met others he would now be able to recall the picture and beware. Then he was shown, in a room full of choking dust, a man sweeping. But, as he swept, the dust only rose and choked all in the room, until another sprinkled the floor with water, and then it became clean. This, he was told, showed the heart of the man who knows not the gospel, the dust being his original sin which, stirred up, rose to defile the whole man, and the water being the gospel. Then, in a second room, he met two children: Passion who pounced eagerly on things that did not last, and Patience who waited for the better things of the life to come. Then, into a third room, where there was a fire burning regardless of water poured on constantly by one who stood near. This, the Interpreter showed him, was because secretly, out of this man's view, another sprinkled the fire with oil. This, he was told, showed how, although the devil might try his hardest, Christ, with the oil of grace, maintained the work begun in his heart.

After this, Christian saw a palace with, on its tall walls, people walking, clothed in gold. Here a man was demanding entrance, and, regardless of the odds of the opposition, fought his way victoriously in. But still the Interpreter had other sights, and he took Christian to see a man languishing in an iron cage and in darkness, because his faith had been killed by lust of the world. Nearby was another man who, as they approached, woke from a nightmare shaking and covered with the sweat of fear. He had dreamed that judgment day had come before he was prepared.

Then, having seen all these things, Christian took his leave of the Interpreter and went on his way between the sheltering walls of Salvation to a hill with a cross and, a little below, a sepulchre. And, as he gazed on the cross, his heavy burden slipped from his weary shoulders and fell down, down to the sepulchre where it was swallowed up. With this relief, joy filled his heart and he hurried on. But once again he happened on something that pulled him up. This time, he came upon three men who lay with their feet fettered. He approached them and offered to loose their bonds, but to no avail, for they refused to let him cut their fetters, so he had no other option but to leave them and get once more on his way.

So he went on until he came to hill Difficulty where one path ran over the hill and two easier ones called Danger and Destruction ran round either side. For a moment he paused, then made his choice and began to ascend the hill, which was as well, for the road Danger led into an open wood, and Destruction went straight to a wide field full of dark monsters.

The way up the hill, however, was very heavy going, and soon Christian's run dropped to a walk, and in time the walk became a crawl. He was, in fact, near to the point of dropping when about half way up he found an arbour where pilgrims could rest. Here he slept until refreshed; then, full of new vigour, made his way quickly up the rest of the hill. At the top he was met by two coming the other way, namely, Timorous and Mistrust, who warned him of the dangers ahead and told him to follow their example and turn back.

He refused, however, and then, when he had left them, he felt for a scroll which had been given to him at the start of his pilgrimage and was indeed a passport, only to find that in his eagerness he had carelessly left it in the arbour. Whereupon, he turned and retraced his steps, found it, and had again to mount the steep last half of the hill. And this was not the worst. For, through his forgetfulness, he had wasted daylight hours and now had to continue through the night. This he did, and the next day came to the stately palace, Beautiful.

Here he met two lions and was afraid until the lodge porter of the place renewed his faith by telling him they were chained. Then he passed them and knocked on the door of the palace.

Nor did he have to wait long before a lovely virgin, Discretion,
answered his call and summoned Prudence, Piety and Charity,
who took him in and showed him a chamber called Peace
where he could sleep.

After he was rested, he was here shown the armoury, where
all pilgrims could fit themselves out; the library, where he
could read records of great antiquity telling of those who
fought great battles, and the museum where were relics of
great ones of the past. The next day they showed him the
Delectable Mountains which were away in Emmanuel's land,
from where, they told him, he would be able to catch his first
glimpse of the Celestial City in the distance. So, having
shown him this, they armed him and accompanied him to
the Valley of Humiliation where, after giving him provisions
for his journey, they wished him God speed and left him to
travel on alone.

He had gone a little way through this valley before he
saw a foul dragon, Apollyon, coming for him across a field.
For a moment he thought of fleeing, then realized that the
armour he wore left no protection for the back. Therefore,
he faced the dragon and started a fight which lasted a long
while before, weary and injured, the dragon knocked the
sword out of Christian's hand. It looked as if his end had
come. Then, as the dragon rose to strike the death blow, a
new strength came on Christian and he stretched out his
hand and grabbed his sword, thrusting it with all the strength
he had left at the monster towering above him. And Apollyon,
scared by this sudden retaliation, spread his wings and
disappeared.

Painfully Christian prepared to go on his way, when a
hand came to him and gave him healing leaves from the tree
of life for his wounds. These he applied, then, with sword
drawn, marched forward and into the Valley of the Shadow
of Death ahead. On its boundary, he met two men who
tried to turn him back, but he kept to his path. This, however, he found no easy matter, for it was exceedingly narrow
and bordered on the right by a very deep ditch where the
blind of all ages have led the blind to perish, and on the left
by a dangerous quag which seemed bottomless. But worse
still was to come. Right in the middle of the Valley and
beside his path was a gaping hole, a veritable mouth of Hell.
And the flames from it seemed to follow him as he went, while
fiends could be heard encircling him nearer and nearer. So

Christian, miserable in this darkness and danger, prayed, and through prayer turned back the fiends. And so he went through the hell of night full of whispered blasphemies to the dawn and welcomed whispered words of God. It was then, in the daylight, that full realization came to him of the extreme narrowness of his path and the great dangers he had come through.

Nevertheless, although dawn had broken, the second part of the valley was even more dangerous than the first, for everywhere were such things as snares, traps and nets, pits, pitfalls and holes. But Christian watched his steps carefully and came to no harm. Neither did he see anyone except Pope and Pagan at the mouth of their cave, and they failed to bother him, for Pagan had been dead for many years and Pope was impotent.

Ahead of this cave was a rise, and, as Christian approached it, he saw ahead his friend Faithful, whom he caught up and joined. As they walked, Faithful told his new companion some of the dangers he had met. First, he had been accosted by Wanton, who promised all sorts of carnal and fleshly content; then by Adam the first, of Deceit, who had offered him home, wages and his daughters, Lust of the Flesh, Lust of the Eyes and Pride of Life for marriage. But Faithful had escaped. Then, he told his friend, he was met by Moses, who beat him until one with holes in his hands and side stopped him. Others he had escaped from included Discontent and Shame, who told him that a tender conscience was soft.

Thus these two journeyed on until they met with Talkative, whom Christian recognized as the son of Say-well. At first his easy manner and fine language nearly deceived Faithful, but, on hearing Christian disclose him as a man of all talk and no action, he spoke to him plainly and sent him on his way.

Shortly after this meeting, the two wanderers came to the town of Vanity, where all the year round there is a fair. Here it was that Christ, when on earth, walked through and, although tempted with all the kingdoms of the world, did not buy. As they entered Vanity, Christian and Faithful, conspicuous by their strange garb and speech, were singled out as strangers by those who sold. But not one stall-holder made a sale, for both replied " We buy truth," and in Vanity Fair none sold truth. Then these two were jeered at and finally arrested, cross-examined, beaten and thrown into a cage where all could spit on them and otherwise hurl insults at them. But to those insults they only answered softly with blessings. Some, admiring their courage, sided with them. But those that did were set upon by the others, with the result that a riot broke out in the fair, for which Christian and Faithful were blamed. As punishment for this they were dragged through the fair in chains. Even this, however, failed to move them from their quiet courage. Seeing this, even more were won to their side, so that their antagonists decided that only death could curb them.

Eventually, they were brought to trial before Judge Lord Hate-God. Faithful was the first to have to answer the charges. Standing very erect, he defied the devil before the judge. Envy, Superstition and Pickthank were called as witnesses for the prosecution. Their word was believed. Faithful was sentenced and tortured to death. But at the moment he died he was taken away in a chariot that came for him and carried him through the clouds to the Celestial Gate while glorious flourishes of trumpets rent the air to welcome him.

Christian fared better, however, being remanded and put back in the cage. Here he stayed a while until, with the aid of God, he escaped and once more continued his journey. Nor did he continue it alone, for he was joined by another good pilgrim called Hopeful. Together they trudged many miles, passing By-ends, who always moved with public opinion, Mr. Hold-the-world, Mr. Money-love and Mr. Save-all on their way. Presently they found some respite from the hard path they had been following in the plain of Ease. This, however, was very short, and in a little while they had passed across it and come to the little hill Lucre, which held rich silver mines. From these came the voice of Demas tempting them to turn from the way and make themselves rich. But they resisted. The others whom they had passed, however, went straight to Demas, where they fell on the deceitful ground on the edge of the pit by the mines.

A little farther on, the pilgrims passed a monument reminding them of what happened to Lot's wife when she looked back; so they pushed forward and came to a river with green trees and fruit on its banks and a cool meadow beside it where they slept and ate.

This respite, though, was brief, and after it the way became very hard. Both Hopeful and Christian became exceedingly tired and their feet were badly blistered and became very painful. In this condition, they noticed a soft path leading through a meadow which appeared to run parallel to their road. By it was Vain-confidence who told them that it led to the Celestial City. The pilgrims believed him. But it was not long before they discovered their mistake; for, walking into the night, they came to a deep pit where the path ended, and, when they turned to retrace their steps, they found the river had swollen making retreat impossible. So they lay in a nearby field and slept.

The next morning they were roughly awakened by a servant of Giant Despair, whose estate this was, and taken to his stronghold Doubting Castle where they were treated as trespassers and thrown into a dungeon. Here they remained alone for four days without food, drink or light, while the giant discussed with his wife, Diffidence, what to do with them. She eventually decided that they should be beaten. But even this had no effect, so finally she got him to try to persuade them to kill themselves, as they were only in the way and could never escape. And still they demanded their freedom, and Giant Despair, hearing this, lost his temper and flew at them. The excitement was too much. As he leapt he fell in a fit, falling to the floor and remaining there helpless for a time.

And while he lay thus, Christian and Hopeful discussed what was best for them to do. Suicide they discarded, as that would be murder and murder meant Hell. They even still defied the giant when he recovered and took them to see the bones and skulls of others who had been obstinate. Then, the night after they had seen these, Christian remembered a key in his bosom. It was called Promise and proved to be a pass key to all the doors. So they let themselves out, and, no doubt, would have escaped unnoticed had not the lock of the iron gate to the castle yard creaked and woken the Giant. Again temper and excitement got the better of him and he fell in another fit.

Once more free, Christian and Hopeful went ahead and reached the peace of the Delectable Mountains, where the shepherds took them to the top of the hill Clear. Here they gave them a perspective glass through which they could see the gates to the Celestial City, but the vision was not clear, so unsteady were their hands.

Then down the hill they went, towards the City, where they met a lad, Conceit, of whom they had been warned by the shepherds. Then a little later they came across Atheist, who, on hearing they were making for the Celestial City, told them there was no such place. But, having already seen the Gate hazily through the perspective glass, they ignored him and proceeded to the Enchanted Ground, of the dangers of which they had also been warned beforehand. Hopeful here nearly fell, but Christian kept his spirit up and they came through its drowsy atmosphere, keeping awake through constant conversation.

And so they came to the sweet, pleasant country of Beulah, which was fertile and abundant and inhabited by angels. And the two looked ahead and saw nearer the Celestial City built from pearls and precious stones with a street which was fashioned from gold and kissed by warm reflected sunbeams. So they went on, led by two Shining Ones clad in raiment that shone like gold and with faces that shone like the light, through vineyards and gardens and orchards to the sight of the gate. But between this and where they stood was a river where there was no bridge. At the sight, therefore, of this river, the pilgrims were much stunned, but the men that were with them said, " You must go through, or you cannot come at the gate."

So they addressed themselves to the water; and entering, Christian began to sink and crying out to his good friend Hopeful, he said, " I sink in deep waters; the billows go over my head, all his waves go over me." And fear filled him. But Hopeful spoke to him bringing fresh encouragement, and thus they got over and on the other bank were met by two angels. Thus they passed out of this world and hurried up the hill on the other side, unencumbered by their mortal garments, while angels sang to them of the wonders that were to come. So they approached the gate where heavenly hosts waited to welcome them in, and here they gave up their certificates and were welcomed in. And, as they entered they were transformed with raiment that shone like gold and given harps with which to give praise, and crowns for honour.

Then, in my dream, I looked back and saw Ignorance being ferried across the cold waters by Vain-hope, but, instead of gaining admittance, he was set upon and bound and carried by the same Shining Ones who had conducted the pilgrims to the City, to a door I had seen in the side of the hill. Then

I saw that there was a way to Hell even from the gates of Heaven as well as from the City of Destruction. So I awoke, and behold it was a dream.

It was some time after this that again I fell asleep and dreamed. And this time I saw a messenger called Secret come to Christian's home and summon his wife Christiana and her four sons to follow in her husband's steps. As he left, Mrs. Timorous and Mercy came to the door, and Christiana told them she must leave on a pilgrimage. In vain Mrs. Timorous tried to dissuade her. Christiana had made her mind up, so she left and Mercy went with her, leaving Mrs. Timorous behind to gossip of such strange happenings with her friends Mrs. Bat's Eyes, Mrs. Inconsiderate, Mrs. Lightmind and Mrs. Know-nothing.

With little trouble, they passed through the Slough of Despond and came to the wicket gate. Here Mercy fainted because she had only joined her friend and had no summons and was afraid that admittance would be denied her. Nevertheless, she gained enough courage to knock. At first, only the barking of a vicious dog could be heard. Then the gate was opened and she was welcomed in.

Once safely on the other side of the gate, she asked about the dog. She was told it was owned by another whose walls came right down to the gate, and was allowed to roam there to scare away pilgrims.

These walls also ran alongside the way the pilgrims had to follow. Behind them grew trees bearing juicy fruit, some of which overhung the path. Regardless of their mother's warnings, the children plucked and ate some of these as they passed by.

They had not gone far past here before Christiana saw two Ill-favoured Ones approaching. Blocking the path, these two attacked the women and, no doubt, would have seriously assaulted them had not they cried out for help. However, their cries were heard and a Reliever came to their aid, driving the men back. Afterwards he told the women that if they had but asked at the gate, a protector would have been sent along the way with them. So they confessed their foolishness and asked that the Reliever should, on his return, petition for such a protector, as they were but weak.

Although hard going, the way was uneventful until the party came to the Interpreter's house. Here they were received with great joy and the old saints rejoiced at the young one's walking in God's ways. Here they were shown the sights that Christiana's husband had seen, and also others. They were shown, for instance, the man who looked always down while just above his head was held a crown. This, Christiana recognized, was he who looked only on worldly things. Then, in the best room, they were shown a venomous spider on the wall to prove that no matter how full of the venom of sin, Faith can let you dwell in the best house of the king. Also, they were shown chickens feeding which lifted their eyes in gratitude to Heaven after each peck, and the slaughter house where the sheep went uncomplaining to their death. Then, in the gardens, the Interpreter pointed out the tree which, although flourishing without, was rotten within.

Having rested a while in this house, they were taken again into the garden and washed and sanctified and a seal put on all their foreheads. Then they were dressed in fine white linen and sent again on their way, but this time with a guide, a man called Great-heart who was well equipped with armour.

As they went, they passed the cross where Christian's burden had fallen from his shoulders, and saw the spot where he had tried to free Simple, Sloth and Presumption. Neither had they moved, for they were there before them, hanged.

Hill Difficulty greatly taxed their strength when they came to it, and they had to rest in the arbour where Christian had forgotten his scroll. Here they ate and drank from a bottle which had been given to them by the Interpreter.

So they came eventually to the lions which had at first so frightened Christian. And they frightened the children likewise, so that they cringed behind in the rear and Great-heart demanded why was it that they loved to go before when there was no danger, yet came behind when the lions appeared.

Then, as Great-heart approached the lions, a certain Giant Grim appeared whom Great-heart engaged in combat and after a hectic fight killed. All were despondent when, at Watchful, the porter's, lodge, Great-heart had to leave them and return, as they had again failed to ask for his guidance throughout their pilgrimage. So they knocked, and were taken in and that night Christiana, at her own request, slept in the same room that her husband had occupied before.

Here it was, too, that after a week Mercy found a sweetheart called Mr. Brisk, of whom she had been warned by the other maidens. So she turned her time to working for the poor, and Mr. Brisk, unable to understand such things, left, saying of her that she was a pretty lass but troubled with ill conditions. Then shortly afterwards, Matthew, the first born, fell ill with terrible pains in his stomach and was taken to Mr. Skill, who diagnosed the trouble as something undigested and prescribed a purge made from the body and blood of Christ, to be taken in tears of repentance and Christiana remembered how the children had disobeyed her orders and eaten of the fruit that had overhung their path by the wicket gate. Fortunately Joseph, another son, remembered after this to send a message to Great-heart that he should be sent to guide them through the rest of the journey.

He arrived shortly afterwards, bringing with him food and drink from his Lord. Then again they set out, Prudence and Piety going a little way with them and Piety giving Christiana a map to help her on her way.

Leaving Prudence and Piety behind, the party went down into the Valley of Humiliation, where Christian had fought Apollyon and Christ had his country home when he was of the world. As they passed they saw a boy tending his father's sheep, singing, and happier in this Valley then all those in other places who were clothed in silk and velvet.

So on and into the Valley of the Shadow of Death which was alive with terrifying groans and the hissing of snakes, and where the ground was shaken with an earthquake, and James, another of Christiana's sons, grew sick with fear. Then, without warning, they met with a monster which blocked their path. Terror, by this time, had struck into the heart of all except Great-heart, who led them on and right up to the dragon which, on being approached so close, disappeared.

Mercy, however, could not resist looking back, and, as she did so, she saw that the monster was now behind them. So Great-heart turned and stood with sword drawn ready for any attack. And, the monster seeing that he was to be resisted, again went away and did not return.

Ahead of them lay yet another danger in the form of a pit completely blocking their way. As they reached it darkness and a blinding mist came down, so that they dared not move for fear they should fall in the pit and be swallowed up by its fire and smoke. Eagerly, they prayed for light, and their prayer was answered.

A little way farther on, fear again struck at them when Giant Maul rushed out of his cave at Great-heart and set about him with a club. But Great-heart stood up to him, and, killing him, cut off his head, which he erected on a pillar as a warning to others.

Then, just past the spot where Christian had met Faithful, they came across Old Honest asleep. Great-heart woke him up and persuaded him to join the party. As they continued, Old Honest told of the strangers he had met on his way, such as Mr. Fearing who had been terrified all the time, not of such things as lions and the jeers of Vanity Fair, but of sin, death and Hell, and his own unworthiness of acceptance in the Celestial City. Then he had met Mr. Self-will, who practised vice as well as virtue. Listening to Old Honest, the time passed quickly and they soon reached Gaius, who owned an inn where they could rest and eat. They were all happy with Gaius and stayed a month, during which time he suggested that Christiana's sons should marry and breed, so that their goodness might flourish on the earth.

Meanwhile, a hunt was organized for Slay-god, who was known to be in the vicinity. When he was found he had Feeble-mind in his clutches. As they approached he robbed him and then prepared to pick his bones. Weak and sickly, this man could have lasted very little longer, had not Great-heart and his companions set about Slay-god, slain him and rescued Feeble-mind.

It was soon after this that Matthew married Mercy, and James married Gaius' daughter Phebe. Ten days later they were all sent again on their way, their host refusing payment.

At Vanity Fair, they stayed at a good man's house owned by Mr. Mason, who had daughters called Grace and Martha. While at his house, these were married to Samuel and Joseph, Christiana's last sons. Actually, they were treated well at Vanity Fair, due to a monster with seven heads and ten horns ravaging the town and being hunted and killed by Great-heart and his friends.

So they went on and came to By-path Meadow, to the stile over which Christian went with Hopeful when they were taken by Giant Despair, and the men decided to seek out this Giant. Now, Giant Despair, being a Giant, thought no man could overcome him, so, Great-heart having challenged him, he harnessed himself and went out. Then the six men made up to him and beset him on all sides. Also, when Diffidence, his wife, came up to help him, Old Honest cut her down with one blow. Then they fought for their lives, and Giant Despair was brought to the ground, but was very loath to die. But

Great-heart was the cause of his death, for he left him not till he had severed his head from his shoulders.

Then they fell to demolishing Doubting Castle, from which place they released one Mr. Despondency, almost starved to death, and one Much-afraid, his daughter. Then again they went on their way and came to a man whose sword was drawn and whose face was all bloody, and who was a pilgrim, Valiant-for-truth, by name, who explained how three strangers had beset him, demanding that he should become one of them, go back from whence he had come, or die where he was. On turning down all three demands, these three, whose names were Wild-head, Inconsiderate and Pragmatic, had thereupon set upon him, but he had valiantly fought on for some three hours so determined in his right, that eventually he had driven them away.

Then they set to talking and the pilgrimage continued past the spot where Faithful had been killed, and past the hill Lucre and to the river by the Delectable Mountains. Here the son's children were left in the care of one put there for that purpose, and the party went on, passing Heedless and Too-bold, too sound asleep to wake, and catching up Stand-fast, who was on his knees giving thanks for being saved from temptation. For, as he joined them, he explained that he had been accosted by a certain Madame Bubble, who had offered him her body, purse and bed.

They came to the land of Beulah, where they rested. And while they waited there, a messenger came to Christiana telling her to prepare herself for crossing the final river. So, ten days after, she went, and crossed fearlessly to where a host of chariots waited to carry her up to the Celestial City. And as Valiant-for-truth answered his summons, and went with firm tread deeper and deeper into the water, he cried:

> " Death where is thy sting—
> Grave where is thy Victory? "

So he passed over, and all the trumpets sounded for him on the other side. And, one by one all the others were called and crossed over, except the sons and their wives who were left, for a while, to increase the Church in that place.

Perhaps they are still there. I do not know, for that was as far as my dream took me, and it was then that I awoke.

PEER GYNT

By HENDRIK IBSEN

*This poetic drama is an attack on egoism, shallowness
and lack of character. Peer Gynt is fundamentally
indolent and boastful, but he has a dangerous charm
which nearly protects him from justice. The piece was
published in 1867 and has been performed in nearly every
European country.*

ACROSS a wooded mountainside of Norway passes Peer
Gynt—a young peasant ne'er-do-well—followed by his
widowed mother. To her scoldings and coaxings he
is alike indifferent, and interrupts her to boast afresh of his
dangerous exploits (all of them imaginary) and of the fine
figure he will cut in the world some day.

The old mother, Aase, unwisely taunts Peer Gynt with
his failure to win Ingrid, the wealthy farmer's daughter, who
is being married that day. Peer, stung to action at last,
responds by lifting her on to a nearby roof—leaving her
there safely out of the way while he goes off to the wedding
—uninvited.

Once there he has to run the gauntlet of chaff from the
guests, who make fun of the unsuccessful suitor, clothed as
he is with his usual rags and bravado. Like the rest, he
gets tipsy, but is sobered a little at meeting for the first time
the sweet and lovely Solveig. She too is attracted, but
repulses his drunken advances, and Peer—finding that
Ingrid, the bride, is hiding from the unwanted bridegroom
—runs off with her into the hills.

Aslak, the blacksmith, swears to repeat the thrashing he
gave Peer Gynt the last time they met; the bride's father
runs out threatening murder and sudden death; while the
bridegroom gives way to weak rage. But it is too late to
stop the runaway pair. They are already almost out of
sight.

The next morning Peer leaves Ingrid on the mountainside.
He longs for Solveig, but though his mother, with Solveig
and her parents, are searching for him, he cannot go to
them, for his rape of the bride has made him an outlaw.

He knows, too, that the rest of the parish are hunting him down, and while in a mood of hard exhilaration, rejoicing in eluding them, he falls in with three bawdy cowherd girls.

From a night with them he embarks directly on another amorous adventure with a strange woman in green, but this time finds he has got into the clutches of the trolls, for the woman is the Troll King's daughter, and before he escapes from these hobglobins he adopts their selfish motto— " To be true to thyself is enough! "

Trolls and goblins are scared away by the sound of church bells which Solveig and her parents have set ringing in the churches in the valley. Peer escapes to the forest. On the way Solveig contrives to send him a basket of food, but runs off when he tries to approach her.

Peer builds himself a log hut, and to him there one day comes Solveig, full of love and pity for the brave lad who is now an outlaw. But Peer's happiness is as short-lived as his forgotten vows to earlier loves, one of whom he finds haunting the hut. It is the Troll King's daughter leading a limping urchin who, she says, is his son. Peer Gynt's ugly past rises before him. He dare not now return to his pure and lovely Solveig, and so he calls to her to wait a little, while he fetches up some logs. The last words, she hears are—

> " Be patient, child:
> Whether the time is long or short,
> You must just wait."

—as he runs off down the mountainside.

In his distress Peer remembers his mother. It is night, and he must be safely away before dawn, but he decides there is time to visit his old home once, before he leaves Norway for ever.

The little farmhouse is tumble-down and windowless, ruined by his dead father's extravagance and Peer's own laziness. His mother lies alone in the bare room, dying —she can scarcely rouse herself to welcome her son—while he sits down beside her on the bed, supporting her in his arms. He tries to cheer her by pretending that he is driving her in a sleigh over the snow—a game she used to play with *him* when he was a little boy. And soon she passes peacefully away in his arms.

*   *   *   *   *

Beneath a grove of palm trees on the coast of Morocco a dining-table is spread under an awning. Peer Gynt, now a good-looking middle-aged man, looks past the bare heads of his four guests, and smiles complacently as he catches sight of his yacht glimmering white in the distance.

Peer Gynt is holding forth to the admiring guests upon his philosophy of life. His success he attributes to his adherence to the troll's motto.

His friends applaud this sentiment, but they are not quite so confident when they hear that their distinguished-looking host made his money by importing slaves to America and exporting idols thence to China. And now he discloses that with their help he intends fully to realize his " Gyntian self " and become an emperor—by the simple process of financing the Greco-Turkish war. But when his friends discover that he proposes to support the common enemy, the Turks, who are " the stronger side," they desert him; and secretly set out and capture his yacht.

Peer Gynt wrings his hands and calls on God to punish the thieves, as he sees them steaming off at full speed. There is a sudden glare and a dull explosion, followed by a thick cloud of smoke. When it clears away the yacht has disappeared. Peer Gynt, prostrated, exclaims—

> " Thanks be to Thee who hast been my protector
> And kept an eye on me in spite of my failings!
> What a wonderful feeling of safety and comfort
> It gives you to know that you're specially guarded! "

Still, he feels that he would be wise to spend the night in a tree and out of reach of prowling lions; but at dawn he is driven out by a swarm of apes, who pelt him with filth.

He wanders off across the desert, at times fearful, at times dreaming dreams of fresh success and power, when, passing through a rocky ravine, suddenly he comes upon an emperor's charger, with robes and jewels to match. The thieves who have stolen them have fled into a cave, imagining they have heard the pursuit approaching, and Peer Gynt delightedly dons the robes and jewels and rides off on the charger.

Arriving in his new-found splendour at an oasis, he is welcomed as the Prophet by the simple people, their Arab chieftain, and his beautiful daughter Anitra.

Before long, however, he becomes bored with a Prophet's dignified isolation. His old failings reassert themselves and he makes advances to Anitra—cunningly beginning by promising to give her a soul, and then make her a houri in Paradise.

Anitra is more interested in his jewels than in his words, and he finds she has an appetite for opals but none for love. Finally he carries her off on his charger into the desert, and there he dismounts, and in his infatuation dances and sings to prove to Anitra how young he really is. Anitra persuades him to hand up to her his heavy money-belt, which impedes his dancing, and at once she turns and gallops back to the camp, leaving him stranded alone in the desert once again.

Peer Gynt wanders along, musing on his experiences, and stripping off his robes as he goes, until he stands once more in European dress. The only thing left for him now, he decides, is to take up archaeology!

*   *   *   *   *

In far away Norway, Solveig, now a handsome middle-aged woman, sits spinning at the door of the self-same hut that Peer had built before he deserted her. As she spins she gazes down the path and sings—

> " It may not be till winter's past,
>   And spring and summer—the whole long year;
>   But I know that you will come at last,
>   And I shall wait, for I promised you, dear."

Meantime Peer Gynt, the centre of Solveig's thoughts, the subject of Solveig's song, has made his way to the Sphinx. Here he falls in with a new admirer of Gyntian philosophy, Professor Begriffenfeldt, who is (though our hero does not know it) the director of the Cairo lunatic asylum.

This new admirer, with many flattering phrases, induces Peer Gynt, the psuedo-antiquarian, to return with him to his " Savants' Club ". On arrival there he immediately locks the keepers into one of the cages, releases the occupants of the others, and whispers to his guest that this was an asylum of which he was Director until " Absolute reason expired at eleven o'clock last night! "

Begriffenfeldt then announces that the inmates are ready to acclaim Peer Gynt Emperor, and that all are worthy followers of Gyntian philosophy.

The horrified Peer Gynt is forced by Begriffenfeldt to

interview and to advise some of the lunatics about their troubles.

One is distressed because nobody will recognize in him a family resemblance to King Apis, whose mummy he carries about with him on his back. Peer Gynt advises him to hang himself, behave like one who is dead, and thus increase the resemblance; but is horrified when his half-jesting advice is immediately taken!

Another lunatic desires to be used by the new Emperor to sign state documents, for his body, he explains, is really a pen. This pen, however, needs sharpening, and the lunatic, seizing a knife, cuts his throat.

Peer Gynt shrieks and sinks down in a swoon, and Begriffenfeldt leaps astride him and thrusts a straw crown on the prostrate Peer's head, shouting.

*   *   *   *   *

Leaning on the gunwale of a ship and gazing at the distant coast of Norway is a vigorous but weather-beaten old man with grey hair and beard. It is Peer Gynt. In the long interval of years he has been many things—trapper of Hudson's Bay, gold-miner of San Francisco—and now he is returning home at last, from Panama.

The captain passes by and Peer Gynt calls to him to remind him of the promised present his passenger is making to the crew when they shall have safely reached the harbour. But when the captain says how pleased their wives and children will be and what a red-letter day this money will make of the home-coming, Peer Gynt bangs his fist on the gunwale—

> " No, I'm damned if they shall have it!
> Do you think me such a fool
> As to fork out for the pleasure
> Of helping other people's children?
> I've worked too hard to get my money!
> No one's waiting for old Peer Gynt."

Night falls and the wind increases. A storm-tossed wreck comes into view and figures can be seen clinging to it. Though Peer Gynt shouts for a boat to be lowered the boatswain refuses—a boat would not live in those mounting seas—and Peer Gynt is left to moralize on the cowardly dogs who would not go to the rescue of their fellows, although they too have wives and children waiting for them.

In the gloom Peer Gynt finds a pale Stranger standing

beside him. The Stranger begs from him, but it appears that he does not want money—he predicts the wreck of the ship and begs the gift of Peer Gynt's corpse.

While Peer Gynt is unsuccessfully trying to rid himself of this uncomfortable companion, a cry of " Breakers ahead ! " is heard, the ship runs on the rocks and, a total wreck, rapidly sinks from sight. On either side of an upturned boat Peer Gynt and the ship's cook come spluttering to the surface, and each immediately clings to the keel. They fight for possession of it. The cook is hurt and cries that he is young and has children waiting for him at home, but old Peer Gynt mercilessly watches him slip off and drown.

And now the pale Stranger again appears to argue with Peer Gynt, and this time tries to show him to himself as he really is.

Peer Gynt's time is not yet at hand however, he reaches land safely.

In his wanderings he comes upon the sale of some rubbishy household goods outside a broken-down mill. A man in mourning disconsolately looks on and talks with a man in grey. Peer Gynt joins in the conversation and discovers he is in the company of his old enemy, Aslak, the blacksmith, who, it seems, eventually married Peer's boyhood sweetheart Ingrid. She has died, the home is being sold up, and Aslak (the man in mourning) is dejectedly recalling the old days, and the young Peer's escapade and deception of the bridegroom, who it turns out is the man in grey.

Peer Gynt remains unrecognized, even when he enter-tains the crowd with some of his tall stories in his old bragging manner; but this bravado cloaks the discomfiture he feels.

At last, on the Eve of Pentecost, he reaches the great forest. Hunger has forced him to grub up wild onions from the ground, and he does not at first notice the log hut which stands amongst the trees. As he roots on all fours in the leaves he mutters to himself of his coming end and composes this epitaph—

> " Here lies Peer Gynt, a decent chap,
>   Who was Emperor of all the Beasts."

And now the hut catches his eye. He starts, and as he recognizes the humble home he built, the home in which he left Solveig, so many years ago, he hears her voice within singing her song of patient waiting, " Dear lad far away, are you coming near ? "

Peer Gynt, deathly pale, rises to his feet, and crying, " Ah misery! *Here* my empire lay! " he runs away into the wood.

By nightfall he reaches a moor covered with charred trees—relics of a forest fire—standing amongst patches of white mist lying near the ground. Running and stumbling, Peer Gynt is tormented by voices—voices of withered leaves, of the sighing of songs he might have sung, of the dew-drops dripping from branches—tears he might have shed, of broken straws who say they are the deeds he left undone.

Last of all he hears his dead mother's voice, and in desperation flees from it to another part of the moor.

But here he meets a button moulder carrying a big casting ladle, which, it appears, is intended for recasting melted down sinners, who (like Peer Gynt) are too bad to go to Heaven and not bad enough to go to Hell.

Peer Gynt, however, argues that his personality has value and needs no re-casting—that he has always been " himself ". The button moulder gives him a chance to find witnesses to prove this statement, and leaves him—but with the warning that they will meet again at the next cross-roads.

Still wandering across the moor, but now looking out desperately for anyone he can find and persuade to bear witness on his behalf, Peer Gynt meets an old beggar. But the old man turns out to be the Troll King, whose daughter Peer Gynt dishonoured in his wild young days. The Troll King refuses to be a witness to Peer Gynt's value, and reminds him of the motto he adopted, the motto that distinguishes trolls from decent human beings—" To be true to thyself is enough ! "? The button moulder appears again.

This time Peer Gynt asks him, " What is it really to be one's self ? " The answer comes, " To be one's self is to slay one's self—one's baser self," and to live according to the Master's intention, as shown to us by insight. But Peer Gynt again decides he is not for the casting-ladle this time because he says he is a great sinner, not a mediocre one—and eventually he is again given a chance to find proof before the next cross-roads is reached. He now hunts everywhere for a parson, and soon meets a thin person in a priest's cassock with a bird-catcher's net over his shoulder.

Noticing a hoof where a right foot should have been

Peer Gynt realizes he is talking to the Devil. So he tries to strike a bargain and obtain " a snug retreat " in Hell.

" A nice warm room? " asks the thin person.

Peer Gynt replies, " But not too warm. And preferably, I should like an easy access, in and out, so that I could retrace my steps if opportunity should offer for something better."

The thin person answers, " My dear friend, I really am extremely sorry, but you can't think how very often exactly similar requests are made to me by people leaving the scene of all their earthly labours." He excuses himself, because, he says, he is in a hurry to find a certain person who " has been persistently himself by day and night."

When Peer Gynt realizes that he himself is this certain person, he sends the Devil off on a wild goose chase to the Cape of Good Hope, where he says he met Peer Gynt.

And now Peer Gynt hears the churchfolk singing on the road below: " Oh blessed day of Pentecost." He turns away in terror and tries to steal into the thickets, but finds himself again at the cross-roads.

The button moulder impatiently asks for the promised list of sins, and Peer Gynt, desperately trying to gain time, points to something shining. " Only the light in a house," says the button moulder. " And that sound, like wailing? " " Only a woman's song," replies the button moulder.

Now the day is dawning, and suddenly they find themselves standing near Solveig's hut. Peer Gynt throws himself down at the threshold, crying, " Pronounce the sentence on a sinner." But Solveig—an almost blind Solveig—gropes for him and gathers him to her arms.

He asks her then to solve a riddle for him, or straightway he must go to his last home in the land of shadows; the riddle, " Where Peer Gynt has been since last we met— where was my real self, complete and true—the Peer who bore the stamp of God upon his brow? "

And Solveig answers, " In my faith, in my hope, and in my love." " But," questions Peer, " so speaks a mother of her child." And Solveig's reply is, " Ah yes; and that is what I am; but He Who grants a pardon for the sake of a mother's prayers—He is his father."

A ray of light seems to flash on Peer Gynt and he cries— " Mother and wife! You stainless woman! Oh hide me, hide me in your love! "

GULLIVER'S TRAVELS

INTO SEVERAL REMOTE NATIONS OF THE WORLD

By JONATHAN SWIFT

This is among the best known satires in the whole of literature. " The work," says " The Oxford Companion to English Literature ", " has, with the exception of certain passages, the rare merit of appealing to both old and young, as a powerful satire on man and human institutions and as a fascinating tale of travels in wonderland." It was published in 1726, the year before Swift's last visit to England. It was the only one of his numerous works for which he received any payment.

O N May 4th, 1699, I left my young wife, with whom I had received a dowry of £400, and as ship's surgeon of the *Antelope* set out on a voyage to the South Sea. A violent storm carried us north-west of Van Dieman's Land, and the ship split against a rock. I found myself, alone, on a deserted sea-shore where I fell asleep, exhausted, on the short, soft grass. On waking and attempting to rise, I was unable to move hand or foot: my arms and legs, and even my hair, were firmly fastened to the ground by strong lengths of twine. All about me was a confused noise. I felt something creep along my left leg and advance up to my chin. Standing on my breast was a human creature, not six inches high, armed with a bow and arrow. At the sight of him I roared with astonishment, and he and his retinue ran away. When I tried to break loose from the strings, a hundred arrows, pricking like needles, were discharged into my left hand. I thought it prudent to lay quiet, and after a while, the crowd around me increasing, an important personage about the size of my middle finger mounted a specially constructed stage and delivered a speech to me. I showed myself to be submissive, and, being almost starved, by means of signs begged for food. By the King's orders, a hundred of the inhabitants mounted ladders and walked towards my mouth to feed me. I ate two or three legs and loins of meat which were smaller than larks' wings, and loaves no bigger than musket bullets, at a mouthful. The inhabitants of Lilliput, for such was the country's name, delighted with my appetite, danced for joy upon my breast. After a Hurgo (as I afterwards learnt they called a great lord) had made me understand that I should be well treated as their prisoner, I fell asleep under the influence of a powerful drug mixed in my wine, and on the kingdom's largest engine was removed by an army of workmen to the Metropolis. The journey was half a mile and took two days. I was lodged and chained in a disused temple where the Emperor came to visit me.

This prince, who by his decision to keep me in custody instead of trying to kill me had already marked himself as more prudent and generous than any in Europe, was taller almost by the breadth of my nail than any of his court, whose members were so richly clad that the ground they stood on resembled an embroidered petticoat. He was then past his prime, being nearly twenty-nine years old, and had reigned happily about seven years. He visited me frequently and helped me to learn the language. At his request I submitted to a search, and two of his officers, whom I picked up and put into my pockets, made the following inventory of my belongings:

"Imprimis, In the right coat pocket of the 'Great Man-Mountain' (for so I interpret the *Quinbus Flestrin*), we found only one great piece of coarse cloth, large enough to be a foot-cloth for your Majesty's chief room of state (the entry referred to my handkerchief). In the left pocket, we saw a huge silver chest, and one of us stepping in, found himself up to the mid leg in a sort of dust, some part whereof flying up to our faces, set us both a-sneezing (my snuff-box). In the left waistcoat pocket, there was a sort of engine, from the back of which were extended twenty long poles, wherewith we conjecture the Man-Mountain combs his head. In each breeches pocket was a hollow pillar of iron (my brace of pistols). In the smaller pocket on the right side, were several round, flat pieces of white and red metal that my comrade and I could hardly lift (my money). Out of the right fob hung a great silver chain, with a wonderful kind of engine at the bottom which made an incessant noise, like that of a water-mill (my watch)." All these articles together with some others were taken away from me.

My gentle behaviour obtained for me the Emperor's good-

will, and one day he entertained me with several of the country
shows, none of which pleased me more than the tight-rope
dancing, practised only by candidates for high positions in
court. But I learnt that the country was not so flourishing
as it appeared to foreigners, being racked by the struggles
of the Tramecksan and Slamecksan, two parties distinguished
by the high or low heels of their shoes. Further, Lilliput was
threatened by invasion from the Island of Blefuscu, the cause
of the war being a difference of opinion as to whether eggs
should be broken at the bigger or the smaller end. The Emperor claimed my assistance against the invaders. The
channel between the two countries being only eight hundred
yards wide, I could see the enemy's fleet of men of war
riding at anchor. I made some cables, pulled off my coat,
shoes and stockings, waded through the sea which was barely
seventy *glumgluffs* (or six feet) deep in the middle, and in
half an hour arrived at the hostile armada. While I hooked
my cables to the prows, the enemy shot thousands of arrows
at me, and I should surely have been blinded if I had not
protected my eyes with my spectacles. But cutting the
anchor cables of the men of war, with the greatest of ease I
hauled fifty of the enemy's largest vessels away with me and
handed them over to the Emperor of Lilliput.

But so ambitious are princes, he desired the reduction of
the whole Empire of Blefuscu to a province governed by a
Viceroy. As I firmly refused to be a party to a people's slavery,
from this time on I was the victim of intrigue. Not even the
service I rendered to his Majesty in putting out a fire in the
Queen's apartments entirely regained his favour: for the only
effective means I could use broke a law of the land against
making water in the palace precincts. Some of the laws and
customs in this empire are very peculiar. Fraud is treated
as a crime more serious than theft. Every law-abiding citizen
is rewarded with a title and money. Good morals are better
credentials for a position than great abilities. Ingratitude is
punished by death. And parents are considered the least
capable of bringing up their own children.

To escape the enmity of the Lord High Admiral, who
was jealous of my naval success and who, I was informed,
was plotting my death on a charge of high treason, I fled to
Blefuscu, where, on the north-east coast, I discovered a real
boat. After this had been renovated and provisioned, I took
my leave. Picked up by an English merchant-man trading

with Japan, the captain thought I was raving when I told him my adventures, until I showed him the cattle and sheep I had put in my pocket as keepsakes.

A Voyage to Brobdingnag

I stayed but two months in England, where I found it profitable to put my diminutive cattle on exhibition, and then I began my second travels in a boat bound for Surat. East of the Molucca Islands we were caught in a monsoon which carried us to the shores of an unknown continent or island. A dozen of us left the ship anchored off a creek to forage for fresh water. Returning from a short walk, I saw the men rowing for their lives away from a prodigious monster who waded after them. I hid in a field of standing corn with stalks remarkable for being forty feet high. But seven monsters as tall as church steeples came to reap the field, and I was trapped under the huge corn stalks. Struck with fear, grief and despair, thoughts of Lilliput where I had been esteemed as the world's greatest prodigy, came to my mind. When one of the giant reapers appeared almost on top of me, I screamed in terror. He looked at me as though I were a dangerous little animal, but my endeavours by voice and gesture to prevent him from destroying me were successful, and, picking me up between his thumb and forefinger, he carried me off to the farmer.

To make a good impression, I walked up and down in front of the farmer, pulled off my hat and bowed, and tried to answer him. He possessed a voice which thundered in my ear like a water-mill. The farmer showed me to his wife who screamed and started like an Englishwomen at the sight of a toad. But she soon became accustomed to me and took me into her family: Her little daughter, Glumdalclitch, looked after me, taught me the language of Brobdingnag, and came to love me as she would a doll. The neighbours were curious to see the strange animal about the size of a *splacknuck* which the farmer had found, so I was taken to the nearest market town to be put on show. As I was placed in a small box and carried on the bumping back of a horse that covered forty feet each step, the journey was most uncomfortable. I was exhibited in the largest room of an inn, made to perform various tricks and repeat them twelve times during the day to new audiences who paid for admission. Seeing how profitable

I would prove to him, the farmer conveyed me to the metropolis called Lorbrulgrud or Pride of the Universe, where I gave ten performances a day to an admiring and wondering populace, and was finally brought before the Queen, who was so delighted that she bought me from the farmer there and then, and engaged Glumdalclitch as my nurse.

I was provided with proper living quarters, and became such a favourite of the Queen's that I always sat with her at dinner, eating off plates that, compared to hers, resembled those sold in the London shops for dolls-houses. For some time the sight of the Queen eating was nauseous to me. She would fill her mouth with the wing of a lark nine times as large as a full-grown turkey, and each bite of bread she took was the size of two twelve-penny loaves. When His Majesty dined with the Queen on Wednesdays, he frequently discoursed with me about the customs of European countries: on one occasion he took me up in his hand and, laughing heartily, asked me whether I was a Whig or a Tory, remarking to his prime minister "how contemptible a thing was human grandeur which could be mimicked by such diminutive insects." I recounted to him the history of our country, and he protested that the last century was nothing but a mass of conspiracies, massacres and revolutions produced by avarice, cruelty, hatred or ambition. "My little friend Grildrig," he said, "you have most admirably sung your country's praises. You have clearly proved that ignorance and vice are the proper qualifications for a legislator, and that laws are best explained, interpreted and applied by those whose interest it is to pervert, confound and elude them. I cannot but conclude the bulk of your natives to be the most pernicious race of little, odious vermin that Nature ever suffered to crawl upon the earth."

Hoping to win back his favour, I offered to initiate him into the mystery and power of the manufacture of gunpowder, by which he could blow to pieces any town that disputed his authority. The King was horrified. He said he would rather lose half his kingdom than take advantage of such a secret.

I had spent two years in Brobdingnag, and was becoming weary of living in conditions comparable to those of a pet canary in a cage, when the Queen took me on a journey with her to the coast. And there, left unguarded for a while, my box houses was seized by an eagle, carried off across the sea, and for some reason dropped into the water. When I first observed the sailors of the ship that rescued me. I thought they

were the most little, contemptible creatures I had ever seen.
In England, I was afraid of trampling on the passers-by,
and shouted to them to get out of my way, and so behaved
myself that my family at first imagined I had gone out of my
mind.

A Voyage to the Houyhnhnms

After another voyage which took me to Laputa, the floating
island of the theoreticians, to Glubbdubdrib, the island of
magicians, where I spoke with the illustrious dead, and to the
kingdom of Luggnag, with its *struldbrugs*, a caste of immortals,
followed by a period of five months at home, I set off again as
captain of the *Adventure*. But in the South Seas I was turned
adrift in the long-boat by buccaneers who set me down by the
shores of an unknown country, where I came face to face with as
objectionable an animal as I ever beheld in my travels. His
head and breast were matted with hair: a long ridge of hair
grew down his spine and on the fore-parts of its leg and feet;
its skin was of a pale brown complexion; its face was flat
and broad, with thick lips and wide nostrils; and its hands
resembled mine except for the excessive length of the nails.
I was horrified to see in this abomination an almost exact
image of a human being. A mob of these filthy creatures
attacked me. But suddenly they all ran away as though
frightened. I looked about me and saw the object of their fear
to be a grey horse walking softly in the field. To my surprise
it neighed most eloquently to a companion, and the two horses
examined me closely, behaving so rationally that I concluded
they were metamorphosed magicians. The grey firmly guided
me to a building, where two nags and three mares seemed
quite at home attending to the domestic affairs usually associated
with ordinary people.

Having a natural propensity for foreign languages, within
ten weeks I could answer most of my master's questions. He
was curious to know how I could appear rational, when all
Yahoos could be taught nothing. I begged him not to think
of me as being of the same kind as those odious animals that the
Houyhnhnms (a word which signifies " horse " or " the perfection
of nature ") employed as their slaves. I assured him that my
fellow countrymen regarded themselves as the only rational
beings. My master found difficulty in accepting my statement;
for he was a stranger to lying, and could not accustom his
mind to the idea of placing a Yahoo higher than a Houyhnhnm.

He pointed out that I was inferior even to a Yahoo in many ways: my nails were useless; my two legs had not the stability of four; and my body was lacking in natural covering. In answer to a request he made, I told him that amongst the innumerable causes of war in Europe could be mentioned: the dissatisfaction of ambitious rulers with the extent of their territory; the cunning of ministers who wish to divert public attention from their own corrupt administration; and differences of opinion as to whether the juice of a certain berry be wine or blood, or whether a post should be kissed or burnt. My description of war and its savage slaughter of thousands, its obliterating bombardments, its rape, avarice and destruction he silenced in horror. He observed that the corruption of the power of reason in humanity appeared worse than the brute state itself. I described the prime minister to him as a man who never tells the truth except that it might be taken as a lie; and that those he censures are most likely to be promoted, while a man he praises can give up all hope. The English aristocracy, I explained, were bred into luxury and idleness, living for little else but to contract money marriages and diseases. My recognition of the Houyhnhnms' superior qualities had made me somewhat critical of man. My master pointed out that the Yahoos likewise hated each other, fought over food, possessions and females; and that their leaders allowed their posteriors to be licked by favourites.

The nobility of the Houyhnhnms is apparent in their cultivation of reason, which for them is not a talent for wranglings and disputes, but a means of securing immediate conviction. The two virtues they most employ are friendship and benevolence. They bring up their children to be industrious, active and clean. Their love of moderation showed itself at one of their Grand Assemblies, when a resolution to exterminate all Yahoos from the face of the earth was modified to one proposing castration so as to allow time for the young Yahoos to be tamed and trained.

From my master's wise lectures I acquired what little knowledge I now possess. I was perfectly happy in the Houyhnhnms' society where I could not be assailed by the treachery of friend or foe, where battening physicians and lawyers, deceiving politicians, vain women, proud pedants and the rest are unknown. I had no desire to return to my family, friends or countrymen whom I valued no more than Yahoos. Unfortunately, certain of the Houyhnhnm representatives

took exception to my master treating me, a Yahoo, as one
equal to themselves.   When my master informed me I should
have to depart, I fell in a swoon at his feet.   My heart heavy
with grief, I took my leave of him, and journeyed to Lisbon.
But my memory was so inspired with the virtues of the
Houyhnhnms that ordinary men and women filled me with
ungovernable terror, and I had to plug my nostrils to keep
out the stench of them.   When my wife kissed me at our meeting after a three years' separation, I fainted, nor could I
endure her presence for a year after.

So, gentle reader, I have presented to you a faithful history
of my travels, not for the sake of fame, but solely for the public
good.   For who can read of the Houyhnhnms' virtues without
feeling ashamed of himself ?   It might be wondered why I
did not take steps to ensure that England could annex those
lands I discovered.   But what happens on such occasions?
A crew of pirates is driven by a storm to an uncharted country:
they land in order to plunder a harmless people: they reward
kindness with appropriation in the name of their king, and thus
establish a new dominion, which is civilized by the sword.
However, the example of the British nation in the planting of
colonies is wholly admirable.   By their vigilant and virtuous
governors, who care only for the happiness of the subject
race, religion is advanced and justice is strictly administered.

As for myself, I shall retire to my little garden in Rotherhithe
to educate the Yahoos of my own family in the virtues of the
excellent Houyhnhnms.   Last week I began to permit my
wife to sit at dinner with me, at the farthest end of a long
table.

THE BHAGAVAD-GITA

THE SONG OF THE LORD

The Bhagavad-Gita, or Song of the Lord, is an episode in the epic of the Mahábhârata, and contains the teachings given by the divine Shrî Krishna to his disciple, Arjuna, on the field of battle. Arjuna, who is of the warrior caste, finds himself obliged to fight against his kinsfolk ; his noble soul is troubled by an apparent conflict of duties. Krishna, in the rôle of his charioteer, replies by voicing the great principle of the Upanishads (the sacred scriptures of India) : the soul is indestructible. It neither comes into existence nor dies, and when it passes to a new life, the wise do not grieve. Arjuna's duty as a warrior is to fight, regardless of consequences. From that point the Song develops into a discourse which gives a complete system of ethics and religion. While adopting the Upanishadic teaching about one reality behind all appearances, the One has become a personal being, incarnate on earth as Krishna, with a nature which makes Him an object of love and devotion to his worshippers. The Song teaches a means of approaching the Lord. It is the practice of training and concentrating the mind called Yoga, which is literally 'yoking' ; the resultant control of the mind makes union with God possible.

1. THE DESPONDENCY OF ARJUNA

MOVED with deepest pity, Arjuna said : "As I see these my people, O Krishna, arrayed eager for battle, my limbs fail, my mouth is parched, my bow slips from my hand, and my mind is in a whirl. I wish not for victory, O Krishna, nor kingship, nor pleasures. Teachers, fathers, sons and other kinsfolk—them I wish not to slay, though slain myself, not even for kingship over the three worlds. Although these, with intelligence overpowered by greed, see no guilt in the destruction of a family, why should not we learn to turn away from such a sin? When a family is destroyed, the eternal family laws of righteousness perish; when unrighteousness prevails, O Krishna, the women of the family are corrupted; when the women are corrupted, there arises confusion of caste. This draggeth to Hell the slayers of the family, and the family; for their ancestors fall, deprived of rice-balls and water offered to the dead. Caste and family customs are abolished, and the abode of men whose family laws of righteousness are ruined is ever in Hell. Thus have we heard. Alas! in committing a great sin are we engaged!"

Thus Arjuna spoke, sank down, dropped his bow and arrow, his mind shaken with grief.

2. SANKHYA, *or* THE DISCRIMINATIVE WISDOM

To Arjuna the Blessed Lord said: "Yield not to impotence, it doth not befit thee. Shake off this paltry faint-heartedness! Stand up, Parantapa! (conqueror of foes)."

Arjuna said: "My mind is confused as to duty. I ask thee which may be the better—that tell me decisively."

The Blessed Lord, smiling, as it were, said: "The wise grieve neither for the living nor for the dead. Nor at any time verily was I not, nor thou, nor these princes of men, nor verily shall we ever cease to be, hereafter. As the dweller in the body experienceth in the body childhood, youth, old age, so passeth he on to another body; the steadfast one grieveth not thereat. Weapons cleave him not, nor fire burneth him, nor waters wet him, nor wind drieth him away. This dweller in the body is ever invulnerable. Looking to thine own duty thou shouldst not tremble. Slain, thou wilt obtain Heaven; victorious, thou wilt enjoy the earth; therefore stand up, O son of Kunti, resolute to fight. This is the Sankhya teaching; hear it now according to Yoga, imbued with which teaching thou shalt cast away the bonds of action. Even a little of this knowledge protects from great fear.

Perform action, renouncing attachments, and balanced evenly in success and failure: equilibrium is called yoga. Cleave thou to yoga; yoga is skill in action. . . ."

Arjuna said: "What is the mark of him whose knowledge is fixed, and who is fixed in concentration? How will he speak, sit or move?"

The Blessed Lord said: "When he abandons all desires of the mind and is satisfied in the SELF by the SELF, then is he called one whose knowledge is fixed.

"If a man meditates on the objects of sense, attachment to them arises; from attachment desire is born; from desire anger is produced. The man who forsakes all desires, without the thought of mine, or I, attains to peace. This is the Brahma-state."

3. ACTION

Arjuna said: "If intellect is deemed by thee to be more excellent than action, why dost thou impose upon me a terrible action?"

The Blessed Lord said: "Do thou prescribed action. Action is more excellent than non-action. Even the maintenance of thy body would not be achieved if thou didst not act. With this nourish ye the Shining Ones and they shall nourish you. Therefore, without attachment, constantly perform action which is duty, for, by performing action without attachment, man verily reacheth the Supreme.

"Resigning all actions to me, with thy thoughts resting on the supreme SELF, from hope and egoism freed, and of mental fever cured, engage in battle.

"Affection and aversion for the objects of sense abide in the senses; let none come under the dominion of these two; they are obstructors of the path."

Arjuna said: "Then by what is the man urged on that he commits sin, even without wishing it, as though constrained by force?"

The Blessed Lord said: "It is desire, it is anger; know that in this world that is the enemy.

"Therefore mastering first the senses, do thou slay this thing of sin, destructive of wisdom and knowledge."

4. KNOWLEDGE

The Blessed Lord said: "This imperishable yoga I declared to Vivasvan; Vivasvan taught it to Manu; Manu to Ikshavaku told it. This, handed on down the line, the King-Sages knew. This yoga by great efflux of time decayed in the world; today it hath been declared to thee by Me, for thou art My devotee and My friend; it is the supreme Secret.

"Whenever there is decay of righteousness and exaltation of unrighteousness, then I Myself come forth; for the protection of the good, for the destruction of evil-doers, I am born from age to age.

"He who thus knoweth My divine birth and action, in its

essence, having abandoned the body, cometh not to birth again, but cometh unto Me, O Arjuna.

"Freed from passion, fear and anger, filled with Me, taking refuge in Me, purified in the fire of wisdom, many have entered into My Being. However men approach Me, even so do I welcome them, for the path men take from every side is Mine.

"'What is action, what inaction?' I will declare to thee the action by knowing which thou shalt be loosed from evil.

"Whose works are all free from the moulding of desire, whose actions are burned up by the fire of wisdom, him the wise have called a Sage.

"Having abandoned attachment to the fruit of action, always content, nowhere seeking refuge, he is not doing anything, although doing actions.

"Hoping for naught, his mind and self controlled, having abandoned all greed, performing actions by the body alone, he doth not commit sin

"Better than material sacrifice is the sacrifice of wisdom, O hero. All actions in their entirety culminate in wisdom. Learn thou this by discipleship, by investigation, and by service. And having known this, thou shalt not again fall into this confusion.

"Even if thou art the most sinful of all sinners, yet shalt thou cross over all sin by the raft of wisdom.

"Therefore, with the sword of the wisdom of the SELF cleaving asunder this ignorance-born doubt, dwelling in thy heart, be established in yoga. Stand up, O Bharata."

5. RENUNCIATION OF ACTIONS

Arjuna said: "Renunciation of actions Thou praisest, O Krishna, and then also yoga. Of the two which one is the better? That tell me conclusively."

The Blessed Lord said: "Renunciation and yoga by action both lead to the highest bliss; of the two, yoga by action is verily better.

"He who is harmonized by yoga, the self-purified, SELF-ruled, the senses subdued, whose SELF is the SELF of all beings, although acting he is not affected.

"Mentally renouncing all actions, the sovereign dweller in the body resteth serenely in the nine-gated city (the body, often called the city of the ETERNAL), neither acting nor causing to act.

" The delights that are contact-born, they are verily wombs of pain, for they have beginning and ending; not in them may rejoice the wise. ͻ

" He who is able to endure here on earth, ere he be liberated from the body, the force born from desire and passion, he is harmonized, he is a happy man.

" The Peace of the Eternal (Nirvâna) lies near to those who know themselves, and are disjoined from desire and passion, subdued in nature, of subdued thoughts.

" Having known Me, as the Enjoyer of sacrifice and of austerity, the mighty Ruler of all the worlds, and the Lover of all beings, he goeth to Peace."

6. MEDITATION

The Blessed Lord said: " He that performeth such action as duty, independently of the fruit of action, he is an ascetic, he is a Yogi, not he that is without fire, and without rites.

" The higher Self of him who is SELF-controlled and peaceful is uniform in cold and heat, pleasure and pain, as well as in honour and dishonour.

" He who regards impartially lovers, friends, and foes, strangers, neutrals, foreigners and relatives, also the righteous and unrighteous, he excelleth.

" Let the Yogi constantly engage himself in yoga, remaining in a secret place by himself, with thought and self subdued, free from hope and greed.

" Having made the mind one-pointed, with thought and the functions of the senses subdued, steady on his seat, he should practise yoga for the purification of the self.

" Verily yoga is not for him who eateth too much, nor who abstaineth to excess, nor who is too much addicted to sleep, nor even to wakefulness, O Arjuna.

" Yoga killeth out all pain for him who is regulated in eating and amusement, regulated in performing actions, regulated in sleeping and waking.

" As a lamp in a windless place flickereth not, to such is likened the Yogi of subdued thought, absorbed in the yoga of the SELF.

" That should be known by the name of yoga, this dis-connection from the union with pain. This yoga must be clung to with a firm conviction and with undesponding mind."

Arjuna said: "This yoga which Thou hast declared to be by equanimity, I see not a stable foundation for it, owing to restlessness; for the mind is verily restless, O Krishna; it is impetuous, strong and difficult to bend. I deem it as hard to curb as the wind."

The Blessed Lord said: "Without doubt the mind is hard to curb and restless; but it may be curbed by constant practice and by dispassion."

Arjuna said: "He who is unsubdued but who possesseth faith, with the mind wandering away from yoga, failing to attain perfection in yoga, what path doth he tread, O Krishna?"

The Blessed Lord said: "Neither in this world nor in the life to come is there destruction for him; never doth any who worketh righteousness, O beloved, tread the path of woe.

"Having attained to the worlds of the pure-doing, and having dwelt there for immemorial years, he who fell from yoga is reborn in a pure and blessed house; or he may even be born into a family of wise Yogis; but such a birth as that is most difficult to obtain in this world.

"The Yogi is greater than the ascetics; he is thought to be greater than even the wise; the Yogi is greater than the men of action; therefore become thou a Yogi, O Arjuna!"

7. KNOWLEDGE OF THE LORD

"With the mind clinging to me, performing yoga, refuged in Me, how thou shalt without doubt know Me to the uttermost, that hear thou.

"Among thousands of men scarce one striveth for perfection; of the successful strivers, scarce one knoweth Me in essence.

"Earth, water, fire, air, space (ether), mind, reason, and the thought of I (individuality), these form my nature in its eightfold division.

"This is my lower nature. But know that other than this is my higher nature. It is the life-principle, O mighty-armed, by which the world is sustained.

"Know Me as the eternal seed of all beings. I am the Reason of the Reason-endowed, the splendour of splendid things am I.

"Fourfold in division are the righteous ones who worship me, O Arjuna: the suffering, the seeker for knowledge, the self-interested and the wise.

"Of these the wise constantly harmonized, worshipping the One, is the best; I am supremely dear to the wise, and he is dear to Me. ;

"Noble are all these, but I hold the wise as verily Myself; he, SELF-united is fixed on Me, the highest Path.

"By the delusion of the pairs of opposites, sprung from attraction and repulsion, all beings walk this universe wholly deluded. But those men of pure deeds, in whom sin is come to an end, they, freed from the delusive pairs of opposites, worship Me, steadfast in vows.

"They who know Me as the knowledge of the elements, as that of the Shining Ones, and as that of the Sacrifice, they, harmonized in mind, know Me verily even in the time of forthgoing."

8. THE LORD AS BRAHMA THE IMPERISHABLE

Arjuna said: "What is that ETERNAL, what SELF-knowledge, what Action? And what is declared to be the knowledge of the Elements, what is called the knowledge of the Shining Ones?"

The Blessed Lord said: "The indestructible, the supreme is the ETERNAL; His essential nature is called SELF-knowledge; the emanation that causes the birth of beings is named Action.

"He who, casting off the body, goeth forth thinking upon Me only at the time of the end, he entereth into My being; there is no doubt of that.

"Therefore at all times think upon Me only, and fight. With mind and reason set on Me, without doubt thou shalt come to Me.

"He who thinketh upon the Ancient, the Omniscient, the All-Ruler, minuter than the minute, the supporter of all, of form unimaginable, refulgent as the sun beyond the darkness, in the time of forthgoing, with unshaken mind, fixed in devotion, by the power of yoga drawing together his life-breath in the centre of the two eyebrows, he goeth to this Spirit, supreme, divine.

"'Aum!' the one-syllabled ETERNAL, reciting, thinking upon Me, he who goeth forth, abandoning the body, he goeth on the highest path.

"From the unmanifested all the manifested stream forth at the coming of day; at the coming of night they dissolve, even in That called the unmanifested.

"That unmanifested, 'the Indestructible', It is called; It is named the highest Path. They who tread it return not. That is My supreme abode.

"Light and darkness, these are thought to be the world's everlasting paths; by the one he goeth who returneth not, by the other he who returneth again.

"Knowing these paths, the Yogi is nowise perplexed. Therefore in all times be firm in yoga, O Arjuna."

9. THE ROYAL SCIENCE AND THE ROYAL SECRET

The Blessed Lord said: "To thee, the uncarping, verily shall I declare this profoundest Secret, wisdom with knowledge combined, which, having known, thou shalt be freed from evil.

"Kingly Science, kingly Secret, supreme Purifier, this; intuitional, according to righteousness, very easy to perform, imperishable.

"By Me all this world is pervaded in My unmanifested aspect; all beings have root in Me, I am not rooted in them.

"As the mighty air everywhere moving is rooted in the ether, so all beings rest rooted in Me—thus know thou.

"I the Father of this universe, the Mother, the Supporter, the Grandsire, the Holy One to be known, the Word of Power.

"I give heat; I hold back and send forth the rain; immortality and also death, being and non-being am I, Arjuna.

"Whatsoever thou doest, whatsoever thou eatest, whatsoever thou offerest, whatsoever thou givest, whatsoever thou doest of austerity, do thou that as an offering unto Me.

"Thus shalt thou be liberated from the bonds of action, yielding good and evil fruits; thyself harmonized by the yoga of renunciation, thou shalt come unto Me when set free.

"The same am I to all beings; there is none hateful to me nor dear. They verily who worship Me with devotion, they are in me, and I also in them.

"Even if the most sinful worship Me, with undivided heart, he too must be accounted righteous, for he hath rightly resolved; speedily he becometh dutiful and goeth to eternal peace, now thou for certain that My devotee perisheth never. On Me fix thy mind; harmonized thus in the SELF, thou shalt come unto Me, having Me as thy supreme goal."

10. THE LORD'S VASTNESS

The Blessed Lord said: "Again, O mighty-armed, hear thou My supreme word, that, desiring thy welfare, I will declare to thee who art beloved.

"He who knoweth Me, unborn, beginningless, the great Lord of the world, he, among mortals without delusion, is liberated from all sin.

"Reason, wisdom, non-illusion, forgiveness, truth, self-restraint, calmness, pleasure, pain, existence, non-existence, fear, and also courage; harmlessness, equanimity, content, austerity, almsgiving, fame and obloquy are the various characteristics of beings issuing from Me.

"I am the Generator of all; all evolves from Me; understanding thus, the wise adore Me in rapt emotion.

"Mindful of Me, their life hidden in Me, illumining each other, ever conversing about Me, they are content and joyful.

"Out of pure compassion for them, dwelling within their SELF, I destroy the ignorance-born darkness by the shining lamp of wisdom.

"I am the SELF, seated in the heart of all beings. And whatsoever is the seed of all beings, that am I, O Arjuna; nor is there aught, moving or unmoving, that may exist bereft of Me. There is no end of My divine powers.

"Whatsoever is glorious, good, beautiful, and mighty, understand thou that to go forth from a fragment of My splendour. Having pervaded this whole universe with one fragment of Myself, I remain."

11. THE LORD AS ALL FORMS

Arjuna said: "This word of the supreme Secret concerning the SELF, Thou hast spoken out of compassion; by this my delusion is taken away. O supreme Lord, even as Thou describest Thyself, I desire to see Thy Form omnipotent."

The Blessed Lord said: "Verily thou art not able to behold Me with these thine eyes; the divine eye I give unto thee. Behold My sovereign Yoga."

Having thus spoken, the great Lord showed his supreme Form as Lord.

Arjuna said:

"Within Thy Form, O God, the Gods I see,
  All grades of beings with distinctive marks;

Brahmâ the Lord, upon His lotus-throne,
The Rishis all, and Serpents, the Divine.
Reveal Thy SELF; what awful Form art Thou?
I worship Thee! Have mercy, God supreme!"

The Blessed Lord said:

" Be not bewildered, be thou not afraid,
Because thou hast beheld this awful Form;
Cast fear away, and let thy heart rejoice;
Behold again Mine own familiar shape."

Arjuna said: "Behold again Thy gentle human Form,
I am restored to my own nature."

The Blessed Lord said: "By devotion to Me alone I may
thus be perceived, Arjuna, and known and seen in essence,
and entered. He who doeth actions for Me, whose supreme
good I am, My devotee, freed from attachment, without hatred
of any being, he cometh unto Me.

12. DEVOTION

Arjuna asked the Lord which is the more learned in yoga,
the one who worships Him, or the one who worships the
Indestructible, the Unmanifested behind all forms.

The Blessed Lord said: " They who with mind fixed on
Me, ever harmonized worship Me, with faith supreme endowed,
these in My opinion, are best in yoga.

" They who worship the Unmanifested, these also come
unto Me; but the path of the Unmanifested is hard for the
embodied to reach. Place thy mind in me, into Me let thy
Reason enter; then without doubt thou shalt abide in Me
hereafter.

" He who beareth no ill-will to any being, friendly and
compassionate, without attachment and egoism, balanced
in pleasure and pain, and forgiving, ever content, harmonious
with the self controlled, resolute, with mind and Reason
dedicated to Me, he, My devotee, is dear to Me.

" Taking equally praise and reproach, silent, wholly content
with what cometh, homeless, firm in mind, full of devotion,
that man is dear to Me.

" They verily who partake of this life-giving wisdom as
taught herein, endued with faith, I their supreme Object,
devotees, they are surpassingly dear to Me."

13. The Field and the Knower of the Field

The Blessed Lord said: "This body is called the Field; that which knoweth it is called the Knower of the Field. Understand me as the Knower of the Field in all Fields.

"Know thou that Matter and Spirit are both without beginning. Spirit seated in Matter useth the qualities born of Matter; attachment to the qualities is the cause of his births in good and evil wombs.

"Whatsoever creature is born, immobile or mobile, know thou that it is from the union between the Field and the Knower of the Field.

"Seated equally in all beings, the supreme Lord, unperishing within the perishing—he who thus seeth, he seeth. Seeing everywhere the same Lord equally dwelling, he doth not destroy the Self by the self, and thus treads the highest Path.

"As the one sun illumineth the whole earth, so the Lord of the Field illumineth the whole Field.

"They who by the eyes of Wisdom perceive this difference between the Field and the Knower of the Field, and the liberations of beings from Matter, they go to the Supreme."

14. Division of the Three Qualities

The Blessed Lord said: "Harmony, Motion, Inertia, such are the qualities, Matter-born; they bind fast in the body, the indestructible dweller in the body.

"Harmony attacheth to bliss, Motion to action; Inertia, verily, having shrouded wisdom, attacheth on the contrary to heedlessness.

"Now Harmony prevaileth, now Motion, and now Inertia.

"When the wisdom-light streameth forth from all the gates of the body, then it may be known that Harmony is increasing.

"Greed, outgoing energy, undertaking of actions, restlessness, desire—these are born of the increase of Motion.

"Darkness, stagnation and heedlessness and also delusion—these are born of the increase of Inertia."

Arjuna said: "What are the marks of him who hath crossed over the three qualities, O Lord?"

The Blessed Lord said: "He who, seated as a neutral, is unshaken by the qualities, standeth apart immovable, balanced in pleasure and pain, self-reliant, to whom a lump of earth, a rock and gold are alike, the same to loved and unloved, firm, the same in censure and in praise—he is said to have crossed over the qualities.

" And he who serveth Me exclusively by the Yoga of devotion, he, crossing beyond the qualities, he is fit to become the ETERNAL."

15. THE LORD AS THE SUPREME SPIRIT

The Blessed Lord said: " With roots above, branches below, the Asvattha (sacred fig-tree) is said to be indestructible; its leaves are the verses. He who knoweth this is a Vedaknower.

" Downwards and upwards spread the branches of it, nourished by the qualities; the objects of the senses its buds; and its roots grow downwards, the bonds of action in the world of men.

" This strongly-rooted Asvattha having been cut down by the unswerving weapon of non-attachment, that path may be sought, treading which there is no return.

" A portion of Mine own Self, transformed in the world of life into an immortal Spirit, draweth round itself the senses of which the mind is the sixth, veiled in Matter.

" I, having become the Fire of Life, take possession of the bodies of breathing things, and united with the life-breaths I digest the four kinds of food.

" There are two energies in this world, the destructible and the indestructible; the destructible is all beings, the unchanging is called the indestructible.

" The highest Energy is verily Another, declared as the supreme SELF, He who pervading all sustaineth the three worlds, the indestructible Lord.

" He who undeluded knoweth Me thus as the Supreme Spirit, he, all-knowing, worshippeth Me with his whole being.

" Thus by Me this most secret teaching hath been told, O sinless one. This known, he hath finished his work."

16. THE BRIGHT AND DARK POWERS

" Fearlessness, cleanness of life, steadfastness in the Yoga of wisdom, almsgiving, self-restraint and sacrifice and study of the Scriptures, austerity and straightforwardness.

" Harmlessness, truth, absence of wrath, renunciation, peacefulness, absence of crookedness, compassion to living beings, uncovetousness, mildness, modesty, absence of fickleness.

"Vigour, forgiveness, fortitude, purity, absence of envy and pride—these are his who is born with the divine properties.

"Twofold is the animal creation in this world, the divine and the demoniacal.

"Demoniacal men know neither right energy nor right abstinence; nor purity, nor even propriety, nor truth is in them.

"Given over to egoism, power, insolence, lust and wrath, these malicious ones hate Me in the bodies of others and in their own.

"Triple is the gate of this hell, destructive of the self—lust, wrath, and greed; therefore let man renounce these.

"Therefore let the Scriptures be thy authority, in determining what ought to be done, or what ought not to be done. Knowing what hath been declared by the ordinances of the Scriptures, thou oughtest to work in this world."

17. The Three-Fold Faith

Arjuna said: "Those that sacrifice full of faith, but casting aside the ordinances of the Scriptures, what is verily their condition, O Krishna?"

The Blessed Lord said: "Threefold by nature the inborn faith of the embodied—pure, passionate, and dark. The man consists of his faith; that which his faith is, he is even that. Pure men worship the Shining Ones; the passionate, the gnomes and giants (gnomes, servants of the Lord of Wealth; giants, the sorcerers of Atlantis); the others, the dark folk, worship ghosts and troops of nature-spirits.

"The men who perform severe austerities, unenjoined by the Scriptures, wedded to vanity and egoism, impelled by the force of their desires and passions; unintelligent, tormenting the aggregated elements forming the body, and Me also, seated in the inner body, know these demoniacal in their resolves.

"Worship given to the Shining Ones, to the twice-born, to the Teachers (Gurus) and to the wise, purity, straight-forwardness, continence and harmlessness, are called the austerity of the body.

"Speech causing no annoyance, truthful, pleasant and

beneficial, the practice of the study of the Scriptures, are called the austerity of speech.

" Mental happiness, equilibrium, silence, self-control, purity of nature—this is called the austerity of the mind.

" This threefold austerity is said to be pure."

18. The Renunciation of Liberation

Arjuna said: " I desire to know severally the essence of renunciation and of relinquishment."

The Blessed Lord said: " Acts of sacrifice, gift and austerity should not be relinquished, but should be performed; but even these actions should be done leaving aside attachment and fruit. Verily renunciation of actions that are prescribed is not proper; the relinquishment thereof from delusion is said to be of darkness.

" Good, evil and mixed—threefold is the fruit of action hereafter for the non-relinquisher; but there is none ever for the renouncer.

" An action which is ordained, done by one undesirous of fruit, that is called pure.

" But an action done by one longing for desires, or again with egoism or much effort, that is declared to be passionate.

" The action undertaken from delusion, without regard to capacity and to consequences—loss and injury to others—that is declared to be dark.

" Listen thou again to My supreme word, most secret of all; beloved art thou of Me, and steadfast in heart, therefore will I speak for thy benefit.

" Merge thy mind in Me, be My devotee, sacrifice to Me, prostrate thyself before Me, thou shalt come even to Me. I pledge thee My troth; thou art dear to Me.

" Abandoning all duties, come unto Me alone for shelter; sorrow not, I will liberate thee from all sins.

" Never is this to be spoken by thee to anyone who is without asceticism, nor without devotion, nor to one who desireth not to listen, nor yet to him who speaketh evil of Me.

" And he who shall study this sacred dialogue of ours, by him I shall be worshipped with the sacrifice of wisdom."

Arjuna said: " Destroyed is my delusion. I have gained knowledge through Thy grace, O Immutable One. I am firm, my doubts have fled away. I will do according to Thy word."

ON THE ORIGIN OF SPECIES

By means of Natural Selection, or the Preservation of Favoured Races in the Struggle for Life

By CHARLES DARWIN

Published in 1859, this great work at once gave rise to tremendous opposition by the fundamentalists. The book has a double interest for us nowadays, as much for the theories expressed in it as for the revelation of a precise scientific mind in operation.

EVER since the days of Linnaeus in the eighteenth century the animals of the world have been classified into groups, according to their likeness to one another. The most fundamental of these groups, the species, can reproduce themselves, but they will not breed with animals of another species.

The number of species of animals in the world is enormous, and is the result of variation of animal patterns. How do these variations arise, and group themselves into surviving species? What is the Origin of Species?

Variability of structure in animals and plants becomes much more noticeable under conditions of domestication than in wild life. Therefore it is reasonable to study the causes of variability under such circumstances. These causes are of two main types—factors acting from outside such as cold and heat, food supply, etc., and factors from within the animal which are inherent in its constitution affecting particularly the reproductive organs. This second factor is the more important because it obviously determines whether a certain variation in structure shall endure through time or not. In short, the factor of inheritance is essential to the development of a new characteristic.

Variations often do not occur alone—they combine sometimes mysteriously with other abnormalities, for example, white, blue-eyed tom cats are nearly always also deaf. Here lack of pigment combines for some unknown reason with deafness. It may easily be seen how this " correlated variation " affects the domestic breeding of animals. For one point may be aimed for and bring another less desirable characteristic in its train.

Use and disuse of parts continued over many generations will also alter the structure of an animal body: witness how in cows which are milked the udders develop to a much greater size than in those which are not milked.

Intercrossing of different breeds also produces variations in the offspring. But this has to be done by man with great skill and care, for otherwise a mixed group of mongrels of all colours and sizes is produced. Now animals and plants under domestication tend to produce a rich harvest of variations—a fact exemplified by the frequency of "monsters" produced under these conditions. Take as an example the varieties of domestic pigeon. These birds have been bred by man ever since the days of the Pharaohs about 3000 B.C. Compare the extraordinarily different shapes of the English carrier, the fantail and the pouter, for instance. These differences would induce many a naturalist, seeing them for the first time, to put them into different species—and yet they are known to have come, all of them, from one species of origin and been modified in domestication by man.

It will be seen from this example that not only is there rich variability under domestic circumstances, but that a special form of selection goes on. That form of an animal which is useful or pleasing to man is selected by him, and is therefore bred from and perpetuated. In this little world of domestic animals Man takes the place of Nature.

We have already mentioned, in our opening remarks, how animal and plant life has been grouped. A species is a relatively clear group, though it is difficult to define. Collections of species form a genus, which in its turn belongs to a family, families group into orders, and orders into classes. Finally classes are included in a phylum. A phylum is the root or basic pattern along which Nature has developed, e.g., the vertebrates or back-boned animals, as opposed to the arthropods or crustaceans, such as the lobster, built on quite a different plan.

Species used to be thought of as special acts of creation by God, as described in the Book of Genesis. These species were therefore fixed, but they could have "variations". Monstrosities are extreme forms of a variety of a species.

Every example of a species shows individual differences, which tend to be inherited—a fact which is obvious to us the moment we consider our own families. These individual differences may be striking, so much so that confusion has often arisen amongst naturalists as to which of two related animal forms is the species, and which is the variety of the species. There is no hard and fast line between species, varieties, and sub-species. All groups blend into each other by imperceptible degrees. Individual differences, such as we all recognize, are the first steps towards new varieties. These in their turn, and in the course of many generations, may develop into new species The circumstances under which this would happen will be governed by inheritance of the variation and its selection from other varieties.

These words—species, variety, etc.—are terms of convenience only. A slight difference, between two forms indicates they are varieties. A greater difference often including the failure of reproduction, indicates they are species.

The larger a genus, the more species and varieties are found in it—far more varieties than develop in a small genus—and thus the forms of life get divided up into " groups subordinate to groups ".

We have now seen how variable are living forms, and how these variations are called names in order to classify them into groups. And we have seen that these groups have no hard and fast boundaries. But variability in itself means nothing—unless it be chaos. How can all these varieties be arranged and grouped into species which we recognize? This sorting is brought about by the process of Natural Selection in the struggle for existence. Any variation which is of use to the animal in its struggle for existence will tend to survive, whereas conversely, any variation which is a drawback to it will disappear with the individual who possesses it. Those animals which survive obviously live to produce offspring in whom the particular variation tends to be reproduced. Whereas the unfavourable variation belongs to an animal which dies early, and therefore leaves few offspring containing this disadvantage, and these, too, tend to be exterminated. And so gradually the number of animals with the useful variation increases, and the variation itself may become altered to an even more useful form—so that a new variety of the original species is formed.

The importance of the struggle for existence is thus manifest. Let us see what forms this struggle can take.

Two dogs fighting for a bone is perhaps the simplest picture symbolizing the struggle—food being the most vital object conditioning survival. But there is something more than this to it. A plant in the desert has a struggle, not only with its fellows but with the chances of weather, and the vital necessity for water. Plants produce thousands of seeds. How many survive? We see that the struggle for existence concerns not only the individual but the power to reproduce its kind. An animal which defeats all its competitors in the jungle, but remains sterile, has failed in the struggle for existence.

The cause of the struggle for existence lies in the great rate of increase in the production of all animals and plants. It is only by virtue of the destruction of individuals and their young that their numbers are kept down. The world would soon become swamped by any species which avoided these destructive forces.

This competition by virtue of rate of increase was first clearly stated by Malthus, who also applied it to the human races, forecasting the dreadful results of over-population!

Apart from theory, however, there are practical examples of prolific breeding in unusually suitable environments, amongst which is the remarkable spread of cattle and horses when first introduced into South America and Australia.

There are many causes in Nature, however, which prevent this enormous rate of increase in the majority of cases, though the exact part which each cause plays is often obscure. First the greater part of destruction occurs in the egg, or larval stage of the animals' life history. In the case of young seedlings slugs destroy an enormous proportion. Scarcity of food is sometimes a cause in itself, particularly where it is at the best of times difficult to obtain, as in the desert or in the polar regions. But often food scarcity acts by increasing the competition, and a species is kept down or even exterminated by its more vigorous rivals. Some animals, however, such as the elephant, are very rarely attacked, so that other factors must be at work in their case. Climate is another factor of obvious significance. Notice how the birds are hit by a particularly severe winter. But here again shortage of food comes into the picture very often.

Epidemics of disease often come along just when one species is multiplying most prolifically. These epidemics are often due to parasitic worms which presumably have benefited in their turn from the flourishing condition of their host-species.

But with all these factors there are others undetected. The variations in prolificity of the human race make this at once evident. The rises and falls in human birth-rate are not open to the above-mentioned factors, and have never been satisfactorily explained.

But this point becomes clear, that the struggle for existence results from prolific reproduction—that this great rate of increase is checked by various factors, some known, probably more unknown. The most important checking factor is competition for light and food from neighbouring species. And since like animals are more likely to need similar foods and materials it is between the animals of the same species that competition is most bitter. For example, where the missel-thrush is introduced and flourishes, the song-thrush disappears.

Emerging from this chaotic struggle for existence come a lesser number of life-forms than entered it. These forms, be they of plant or animal life, have passed through Nature's sieve of selection whose meshes exist wherever life exists. Just as Man selected the variations that he liked or found useful, so Nature, in far more radical fashion, lays her blessing on certain varieties, condemning others with merciless cruelty: and in yet a third group of irrelevant variations, letting them pass by without approval or disapproval. Natural Selection, therefore, has no influence at all over what kind of variation is produced. It acts only by weeding out some variations from others, just as man breeds by selecting certain variations as desirable. But Man cannot thrust a variation on a species.

What variations does Nature select? Unlike man, she is not concerned with the beauty of the animal to the human eye. She is concerned only with what is useful to it. Whereas Man selects for his own benefit Nature does so for the benefit of the animal or plant concerned—and only for this. And Nature has longer to work in: the whole stretch of Time is hers, and her handiwork is in consequence far finer and more marvellous to behold than Man's.

Again, whereas man selects only rather obvious character-istics, and these usually external, Nature selects *any* characteristic, however slight, which benefits the animal in its struggle for life. Often apparently small variations such as the down on the surface of a fruit have been found to make all the difference in survival. The smooth fruit in this case was attacked by a beetle far oftener than the downy one.

Many animals, including Man, are social—*i.e*, congregate into a community. In this case, the selected variation in the individual will be that which benefits the community as a whole.

As a result of Natural Selection then the animal or plant is improved as regards its circumstances of living; it has advanced in its organization. This does not contradict the fact that under certain circumstances a simple structure is quite sufficient, so that through all the ages simple forms, such as worms, exist perfectly adapted to their simple conditions, with no possibility of advance in organization unless their conditions alter.

Already the importance of reproduction from the point of view of inheritance of variations has been emphasized. This factor brings to the fore the question of sex. One form of selection necessary to reproduction experienced by nearly all animals is sexual selection whereby a mate is found. The qualities necessary in this sphere are rather different from those of the struggle for existence. Here there is a struggle between the males, usually for the possession of the female. Here the unsuccessful competitor is not usually killed—he simply remains unproductive of his type. Courage, vigour and a good supply of male sexual weapons such as horns, antlers or spurs are the chief criteria of success in sexual selection. Animals of all kinds have these competitive combats; male alligators have been described whirling round " like Indians in a war dance " bellowing defiance of their fellow competitors for the female. Birds often adopt a more gentle method—that of song, or elaborate display of plumage, as in the birds of paradise.

The differences between the appearance of the male and female of a species is mainly due to sexual selection; by which, on the whole, the most vigorous males are chosen to perpetuate their kind.

Natural Selection, it will be seen, is a double-edged sword. Just as it selects some varieties which persist and reproduce their kind, so it rejects others into the limbo of life's mistakes. Such forms of life become extinct. How large a proportion of Nature's experiments have been mistakes is vividly shown by the fossils in the rocks. All these past species have given way to their more vigorous successors. In actual fact, the number of species has not greatly increased—for each new species as it is formed exterminates its neighbouring inferior species. This phenomenon is well illustrated in domestication. The old Yorkshire black cattle soon vanished when the long-horn type came on the scene. These in turn were " swept away " by the short-horns.

Natural Selection also encourages divergence of characteristics. The more dissimilar animals are, the less the competition, as we have seen. To take another example from domestication—horses are selected by man for different purposes, for swiftness and for strength. Race horses and cart horses come from a common stock. They do not compete against each other now, as their divergence of form is sufficiently wide. But if man had been looking for one quality only, say strength, in a horse, then those which were swifter and lighter would have become extinct. In Nature divergences of character will enable new fields to be explored, will expand the living room of the species. And the new type formed by this divergence will in time form a new species on its own.

One can also see from this how the larger genera occupy the largest geographical areas—and how the species of these genera tend to vary most. These types become dominant in their respective countries, transmitting their characteristics to their offspring. Thus we find plants and animals formed in groups with similar forms which derive from previous groups such as genera, classes, etc.

The simplest picture of the process is that of a tree with the green buds representing species—the scars of old buds extinct species. The growing twigs branch out and try to kill off other twigs, species overpowering neighbouring species. The great branches of the tree, which now divide into so many lesser branches and twigs, were once themselves small twigs. This illustrates how what at one time was a species becomes, in the course of geological time, a genus or class. There were many twigs when the tree was merely a bush. Of these only one or two survive now as great main branches—the phyla of surviving living forms. Some great branches may have rotted and fallen off—orders or genera which are now quite extinct, and known to us only as fossils.

The importance of variation as the material, so to speak, upon which Natural Selection works has been already emphasized. We are now in a position to enquire a little further into its causes. Ignorance of its mechanism is the most noticeable fact (though some light has been thrown on the matter since Darwin's day). But whatever the laws, they seem to apply both for slight individual differences between varieties of species, and between different species themselves. How far changed conditions act is doubtful. Use and disuse we have already noted as factors inducing variation. An alteration of a hard part of the anatomy, such as bone, always carries with it alteration of soft tissue. Development of one part to unusual size necessitates a blood and nervous supply, and since, as **Goethe** said " In order to spend on one side, Nature is forced to economize on the other ", balance is often restored by diminution of some other part of the organisms. Cows which give a lot of milk do not fatten well—when the seeds of fruit atrophy the fruit itself becomes large and more luscious, and vice versa. Multiple organs, such as the vertebrae, are very liable to variation in number in all animals. Rudimentary parts are also highly variable—possibly as a result of their uselessness. The human appendix is a good example. Extraordinary development of a part in an isolated species always results in great variation in this part. The best example would be the pigeon types which we have already mentioned—the crop of the pouter is a very variable characteristic in successive generations. Only rigid selection by man keeps it constant. One may go further than this and say that recently acquired, specific characteristics are much more variable than generic or older types.

Secondary sexual characteristics, such as combs and spurs of cocks, are very variable. This is really to be expected, since sexual selection is not so rigid as Natural Selection. Failure in it does not result in death.

Like species, being related in ancestry, tend to vary in similar fashions—analogous variations. Sometimes variations occur which revert to some ancient progenitor. Dun horses are particularly liable to have foals with stripes on their legs like a zebra. The ordinary mule—produced by crossing an ass and a horse—commonly has striped bars on its legs. In both these cases the bars are very much more conspicuous in the very young animal, and may disappear in the adult. These bars are a reversion to the markings on the common ancestor of horse, zebra, and ass.

The picture of Natural Selection is made clearer by discussing very briefly some of the difficulties and objections which arise to the theory.

First, why if descent has been by such fine differences do we not find many transitional or intermediate forms of life, in more profusion than order?

This is because Natural Selection preserves only useful variations. A species with such a variation exterminates one without it, or with it less well-developed. Such a species will exterminate even its own ancestor from which it sprang, so finally standing out alone and distinct. Species scattered over a wide area are numerous at the centre of this area, disappearing abruptly at the boundaries, where they come into contact with a different species. Any intermediate species between the two becomes gradually engulfed by one or other neighbour, until the two distinct varieties come into contact. The neutral territory between two well-marked species is always narrow, when compared with the territory they occupy.

These exterminated species—transitional forms—exist now only as fossils.

How could a flesh-eating land animal be converted into a swimming one? It seems difficult to see how any animal could survive whilst in the transitional stage. Actually there exist animals at present making this change. In North America the Mustela vison has webbed feet, fur like an otter, short legs and a tail. It feeds on fish in summer—but during the winter when the ponds are frozen it preys on mice. It combines land and water life successfully enough for the approval of Natural Selection.

Can Natural Selection produce an organ so wonderful as the human eye? The earliest cells sensitive to light are pigment spots on the skin. In some star fishes small holes in the pigment are filled by a jelly. To this runs an optic nerve. Here are all the essential components of an eye as found in the human. Through fishes, with eyes similar to the young human embryo, to other vertebrate eyes we see a steady progress, until the marvels of the human eye are reached. And what is true for the eye is true for all organs. They can each and all be produced by fine gradations from more primitive or different patterns. For example, the swimbladder of fishes has by gradation become the lung of the vertebrate. Even in the human, food passes over the opening of the windpipe—a remnant of this strange mode of development.

Does Beauty come under the sway of Natural Selection? Natural Selection is concerned with the perfection of an organ from a utilitarian point of view. It can never produce absolute perfection—beauty as admired by the human eye is incidental. Natural Selection never produces a modification for the benefit of *another* species, even human!

It is often asked how these useful variations began. For example, in the case of the giraffe—the first ungulate with a slightly longer neck than others browsed on food out of the reach of its less favoured neighbours—a great advantage, particularly in times of food shortage. Competition now comes from other forms of giraffes—those with shorter necks are exterminated. An insect, which at first accidentally resembles a leaf, for example, is the foundation for the work of Natural Selection whereby the resemblance is increased.

The mammae of higher animals originated as small specialized skin glands in the marsupial sac, as in kangaroos, where many small skin glands secrete nourishing fluid. As these glands became larger and contained more nourishment they became localized to certain parts of the body, forming the mammae of mammals.

All these changes be it noted are gradual. It is only on very rare occasions that Nature makes leaps.

But the laws of Natural Selection apply to the instincts of animals, as well as to their bodily structure. Instinctive actions are devoid of conscious reason and judgment—often having a similarity to habits. Such actions do not need practice for they are born in, and develop like an organ of, the body. Mozart played the piano at the age of three years with but little practice. If he had played a tune with no practice at all the action could have been called instinctive. Habitual action can become inherited—but many of the strangest and most complex examples of instinctive behaviour cannot belong to this category. One has only to think of the honey-bee building its beehive instinctively, or the ant its ant-hill to see this. Instincts in animals vary, and Natural Selection works on these variations in the same way as it does on bodily differences, choosing those which are beneficial and rejecting the others. Just as use and habit develop an organ, so they develop an instinct. If an instinct is not used it fades away.

Under domestication instincts are relatively rapidly developed or changed—just as body-structure is, so that a young pointer " points " the first time he is taken out, a young retriever will retrieve, and a young sheepdog runs round a flock of sheep instead of towards it. These are all instinctive actions which appeared as variations of instinct by accident. To Man they were useful, so that he selected and bred for these properties, and pointers, retrievers, and sheepdogs resulted.

Only a common inheritance of instinct can account for the thrush of South America having the same habit as the thrush of England of lining its nest with mud. How else could their very separate existences through the ages have acquired this strange link in behaviour?

We have already mentioned that as a rule animals of different species do not interbreed. This is a fundamental tenet of the creationists' point of view, in which the animals had been created as different species which did not cross fertilize each other. In actual fact the cross fertilization of different so-called species is often possible, andt here is every variation between complete sterility and normal fruitfulness. Different varieties when crossed are usually fertile, but even here not always so. So again we have an example of how dim is the border-line between varieties and species: a point of great importance when by Natural Selection it is held that the variety merges through the generations into the more clearly defined species. Crossing of different varieties of a species produces mongrels, which are themselves notoriously variable as well as fertile.

The theory of Natural Selection as has been here outlined automatically includes the conception that countless forms of life have existed, and become extinct during the vast geological progress of time. These forms should therefore be found in all their infinite variety in the book of the rocks. Palaeontologists as a group vehemently upheld the theory of the immutability of species until Sir Charles Lyell first took up the cudgels for Natural Selection. Fossils have formed a very imperfect record of previous living forms, and this imperfection is due to the comparatively recent study of the subject. Our museums still contain only a fraction of organic beings that have existed, and lie in various parts of the world as undiscovered fossils.

Other obscuring features which cloud this aspect of the problem are, the enormous time factor, the tendency of fossils to collect in areas of subsidence of land when extinction was probably more dominant than in periods of elevation where variation was more common. Migration also adds complications. This adds new species to any area; and species which range widely produce the most variations, so giving rise to new species. Again the periods during which the forms of life have been changing have been probably short compared with those during which the forms have remained comparatively constant.

When we observe the manner in which species are distributed in the world we are often tempted to exaggerate the importance of climate. But this is obviously not the most important factor. Comparable climates of all kinds can be found in the Old World and the New—and how different, in spite of this, are the plants and animals of each.

Of great importance in dividing up animals into groups are the great barriers to migration such as mountain ranges, deserts, and oceans. Resulting in part from this, one notices the close relationship of life on each continent; for example, American types have existed throughout the geological ages on the American continent, related to each other—and not to the types of other continents. These forms are linked to each other by the strong bond of inheritance, though separated later, perhaps, by subsidence or elevation of land levels, forming islands or mountain ranges which act by checking migration. Life has started from certain centres, as it were, on the surface of the earth, from which it has diffused in all directions suffering various changes in environment which have demanded variation and adaptation as the price of survival. The dispersal of these forms of life has then depended on climate and changes of land levels so that seas replace land and land appears elsewhere above the surface of the waters. Dispersal of plants often utilizes the subtlest methods which conquer the obvious barriers of sea and mountain. Many seeds can float over a thousand miles in sea water and germinate at the end. Birds in their migration carry seeds from continent to continent, either in their crops or entangled in their feet.

In the glacial periods the vast pendulum of climatic change spread down towards the equator, leaving on its recession plants on mountain tops separated by areas in which they could not possibly have existed. Similar plants, for example, existing on the mountain-tops of the Pyrenees, the Alps and the peaks of northern Europe come from this origin.

Living beings, plant or animal, can as we have already seen, be arranged in " groups subordinate to groups ". One dominant spreading group becomes larger and more divergent in character whilst new varieties gradually change into new smaller groups or species—exterminating those parental types from whose stem they sprang.

Animals and plants have been arranged by naturalists into a setting of groups or a classification known as the Natural System, in which there is a deeper bond than mere likeness to one another. And this bond is not the separate plan of a creator, but the bond of community of descent. This gives a clue to fundamental pattern, though use and disuse may distort this pattern. So it is that vestigial organs are so important. They indicate a similarity of basic architecture modified by recent disuse. The importance of an organ physiologically bears no relation, therefore, to its importance in Natural Classification. And since classification includes, of course, animals at all ages of their existence, features in the embryo are of singular importance in this matter. The main types of flowering plants are classified on an embryological characteristic—the number of cotyledons and the development of plumule and radicle.

These features and difficulties of classification are answered by the theory of descent with modification—that affinity of animal types is due to their having common ancestors from which they have inherited basically similar patterns—with modification: animals may resemble each other by virtue of acquiring similar mechanisms under similar environments. Such similarity is known as analogical. Dugongs and whales are of similar shape—the one a fish, the other a mammal. Similar problems have produced the similar shape of body. One might even note the resemblance between the greyhound and the racehorse in this connection.

Extinction rules definite lines between groups of living animals —emphasizing the difference, for example, between birds and all other vertebrate animals by cutting out all intermediate forms.

Members of a group or class of animals have resemblances of fundamental pattern in their structure. The parts which resemble each other are termed homologous. The hand of a man, the leg of a horse, the wing of a bat, are all built on the same pattern, though modified for their different uses. Through this, the bones of limbs can be named for all related species, as their relationships to each other are always similar. All these similarities can be explained by descent with modification.

Embryology is another subject which throws light on the natural affinity of animals. Everyone is familiar with successive changes in the development of an insect—egg, larva, pupa, to adult form. Parts of the body, very similar in embryo, become very different as development proceeds. This applies to different animals also. As Von Baer says, " embryos of mammals, birds, lizards and snakes . . . are in their earliest states exceedingly like one another, both as a whole, and in the mode of development of their parts ". The larvae of crustaceans are very similar. Sometimes these resemblances persist until a relatively late age, as, for example, in the similar immature plumage of birds of different genera.

Larvae (or insects in embryo) sometimes have to live active lives—the embryo then adapts itself as wonderfully as the adult to conditions of existence—the variations in caterpillar colour, hair and shape being an example.

Some insects such as the spider and the cuttle-fish do not pass through stages of metamorphosis or change at all. In these the young, as soon as they are born, must fend for themselves. They therefore adopt the stamp of the adult pattern early—thereby losing the power to learn and make further modifications.

The structure of the embryo shows relationships between living forms deeper than that of the adult. It is of great importance, therefore, in classification. Similarity of embryo means similar ancestry, however different the final adult forms may be. But dissimilarity of embryonic form does not mean that there is no relation of descent, for in one group development may have been suppressed altogether, as in the spider, whereas in another it may have been modified and lengthened in such a way as to be barely recognizable.

Embryos often resemble some ancestral form—thus many extinct fossil species closely resemble the embryos of living forms.

Rudimentary organs are very common in animals. This term is applied to organs which are useless. Men, for example, possess rudimentary mammae—foetal whales have teeth; adult whales are toothless! These organs are useless, and seem a nonsensical sport of nature. They cannot have been produced therefore by Natural Selection, which preserves only useful parts.

Rudimentary organs vary widely in different individuals in size, shape and position, and are larger relatively in the embryo than in the adult.

Disuse is the main factor in producing rudimentary organs. An organ that, owing to change of environment, has lost its usefulness to the animal, shrinks, but by inheritance persists from generation to generation, until eventually it becomes obliterated altogether. " Rudimentary organs may be compared with the letters in a word still retained in the spelling, useless in the pronunciation but which serve as a clue for its derivation."

The facts as related above are convincing evidence that modification has gone on during the long course of the descent of life from primitive forms. How life originally arose is outside the problem.

DAS KAPITAL

By KARL MARX

The first volume of this monumental work appeared in 1867, the rest being completed by Engels after Marx's death in 1883. It is, as will be seen, a criticism of the capitalist system and a plea for the abolition of private property. The inclusion of "Das Kapital" in this volume does not necessarily mean that the editors and publishers hold identical views with the author.

IN any society where production is carried on by the capitalist method, wealth consists of a great accumulation of commodities. The simple units in such a society are the individual commodities. So let us begin by finding out just what a commodity is.

First of all, a commodity is something outside us, something that satisfies a human want. It does not matter whether these wants spring from the stomach or from the imagination. Nor does it matter whether the commodity satisfies a want directly (as a loaf of bread satisfies our hunger) or whether it satisfies a want indirectly (as a baking tin, in which bread is baked, indirectly satisfies our hunger).

The extent to which a commodity satisfies wants, that is to say its "utility", makes it a *use-value*. The proportions in which a use-value can be exchanged for other use-values gives it its *exchange-value*. Obviously we must be able to express the exchange-values of commodities in something common to them all. What is this "common something"? It cannot be some individual property of the different commodities. When we compare use-values we are interested in differences of quality. But when we compare exchange values, we are interested in differences of quantity. We want to be able to say x lb. of silk can be exchanged for y lb. of gold. These exchange-values do not take into account the particular wants that the commodities supply. Use-values, therefore, do not enter into exchange-value.

This being so, there remains only one "common something" to be found in all commodities and that is the fact that they are all the products of labour.

And since we are leaving use-value out of it, the particular kind of labour must be left out of it too. The value of a table is not determined by joiner's labour, nor the value of a house by builder's labour. Obviously not, because no individual type of labour (like builder's labour or joiner's labour) is common to every commodity. Labour, to be the " common something " of all commodities, must be plain, undifferentiated labour— human labour in the abstract. What gives a commodity its exchange-value is the fact that labour was needed to produce it, that labour is stored up in it. In short, the labour stored up inside a commodity is its value. Its exchange-value is the outward form of this value; it is the only form in which this value can be expressed.

Thus a use-value or commodity has value solely because human labour in the abstract has been used in producing it. This value can be measured only in terms of the quantity of labour used. We measure the quantity of labour in time : that is, we say, " Six hours of labour-time were needed to produce such and such a commodity ".

Some people will at once object and say that this means that if a thing is made by a lazy man or an unskilled man it will be more valuable because such a man will take more time over making it. But this is an unfair criticism. We are talking not of the labour of a particular man but of human labour in the abstract, of average labour. The thing which determines the value of an article is the *socially necessary labour-time* required to produce it.

Socially necessary labour-time is the time necessary to pro- duce an article under the normal conditions of production and with the average degree of skill and intensity. Suppose someone makes an invention enabling some commodity to be produced in half the time. It is true that a man who sticks to the old system has to work twice as long as men working by the new method, but the time he takes is twice as long as is " socially necessary " and therefore the product of one hour of his labour is now worth only half what it was before.

Speaking generally, then, every commodity has the value of the average sample of its class, and any two sorts of commodity which contain the same quantities of labour have the same magnitude of value. The proportion between the values of two commodities is the same as the proportion between the periods of necessary labour-time embodied in them. As values, commodities are simply individual jellies of labour-time.

The value of a certain sort of commodity would, of course, remain constant if the labour-time needed for its production remained constant, but the necessary labour-time varies with every change in the productivity of labour. The productivity of labour is determined by such things as the worker's average skill, the type of machinery used, the social organization of production, weather conditions, and so on, and so on.

A thing can be a use-value although it has no value. Examples of this are air, virgin soil, primeval forests and such things. ﹂They satisfy wants but no labour has been expended on them. A thing can also be a use-value *and* the product of human labour and still not be a commodity. A man who uses his labour to satisfy his own wants does not produce a commodity. Commodities are not merely use-values but use-values for others—*social* use-values. (A thing like the tithe-corn produced by the medieval peasant for the priest is also not a commodity, although it is produced " for others ". To become a commodity, a product must pass by way of *exchange* into the hands of another person.) Finally, nothing can have value unless it has use-value. If a thing is useless, then the labour spent on making it has been useless. Such labour cannot be counted as labour and cannot produce value.

At first sight, a commodity seems a simple enough thing to understand, but on examination it turns out to be a very queer thing indeed. Commodities have a fetishistic* character because they embody human labour and therefore the social relations between men become mirrored in the relations between commodities. Thus men see the social relations between one another, not as they are, but in the form of relations between things. And there is nothing about these things themselves to suggest they have this fetishistic character. They assume this character, not because of what they are, but because they have become commodities.

All this really arises from the fact that the different producers in society do not come into social contact with one another during the period of their labour but only when they come to exchange their labour-products. This disguises the specifically social character of their labour. Social relations do not seem, therefore, to exist between the producers but between the things they produce.

For simplicity, let us assume throughout this work that gold is the money-commodity. It is not because there is money that we can measure the value of commodities. Their value can be measured and compared with one another because there is labour embodied in them. But money provides a simple outward way of expressing the values embodied in commodities. The money-value of a commodity (x commodity A = y gold) is its money form of *price*.

Money has two quite distinct functions. First, it is the measure of value; and secondly, it is the standard of price. It is the measure of value because it tells us in what proportions labour-time is embodied in various commodities. It is the standard of price because it tells us the proportions in which commodities can be exchanged for one another. Broadly speaking, the magnitude of value and the price are the same. But there may be a small quantitative difference between price and value. This is natural in a system of production which is full of apparently lawless irregularities which compensate one another. There may also be a qualitative difference between price and value. Examples of this are things like conscience and honour, which can be sold by their owners. These things assume the commodity form and have a price, but they cannot be said to have value, since no labour is embodied in them. Their price is an imaginary one. In cases of this kind price wholly ceases to be an expression of value—in spite of the fact that money is the value-form of commodities.

In order to be quite clear how the process of exchange of commodities takes place, let us follow some owner of a commodity to market and watch him in action. Say he has twenty yards of linen. Its price is £2. He exchanges it for £2 and being an old-fashioned sort of a chap he then exchanges his £2 for a family bible. His process of exchanging commodities has been performed in two separate and opposed phases. First he exchanges a commodity for money. Then he exchanges money for a commodity. The net result is that he has exchanged one commodity for another commodity. Where before he had linen, he now has a bible—a commodity of equal value but of different utility. We can express the whole transaction like this:

$$Commodity—Money—Commodity$$
$$\text{or} \qquad C—M—C$$

As far as the commodities themselves go, the transaction simply boils down to C—C.

This form of circulation of commodities we can call selling in order to buy. But there is another form of circulation—

buying in order to sell: a man having so much money buys a commodity, and having bought it he sells it again. This transaction can be expressed $M—C—M$. Money which circulates in this way is thereby transformed into capital. It is already potential capital. The first difference that we notice between money which is mere money and money which is capital is simply this difference in the form of circulation.

Obviously the transaction $M—C—M$ would be meaningless if the owner of the money ended up with the same amount of money that he started with. To exchange £100 for 2000 lb. of cotton and then to sell the cotton for £100 brings a man no advantage. The hoarder has a much safer way of achieving the same result. He holds tight to his original £100. But if a man exchanges £100 for 2000 lb. of cotton and then sells the cotton for £110, he has in fact exchanged £100 for £110.

We shall obviously learn a great deal if we make it our business to study the real difference between the respective transactions $M—C—M$ and $C—M—C$. In one case, money forms both the starting point and the finishing point. In the case of the other a commodity forms both the starting point and the finishing point. This is important. The man who sells his linen to buy a bible has completed his transaction altogether. The bible falls out of circulation and into consumption. The aim of $C—M—C$ is consumption, the satisfaction of wants—in a word, use-value. The man who uses his £100 to bring him back £110 has not brought his transaction to a dead end. He is in a position with his £110 to start the whole process over again. The money itself cannot be consumed. It is only useful if it is put back into circulation. The aim of the transaction $M—C—M$ is not use-value but exchange-value.

Actually it would be fairer to write this transaction as $M—C—M'$ (in which $M' = M + xM$), because the final amount of money is equal to the original amount advanced plus an increment. (In our example, the £100 had added to it an increment of £10.) Let us call this increment, or excess over the original value, "*surplus value*". It is this process of adding to itself a surplus value that converts money into capital.

Of course it is possible that sometimes in the transaction $C—M—C$ the final C may be more valuable than the original C. One party to the transaction may be taken advantage of. But such differences of value are purely accidental. The aim of C—M—C is to bring about a qualitative difference—to exchange one commodity for a different one with the same value but a different utility. The aim of M—C—M is to bring about a quantitative difference—to exchange one amount of money for a greater amount.

M—C—M', buying in order to sell (or better, buying in order to sell at a higher price), appears to be only one form of capital—merchants' capital—but as a matter of fact industrial capital, too, is money that has been spent on commodities and has then been reconverted into more money than before by the sale of these commodities. Events that take place in the interval between the buying and the selling outside the sphere of circulation do not affect the form of the transaction. And finally, in the case of interest-bearing capital, the transaction M—C—M' occurs in an abridged form. There is no intermediate stage. Money invested brings back in return a sum greater than itself. We can write this, M—M'.

Thus, M—C—M' is the *general formula of capital* as it presents itself within the sphere of circulation.

The creation of surplus value does not seem to fit in at all with the laws we have studied about commodities and their values. How can a mere transaction create value? It is no good saying, as some people have tried to do, that the seller sells commodities above their value or that the buyer buys them below their value, because all people are at some times buyers and at some times sellers. If they gained in one place what they lost in others, they would not be any better off. Surplus value cannot be created by circulation. There must be something at work behind the scenes, something that cannot be seen on the surface.

So here we find a problem. It is a problem that is very important if we are to understand the laws that govern capitalist society. Let us put the problem this way: Mr. Moneybags must buy his commodities at their value. He must also sell them at their value. Nevertheless at the end of the transaction he must draw more money out of circulation than he put into it to start with. How does he do it?

He does it this way. When he performs the first phase of the transaction, M—C—M', he must buy a commodity whose use-value is that it itself creates value. Otherwise he cannot sell it again later at a higher price than he paid for it. He must find a commodity whose consumption is a process in which labour is embodied and value is created. There exists in the market precisely one such commodity—capacity for labour or *labour-power*.

Labour-power is all those physical and mental abilities in a human being which he employs whenever he produces a use-value of any kind. '

Now if Mr. Moneybags is to be in a position to buy labour-power on the market, two things are necessary. Labour-power can be sold only if its owner—the person whose labour-power it is—actually has it at his disposal to sell. When the owner of labour-power and the owner of money meet in the market, it must be definitely understood that the seller sells his labour-power for only a definite time and no longer. If he sells it for good and all, then he sells himself. He turns himself from a freeman into a slave, from an owner of a commodity into a commodity. It is most important to grasp that in capitalist society the owner of capital purchases not labour but labour-power; not the worker himself, but a claim on his services for a certain period of time.

In the second place, Mr. Moneybags can buy labour-power in the market only if the owner of labour is one who, instead of being able to sell commodities in which labour has already been embodied, has to sell his labour-power itself—which exists only in his living being.

If a man is to be able to sell commodities he has produced—as distinct from his labour-power—he must own the means of production, machinery, raw materials and so on. If a man has no resources of this kind, then he cannot sell commodities embodying his own labour. He therefore sells his labour-power to Mr. Moneybags. The capitalist period is marked by the fact that in the worker's eyes labour-power takes the form of a commodity which is his own property. His labour becomes wage-labour. ' It is only from this moment that the products of labour universally take the form of commodities.

This peculiar commodity, labour-power, must now be examined carefully. It must have a value like any other commodity. How is this value fixed?

It is fixed in the same way as the value of any other commodity—by the labour-time necessary for its production (and consequently for its reproduction). Labour-power is useful only because its owner is a living human being, and a living human being requires a certain amount of the means of subsistence. Thus the labour-time necessary for the production of labour-power is the labour-time necessary for the production of these means of subsistence. In other words, the value of labour-power is the value of the means of subsistence necessary to maintain the labourer. His means of subsistence must be enough to enable him after a day's labour to strengthen and refresh himself so that he returns equally strong to the next day's labour. In different countries, by long development and custom, varying subsistence standards have sprung up. Thus a historical and moral element enters into the value of labour-power. But in a given country at a given time the means of subsistence necessary to maintain a labourer can be taken as a fixed quantity.

The labourer is sure sooner or later to die. It is therefore in the interests of Mr. Moneybags and his fellows that he shall perpetuate himself. His means of subsistence must include an amount big enough to enable him to marry and raise a family. In the case of a skilled labourer, his means of subsistence must include facilities and time for training himself.

Let us assume that the sum of money that must be paid to a labourer to provide himself with all the necessary means of subsistence works out at an average of 3s. a day. In this case 3s. a day will be the price that Mr. Moneybags will have to pay for his labour-power. Let us further assume that when Mr. Moneybags sets him to work, the labourer has to work for six hours each day before he has produced commodities worth 3s.—that is to say, commodities of equivalent value to the commodities necessary for his subsistence. In this case, by working six hours a day, he will have enabled Mr. Moneybags to pay him 3s. each day for something that is worth precisely 3s. Mr. Moneybags has not lost anything, neither has he gained anything.

This will hardly suit Mr. Moneybags. But suppose the labourer is made to work for more than six hours! Suppose that he works for a twelve-hour day. We are beginning now to see how surplus value is created. We must in a moment or two examine in detail just how this prolonging of the working-day benefits the capitalist. But first let us be quite clear about the nature of the labour-process—the process by which labour-power is used up by the capitalist.

It has two important features. First, the worker does his work under the control of the capitalist to whom his labour-power belongs. The capitalist sees to it that not a moment of the working day is wasted, that all the means of production are used to the fullest advantage. And secondly, the product of the labour-process is the property of the capitalist and not of the worker who is its direct producer. The capitalist hires the worker's labour-power for the day and during the day that labour-power belongs to him. From the capitalist's point of view the labour-process is only the consumption of the commodity, labour-power, which he has bought. The labour-process takes place between the various things he has bought—raw material, machinery, labour-power, and so on—and the product of this process naturally belongs to him.

The product, when the process is over, is a use-value, such as yarn or boots, but the capitalist does not make boots just for the fun of the thing. He makes them with two aims in mind. He wants, first, to make a use-value that is an exchange-value; he wants to make something he can sell. He wants, secondly, to produce a commodity whose value is greater than the total of the values of the commodities used up in making it. He wants not only to produce exchange-value, but surplus value in addition.

All this can happen because the daily cost of maintaining labour and the daily output of labour are very different things. The cost of maintenance determines the exchange-value of labour; that is to say, how much the worker will be paid. The output of labour determines its use-value. The value of labour-power and the value which labour-power creates during the labour-process are therefore two entirely different magnitudes. It was precisely this difference in magnitude that the capitalist knew of when he bought the labour-power. We can now see that the process of creating surplus value is the process of creating value prolonged beyond a certain point. If the process of creating value stops at the point when the worker has made a product equivalent only to the cost of his own maintenance, then there is no more than a mere process of creating value, but as soon as the worker goes on working beyond this point he is creating surplus value.

Now why should it be that labour-power alone should be a commodity yielding surplus value to the capital? The answer is simply that, unlike every other commodity, labour-power has for its use-value the fact that it itself *creates value*. Labour-power is the source of all value, it is the determinant of the value of commodities, it has the specific power of being able to produce more value than it itself has. No other commodity has this power.

UTOPIA

By SIR THOMAS MORE

A speculative political essay written in Latin and first published in 1516. It is an early example of communism and was immediately popular, being translated into most of the European languages.

HENRY VIII was king of England when Thomas More, his ambassador in Flanders, heard from Raphael Hythloday of the happy island called Utopia. If the clearest and brightest mind of his age, who in ours has been made a saint, invented Hythloday and Utopia that they might carry his criticism of contemporary ideas, what matter? He gave to us a witty and pungent book, and a new word to our language—Utopia, the ideal and unreachable country.

On a certain day in the summer of 1515, Thomas More was coming out of the Church of Our Lady, in Antwerp, when he saw across the way his friend Peter Giles talking with an elderly man, whose sunburnt face and carelessly worn cloak gave him the look of a sailor. He had indeed sailed far seas, as presently appeared, but rather as wandering Ulysses, seeking strange encounters, than as a mariner earning his bread. His strangest tale (for what can be stranger in this woeful world than a happy and virtuous commonwealth?) was told to Thomas More and Peter Giles in the garden of More's lodging, after dinner, on that summer afternoon.

This island of Utopia (said Hythloday) is crescent-shaped and the horns of the crescent enclose a wide harbour where the sea flows quietly and the winds are kept out. There are dangerous rocks and perilous channels outside the harbour, which only the Utopians can safely pass, but once within it a ship may ride at ease. King Utopus, the long-ago conqueror who brought a wild people to perfect excellence in humanity and civil gentleness, made the land an island by cutting through fifteen miles of upland ground that joined it to the neighbouring continent.

The cities of this island are large and fair, in all points fashioned and governed alike, but set not less than twenty-four miles apart. None of them tries to enlarge its borders or trespass upon the cornland and pastures that lie about it. In this open country there are farmhouses, well built and provided with all the tools of husbandry. All citizens dwell in them by turn, forty at a time, under the rule of the farmer and his wife; for it is held in Utopia that every man should be expert in husbandry, lest food should grow scarce for lack of skilled culture. The farms are grouped by thirties under a headman or bailiff, who is called the Philarch, and superintends the come and go of citizens serving at the farms. Tillage, cattle-breeding, and timber-growing are thus familiar to every man; and likewise the nurture of poultry, which in Utopia is of a novel fashion. "For" (said Master Hythloday, and Thomas More records the marvel) "the hens do not sit upon the eggs; but by keeping them in a certain equal heat they bring life into them and hatch them, and the chickens as soon as they come out of the shell follow men and women instead of the hens."

Few horses are used in the farm work, most of them being kept to exercise the young men in riding and feats of arms. Oxen are put to the work of ploughing and drawing carts, as willing to abide more labour than the horse, though less good at a dead weight. Corn is sown only for bread, as no ale is brewed; for the Utopians drink wine made of grapes, apples or pears, when they do not content themselves with clear water. At the harvest season, men are sent from the cities for the ingathering, and so many of them that the work is quickly done.

It has been said that all the cities of Utopia are fashioned alike. So a description of Amaurote, the capital, will serve for them all. To Amaurote three old and wise men go yearly from every city to debate on national policy and affairs. It stands upon the side of a low hill above the river Anyder, which is there fully half a mile broad and widens as it flows a further forty miles to the sea. The tides and the salt of the ocean do not reach as far as Amaurote, where the river runs fresh and pleasant below the city walls. A stone bridge of strong arches crosses the river at the end of the city which is farthest from the sea, so that ships can sail alongside the wall, without hindrance, full two miles. The wall is high and strong and built of stone, with many turrets upon it, and on every side of the city, save only where the river runs, there is a deep broad ditch below the wall. The streets are clean and handsome, the houses built close together, and at the back of

them lie large gardens. The doors are never locked, so that
who so will may enter, for nothing in the house is a man's
own, seeing that every tenth year they exchange their houses
by drawing lots. They set great store by their gardens, which
are furnished so fully with all manner of fruit and flowers
that Master Hythloday said he had never seen gardens better
trimmed. In the making of these gardens they express the
fashion of their own minds. For King Utopus, when he
prescribed the shape and size of the city, left to posterity the
gallant garnishing of it. And posterity has made fair gardens,
and built comely houses three storeys high, in place of the
rude huts thatched with straw of King Utopus' day.

The government of this commonwealth is by officers called
Syphogrants, chosen by the people with the approval of the
Prince, who is elected by the Syphogrants from among four fit
and experienced men named by the people. Nothing touching
the common weal is decreed until it has been debated not less
than three days by the officers in council, where alone such
matters may be argued. And it is further ordained that no
matter may be argued on the day it is mooted, lest any man
who has spoken his opinion in haste may feel bound to maintain
it later (though it be never so ill-advised) for consistency's sake,
being willing rather to do public harm than to hurt his own
conceit.

It has been said that husbandry is a science common to all
the people, both men and women, but besides husbandry each
one learns another science as his proper craft. This is most
commonly clothworking in wool or flax, masonry, smith's
work or carpentry. There are but few other occupations;
none that minister to the vanities of life. For the garments of
these islanders are of one kind and fashion, save that there
are differences between the man's garment and the woman's,
and between that of the married and the unmarried. This
universal dress is pleasant to the eye and does not in any sort
impede the movements of the body. It serves comfortably for
both summer and winter, with no more than a cloak cast over
it for warmth or for covering the coarse working dress of leather
that lasts a man perhaps as long as seven years. The cloaks
are everywhere of the same colour and that the natural colour
of the wool. For in linen only whiteness, in wool only cleanliness, are regarded. "Not," said Master Hythloday, turning his
black eyes reprovingly upon Thomas More, servant of the
gorgeous Tudor king, and upon Peter Giles, a merchant of

rich, befurred Antwerp, " not as in some countries we know,
where a man may have four or five cloth gowns of divers
colours and many silk coats. As though he might be
better happed against the cold by a blue coat than by a
green ! "

Every family makes its own clothes, so there is none that lives
by the tailor's craft, as in countries where vain adornment is
the custom. But every man must learn one trade, and every
woman, too; the women, as the weaker sort, being put to the
easier work, such as spinning and weaving. In general a man
follows his father's craft, but if he have a mind towards another
he is adopted into a family that pursues the craft he desires.
The Syphogrants see to it that no man is idle, though none is
wearied with continual toil from dawn to dark. That is to
live like slaves and not as free men, though it is the fate of
free workmen almost everywhere save in Utopia. There the
day is justly divided. Six hours are given to work and eight
to sleep, the rest being bestowed as a man will, save only that
he spend his time virtuously, as in hearing lectures (in which
the Utopians take great delight), or in thriftily improving his
understanding in some other sort. After supper there is play;
but play of honest kind. Dice and such pernicious games they
do not know; but they have pleasant games, not unlike chess,
and one in which vices contend with virtues, exceedingly
improving to the mind.

In Thomas More's England, in Peter Giles's Flanders, the
life of the labouring poor was harsh and toilsome, and beggars
roved the country, asking charity at the monastery gates.
The listeners may have looked grave at the tale of the Utopian
six-hour day, for Hythloday said:

" You must not think, for all that they labour so few hours,
that the commonwealth is poor. Not so. Consider how many
idlers there are in the countries you know. Rich men, proud
women, the vicious crowd of lacqueys and serving-men, lazy
priests and monks, nobles and beggars—if you so consider you
will find that the work of the country is done by fewer men
than you thought. If all those do-nothings were put to honest
crafts—and in Utopia there are none other—you can suppose
with what plenty the land would be furnished."

Yet even in Utopia there are some who do not labour—the
old, the infirm, those who are proved fit for the rarer labour
of the mind (though if one of these prove later unfit he is plucked
back into the company of the artificers). This is regarded as

the more shameful in that the Utopians reckon the felicity of
this life to consist in the exercise of the mind and the garnishing
of the same.

In order that the number of the people should not decrease
or increase above measure it is ordained that no household
shall contain less than ten children or more than sixteen about
the age of thirteen years. This proportion can be observed
by putting children from the more prolific families into the
households that are slower to increase. In regard to the
population of the cities, if it grow unwieldy in one city a part
of it is transferred to a city where it is scant, and if by ill-hap
the people of the whole island multiply beyond reason, a
number of citizens are chosen from each city and a new
city builded for them on any land that a neighbour country
has lying idle. Should the neighbour country accept this
mildly, all is well, but should it resent the newcomers the land
is taken by force of arms. " For the Utopians count this a
reasonable cause of war, if any people hold a piece of ground
void and vacant, keeping others from the use of it that ought
thereby to be nourished and relieved."

The cities are divided into four quarters, and in the midst
of each quarter there is a market-place with storehouses, from
whence the father of a family fetches what his household needs,
without payment, without exchange or pledge. For why
should anything be denied him, seeing that there is abundance
of all things? And no man will take more than he needs
when he knows his needs will always be satisfied. Hard by the
storehouse is the market, where fruit and herbs, bread, meat
and fowl may be had in plenty. It is the cleanly custom to
slaughter beasts for food outside the city at appointed places
where running water may be had for washing the meat. The
butchers are always bond-servants, for the Utopians hold that
the killing of beasts causes little by little the gentlest affection
of our nature, which is pitifulness, to perish in us, and therefore
they think it unfitting work for a free man.

For the due care of the sick they have four hospitals outside
each city, so wide and ample that they seem like four little
towns. In these hospitals the sick need not lie too close, and
so in discomfort, and they which suffer from contagious disease
(which is wont to creep from one to another) can be laid far
apart from the rest. The hospitals are well appointed with
everything necessary to health and good diet, and skilled
physicians are in constant attendance. No man is sent thither

against his will, but there is no sick person that would not
rather lie there than at home.

It is the custom of those who live in the cities to dine together
in halls appointed for the purpose. At the set hour of dinner
and supper the whole Syphogranty, or ward, assembles in
their hall, summoned by the sound of a brazen trumpet, save
only the sick and those who for other good reason are unable
to come. No man is forbid to dine at home, yet none does so
willingly, for it were folly to dress a bad dinner at home when
good fare may be had near at hand in the hall. All the
laborious tasks of preparation are done by bondmen, but the
women of every family take turns in cooking and arranging
the meals. The company sits at three tables or more, young
and old mingled, so that the wise converse of the elder, which
is never harsh or tutorial, may benefit the younger and the
freshness of youth may enliven the old. The men sit on
benches against the wall, the women opposite, which makes
it the more easy to withdraw without disturbance of others if
a woman with child should feel the pangs of labour come
upon her suddenly.

The nursing mothers sit apart with their infants in a parlour
appointed for them and all the children under five years old.
This parlour is never without fire and clean water, nor yet
without cradles in which the child may be laid at will. Every
mother nurses her own child, except death or disability prevent.
In such a case, the wives of the Syphogrants seek out a foster-
mother, any woman who is able proffering herself at once;
for this kind of beneficence is much praised and the foster-
child ever after treats his nurse as if she were his mother. The
other children, all, that is, above the age of five, either wait
on their elders at table, or, if too young to do this, stand by
in silence, taking what food is given them. Food is served
first to the old and then in order of age to the younger folk.
They begin each meal by reading from some worthy book, but
the reading is short that none may feel it burdensome, and
though the elders may discourse of what is read they are careful
to hear the opinions of the younger men, as the freedom of the
occasion unlooses their wit. Dinner is short; supper somewhat
longer, for after supper comes recreation and sleep, which
allows of good digestion, and after dinner comes work. At
supper, too, they have music, and for further delight they burn
spices and sprinkle sweet scents abroad. For they think no
pleasant thing need be forbidden, so it be innocent.

There is little travelling from place to place. Any who
would visit another city must first get leave of his Syphogrant,
and no man goes alone, but in a company, bearing letters of
permission which likewise prescribe the day of return. They
are given a wagon and a bond-servant to drive the oxen, but
they seldom use it, save there be women in the party, for they
need carry no provision. Wherever they tarry they are
welcome, but should they tarry longer than a day in any place
each man must work there among those of his own craft, and
in whatsoever part of the country he comes, there is no food
given to him until he has done a morning's work or as much
as is commonly done before supper. There is so little approval
of idle wandering, that if a man wishes even to walk in the
fields outside his own city he must have the consent of his
father and his wife. " As there are neither wine-taverns nor
ale-houses, nor other haunts of vice," said the traveller, who
had voyaged from less virtuous lands, " they are driven to
more laudable pastimes, willy-nilly."

And it is by no means the only matter in which Utopia
surpasses the countries of Europe. In More's England, men
who have toiled their life through with spade and mattock
for hard fare and small wage may perish miserably of hunger,
and soldiers broken in the wars beg their bread. " Your very
sheep," said Master Hythloday, fixing his dark regard upon
King Henry's ambassador, " your sheep that were wont to be
so meek and tame, have become so great devourers that they
swallow down the very men themselves. For your rich nobles
leave no ground for tillage, but enclose all into pasture. They
throw down houses and leave all desolate, so that your
husbandmen must trudge away from their accustomed homes,
with their wives and children; for one shepherd can mind
many sheep on the land that employed many husbandmen.
And when these outcast men have wandered till all be spent,
what can they do but steal and be hanged? It is otherwise
in Utopia, where, seeing that all men be partners equally in
the commonwealth, none be needy."

In Utopia what is lacking in one part of the country is
supplied by the abundance of another, so that the whole
island is as it were one household. Only when they have laid
up enough for next year's store do they convey their grain,
wool, madder, wood, purple-dyed skins, honey, flax and other
goods into foreign lands, where they give a seventh part of
them to the poor, selling the rest at a moderate price, and

bringing home (besides gold and silver) iron, which is their only lack. By these means they have great abundance of all things needful for life, and of treasure plenty to succour them in sudden jeopardy, when they use it to hire foreign soldiers, whom they pay very highly.

Save in this respect they have none but the basest uses for gold and silver, esteeming them of far less value than iron. For to gold and silver Nature has given no serviceableness, if the folly of men had not exalted them for their rarity. Nature, like a tender mother, has placed the best and most necessary things where all may reach their goodness—the air, the water, the earth itself—and has hidden farthest from us the vain unprofitable things, such as gold and silver and precious stones. The Utopians, judging their several values as no other people in the world judges them, eat and drink from glass and earthen vessels, finely shaped though of small cost, and use gold and silver for the meanest household pots and for the fetters of criminals. They hang rings of gold in the ears of felons and set diadems on their heads in sign of infamy, contrary to the custom of those nations who crown with them their royal princes. They do, indeed, deck their young children with pearls and precious stones, thinking that only those of tender years should care for such trifling toys, and the children as they grow cast them by of their own accord, as our children cast away their dolls.

" Touching this matter of gold and gems," said Master Raphael, " the Ambassadors of the Anemolians came to the country while I was there." Knowing little of the Utopians, save that they wore all the same fashion of dress and that very homely, the ambassadors supposed them to lack what they did not display. They thought, therefore, to dazzle the poor Utopians and to show themselves the emissaries of a great and rich nation by attiring themselves in silks of gorgeous colour and cloth-of-gold, with chains of gold about their necks and caps sewn with pearls. The Utopians, swarming into the streets to see them, bowed courteously to the ambassadors' servants, taking them, in their stuff coats, for the ambassadors, and the ambassadors, tricked out with gold and silks, for persons in attendance. A child who saw baubles he had cast aside but lately sticking in the ambassadors' caps, plucked at his mother's gown and cried out, " Look, mother, at the great lubber wearing pearls as though he were still a baby! "
" Hush, son," said the mother, " I think he be the ambassa-

dor's fool." Some of the wiseheads said that the chains of
gold and gems were too slight—that the bond-servants who
wore them would break them easily.

The killing of harmless animals for sport they utterly despise.
Why is there more pleasure to be felt, they ask, when a dog
pursues a hare than when a dog runs after a dog, seeing that
one thing is done in both cases, namely, running? If the
slaughter and tearing in pieces of the creature delights you,
the weak taken by the strong, the timid by the fierce, you should
rather be moved with pity than with pleasure. Therefore
they leave hunting as they leave butchers' work, to their bond-
servants, as unworthy of free men. Hunting they account the
worser work, because the hunter seeks only the pleasure of an
innocent creature's death, whereas a butcher kills of necessity.

There are, nevertheless, lawful pleasures of the body:
steadfast quiet health, the refreshment of food and drink, the
strength and nimbleness of the limbs. They themselves are
light and quick of body, and stronger than you would suppose
from their stature, which is but middling; and though their
soil is not very fertile, nor their climate kindly, they use such
temperance of diet and behaviour and so carefully till and care
for their fields that no people enjoys greater plenty of the
fruits of the earth or better health of body.

When the work of their hands is finished, the better sort
give their leisure to learning. Until Master Hythloday and
his companions came there they were not acquainted with
the philosophy of Greece, but they had discovered for themselves much wisdom, especially in the science of astronomy.
They are ingenious in the invention of instruments for observing
the movements of the stars, but of astrology or the vain science
of divination thereby, they make no use. They hold many of
the ideas concerning the origin of the world that our ancient
philosophers have propounded and in debating the nature of
the soul and the meaning of goodness they have concluded
that the soul is immortal and by God's bountiful mercy set
towards ultimate felicity. They think that evil deeds will be
punished and good rewarded after this life, but none among
them mortify and mutilate the body in the hope of sustaining
the soul. For they count it folly that a man should deny
himself happiness if it will not later prove hurtful to himself
or another. Nature, they say, bids us be gentle to our fellows,
but does not therefore command us to be cruel to ourselves,
though in taking our pleasure we must not stand in the way

of another man obtaining his.   They hold that happiness does
not lie in all and any pleasure but only in that which is honest.
The perverse flickering enticements of mere desire, the gauds
of worldly honours, they esteem as outside the bounds of
happiness.   To vie with one another as to who shall wear the
finer coat they think childishness.   Why should a fine-spun
thread be thought better than a coarse, seeing that both came
from the back of a sheep?   Will it comfort your heart in sorrow
to have men bow the knee before you?   Not so.   Happiness,
like virtue, is life ordered according to nature, the desiring
and refusing of things in the light of high reason, which kindles
in man a love of God's divine majesty that has endowed us
with knowledge of good and evil.

"They are gentle, cheerful and intelligent, delighting in
quiet and comely pleasures," Master Raphael said, as the
shadows lengthened in the walled garden and the turfed banks
grew cool and more evenly green.   "But they prefer the exercise of the mind to great bodily labour, though at need they
can endure it hardily.   When I spoke to them of Greek
literature they very earnestly asked me to instruct them in the
language, and, though I had little hope that many of them
would profit, I did so, that I might not seem ungracious.   I
soon perceived by their diligence that I should not labour in
vain.   They quickly learned to fashion the letters and to
pronounce the words, and they studied with such understanding that in less than a year the forwardest of them could
read the simplest Greek authors without difficulty.   I have
thought that their nation may derive distantly from the Greeks,
because their speech, which in many respects is not unlike
Persian, shows divers tokens of a Greek origin, as in the names
of their cities and their magistrates.   When I went thither for
the fourth time I took with me, instead of merchandise, a great
bundle of books;   the most of Plato and Aristotle, and
Theophrastus, though this, I am sorry to say, was imperfect.
For while we were aboard ship a marmoset chanced upon the
book and playing with it wantonly plucked out several leaves
and tore them to pieces.   They set great store by Plutarch,
and were delighted with the quips and jests of Lucian.   Of the
poets they have Homer, Euripedes and Sophocles, in the
small Aldine type.   We took with us, also, the smaller works
of Galen, for though no nation under heaven has less need of
physic than they, none honours the science of medicine more."

Besides bringing to the Utopians the wisdom of Greece,

Master Hythloday was able to introduce to them the arts of printing and papermaking. He was imperfectly instructed in both, but they proved so quick to understand that they soon learned, with some pains, to make paper and type, though formerly they had written upon skins and the bark of trees. They are always willing to learn of any stranger who comes into their country, and make especially welcome one who is expert in any art or rich in learning.

The bond-servants whom they use for the baser tasks (as butchery and the heavier labour of the kitchen) are not enslaved prisoners taken in battle, but persons condemned for heinous offences. They sometimes buy the offenders of other nations for this purpose and there are likewise poor folk who have fled from harsh treatment elsewhere and willingly become bondmen of the Utopians. These they treat with great kindness, and if any wish to depart they do not hold him against his will, nor send him away empty-handed. They do not make bond-servants of the children of bondmen, for every man among them is born free.

Their women are not married before eighteen years of age and the men must be four years older. If either man or woman has lain with another before marriage, the sinner is sharply punished, and the head of the household to which he belonged is admonished as lacking care and circumspection. In choosing wife or husband they have one other custom that seemed to the strangers from Europe singular, but not unwise. A discreet matron is called upon to show the woman naked before her wooer and a discreet man shows the wooer naked to the woman. For they wonder much at other nations who in buying a colt will see him stripped of saddle and harness lest there be a hidden gall or sore, but in choosing a wife are willing to judge her by scarcely more than a handbreadth, seeing no more of her but only her face. And all men are not so sage as to be content with virtue in an ill-made casket.

The Utopians, unlike most nations in that part of the world, have but one wife apiece. The more need, therefore, to be careful in the choice of her. For only unfaithfulness can break the bond of marriage or else some intolerable waywardness of either party, and once divorced the guilty may not marry another spouse. For a husband to put away his wife for no other cause but age or the failure of bodily health is regarded as extreme cruelty, seeing that to do so is to cast off one who is in need of help and comfort. Adulterers they punish with grievous bondage, though by repentance and amendment of life they may win pardon. Other offences are punished according to their degree of heinousness, at the discretion of the council, there being no penalty fixed by law for such and such a crime. ᛉ The penalty is in general bondage, not death, for they hold strait bondage to be no less grief to the offender and of some use to the commonwealth, which can exact no labour from a dead man. And these bondmen may with diligence and patience win release and the forgiveness of their fellows, which in the grave could not have reached them. " In England," said Raphael Hythloday, " you hang many men every year for robbery or riot who are driven thereto by hunger, and many more who commit murder because they know that mere robbery has the same punishment, and, as the proverb says, it is as well to be hanged for a sheep as for a lamb."

They do not only warn their people from evil by punishment, but they allure them to virtue by setting up in the market-place the statues of men who have been benefactors to the commonwealth. They live together lovingly. For no magistrate is haughty or threatening. " Fathers " they are called and like fathers they use the erring and the poor. They have no symbols of power to daunt the multitude. Even the prince is known from the commonalty not by a crown or robe of state, but by a little sheaf of corn carried before him. They have no long and complex code of laws, thinking that the law should be so plain that the unlearned may understand it. For this reason also they have no lawyers who subtly dispute points of law to the confusion of the simple. They make no alliances with other countries (which so often are concluded, broken and renewed), thinking that nature enjoins love between man and man and that whosoever is not bound by love of his fellowmen is not likely to be bound by leagues and treaties, which, though knit up with oaths and solemnity, are made void by dishonest reading of their meaning. Nations, in their dealings with each other, use a craftiness and deceit which, if it were practised by private men, would be cried out upon as detestable. And why should nations, because they are separated by a river or a little hill, think themselves born adversaries? ᛬

War, contrary to the custom of other peoples, is held in no honour among the Utopians. They daily practise themselves, both men and women, in the exercise and discipline of arms, but they do not go to war, save in defence of their country or to deliver from tyranny an oppressed people, if their help is asked. And they do not rejoice in bloodshed, preferring to vanquish their enemies, if it be possible, by cunning political moves. For brute force, they say, is the weapon of brutes alone. And if they can bring about by any means the death of the enemy's leaders they count it a worthy deed, because by the death of a few the lives of many innocent people, driven to war by the will of their leaders, may be saved. They no less pity the common people in their enemies' country than in their own. And they send no man to war against his will, believing that the faint-hearted will do no manful part himself and be an occasion of cowardice in others. But if Utopia itself be attacked they put these timorous ones (provided they be not infirm of body) on shipboard among the boldest of their men, or set them to man the walls of the cities, where, because there is no chance of flight, they may forget fear. For many times extreme necessity turns cowards into brave men. In battle, when battle must be, wives stand at their husbands' side and their kinsfolk about them; all whom nature has bound together mutually succouring each other. They are stubborn fighters, disdaining to give back an inch, and that fear which often weakens the men of other nations—namely, the thought of leaving their children to poverty—has no power over them who know that the commonwealth makes every man's livelihood safe. Their armour is strong, and so easy in the wearing that it is not unwieldy even for swimming. And they have many ingenious engines of war, which they keep very secretly. They are merciful in victory, slaying no man unarmed, unless he be a spy and forbearing to waste or ravage the land.

There are diverse religions in Utopia. Some worship the sun, some the moon, some a great and good man that once lived on earth. But the wisest hold that there is a certain Power unknown, everlasting and incomprehensible, whose virtue is dispersed throughout the world. Him they call the Father of all. Even those who follow another religion share this belief in a chief and almighty God, maker and ruler of the world, whom in their tongue they call Mythra. And they seem little by little to be casting off the baser superstitions and to agree in the religion of the wisest among them. Moreover, when the travellers spoke to them of Christ, they accepted his godhead with willingness and joy, finding it an apt consummation of their own philosophy. Many of them were baptized into the Christian faith, but those who hold it do not constrain those who do not. They like religious exclusiveness so little that one of Hythloday's company, who went about proclaiming that all religions save that of Christ were wicked and devilish, was sent out of the country as a raiser up of dissension. For ever since King Utopus' day, they have held that every man shall follow what religion he will (so he do it peaceably), and may try to bring others to his opinion, so he do it without harsh rebuke. King Utopus, believing that truth must prevail, did not prescribe one form of faith for his people, save only that he straitly charged them not to have so base an opinion of the dignity of man as to think that the soul dies with the body, or that there is no divinity concerned to shape our ends. For this reason, they mourn only those who die unwillingly and in despair, thinking they shall not be welcome to God. But the man who dies in peace they follow to the grave with joyous singing, sharing the joy of him who, when called of God, ran to Him gladly.

They think the contemplation of nature and the praise of God's wonders therein very acceptable to Him. But none turns apart from life's labour to this end alone. Idleness they abhor. Some, therefore, attend on the sick, some fell wood, dig turf, mend the highways, labouring for the good of others willingly, neither reproving the lives of their fellow-men nor glorying in their own. There be two sects of these religious-minded. One abstains from the eating of meat and lives celibate. The other, though no less desirous of labour in the common cause, eats meat and accepts matrimony, the first as making them hardier to labour, the second as a service to the country by the procreation of children. Their priests are men of very holy life, and therefore few—not more than thirteen in each city. Both childhood and youth are instructed by them, and they endeavour heartily to put good thoughts into the minds of children, while they be pliant and tender, which may tend to the common weal when they grow older. For ideas once rooted in children remain with them all their life. There are women-priests, but very few, and none but widows and old women, and the men-priests may marry, if they will.

They keep holy the first and last day of every month and year, and their churches, which are of fine and curious workmanship, are very large, though somewhat dark. This is not due to ignorance, but to the belief that over much light disperses men's thoughts, whereas in a dim light thought is more easily concentrated. There is nothing in their ceremonies nor in the church itself peculiar to one form of belief. No image of any god is to be seen, so that every man may be free to conceive God after what likeness he will, though all call upon Him by the one name of Mythra. They kill no living beast in sacrifice, thinking that the merciful God has no delight in blood and slaughter, and gave life to the beasts that they should rejoice in it, even as man himself. They do not disdain to burn incense and other sweet savours, and they light a great number of tapers, not supposing any of this gear to be pleasing to the divine nature, but because by such sweet savours and burning light men feel themselves secretly lifted up towards devoutness; as likewise by the music that accompanies their worship.

There was much else that Thomas More would have liked to know concerning the perfect commonwealth, but perceiving that Master Hythloday was tired, and observing his sharpness in criticism (which commonly is accompanied by a sharp resentment of being criticized), he led the way to the house and supper, saying they would talk more of Utopia on another occasion. But the occasion did not come. Thomas More went home to England and wrote down the tale Raphael had told him. Only one thing, as he found when he came to write, Raphael had not told, namely, in what part of the world Utopia lies. He had begun to speak of it, indeed, but, at the moment, one of More's servants came with a message, distracting his attention, and Peter Giles, by reason of a cold caught (he regretfully supposed) aboard ship, coughed at that very instant so loudly that he lost what Raphael was saying. They resolved to question Raphael when he returned to Europe (for he was gone again on his far voyage).

But they never learned where Utopia is situate. Perhaps Raphael never returned. Perhaps—as the name Utopia in English means Nowhere—he had never been there.

THE REPUBLIC

By PLATO

*Any digest of a work so closely knit as this famous dialogue
must necessarily omit many essentials. Thus the famous
Apologue of the Cavern in Book VII is not included for
reasons of space. It is hoped that readers may be encouraged
by this foretaste to read the original.*

AFTERNOON at the Piræus, seaport of ancient Athens.
Against the limpid blue background of the Aegean Sea
file the processions in honour of the goddess Diana.
Among the holiday makers going towards the city is a vigorous,
middle-aged man with a broad, powerful brow and a kindly,
rather flat face. It is Socrates, idol of the youths of Athens,
and truly their " guide, philosopher and friend ". With him
walks his pupil, Glaucon.

Even now, from the throng behind, a group of young men,
catching sight of him ahead, hurry forward, and, closing round
him, make it impossible for Socrates to proceed.

One among them, Polemarchus, persuades Socrates and
Glaucon to return with them to the house of his father,
Cephelus.

Here it was, in the cool marble hall of the country villa,
looking out between pillars on the wide sweep of the sea, among
the eager, flushed young men, that Plato imagines Socrates
propounding the immortal conception of the ideal state and the
ideal man.

Their ancient host, Cephelus, starts the discussion by a chance
remark about justice. But when he is asked by Socrates to
define justice, he goes out to attend a sacrifice and leaves his
son, Polemarchus, to speak in his place.

Various definitions are put forward by the young men, such
as, " justice means restoring to everybody what is due to him "
and " justice is the interest of the stronger ". The second
definition was proposed by Thrasymachus, an impetuous
young man. He enters into a vehement comparison between
the just and the unjust man, striving to make out that the latter
is not only far better off materially but is also a much happier
man. As an illustration he takes injustice in its most terrible
form.

"This form is a despotism, which proceeds not by small degrees, but by wholesale, in its open or fraudulent appropriation of the property of others, whether it be sacred or profane, public or private; perpetuating offences, which if a person commits in detail and is found out, he becomes liable to a penalty and incurs deep disgrace. But when a man not only seizes the property of his fellow-citizens but captures and enslaves their persons also, instead of those dishonourable titles, he is called happy and highly favoured by all who hear of the comprehensive injustice which he has wrought. For when people abuse injustice, they do so because they are afraid, not of committing it, but of suffering it."

"After deluging our ears like a bathing-man with this copious and unbroken flood of words", Thrasymachus was for taking his leave, but the others make him stay to hear out Socrates' answer.

Before Socrates starts on his task of refutation, Glaucon tries further to establish the rather dogmatic position that Thrasymachus has sought to hold. Glaucon, in order to draw the best from his beloved master, puts a case for injustice by means of the fable of Gyges. This man was a shepherd who found a ring that made the wearer invisible. The story tells how Gyges immediately went to court, seduced the king's wife and murdered the king. Since he was invisible and could not be found out, all considerations of justice went by the board. Would not, Glaucon asks, the just and the unjust man both behave in a similar way, that is to say, an unjust way, if they possessed that magic ring? Justice, in short, is a compromise for the necessities of social life.

Socrates is now told to go ahead with his confutation. He asks that he may be allowed, since the inquiry is likely to prove arduous, to examine first where justice is found in the state, and only after that to narrow down the search to the individual.

Permission is granted, and Socrates proceeds to trace the growth of a state, starting with the primitive needs of men that bring them together, sorting them out into the occupations they are best fitted for—one being a builder, another a husbandman, a third a weaver, and so on. As the state grows, more occupations will spring up. Eventually, it will scarcely be possible for the state to do without imports. Thus a merchant class will come into being. To provide for the exchange of goods a currency must be instituted and public markets for buying and selling. A retail trade will arise, and there will be a class of shopkeepers. Besides all these, some persons whose mental qualifications do not fit them to be associates of the producers, artisans and barterers, will be employed as hired labourers.

At this point, where the people still live simply, without luxuries of any kind, Socrates believes the good state has been attained. He is about to search for justice in it, when Glaucon objects that the state he has constructed is fit only for swine to live in. "Very well," says Socrates, "if you wish it so, we will change it from a simple to a bloated state. Perhaps then we shall find justice and injustice more easily." So Socrates goes on to enumerate the various needs of citizens who have ceased to be contented with the prime necessities of life; now they want in addition painting, embroidery, gold, ivory, music, articles of finery for the women. Gratification of these increased appetites will mean great addition to the population. There will come a time when the state will be forced to expand and take its neighbour's territory. But this means war, and the addition of another class, the soldiers.

Now the perfect state in these conditions must needs have for its guardians, that is to say, for its rulers and its soldiers, the perfectly educated man. The guardians, as distinct from the producers, tradesmen and labourers, are the cream of the community. "Then," says Socrates, "in our judgment the man whose natural gifts promise to make him a perfect guardian of the state will be philosophical, high-spirited, swift-footed, and strong."

How is he to be educated to fulfil this ideal? Socrates describes the education of the guardian. First, religious instruction. "God," Socrates affirms, "inasmuch as he is good, cannot be the cause of all things. On the contrary, he is the author of only a small part of human affairs; of the larger part he is not the author: for our evil things far outnumber our good things." It follows that many acts ascribed to the gods by the poet Homer, as for instance their immorality, their jealousy, and their vengefulness, create a harmful impression of deity. And so poets in the ideal state must represent God as the author only of good.

Then Socrates goes on to describe the importance of harmony, that is to say music and poetry, and of gymnastic, and the manner in which these two subjects must tone the whole man to a perfect concord of his faculties. The poetry that is taught the young guardians must be narrative, or epic, as distinct from imitative, or dramatic. Socrates believes that drama is bad for the formation of a soldier's mind, because the author translates himself as it were into all his various characters, some of whom are bad, some ridiculous, some of mean callings, and because he represents passions and emotions, wailings of women, greed and licentiousness.

Music must be simple and such as stirs to noble endeavour or philosophical tranquillity. Music, to Socrates, is of prime importance, " because rhythm and harmony sink most deeply into the recesses of the soul, and take most powerful hold on it, bringing gracefulness in their train ".

What music is to the mind, so is gymnastic to the body. Yet the two exercises are not to be separated, as if soul and body did not interact one upon the other. Music and gymnastic are meant to temper the two elements in a noble nature, mettle, or spiritedness and philosophy. Without the two supplementary aids, either mettle or mind would tend to become dominant and lead to roughness or inactivity.

Philosophy consists in the harmony of the mind with the eternal realities. To acquire the philosophical attitude that looks upwards at first principles, at the ultimate reality instead of at the images and changing shapes of things, we must first be able to distinguish the appearance from the substance.

There are two worlds, that visible to the eye only, and that which can be perceived only by the intellect, or the eye of reason. Each world falls into two parts: that visible to the eye contains: least certain, *images*, that is to say, shadows and reflections; more certain, substances themselves that make the reflections or cast the shadows. The world that is perceived only by the intellect is revealed to us firstly and with least certainty by way of reasoning from an hypothesis to a conclusion. This is the geometrical method, and for purposes of illustration it employs objects visible to the eye, that is to say, lines. Secondly, the intellectual world is reached by the process of pure reason, without the aid of any material illustrations; its objects are first principles from which unerring conclusions may be deduced.

Socrates goes on to show how, corresponding with the four divisions of the two worlds, there are four mental states: Conjecture, Belief, Understanding, Reason. He uses symbolism to explain the four stages. The first stage is to be able easily to distinguish shadows and reflections; this is the conjectural stage. Next to believe that reflections are made by solid bodies; this is the stage of belief. He who raises his head to the heaven, the moon and stars symbolizes his rational approach to reality, and the sun itself represents the supreme good. For, as Socrates says, " the essential Form of the Good is the highest object of science; this essence, by blending with just things and all other created objects, renders them useful and advantageous ".

Now that Socrates has revealed the nature of the highest reality, which is also the highest good, and the object of philosophy, he shows how the guardians of his ideal state, and especially those of them who are selected on account of their special aptitude for *rule* as apart from *protection*, must be instructed in this science.

The qualities a philosopher must possess are these: (1) an eager desire for the knowledge of all real existence; (2) hatred of falsehood and devotion to truth; (3) contempt for all sensual pleasures; (4) indifference to money; (5) high-mindedness and generosity; (6) justice and gentleness; (7) a quick understanding and good memory; (8) a musical, regular, and harmonious disposition.

The training of the philosopher must consist of the abstract sciences that train the reasoning element in the soul and quicken the intellectual vision: arithmetic, geometry, astronomy considered as the abstract science of motion, harmonics, and dialectics, or the study of real existence.

Such must be the education of the rulers. To the objection that philosophers are found to be inept in public affairs and to shun them, Socrates answers that this diffidence is not inherent in the philosopher as such; he has been brought to despise public offices by observing the class of opportunists who fill them.

Now that Socrates has built up his ideal state, with its rulers, its auxiliaries or soldiers, its members who are occupied in agriculture, crafts and trade, he perceives that one thing is needful to cement it, as it were, and to prevent the three classes from becoming embroiled with one another or indiscriminately intermixed. He proposes that a myth about the origin of men should be inculcated in the consciousness of all the constituent members, even of the rulers, if that be possible. It will be a falsehood, but a " golden " falsehood, leading to the people's own good.

" I shall try to persuade first the rulers themselves and the military class, and after them the rest of the city, that when we were training and instructing them, they only fancied, as in dreams, that all this was happening to them and about them, while in reality they were in course of formation and training in the bowels of the earth, where they themselves, their armour, and the rest of their equipment were manufactured, and from whence, as soon as they were thoroughly elaborated, the earth, their real mother, sent them up to the surface; and, consequently, that they ought now to take thought for the land in which they dwell, as their mother and nurse, and repel all attacks upon it, and feel towards their brother citizens as brother children of the soil.

" We shall tell our people, in mythical language: You are doubtless all brethren, as many as inhabit the city, but the God who created you mixed gold in the composition of such of you as are qualified to rule, which gives them the highest value; while in the auxiliaries he made silver an ingredient, assigning iron and copper to the cultivators of the soil and the other workmen. Therefore, inasmuch as you are all related to one another, although your children will generally resemble their parents, yet sometimes a golden parent will produce a silver child, and a silver parent a golden child, and so on, each producing any. The rulers therefore have received this in charge first and above all from the gods, to observe nothing more closely, in their character of vigilant guardians, than the children that are born, to see which of these metals enters into the composition of their souls; and if a child be born in their class with an alloy of copper or iron, they are to have no manner of pity upon it, but giving it the value that belongs to its nature, they are to thrust it away into the class of artisans or agriculturists; and if again among these a child be born with any admixture of gold or silver, when they have assayed it, they are to raise it either to the class of guardians, or to that of auxiliaries: because there is an oracle that declares the city shall then perish when it is guarded by iron or copper."

The " golden lie " is designed to keep the classes contented. But it is perhaps even more important that the class to whose hands the keeping of the state is entrusted, both to guard it from foreign foes and to maintain interior order, that this soldier class does not fall out among itself. To preclude this possibility Socrates proposes the following regimen. The guardians must remove themselves to a quarter outside the city, where they will live as it were in barracks, without any personal property, maintained at the expense of the state. Their wants will be provided, but they will be given no luxuries.

But wives and children themselves constitute private property; therefore Socrates proposes that these too should be shared in common. Otherwise, envy, lust, jealousy, would disturb the harmonious composition of the state's *élite*.

When Socrates is interrupted and asked what the position of women would be in his ideal state, he answers that women, in as far as they were fitted, would be eligible for any position in the state. There would be no reason why they should not become auxiliaries, if their constitutions were hardy enough. Therefore the athletic women will live a barrack life with the soldiery, exercising with them naked in the gymnasium, learning to bear arms and accompanying the men to battle.

Living thus in common with the men it would be natural that they should not be the exclusive property of any one man. Mating among this select class would be arranged hygenically by specially equipped guardians, so that the best results might accrue to the state.

To prevent property in children, immediately on birth, trained nurses must take them away from their mothers, who will not see them again. All children born within three months of the same age are to be regarded as brothers and sisters. This will create a larger family bond to unify the state, prevent jealousy and encourage sacrifice and heroism in battle. These " sisters " and " brothers " may mate together if both are found to possess the prescribed qualifications for propagating. Speedy increase of population would not be encouraged.

Here Adeimantus, Glaucon's brother, interposed, with the criticism that Socrates provided only a scant ration of happiness for his guardians. For though the city state really belonged to them, they received less from it than anybody else.

" We shall reply that, though it would not surprise us if even this class in the given circumstances were very happy, yet that our object in the construction of our state is not to make any one class pre-eminently happy, but to make the whole state as happy as it can be made. For we thought that in such a state we should be most likely to discover justice."

And now Socrates has reached the point in his search after justice where he has his quarry, that elusive definition of justice, enclosed within the city walls of his republic. For since this is the perfect state, justice must somewhere have come into it. But there are three other qualities inside it: the re-

maining moral virtues, Wisdom, Temperance, Fortitude.
Socrates's plan is to locate these first, for then the remaining
moral constituent of his state must be Justice.

He proceeds to do this by proving that wisdom resides in
that highly trained class of searcher into absolute reality, the
rulers; fortitude is the virtue of the auxiliaries, or soldiers.

To locate temperance in his state, Socrates reminds his
audience of the common phrase, that declares a man to be
" master of himself " :

" Well, I continued, it appears to me that the meaning of the
expression is, that in the man himself, that is, in his soul,
there resides a good principle and a bad, and when the naturally
good principle is master of the bad, this state of things is described by the term ' master of himself'; when, in consequence of evil training, or the influence of associates, the smaller
force of the good principle is overpowered by the superior
numbers of the bad, the person so situated is described in terms
of reproach and condemnation, as a slave of self, and a
dissolute person.

" Do you not see that the parallel to this exists in your state;
in other words that the desires of the vulgar many are there
controlled by the desires and the wisdom of the cultivated
few? "

And then Socrates proceeds to show how temperance may
be said to reside not in any one class, as wisdom and fortitude
were found to do, but in both rulers and subjects alike, since
governors and governed are unanimous on the question of who
ought to govern. Temperance, then, resembles a kind of
harmony, spreading throughout the whole in literal diapason,
producing a unison between the weakest and the strongest and
the middle class.

" Now then, Glaucon," Socrates exclaims, " we must be
like hunters surrounding a cover, and must give close attention
that justice may nowhere escape us, and disappear from our
view: for it is manifest that she is somewhere here; so look for
her and strive to gain a sight of her. Ho! ho! Glaucon, here
is something that looks like a track, and I believe the game will
not altogether escape us. Upon my word, we are in a most
foolish predicament, for it appears that what we were looking
for has been all this time rolling before our feet, and we never
saw it. What at the commencement we laid down as a universal rule of action, when we were founding our state, this, if
I mistake not, or some modification of it, is justice. I think

we affirmed, if you recollect, and frequently repeated, that every individual ought to have some one occupation in the state, which should be that to which his natural capacity was best adapted.

" And again, we have often heard people say, that to mind one's own business, and not be meddlesome, is justice. I think that the remainder left in the state, after eliminating the quàlities which we have considered, I mean temperance, and courage, and wisdom, must be that which made their entrance into it possible, and which preserves them there so long as they exist in it. Now we affirmed that the remaining quality, when three out of the four were found, would be justice."

" Yes, unquestionably it would."

" If, however, it were required to decide which of these qualities will have most influence in perfecting by its presence the virtue of our state, it would be difficult to determine; whether it will be in the harmony of opinion between the governors and the governed, or the faithful adherence on the part of the soldiers to the lawful belief concerning the things that are, and the things which are not, to be feared; or the existence of wisdom and watchfulness in the rulers; or whether the virtue of the state may not chiefly be traced to the presence of that fourth principle in every child and woman, in every slave, freeman, and artisan, in the ruler and in the subject, requiring each to do his own work, and not meddle with many things."

" Minding one's own business ", that simple phrase, then, would seem to be something equivalent to virtue. But, before deciding definitely, Socrates must try another line of approach. For he reminds his hearers that his attempt to locate justice in the state was only a means to an end—to find it in the individual.

The first step must be to equate, if possible, the three qualities already found in the ideal state with three qualities residing in a man's soul. Then, if this is managed satisfactorily, and man is found to be a state in miniature in so far as the three determining qualities of wisdom, fortitude and temperance are concerned, the remaining quality of " minding one's own business ", which has been found to emerge out of a concord of these three, may also be predicated of the wise, brave and temperate man.

Socrates argues thus: two contradictory impulses, existing together in the mind, cannot proceed from the same source. A thirsty man is sometimes unwilling to drink, for instance. He wants to satisfy his desire, but the impulse of reason tells him not to because the water may be infected, or the wine may make him indecorously drunk. It follows there must be at least two principles within him. One that has its seat in concupiscence, the other in the reason.

What about that third principle that must be found in the individual to make the needed parallel with the state? This Socrates tracks down to the irascible, passionate or spirited principle. He shows how this element, when reason is warring with concupiscence, sides with the former, and quotes the story of how Leontius, walking up from the Piræus, saw some dead bodies on the ground. His desire was to look at them, but at the same time his reason tried to prevent him from indulging the morbid longing. At length the desire over-mastered him. Opening his eyes wide with his fingers, and running up to the bodies, he exclaimed, " There, you wretches! gaze your fill at the beautiful spectacle."

Here, then, are the three principles in the individual corresponding with the principles that distinguished the three classes in the state of guardians, auxiliaries and producers. Hence, considering the individual, he is wise in virtue of the rational element; courageous when in possession of the spirited element; temperate when concupiscence and spirit concur in desiring the rule of reason. Lastly, therefore, a man is just in allowing each of the elements in his soul its own province, and preventing their intermeddling with each other. Justice, in short, is the harmony of the soul's constituent parts, a harmony that shows itself outwardly in the performance of all those acts that are usually considered just.

Now from the deductions Socrates has made and working on his parallel between the elements in a man's soul and the component elements in the state, he proceeds to conclusions about the four other possible constitutions of the state. His ideal state is an autocracy, his ideal man an autocrat, for in both wisdom is the principle that rules. But what has a beginning must have an end, and Socrates represents the successive decline through four stages of this state until, finally, under the despot, or tyrannical man, unbridled desire is ruler in the state.

The process of degeneration begins when the guardians and the auxiliaries become dissatisfied and agree to share out between them the property of the producers and reduce them

to slaves.   The plundering of the propertied populace is effected
by force, and it is the spirited man, the soldier, who comes to
the fore in this constitution, wherefore Socrates calls it a Timocracy, or rule of honour.   Wisdom will still be prominent, but
the soldier and the soldier's interests will be more prominent
still.

The next stage will be oligarchy, or rule of the rich.   Now
that the soldiery, under the timocracy, have become possessed
of property, many of them will cease to pursue their honourable
profession and give themselves over more and more to the
acquisition of wealth.

The oligarchical state is succeeded naturally by the demo-
cratical one.   Here that class which has been impoverished
by the depredations of the oligarchical man establishes itself
in power through force of arms and expels the rich.   Equality
of civic rights is established.   Liberty degenerates into licentiousness, and licentiousness, called liberty, is the distinguishing
feature of democracy.

Socrates describes the democratic man.   His father, the
oligarch, having neglected wisdom, has left a small enough
dower of it to his son, who is thus unable to cope with the
desires he feels and ends up by abusing all the liberties the
revolution has won for him.

Finally, there is the Tyranny, which corresponds with the
tyrannical man, *is*, in fact the Tyrant, who has started as the
champion of the democrats and who turns his power against
the very people whose rights he once fought for, dominating
them, as he is himself dominated by an absorbing passion for
power that takes to itself every evil passion there is.

And, now, with the completion of his review of the human
soul and of human society, with Thrasymachus's assertion that
justice is the interest of the stronger completely refuted, Socrates
has one last point left to prove: that the soul is immortal.

"Everything that exists", says Socrates, "has a peculiar and
fatal infirmity attached to it.   Blindness destroys sight, mildew
destroys corn, rot destroys wood.   What then is the infirmity
that attacks the soul? Evidently, it is vice; that is to say
intemperance, ignorance, cowardice, injustice.   But none of
these can immediately destroy the soul, though they may be
the mediate cause of a man's being put to death by other
people.   But if wickedness cannot destroy the soul, then
nothing can.   The soul, therefore, must be immortal."